Healthy Highways
The Traveler's Guide to Healthy Eating
Second Edition

Nikki & David Goldbeck

CERES PRESS
WOODSTOCK, NY

About the Cover: On the left is David Lewis biking. David, a teacher, is active in local politics. We think of him as the future. Representing our history is hiker Beatrice Trum Hunter, a courageous food activist whom we consider our mentor. After more than four decades of alerting the public, she continues to write on food and environmental issues. In the car, your guides for this adventure, Nikki and David Goldbeck.

Cover Concept: David Goldbeck
Cover Design: Naomi Schmidt www.naomigraphics.com
Cover Illustration: Jeff Mandel
Interior Layout: Nikki Goldbeck, Teal Hutton, Naomi Schmidt
CERES PRESS
PO Box 87
Woodstock, NY 12498
Ceres Press Catalog: www.HealthyHighways.com
Phone/Fax 845-679-5573
Email Cem620@aol.com
Copyright © 2009 Nikki & David Goldbeck
Printed in Canada on recycled paper with canola based ink

Library of Congress Control Number (LCCN) 2009 902192
CIP Data by Amy Booth Raff
Goldbeck, Nikki and David.
Healthy highways : the traveler's guide to healthy eating / Nikki & David Goldbeck.
488 p. : maps, 21 cm.
ISBN 1-886101-13-2   ISBN (13 digit) 978-1-886101-13-5
1. Natural food restaurants—United States—Guidebooks.
2. Vegetarian restaurants-United States-Directories. I. Title.
"2800 Eateries & Natural Food Stores with Directions." – Cover
641.302
TX907.2 G64 2009

Other Books by Nikki & David Goldbeck
*Cooking What Comes Naturally**
The Supermarket Handbook
The Dieters' Companion
American Wholefoods Cuisine
Goldbecks' Guide to Good Food
*The Smart Kitchen***
The Good Breakfast Book
Choose to Reuse
The Healthiest Diet in the World
Eat Well the YoChee Way
The ABC's of Fruits & Vegetables and Beyond (with Steve Charney) ***
* Nikki Goldbeck,sole author ** David Goldbeck, sole author

CONTENTS

Introduction IV
Symbols & Descriptions VI

Alabama 1
Alaska 5
Arizona 7
Arkansas 15
California, Northern 18
California, Southern 45
Colorado 76
Connecticut 88
Delaware 95
District of Columbia 97
Florida 102
Georgia 132
Hawaii 141
Idaho 146
Illinois 150
Indiana 162
Iowa 168
Kansas 173
Kentucky 177
Louisiana 180
Maine 184
Maryland 190
Massachusetts 200
Michigan 216
Minnesota 228
Mississippi 239

Missouri 241
Montana 246
Nebraska 250
Nevada 253
New Hampshire 255
New Jersey 259
New Mexico 273
New York 278
North Carolina 314
North Dakota 324
Ohio 325
Oklahoma 336
Oregon 339
Pennsylvania 358
Rhode Island 380
South Carolina 383
South Dakota 388
Tennessee 390
Texas 394
Utah 410
Vermont 415
Virginia 420
Washington 432
West Virginia 447
Wisconsin 450
Wyoming 460

Eating On and Off the Healthy Highways 463
Resources 469

INTRODUCTION

Welcome to the second edition of *Healthy Highways*, a unique guide for anyone who wants to eat healthfully, particularly while away from home. We are pleased to see it grow by almost one-third. With this resource, you aren't restricted to chance roadside eateries and highway rest stops, but instead can make informed, planned choices as to where to find a nourishing meal or snack, or restock your cooler. *Healthy Highways* offers real alternatives to the standard fare of supersized, fatty, calorie-laden, repetitious, fast food and restaurant meals. Moreover, it provides an opportunity to explore new territory, as you take the healthy highway rather than the fast food lane.

Healthy Highways features more than 2,800 natural food stores, co-ops and health-minded restaurants throughout the U.S.A. Each entry includes address, phone number and hours of operation, and is keyed to such details as organic produce, vegetarian and vegan friendly, organic focus, salad bar, fresh juice, alcohol, deli, bakery, kosher, type of service, co-op, and handicap access,

Most important, with *Healthy Highways* you can easily find upcoming locations and plan refreshment stops by using the keyed maps found at the beginning of every state chapter. Once you have selected your stop, local directions, included with each listing, guide you from the nearest highway or main road.

This guide is designed with motorists, bikers and hikers in mind. It will, of course, be useful to everyone who is concerned about their health and weight, is a vegetarian or vegan, even if they aren't venturing far from home.

Types of Listings

Natural food stores. In order to qualify for a listing, natural food stores must have a good selection of groceries. We have also noted when stores offer a cafe or deli and a place to sit and eat.

Eateries. All of the eating places listed provide a reasonable selection of vegetarian options and serve freshly prepared food using a minimum of processed ingredients. We also note those that emphasize wholefoods cooking, pay attention to organic or locally grown ingredients, or cater to vegans. Restaurants noted as vegan are done so according to their own description, however some dishes may not meet strict vegan standards, since they may contain whey, casein (present in some soy cheeses), honey or sugar.

You will also notice some listings described as "Certified Green Restaurants." These establishments meet the Green Restaurant Association's standards for an ecologically sustainable restaurant industry (see Resources).

In general, restaurants serving ethnic cuisines that traditionally include vegetarian options—Indian, Mexican, Middle Eastern, Asian, etc.—are not listed. There are simply too many of them. However, we do list those that are exclusively vegetarian, surpass the usual expectations in terms of meat-free or wholefoods choices, or have an organic or sustainable focus.

Road Maps & Driving Directions
Guide You to Local Options

We have done our best to provide concise and accurate directions. However, there are often different ways to arrive at the same place, as well as various possible points of origin. Many of the directions were furnished by the establishments themselves; others were culled from online and telephone research. If you have ever asked for (or given) a driving route, you know that furnishing good directions is an art. Likewise, online routing is not always the most direct or reliable. Hopefully, you won't encounter any errors, but if you think you may be lost (or even confused), we suggest you call.

The maps that appear at the beginning of each state chapter orient you in relation to cities and towns that have *Healthy Highways* listings. We have attempted to place the arrows as accurately as possible, but these are not designed to be road maps.

Join the *Healthy Highways* Community

We invite you to become a "HH Tripster" and help make *Healthy Highways* grow. It is our intention to keep this guide up to date and to see it expand. You can lend a hand by informing us of new places you find or changes in our listings via our website at www.HealthyHighways.com or by writing or faxing us (see details on the copyright page).

Bon Appetit!

We have been fortunate, to borrow from Napoleon, to have "traveled on our stomachs." We have ventured throughout the U.S. and many other parts of the world in search of healthful and interesting cuisines and have returned to share our culinary experiences in our cookbooks and other writings. While there are many important health, social and environmental problems related to diet, our search for solutions has always included the delight food gives, along with the sustenance. Although we have not visited all the establishments listed in *Healthy Highways* (yet!), it gives us great joy knowing that you will.

Happy Trails,

Nikki & David Goldbeck

Call Ahead

We suggest you call first if possible before visiting a location. Stores and restaurants have a habit of moving (and closing), and hours, services, etc. change more often than you might expect.

SYMBOLS & DESCRIPTIONS

The symbols and standard list of features we employed are explained below. Because not all establishments responded in full to our questionnaire, some details will inevitably be missing.

🛍   natural food store

🍴   restaurant

🛍 🍴   natural food store with an eating area

♿   handicap restrooms

🚫💳   no credit cards accepted

alcohol indicates beer, wine and/or hard liquor is served.

bakery denotes baked goods made on site.

cafe signifies a store with an eating area.

co-op refers to ownership.

counter and **tables** refer to seating options.

deli implies a display case with freshly made food.

fresh juice signifies that fresh juice is made on the premises.

kosher is for kitchens that have been so certified.

organic focus means a significant portion of the menu incorporates organic ingredients.

organic produce is noted where we have been able to verify a reasonable selection. These stores may also sell conventional produce.

salad bar is just what it says.

self-service includes buffets, cafeterias, salad bars, and venues where orders are placed at the counter (even if the food is brought to your table).

take-out is noted when we know it to be a significant feature.

vegan means no animal products at all are served.

vegan-friendly signifies attention to providing animal-free choices.

vegetarian means no animal flesh is served.

vegetarian-friendly signifies fish, poultry or meat may also be served.

wait staff denotes full table service. When both self-service and wait staff appear, orders are taken at the table and there is also either a buffet or salad bar option.

Editorial note regarding the use of periods. Fussy readers please note that to save space we did not use periods in the following abbreviations, except in addresses: Days of the week, Ave, Blvd, Bus (business route), Ctr, Dr, Ln, Pkwy, Rd, Rt, St, and NESW.

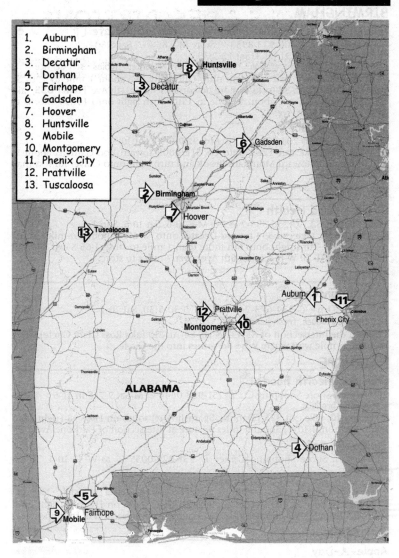

1. Auburn
2. Birmingham
3. Decatur
4. Dothan
5. Fairhope
6. Gadsden
7. Hoover
8. Huntsville
9. Mobile
10. Montgomery
11. Phenix City
12. Prattville
13. Tuscaloosa

AUBURN

Dayspring Natural Foods 🛍

223 Opelika Rd. ☎ 334-821-1965 ⏱ M-Sat 10-6

• organic produce

🛏 **From I-85**, take exit 51 (US 29) toward Auburn. Turn north (left from 85N, right from 85S) onto S College St about 4 miles to Micham Ave (just past railroad tracks). Turn right onto Micham Ave 1 block to N Gay St. Turn left onto N Gay 1 block to Opelika Rd. Turn right onto Opelika to store on left.

BIRMINGHAM

Golden Temple Natural Grocery & Vegetarian Cafe 🛍️ 🍴 &

1901 11th Ave. S. ✆ 205-933-8933 ⏰ Store M-F 8:30-7, Sat 8:30-5:30,
Sun 1-5:30 Cafe M-F 11:30-3, Sat 12-2:30
• organic produce • vegetarian • fresh juice • cafe • counter • tables • self-service

🛍️ **From I-65N**, take exit 259 right onto University Ave about 1 mile to 19th St.
Turn right onto 19th 3 blocks to store on corner 19th & 11th Ave. **From I-65S,** take
exit 259B onto 4th Ave about ¾ mile to 19th. Turn right onto 19th 7 blocks to
store at 19th & 11th Ave.

The Green Door 🛍️

2843 Culver Rd. ✆ 205-871-2651 ⏰ M-F 9:30-5:30, Sat 10-5

🛍️ **From I-59**, take exit 126A onto US 31E/280E toward Zoo-Gardens about ½
mile. Take ramp toward Mountain Brook and turn right onto Culver Rd less than
¼ mile to store.

DECATUR

Gloria's Good Health 🛍️

1820 6th Ave. S.E. ✆ 256-355-2439 ⏰ M-F 10-6, Sat 10-5, Sun 1-5

🛍️ **From I-65N**, take exit 334 toward Decatur onto AL 67N about 4½ miles to 6th
Ave (US 31N). Turn right onto 6th more than 1 mile to store. I-65 S exit 340A or
I-565W, take AL 20 W (becomes 6th Ave) over 7 miles to store.

DOTHAN

Health Concepts 🛍️

1901 Wise Drive ✆ 334-673-2444 ⏰ M-F 9:30-5:30, Sat 10-1
• organic produce, fresh juice

🛍️ From the intersection of AL 431 & US 84/AL 210 (aka Ross Clark Circle), store
is about ½ mile west where Wise Rd comes into the Circle.

FAIRHOPE

Fairhope Health Foods 🛍️

280 Eastern Shore Shopping Ctr ✆ 251-928-0644 ⏰ M-Sat 9-7, Sun 11-6
• organic produce

🛍️ **From I-10**, take exit 35A (Daphne/Spanish Fort) south on Hwy 98 (right from
I-10E, left from I-10W) about 9 miles to store at intersection of Fairhope Ave.

Sunflower Cafe 🍴

329 Eastern Shore Shopping Center ✆ 251-929-0055 ⏰ M-W 10:30-4, Th-Sat
10:30-9
Vegetarian, vegan, shrimp and poultry choices.
• vegetarian friendly • vegan friendly • organic focus • alcohol • tables • wait staff • take-out

🛍️ **From I-10**, take exit 35A (Daphne/Spanish Fort) south on Hwy 98 (right from
I-10E, left from I-10W) about 9 miles to restaurant at intersection of Fairhope Ave.

GADSDEN

Apple-A-Day 🛍️

280 N. 3rd St. ✆ 256-546-8458 ⏰ M-F 9-6, F-Sat 9-5, Sun 12:30-5
• organic produce

🛍️ **From I-59**, take exit 182 onto I-759E about 5 miles to exit 4B (Rt 411N)
toward Gasden. Take 411N about 2 miles and turn left to merge onto US 278W/W
Meighan Blvd ¼ mile to 3rd St. Turn left onto 3rd to store in Midtown Plaza
(inside Foodmax).

HOOVER

Golden Temple Natural Grocery 🛍

3309 Lorna Rd. ℭ 205-823-7002 ⏰ M-F 10-6:30, Sat 10-6

🍎 **From I-65S**, take exit 252 onto Montgomery Hwy/US 31S about 1¼ miles to Patton Chapel Rd. Turn on left onto Patton Chapel about ½ mile to Lorna Rd. Turn right onto Lorna to store on left. **From I-65N,** take exit 250 onto I-459S toward Hoover about 1½ miles to exit 13 (Montgomery Hwy/ US 31). **From I-459** exit 13, take US 31N about 1 mile to Patton Chapel. Turn right onto Patton Chapel about ½ mile to Lorna. Turn right onto Lorna to store on left.

HUNTSVILLE

Garden Cove Produce Center 🛍

628 Meridian St. ℭ256-534-2683 ⏰ M-Tues 10-7, W 9-6, Th 9-7, F 9-3, Sun 11-5
• organic produce

🍎 **From I-565E**, take exit 19C (Washington St/Jefferson St) toward Downtown. Merge onto Washington St NW to Pratt Ave NW. Turn right onto Pratt about ¼ mile to Meridian St. Turn right onto Meridian to store. **From I-565W**, take exit 19B toward Washington St and make sharp left onto Pratt under ¼ mile to Meridian. Turn right onto Meridian to store.

Pearly Gates Natural Foods, Inc. 🛍

2308 Memorial Pkwy. S. ℭ 256-534-6233 ⏰ M-Sat 10-6:30

🍎 **From I-565E**, take exit 19A onto Memorial Pkwy/Hwy 231S almost 1½ miles to store on west side. **From I-565W**, take exit 19B onto Memorial Pkwy/Hwy 231S almost 2⅔ miles to store.

MOBILE

Virginia's Health Food 🛍

3170 B Dauphin St. ℭ 251-479-3952 ⏰ M-Sat 9-7, Sun 11-6
• organic produce

🍎 **From I-65**, take exit 4 east on Dauphin St (left from I-65S, right from I-65N) about ½ mile (past two lights) to store on left in Food World Shopping Ctr.

MONTGOMERY

Health Wise Foods 🛍

5147 Atlanta Hwy. ⏰ M-F 10-7, Sat 10-6, Sun 1-6
• organic produce

🍎 **From I-85**, take exit 6 (US 231N/80E) toward Wetumpka and merge onto Eastern Blvd heading north about ¾ mile. Take the ramp onto Easter Bypass/US 80 about ½ mile. Veer right then left to stay on Eastern Blvd/US 80 to 80/AL 108/Atlanta Hwy. Turn left onto 108 about ¾ mile to store on right.

PHENIX CITY

Peachtree Natural Foods 🛍

1811 Stadium Drive ℭ 334-480-0284 ⏰ M-F 10-7, Sat 10-5

🍎 **From US 80E**, turn right onto Stadium Dr 1½ miles to store on right at Summerville Rd. **From US 80W**, take Summerville exit right onto Summerville under ¼ mile to 43rd St. Turn right onto 43rd under ½ mile to 13th Ave. Turn right onto 13th past hwy to Airport Rd. Turn right onto Airport continuing onto Stadium to store on left after Summerville.

PRATTVILLE

🛏 Fountain City Health Foods 🍴

111 S. Memorial Drive © 334-361-7550 ⊕ M-Sat 9-6

From I-65, take exit 118 southwest on AL 14 (right from I-65S, left from I-65N) about 3 miles veering left onto Memorial Dr about 1 block to store on left after Wright St (across from Baptist Memorial Hosp).

TUSCALOOSA

Manna Grocery Natural Gourmet & Ethnic Foods 🍴 🍴

2300 McFarland Blvd. #12 © 205-752-9955 ⊕ M-Sat 9-7

• organic produce, vegetarian friendly • deli • tables • self-service • take-out

🛏 **From I-20/59**, take exit 73 onto US 82W/McFarland Blvd E (right from I-20W/59S, left from I-20E/59N) about 1 mile to store on left in Meadowbrook Shopping Ctr (across from Snow Hinton Park).

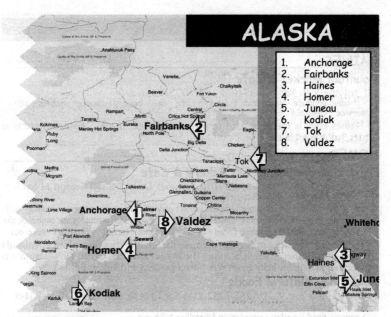

ALASKA

1. Anchorage
2. Fairbanks
3. Haines
4. Homer
5. Juneau
6. Kodiak
7. Tok
8. Valdez

ANCHORAGE

Middleway Cafe 🍴

1200 W. Northern Lights Blvd.© 907-272-6433 ⏰ M-F 7-5:30, Sat-Sun 8-5:30
coffee and baked goods, Lunch Daily 10:30-4:30
Emphasis is healthy food including whole grains and some organic ingredients. Choices for vegetarians and vegans but also poultry and fish.
  · vegetarian friendly · vegan friendly · fresh juice · tables · self-service
🚗 **From Seward Hwy (Rt 1),** take Northern Lights Blvd exit west about 1¼ miles to restaurant.

Natural Pantry 🛍️🍴

3801 Old Seward Hwy. © 907-770-1444 ⏰ M-Sat 9-9
  · organic produce · vegetarian friendly · cafe · tables · self-service ·take-out
🚗 **From Seward Hwy (Rt 1),** take E Tudor Rd exit west about ¼ mile to Old Seward Hwy. Turn right onto Old Seward under ½ mile to store at Telephone Ave.

Organic Oasi Restaurant & Juice Bar 🍴

2610 Spenard Rd.© 907-277-7882 ⏰M, Sat 11-8, Tues-F 11-9, Sun 12-4
  · vegetarian friendly · vegan friendly · organic focus · alcohol ·tables · wait staff
🚗 **From Seward Hwy (Rt 1),** take Northern Lights Blvd exit west about 1¼ miles to Spenard Rd. Turn right onto Spenard to restaurant at 26th Ave.

Snow City Cafe 🍴

1034 W. 4th Ave. © 907-272-2489 ⏰ M-F 7-3, Sat-Sun 7-4
All-day breakfast with homemade granola, real oatmeal and tofu scramble.
  · vegetarian friendly · vegan friendly · alcohol · counter · tables · wait staff · take-out
🚗 **From south of Anchorage,** take Seward Hwy (Rt 1N) to 5th Ave. Turn left onto 5th about 1 mile to K St. Turn right onto K and left onto 4th Ave to restaurant on left between K & L St. **From north of Anchorage,** take Glenn Hwy west (becomes 5th Ave) to K St and follow directions above.

FAIRBANKS

Sunshine Health Foods 🛍️

410 Trainor Gate Rd. © 907-456-5433 ⏰ M-F 9:30-6, Sat 10-6
🚗 **From Steese Hwy/AK 2,** go east (left from AK 2N, right from AK 2S) on Trainor Gate Rd ½ mile to store on left after D St..

HAINES

Mountain Market & Cafe 🛍 🍴

151 3rd Ave. S. ✆ 907-766-3340 ① M-F 7-7, Sat-Sun 8-7
• organic produce • vegetarian friendly • cafe • deli • bakery • counter • tables • self-service • take-out

🍎 Haines Hwy is the only road to town from the Canadian Border. Store is at corner 3rd Ave & Haines 1 block off Main St.

HOMER

Fresh Sourdough Express Bakery & Cafe 🍴 &

1316 Ocean Drive ✆ 907-235-7571 ① Summer Daily 7-8 Off Season M-Sat 8-3, Sun 10-3 Closed for part of winter
Alaska's first certified green restaurant. Alaskan seafood, good vegetarian options, reindeer sausage and buffalo burgers along with more conventional offerings. Baking done with organic grains ground on site.
• vegetarian friendly • organic focus • bakery • alcohol • tables • wait staff • take-out

🍎 The Seward Hwy from Anchorage becomes the Sterling Hwy on the lower peninsula and runs into Homer where it becomes the Bypass and then Ocean Dr. Restaurant is on Ocean Dr (look for kelly green van, flower gardens and kids' sandbox).

Smoky Bay Natural Foods 🛍

248 W. Pioneer Ave. ✆ 907-235-7252 ✆ M-Sat 10-6:30, Sun 12-5 Deli M-F 11-3
Soups and sandwiches.
• organic produce • deli • vegetarian friendly • take-out

🍎 **From Sterling Hwy (AK 1)**, go north (inland) on Pioneer Ave about ¼ mile to store (in bright yellow bldg).

JUNEAU

Rainbow Foods 🛍 🍴

224 4th St. ✆ 907-586-6476 ① M-F 9-7, Sat 10-6, Sun 12-6
• organic produce • vegetarian friendly • organic focus • deli • tables • self-service

🍎 **From AK 7** (Glacier Hwy), go inland on Main St 4 blocks to 4th St. Turn right onto 4th 2 blocks to store at Franklin Ave.

KODIAK

Cactus Flats 🛍

338 Mission Rd. ✆ 907-486-4677 ① Daily 10-6
• organic produce • fresh juice

🍎 **From Kodiak Alaska Marine Hwy**, go right onto W Marine Way and right onto Mission Rd under ¼ mile to store on right.

TOK

Tok General Store 🛍

mp 1313.5 Alaska Hwy. ✆ 907-883-8343 ① Winter M-Th 12-6, F, Sun 12-4 Summer opens earlier and closes a little later

🍎 **Tok is about 200 miles SE** of Fairbanks and over 1,600 miles NW of Juneau. Store is on main hwy that runs between them.

VALDEZ

A Rogues Garden 🛍

354 Fairbanks Drive ✆ 907-835-5880 ① M-F 7-6, Sat 9-5
• organic produce

🍎 **At the southern tip of Richardson Hwy** turn right onto Hazelet Ave. Take next right onto Fairbanks Dr to store.

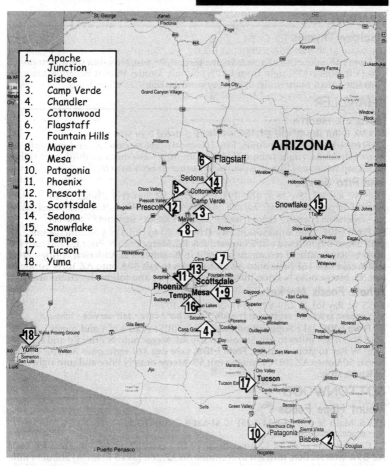

ARIZONA

1. Apache Junction
2. Bisbee
3. Camp Verde
4. Chandler
5. Cottonwood
6. Flagstaff
7. Fountain Hills
8. Mayer
9. Mesa
10. Patagonia
11. Phoenix
12. Prescott
13. Scottsdale
14. Sedona
15. Snowflake
16. Tempe
17. Tucson
18. Yuma

APACHE JUNCTION

The Good Apple Natural Market 🛍️

100 N. Plaza Drive   ✆ 480-982-2239   ⏲ M-Sat 8-8, Sun 10-6
  • organic produce

📇 **From Hwy 60,** take exit 195 north on Ironwood Drive (left from 60E, right from 60W) about 2½ miles to third light (Apache Trail). Turn right onto Apache (aka Main St). Stay left and turn left at first light to continue on Apache to store in plaza on left.

BISBEE

Bisbee Food Coop 🛍️ 🍴   ♿

72 Erie St. ✆ 520-432-4011   ⏲ M-Sat 9-7, Sun 10-5
  • organic produce • vegetarian friendly • deli • tables • self-service • take-out • co-op

📇 **From Hwy 80,** go through Old Bisbee to end of copper pit. Store is on right in Lowell Plaza. **From Hwy 92 (from Sierra Vista),** go through traffic circle, turn left at Chevron Station and go under overpass to store.

CAMP VERDE

Healthy Thymes 🛍
545 Main St. © 928-567-5585 ⏱ M-F 9-6
🍎 **From I-17**, take exit 287 toward Cottonwood/Payson/Hwy 89A southwest on AZ 260 (left from I-17S, right from I-17N) almost 3 miles until it becomes Main St. Turn left onto S Main under ½ mile to store on right.

CHANDLER

Nature's Health 🛍
973 W. Elliot Rd. © 480-821-1986 ⏱ M-F 9-8, Sat 9-6, Sun 10-5
🍎 **From I-10**, take Superstition Fwy (Hwy 60) east to exit 178 and go south on Alma School Rd (right from 60E, left from 60W) 2½ miles to third light (Elliot Rd). Turn left onto Elliot to store on SE corner in Fry's strip mall.

The Pita Jungle 🍴
1949 W. Ray Rd., Ste 28 © 480-855-3232 ⏱ M-W, Sun 11-9, Th-Sat 11-10
Meatless burgers, pizza, salads, hot and cold pita sandwiches. Vegetarian, chicken and fish.
• vegetarian friendly • vegan friendly • alcohol • tables • wait staff • take-out
🍎 **From I-10E**, take Superstition Fwy (Hwy 60E) to exit 176A and merge onto AZ 101S about 3½ miles to exit 59 toward Ray Rd. Merge onto N Price Rd and turn left onto W Ray 1 mile to restaurant on right in Boardwalk at Andersen Springs. **From I-10W**, take exit 161 right onto AZ 202 4 miles to exit 50A onto AZ 101N 1 mile to exit 59. Merge onto N Price, turn right onto W Ray and follow directions above.

Whole Foods Market 🛍 🍴
2955 W. Ray Rd. © 480-821-9447 ⏱ Daily 8-10
• organic produce • vegetarian friendly • salad bar • cafe • self-service • take-out
🍎 **From I-10E**, take Superstition Fwy (Hwy 60E) to exit 176A and merge onto AZ 101S about 3½ miles to exit 59 toward Ray Rd. Merge onto N Price Rd and turn left onto W Ray to store on right. **From I-10W**, take exit 161 right onto AZ 202 4 miles to exit 50A onto AZ 101N 1 mile to exit 59. Merge onto N Price and turn right onto W Ray to store.

COTTONWOOD

Mount Hope Foods 🛍
853 S. Main St. © 928-634-8251 ⏱ M-Sat 9-7, Sun 10-5
• organic produce
🍎 Cottonwood is about 12 miles north of I-17 exit 287 on AZ 260. **From AZ 260/ AZ 89A intersection**, turn left to continue on AZ 260 (aka S Main St) about ¼ mile to store on right.

FLAGSTAFF

Cafe Espress 🍴
16 N. San Francisco St. © 928-774-0541 ⏱ M, Th-Sun 7-2
• vegetarian friendly • alcohol • counter • tables • wait staff • take-out
🍎 **From I-17N**, merge onto 89A (Milton Rd) about 1¾ miles and continue right onto I-40 Bus about ¼ mile to San Francisco St. Turn left onto San Francisco to restaurant on right ½ block north of train station. **From I-40E**, take exit 195 toward AZ 89A/Flagstaff onto I-17N and follow directions above. **From I-40W**, take exit 198 toward Flagstaff right onto Butler Ave ¼ mile to Enterprise Rd. Turn right onto Enterprise about ¼ mile to S Santa Fe Ave (40 Bus). Turn left onto Santa Fe about 1¼ miles to San Francisco St. Turn left onto San Francisco to restaurant.

Macy's European Coffee House Bakery & Vegetarian Restaurant 🍴
14 S. Beaver St. © 928-774-2243 ⏱ Daily 6am-10pm Kitchen closes at 4
Vegetarian (mostly vegan) soups, salads, sandwiches, daily specials and vegan baked goods.
• vegetarian • vegan friendly • tables • self-service

🛍 **From I-17N,** merge onto 89A (Milton Rd) about 1¾ miles and continue right on I-40 Bus under ¼ mile to Beaver St. Turn right onto Beaver ½ block to restaurant. **From I-40E,** take exit 195 toward AZ 89A/Flagstaff onto I-17N and follow directions above. **From I-40W,** take exit 198 toward Flagstaff right onto Butler Ave ¼ mile to Enterprise Rd. Turn right onto Enterprise about ¼ mile to S Santa Fe Ave (40 Bus). Turn left onto Santa Fe about 1¼ miles to Beaver. Turn left onto Beaver ½ block to restaurant.

New Frontiers Natural Marketplace 🛍 🍴   ♿

320 S. Cambridge Lane ✆ 928-774-5747 ⏱ M-Sat 8-9 Sun 8-8
• organic produce • vegetarian friendly • deli • bakery • tables • self-service • take-out

🛍 **From I-40,** take exit 198 toward Flagstaff west on E Butler Ave (left from I-40E, right from I-40W) about 1¼ miles to store on right at Cambridge Ln.

FOUNTAIN HILLS

Nature's Finest 🛍

16838 E. Parkview Ave. ✆ 480-837-4588 ⏱ M-F 10-6, Sat 10-5
Mainly supplements with some food.

🛍 **From AZ 87/Beeline Hwy,** go west on E Shea Blvd (left from 87S, right from 87N) about ½ mile to N Saguaro Blvd. Turn right onto N Saguaro about 2¾ miles to E Parkview Ave (Fountain Park on right). Turn left onto E Parkview to store on right. **From the east,** take Shea Blvd to N Fountain Hills Blvd. Turn left onto N Fountain Hills almost 1½ miles to N Chama Dr. Turn right onto N Chama under ½ mile to E Gunsight Dr. Turn right onto E Gunsight ⅓ mile to N Saguaro. Turn left onto N Saguaro ½ mile to E Parkview. Turn left onto E Parkview to store.

MAYER

Cafe at Arcosanti 🍴

Off I-17, exit 262 (Cordes Junction) ✆ 928-632-6217 ⏱ Daily 7-9, 12-2, 6-7
At Paolo Solari's experimental town. Lunch and dinner buffets include one meat and one vegetarian main plus sides. Onsite baking with organic flours.
• vegetarian friendly • bakery • tables • self service

🛍 **From I-17,** take exit 262 (Cordes Junction). Follow signs to Arcosanti, including 2½ miles of unpaved road.

MESA

Nature's Finest 🛍

1925 E. Brown Rd. ✆ 480-962-8288 ⏱ M-F 9:30-6, Sat 9:30-5
Mainly supplements with some food.

🛍 **From Hwy 202E,** take exit 16 south (right) onto N Gilbert St 2 miles to E Brown St. Turn left onto E Brown to store on left. **From 202W,** take exit 17 and turn right onto E McDowell Rd to N Gilbert. Turn left onto N Gilbert and follow directions above. **From US 60,** take exit 182 north on S Gilbert (left from 60E, right from 60W) 3½ miles to E Brown. Turn left onto E Brown to store on left.

The Pita Jungle 🍴

1850 W. Southern Ave. ✆ 480-615-7482 ⏱ Daily 10:30-10
See Chandler location for description.
• vegetarian friendly • vegan friendly • alcohol • tables • wait staff • take-out

🍴 **From US 60W** (Superstition Fwy), turn right onto Alma School Rd ½ mile to W Southern Ave. Turn left onto W Southern under 1 mile to restaurant on right. **From US 60E,** take exit 177 right onto S Dobson Rd to W Isabella Ave and U-turn back onto S Dobson heading north over ½ mile to Mesa Community Coll. Follow Mesa Community to W Southern and turn left to restaurant. **From AZ 101S,** take exit 54 onto S Price Rd and left onto S Southern Ave 1¼ miles to restaurant on left. **From AZ 101N,** take exit 55C onto S Price, right onto S Southern and follow directions above.

PATAGONIA

Red Mountain Foods 🛒
376 Naugle Ave. ✆ 520-394-2786 ◷ M-Sat 9-6
• organic produce◷
🛒**Take Hwy 82 into Patagonia**. Store is near corner Naugle Ave (aka Hwy 82) & 4th Ave.

Tree of Life Cafe 🍴 ♿
771 Harshaw Rd. ✆ 520-394-2520 ◷ M-F 8am-9am, 1-2, Sat-Sun 10:30am-noon
Daily dinner beginning at sunset
Part of the Tree of Life Foundation eco-retreat and holistic health center. Come stay or just for the food buffet. Reservations required.
• vegan • organic focus • kosher • tables • self-service
🍎 **Take Hwy 82 into Patagonia**. Make second left after high school onto 3rd Ave 1 block to stop sign at McKeown. Turn left onto McKeown (bends right and becomes Harshaw Rd) under 1 mile to Tree of Life Rejuvenation Ctr on right (short, pink stucco walls and sign mark entrance). Turn right onto grounds and continue up hill to dark pink stucco Cafe.

PHOENIX

Chakra 4 Organic Vegetarian Cafe, Herb & Tea House 🛒 🍴 ♿
4773 N. 20th St. ✆ 602-283-1210 ◷ Store M-Sat 10-7, Sun 11-5 Cafe Daily 11-3
• vegetarian • vegan friendly • organic focus • tables • wait staff
🍎 **From I-17S**, take exit 203 left onto Camelback Rd about 4⅓ miles to 20th St. Turn right onto 20th to store on left in Town & Country Shopping Ctr. **From I-10E**, take exit 147B on left onto Hwy 51N 3 miles to exit 4A. Take exit right onto E Highland Ave and first left onto 20th to store on right. **From I-10W,** turn right onto Hwy 51N about 3¾ to exit 4A and follow directions above.

Healthy Habit Health Foods 🛒
6029 N. 7th St. ✆ 602-252-6000 ◷ M-Sat 9-6
🍎 **From I-17**, go east on W Bethany Home Rd (left from I-17S, right from I-17N) about 2¾ miles to N 7th St. Turn left onto N 7th to store on right. **From Hwy 51**, take exit 4B west on W Bethany Home (right from 51S, left from 51N) about 1¼miles to N 7th. Turn left onto N 7th to store on right.

Persian Garden Cafe 🍴
1335 W. Thomas Rd. ✆ 602-263-1915 ◷ Tues-Th 11-3, 5-9, F 11-3, 5-10, Sat 5-10
Middleastern with a strong vegetarian and vegan focus including vegetable-based soups, exotic stews, tofu dishes and several vegan desserts.
• vegetarian friendly • vegan friendly • organic focus • tables • wait staff
🍎 **From I-17**, go east on N Thomas Rd (left from I-17S, right from I-17N) about 1⅓ miles to restaurant on right after 15th Ave.

Supreme Master Ching Hai Vegetarian House 🍴
3239 E. Indian School Rd. ✆ 602-264-3480 ◷ Tues-Sat 11-2:30, 5-9
Chinese Buddhist vegetarian cooking.
• vegetarian • vegan friendly • tables • wait staff • take-out
🍎 **From I-10,** take exit 147 (147B from I-10E) onto AZ 51N under 2½ miles to exit 3. Turn right onto Indian School Rd about 1¾ miles to restaurant at 32nd St. **From I-17**, take exit 202 toward Indian School onto Black Canyon Hwy to Indian School. Turn east onto Indian School (left from I-17S, right from I-17N) under 6 miles to restaurant.

The Pita Jungle 🍴
4340 E. Indian School Rd. Phoenix ✆ 602-955-7482 ◷ Daily 10:30-10
See Chandler location for description.
• vegetarian friendly • vegan friendly • alcohol • tables • wait staff • take-out
🍎 **From I-10**, take exit 147 (147B from I-10E) onto AZ 51N under 2½ miles to exit

3. Turn right onto Indian School Rd about 3¼ miles to restaurant on left before N 44th St. **From I-17**, take exit 202 toward Indian School onto Black Canyon Hwy to Indian School. Turn east onto Indian School (left from I-17S, right from I-17N) about 7¼ miles to restaurant.

True Food Kitchen 🍴 &

2502 E Camelback Rd. ✆ 602-774-3488 ⏱ M-Th, Sun 11-10, F-Sat 11-11
Developed in partnership with Dr. Andrew Weil.
   • vegetarian friendly • vegan friendly • organic focus • alcohol • tables • wait staff
🍎 **From I-17S**, take exit 203 left onto Camelback Rd about 5 miles to restaurant on left at 24th St in Biltmore Fashion Park. **From I-10E**, take exit 147B on left onto Hwy 51N to exit 4A. Take exit right onto E Highland Ave and first left onto 20th St 1 block to Camelback. Turn right onto Camelback about ½ mile to restaurant. **From I-10W**, turn right onto Hwy 51N about 3¾ to exit 4A and follow directions above.

Whole Foods Market 🛒 🍴 &

10810 N. Tatum Blvd. ✆ 602-569-7600 ⏱ Daily 7-10
   • organic produce • vegetarian friendly • salad bar • cafe • self-service • take-out
🍎 **From north of Phoenix on I-17S**, take exit 215 on left onto AZ 101 Loop E about 7¼ miles to exit 31. Merge right onto N Tatum Blvd about 6½ miles to store. **From 101 Loop N**, take exit 41 west on Shea Blvd 5 miles to N Tatum. Turn right onto N Tatum to store.

Wild Oats Market 🛒 🍴 &

3933 E. Camelback Rd. ✆ 602-954-0584 ⏱ Daily 7-10
   • organic produce • vegetarian friendly • salad bar • cafe • self-service • take-out
🍎 **From I-17**, take exit 203 east on Camelback Rd about 10 miles to store on SW corner at 40th St.

PRESCOTT

New Frontiers Natural Marketplace 🛒 🍴 &

1112 Iron Springs Rd. ✆ 928-445-7370 ⏱ Daily 8-8
   • organic produce • ve©getarian friendly • fresh juice • salad bar • cafe • deli • bakery
   • counter • tables • self service • take-out
🍎 **Take Hwy 69 (via I-17) or Hwy 89 (via I-40) to Prescott**. Go west on Sheldon St or Gurley St (aka Hwy 69) to Montezuma St. Turn right onto Montezuma (becomes Whipple, then Iron Springs Rd) about 1¼-1½ miles to store on right 1 block past Yavapai Regional Medical Hospital.

SCOTTSDALE

Mandala Tearoom 🍴

7027 E. 5th Ave. ✆ 480-423-3411 ⏱ M-F 11-9, Sat 10-9, Sun 10-6
Tea lounge and vegan kitchen in a contemporary fine arts gallery with a performance stage.
   • vegan • organic focus • alcohol • tables • wait staff
🍎 **From Hwy 202,** take exit 7 north on N Scottsdale Rd about 4½ miles to E Indian School Rd. Turn left onto E Indian School about ¼ mile to N Marshall Way. Turn right onto N Marshall about ¼ mile to traffic circle. Take second exit onto E 5th Ave ⅓ mile to restaurant on left at Goldwater Blvd.

The Pita Jungle 🍴

7366 E. Shea Blvd. ✆ 480-922-7482 ⏱ Daily 11-10
See Chandler location for description.
   • vegetarian friendly • vegan friendly • alcohol • tables • wait staff • take-out
🍎 **From AZ 101**, take exit 41 west on Shea Blvd (left from AZ 101N, right from AZ 101E) under 2 miles to restaurant on right in Shea Scottsdale Shopping Ctr.

Wild Oats Market 🛒🍴
8688 E. Raintree Dr. ✆ 480-368-1279 ⏱ Daily 7-10
· organic produce · vegetarian friendly · salad bar · cafe · self-service · take-out
🍎 **From AZ 101**, take exit 39 west on E Raintree Dr (right from AZ 101N, left from AZ 101S) to store on right.

SEDONA

D'Lish 🍴
3190 W. Hwy 89A ✆ 928-203-9393 ⏱ Daily 11-8
Soups, salads, sandwiches, wraps and south-of-the border selections.
· vegan · organic focus · fresh juice · tables · self-service · take-out
🍎 **Hwy 89A runs through Sedona**. Restaurant is on corner 89A & Dry Creek Rd.

New Frontiers Natural Foods 🛒🍴
1420 W. Hwy. 89A ✆ 928-282-6311 ⏱ M-Sat 8-9, Sun 8-8
· organic produce · vegetarian friendly · deli · tables · self-service · take-out
🍎 Hwy 89A runs through Sedona. Store is west of the center between Soldier's Pass Rd & Oak Creek Blvd on west side.

SNOWFLAKE

Amelia's Garden 🛒🍴
305 S. Main St. ✆ 928-536-2046 ⏱ M-F 9-5:30, Sat 9-5 Cafe M-Sat 9-2:30
· organic produce · vegetarian friendly · organic focus · cafe · tables · wait staff
🍎 Store is ½ mile south of Hwy 277 on Hwy 77 (Main St in town).

TEMPE

Green 🍴
2240 N. Scottsdale Rd. ✆ 480-941-9003 ⏱ M-Sat 11-9
Salads, flatbread pizzas, noodle bowls and other vegan "comfort" foods. Homemade vegan soft-serve ice cream.
· vegan · organic focus · tables · self-service
🍎 **From Hwy 202**, take exit 7 north on N Scottsdale Rd almost 2 miles to E Continental Dr. U-turn at Continental and go south on N Scottsdale about ⅓ mile to restaurant on right.

The Pita Jungle 🍴
1250 E. Apache Blvd. ✆ 480-804-0234 ⏱ Daily 9-10
See Chandler location for description.
· vegetarian friendly · vegan friendly · alcohol · tables · wait staff · take-out
🍎 **From Hwy 101N**, take exit 53 onto S Price Rd about ½ mile and left onto E Apache Blvd about 1½ miles to restaurant on right. **From Hwy 101S,** take exit 52 for Rio Salado Pkwy onto S Price 1 mile to E Apache. Turn right onto E Apache and follow directions above. **From Hwy 202W**, take exit 53 onto S Price and turn left onto E Broadway Rd 1 mile to S McClintock Dr. Turn right onto S McClintock Dr ½ mile to E Apache. Turn left onto E Apache to restaurant. **From Hwy 202E**, take exit 8 right onto N McClintock Dr 1½ miles to E Apache. Turn right onto E Apache to restaurant.

Udupi Cafe 🍴
1636 N. Scottsdale Rd. ✆ 480-994-8787 ⏱ Lunch M, W-Sun 11-3 Dinner M, W-Th, Sun 5-9:30, F-Sat 11-3, 5-10
Indian vegetarian with a lunch buffet.
· vegetarian · vegan friendly · tables · self-service · wait staff
🍎 **From Hwy 202**, take exit 7 north on N Scottsdale Rd 1¼ miles to E Lilac Dr. U-turn at E Lila to restaurant on right side of N Scottsdale.

Whole Foods Market 🛍️ 🍴 ♿

5120 S. Rural Rd. © 480-456-1400 ⏰ Daily 8-10
• organic produce • vegetarian friendly • salad bar • cafe • self-service • take-out •

🍎 **From Hwy 60**, take exit 174 toward Scottsdale south on Rural Rd (right from 60E, left from 60W) about ½ mile to store at Baseline Rd.

TUCSON

Aqua Vita 🛍️

2801 N. Country Club Rd. © 520-293-7770 ⏰ M-Sat 8-8, Sun 8-6
• organic produce

🍎 **From I-10**, take exit 255 onto N Freeway Rd to Miracle Mile. Turn east on Miracle Mile (left from I-10E, right from I-10W) 1¾ miles to W Oracle Rd. Turn left onto Oracle 2 blocks to E Ft Lowell Rd. Turn right onto E Ft Lowell 2 miles to N Country Club Rd. Turn right onto Country Club ½ mile to store.

Casbah Tea House 🍴

628 N. 4th Ave. © 520-740-0393 ⏰ M-Th, Sun 9-10, F-Sat 9-11
• vegetarian • vegan friendly • organic focus • tables • wait staff

🍎 **From I-10W**, take exit 257A right onto St Mary's Rd (becomes W 6th St) 1 mile to 4th Ave. Turn left onto 4th to restaurant on right. **From I-10E**, take exit 257 (Speedway Blvd) but continue past Speedway along N Freeway Rd to St Mary's/6th St. Turn left onto St Mary's and follow directions above.

Food Conspiracy Co-op 🛍️ ♿

412 N. 4th Ave. © 520-624-4821 ⏰ Daily 8-8
• organic produce • deli • take-out • co-op

🍎 **From I-10W,** take exit 257A right onto St Mary's Rd (becomes W 6th St) 1 mile to 4th Ave. Turn right onto 4th to store on left between 6th & 7th St (blue bldg with pink and turquoise highlights). **From I-10E**, take exit 257 (Speedway Blvd) but continue past Speedway along N Freeway Rd to St Mary's/6th St. Turn left onto St Mary's and follow directions above.

Govinda's Natural Foods Buffet 🍴 ♿

711 E. Blacklidge Drive © 520-792-0630 ⏰ Lunch W-Sun 11:30-2:30, Dinner Tues-Sat 5-9
Mostly vegan buffet including salad bar, pastas, rice dishes, hot entrees, homemade bread, natural desserts. Eat inside or outdoors among the landscaped gardens, waterfall, fountains, koi pond and bird aviaries.
• vegetarian • vegan friendly • organic focus • salad bar • tables • self-service

🍎 **From I-10,** merge onto N Freeway Rd to Grant Rd. Turn east onto Grant Rd (left from I-10E, right from I-10W) 5 lights (almost 2 miles) to 1st Ave. Turn left onto 1st under 1 mile to second light (Blacklidge Dr). Turn right onto Blacklidge to restaurant in the Chaitanya Cultural Ctr.

Lovin' Spoonfuls 🍴

2990 N. Campbell, Ste. 120 © 520-325-7766 ⏰ M-Sat 9:30-9, Sun 10-3
Eclectic homey menu.
• vegan • alcohol • tables • wait staff

🍎 **From I-10**, merge onto N Freeway Rd to Grant Rd. Turn east onto Grant Rd (left from I-10E, right from I-10W) almost 3 miles to N Campbell Ave. Turn left onto N Campbell about ¾ mile to restaurant at Blacklidge Dr.

New Life Health Center 🛍️

3954 N. Oracle Rd. © 520-888-4830 ⏰ M-F 9-7, Sat 10-7, Sun 10-5
🍎 **From I-10**, merge onto N Freeway Rd to Prince Rd. Take Prince almost 2 miles to Oracle Rd. Turn left on Oracle to store on right before Roger Rd.

New Life Health Center 🛍

1745 W. Ajo Way ✆ 520-294-4926 ⏰ M-F 9-7, Sat 9-6, Sun 9-4

🚘 **From I-19,** take exit 99 west on Ajo Way (left from I-19N, right from I-19S) about 1 mile to store parking on left before Mission Rd.

New Life Health Center 🛍

5612 E. Broadway ✆ 520-747-0209 ⏰ M-F 9-7:30, Sat 9:30-6:30, Sun 10-5
   • organic produce

🚘 **From I-10,** merge onto N Freeway Rd to W Congress St. Take W Congress east (left from I-10E, right from I-0W) ⅓ mile to Broadway Blvd. Continue on W Broadway (becomes E Broadway) about 6 miles to store on right after N Craycroft Rd.

New Life Health Center 🛍

4841 E. Speedway Blvd. ✆ 520-795-7862 ⏰M-F 8-8, Sat-Sun 9-7
   • organic produce

🚘 **From I-10,** merge onto N Freeway Rd to Speedway Blvd. Take Speedway east (left from I-10E, right from I-10W) 5½ miles to N Arcadia. U-turn at N Arcadia to store on right.

The Garland 🍴

119 E. Speedway Blvd. ✆ 520-882-3999 ⏰ W-Th, Sun 8-3, F-Sat 8-3, 5-9
Mostly vegetarian, natural foods orientation with some tuna and chicken.
   • vegetarian friendly • alcohol • tables • wait staff

🚘 **From I-10,** merge onto N Freeway Rd to Speedway Blvd. Take Speedway east (left from I-10E, right from I-10W) under 1 mile to restaurant.

Wild Oats Market 🛍 🍴   ♿

7133 N. Oracle Rd. ✆ 520-297-5394 ⏰ Daily 7-10
   • organic produce • vegetarian friendly • salad bar • cafe • self-service • take-out

🍎 **From I-10,** take exit 248 east on Ina Rd (left from I-10E, right from I-10W) about 5¼ miles to N Oracle Rd. Turn right onto N Oracle Rd to store in shopping plaza on right.

Wild Oats Market 🛍 🍴   ♿

3360 E. Speedway Blvd. ✆ 520-795-9844 ⏰ Daily 7-10
   • organic produce • vegetarian friendly • salad bar • cafe • self-service • take-out

🚘 **From I-10,** take exit 257 onto N Freeway Rd to Speedway Blvd. Turn east onto Speedway (left from I-10E, right from I-10W) about 6 miles to store past Tucson Blvd on right in strip mall .

YUMA

Full Circle Health Foods 🛍

2099 S. 4th Ave. ✆ 928-783-8080 ⏰ Tues-F 9:30-6, Sat 9:30-5

🚘 **From I-8,** take exit 2 toward San Luis west on 16th St (left from I-8W, right from I -8E) about 1 mile to 4th Ave (Bus 8). Turn left onto 4th about ¾ mile to store at 21st St.

Nature's Express 🍴

2905 S. 4th Ave. ✆ 928-317-8300 ⏰ M-F 7-10 Drive-through 7-11 Sat-Sun 10-9:30 Drive-through 10-11
Healthier fast food with vegan burgers, dogs, fries, shakes and an environmental approach.
   • vegan • organic focus • fresh juice • tables • self-service

🚘 **From I-8,** take exit 2 toward San Luis west on 16th St (left from I-8W, right from I-8E) about 1 mile to 4th Ave (Bus 8). Turn left onto 4th about 1 mile to store on left between 28th & 29th St.

ARKANSAS

1. Decatur
2. El Dorado
3. Eureka Springs
4. Fayetteville
5. Fort Smith
6. Harrison
7. Hot Springs
8. Little Rock
9. Mountain View
10. Pine Bluff
11. Rogers
12. Sherwood
13. Van Buren

DECATUR

Wellness Secrets 🍴

891 E. Roller Ave. ℂ 479-752-8555 ⏰ Sun-Th 11-3
In the Wellness Secrets health clinic. One daily lunch menu.

• vegan, tables • wait staff

🗓 **From I-540**, take exit 86 west on Hwy 102 to store on left ½ mile before the center of town.

EL DORADO

The Olde Towne Store 🛍

113 N. Jefferson Ave. ℂ 870-862-1060 ⏰ M-F 9-6, Sat 9-5

🗓 **From US 167**, take E Main St over 1½ miles into town to N Jefferson St. Turn right onto N Jefferson to store on right. **From US Hwy 82W**, take Southfield Rd exit toward El Dorado right onto Southfield (signs for S West Ave) under ½ mile continuing onto S West then S Washington Ave another 1½ miles to E Cedar St. Turn right onto E Cedar 1 block to N Jefferson. Turn right onto N Jefferson 1 block to store on right. **From 82E**, continue onto W Hillsboro St to S West. Turn left onto S West 4 blocks to W Main. Turn right onto W Main 3 blocks to N Jefferson. Turn left onto N Jefferson 1 block to store.

EUREKA SPRINGS

The Eureka Market 🛍

121 E. Van Buren, Ste. B ℂ 479-253-8136 ⏰ Daily 8-7
• organic produce

🗓 Store is on US 62 (Van Buren Hwy) just east of S Main St in the Quarter Marketplace.

FAYETTEVILLE

Ozark Natural Foods Co-op 🛍 🍴

1554 N. College Ave. ✆ 479-521-7558 ⏱ M-Sat 8-9, Sun 10-6
• organic produce • vegetarian friendly • deli • tables • self-service • take-out • co-op

🛒 **From I-540**, take exit 66 right onto AR 112 (Garland Ave) to AR 180. Veer left onto 180 (W Drake St, becomes W Township St) 1¾ miles to US 71Bus. Turn right onto US 71Bus (aka N College Ave) under 1 mile to store between E Sycamore & E North St.

The Greenhouse Grille 🍴

318 S. Archibald Yellow Blvd. ✆ 479-444-8909 ⏱Tues-Sat 11-9
A good vegetarian selection plus organic poultry and buffalo meat.
• vegetarian friendly • organic focus • tables • wait staff

🛒 **From I-540S**, take exit 62 (Hwy 180 E/US-62 W) toward Farmington to W 6th St. Turn east onto W 6th (left from I-540S, right from I-540N) 1½-2 miles to S School Ave. Turn left onto S School ¼ mile to restaurant.

FORT SMITH

Olde Fashioned Foods 🛍

123 N. 18th St. ✆ 479-782-6183 ⏱ M-Sat 9-6
• organic produce

🛒 **From I-540**, take exit 8 (8A from I-540S) west on AR 22W/Rogers Ave over 3 miles to N 18th St. Turn right onto 18th to store on left.

HARRISON

Natural Way 🛍

2508 S. Olive St. ✆ 870-534-5335 ⏱ M-F 9-6, Sat 10-5:30
🛒 **From Hwy 62/65N and W Central Ave/AR 7 intersection**, go north on Hwy 62/65N and make first right onto N Olive St to store.

HOT SPRINGS

Good Earth Natural Foods 🛍

3955 Central Ave. ✆ 501-520-4551 ⏱ M-F 9:30-6:30, Sat 10-5
• organic produce

🛒 **From US 270/70/MLK Expwy**, take exit 5 south on Central Ave (right from 270E, left from 270W) 1 mile to Files Rd. U-turn back onto Central ½ mile to store on right.

The Old Country Store 🛍

455 Broadway ✆ 501-624-1172 ⏱ M-Th 9-5:30, F 9-4
• organic produce

🛒 **From US 270/70/MLK Expwy**, take exit 5 north on Central Ave (left from 270E, right from 270W) about 2¾ miles to E Grand Ave. U-turn and turn left (east) onto Grand 3 blocks to Broadway. Turn left onto Broadway to store on right.

LITTLE ROCK

Vitamins Plus 🛍

9112 Rodney Parham Rd. ✆ 501-223-2650 ⏱ M-Sat 9-9, Sun 10-6
🛒 **From I-430S**, take to exit 6 toward Downtown right at fork, right onto S Shakleford Rd and right onto S Markham Rd 1½ miles to Rodney Parham Rd. Turn right onto Rodney Parham to store on right. **From I-430N**, take exit 6 toward downtown right onto I-630E 2 miles to exit 6A. Merge onto S Rodney Parham and stay left to continue on S Rodney Parham about ¾ mile to store on left.

Whole Foods Market 🛍 🍴   ♿

10700 N. Rodney Parham Rd. ✆ 501-221-2331 ⏱ Daily 8-10
• organic produce • vegetarian friendly • salad bar • cafe • self-service • take-out

🛒 **From I-430**, take exit 8 west on N Rodney Parham Rd (right from I-430S, left from I-430N) to store at first intersection on right in shopping mall.

MOUNTAIN VIEW

Stone Ground Natural Foods 🛍

422 Sylamore Ave. ℂ 870-269-8164 ◷ M-F 10-5

🚘 AR 66, 14, 9, 5 and 87 all come into Mt View. Store is ⅓ mile north of AR 66 (W Main St) and AR14/87 (E Main) on west side of AR 14/8/5 (Sylamore Ave).

PINE BLUFF

Sweet Clover Health Foods 🛍

2624 W. 28th Ave. ℂ 870-536-0107 ◷ M-F 10-5, Sat 10-4

🚘 **From I-530**, take exit 39 (US 79/79Bus) north on Camden Rd (left from I-530S, right from I-530N) about 1 mile to W 28th Ave. Turn right onto W 28th about 1 mile to store in Oak Park Village.

ROGERS

Cook's Natural Foods & Cafe 🛍 🍴

726 W. Walnut St. ℂ 479-936-8484 ◷ M-F 8-6, Sat 9-5
• organic produce • vegetarian friendly • deli • tables • self-service • take-out

🚘 **From I-540**, take exit 85 (US 71B) toward Rogers east on W Walnut St (left from I-540S, right from I-540N) about 3¼ miles to store on left between 8th & 7th St.

Roger's Natural 🛍

310 N. 13th St. ℂ 479-636-7331 ◷ M-F 9-6, Sat 8:30-5

🚘 **From I-540**, take exit 85 (US 71B) toward Rogers east on W Walnut St (left from I-540S, right from I-540N) about 2½ miles to N 13th St. Turn left onto N 13th under ¼ mile to store on left.

SHERWOOD

Ann's Health Food Store 🛍

9800 Hwy. 107 ℂ 501-835-6415 ◷ M-F 8:30-5:30

🚘 **From I-40**, take exit 153A onto Hwy 107N about 5½ miles to store.

VAN BUREN

Squash Blossom 🛍

5005 Dora Rd. ℂ 479-474-1147 ◷ M-F 9-6, Sat 9-5
• organic produce

🚘 **From I-40W**, take exit 1 toward Fort Smith onto Dora Rd about ⅔ mile to store on left (in century-old restored general store). **From I-40E**, take exit 330 toward Dora/Fort Smith left onto Greenwood Rd to Dora Rd. Turn left onto Dora about ¼ mile to store.

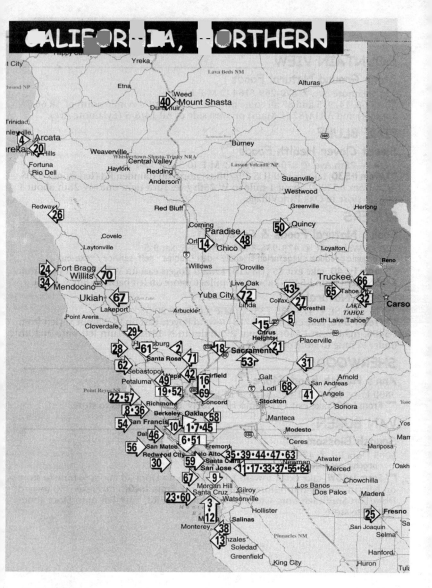

ALAMEEDA

Alameda Natural Grocery 🛍

1650 Park St. ✆ 510-865-1500 ⏰ M-Sat 8-8, Sun 8-7
In the Alameda Marketplace along with a bakery, juice bar, fish market, natural meat market and organic take-out/eat-in deli.

· organic produce

🛍 **From I-880S,** take 23rd Ave exit toward Alameda. Follow 23rd (becomes 29th Ave) across bridge onto Park Ave 4 blocks to store on left. **From I-880N,** take 29th Ave exit toward Fruitvale Rd. Turn right onto 29th 1 block then U-turn back onto 29th about ¼ mile to Ford Ave. Turn right onto Ford, left onto 23rd and merge back onto 29th across bridge onto Park Ave 4 blocks to store on left.

1. Alameeda	19. El Cerrito	38. Monterey	55. San Jose
2. Angwin	20. Eureka	39. Mountain View	56. San Mateo
3. Aptos	21. Fair Oaks		57. San Rafael
4. Arcata	22. Fairfax	40. Mt. Shasta	58. San Ramon
5. Auburn	23. Felton	41. Murphys	59. Santa Clara
6. Belmont	24. Fort Bragg	42. Napa	60. Santa Cruz
7. Berkeley	25. Fresno	43. Nevada City	61. Santa Rosa
8. Bolinas	26. Garberville	44. Newark	62. Sebastopol
9. Boulder Creek	27. Grass Valley	45. Oakland	63. Stanford
	28. Guerneville	46. Pacifica	64. Sunnyvale
10. Burlingame	29. Half Moon Bay	47. Palo Alto	65. Tahoe City
11. Campbell		48. Paradise	66. Truckee
12. Capitola	30. Healdsburg	49. Petaluma	67. Ukiah
13. Carmel	31. Jackson	50. Quincy	68. Valley Springs
14. Chico	32. Lake Tahoe	51. Redwood City	
15. Citrus Heights	33. Los Gatos	52. Richmond	69. Walnut Creek
	34. Mendocino	53. Sacramento	70. Willits
16. Concord	35. Menlo Park	54. San Francisco	71. Yountville
17. Cupertino	36. Mill Valley		72. Yuba City
18. Davis	37. Milpitas		

ANGWIN

College Market 🛒
15 Angwin Plaza © 707-965-6321 ⏰ M-Th, Sun 7:30-7:30, F 7:30-3:30 (5:30 in summer)
organic produce, vegetarian friendly, salad bar, deli, take-out
🚗 **From Rt 29** about 6 miles north of St Helena, head northeast on Deer Park Rd toward Pacific Union College (becomes Howell Mt Rd) about 1⅔ miles to store at top of hill on college campus.

APTOS

Aptos Natural Foods 🛒
7506 Soquel Drive © 831-685-3334 ⏰ Daily 8-8
🚗 **From Rt 1**, take State Park Dr north on State Park (left from 1S, right from 1N) about ⅓ mile to Soquel Dr. Turn left onto Soquel about ¼ mile to store on left.

ARCATA

Arcata Food Co-op 🛒
811 I St. © 707-822-5947 ⏰ Daily 6-9
• organic produce • vegetarian friendly • deli • bakery • take-out • co-op
🚗 **From Hwy 101**, take Samoa Blvd west about ½ mile to I St. Turn right onto I about ¼ mile (4 blocks) to store on left (1 block west of town plaza).

Daybreak Cafe 🍴
768 18th St. © 707-826-7543 ⏰ Daily 8-4
Locally grown, organic, vegetarian fare with a few "token" meat dishes.
• vegetarian friendly • organic focus • counter • tables, wait staff
🚗 **From Hwy 101**, take Sunset Ave/Humboldt State U exit. **From 101N**, turn left at stop sign, go over bridge and turn left onto H St to restaurant at H & 18th St. **From 101S**, go straight onto H St 2 blocks to restaurant at 18th.

Wildflower Cafe 🍴
1604 G St. © 707-822-0360 ⏰ M-Th, Sun 8-8, F-Sat 8-9
• vegetarian • vegan friendly • organic focus • alcohol • tables • wait staff
🚗 **From Hwy 101S**, take exit 714 for Sunset Ave onto H St and turn left onto 16th St 1 block to G St. Turn left onto G to restaurant on right. **From Hwy 101N**, take exit 714A left (across hwy) 2 blocks to G. Turn right onto G 2 blocks to restaurant on right after 16th.

AUBURN

Sunrise Natural Foods 🛍️

2160 Grass Valley Hwy. ✆ 530-888-8973 🕐 M-F 9:30-6:30, Sat 9:30-5, Sun 12-5
🚗 **From I-80,** take Hwy 49 exit north toward Grass Valley about 2 miles to store on right.

BELMONT

Hobee's 🍴

1101 Shoreway Rd. ✆650-596-0400 🕐 M-F 7-2:30, Sat-Sun 8-3
See Mountain View location for description.
   • vegetarian friendly • salad bar • alcohol • tables • wait staff • take-out
🚗 **From Hwy 101,** take Ralston Ave exit and take ramp toward Marine World Pkwy
onto Ralston. Restaurant is at intersection next to Motel 6.

BERKELEY

Ashkenaz Music & Dance Community Center 🍴   ♿

1317 San Pablo Ave. ✆ 510-525-5099 🕐 Cafe hours vary with show schedule Call
510-525-5054 for show times
World music and dance performances, classes and vegetarian food in a warehouse trans-
formed to look like an old wooden synagogue.
   • vegetarian • organic focus • alcohol • tables, self-service
🚗 **From I-80,** take Gillman St east about ⅔ mile to San Pablo Ave. Turn right onto
San Pablo to center on left (across from mini shopping center and REI).

Barney's Gourmet Hamburgers 🍴

1600 Shattuck Ave. ✆ 510-849-2827 🕐 M-Th, Sun 11-10, F-Sat 11-10:30
The attraction for vegetarians is garden and tofu burgers with toppings and plenty of salad.
   • vegetarian friendly • vegan friendly • alcohol • tables • wait staff
🚗 **From I-80,** take University Ave east about 2 miles to MKL Jr Way. Turn left onto
MLK about ½ mile to Cedar St. Turn right onto Cedar 4 blocks to restaurant on
right at Shattuck Ave.

Barney's Gourmet Hamburgers 🍴

1591 Solano Ave. ✆ 510-526-8185 🕐 M-Th 11-10, F-Sat 11-10:30, Sun 11-9:30
See Shattuck Ave location for description.
   • vegetarian friendly • vegan friendly • alcohol • tables • wait staff
🚗 **From I-80,** take Buchanan St east ½ mile and continue onto Marin Ave under
1 mile to Peralta Ave. Turn left onto Peralta 1 block to Solano Ave. Turn right onto
Solano about 1 block to restaurant on left.

Berkeley Natural Grocery Company 🛍️

1336 Gilman St. ✆ 510-526-2456 🕐 Daily 9-8
   • organic produce
🚗 **From I-80,** take Gilman St east 1 mile to store on right.

Cafe Gratitude 🍴

1730 Shattuck Ave. ✆ 415-824-4652 🕐 Daily 10-10
Focus is on raw food.
   • vegan • organic focus • fresh juice • alcohol • tables • wait staff • take-out
🚗 **From I-80,** take University Ave east 2 miles to Shattuck Ave. Turn left onto
Shattuck 5 blocks to restaurant on right at Virginia St.

Cafe Muse 🍴

2625 Durant Ave. ✆ 510-548-4366 🕐 Daily 11-3
About half the menu is raw and vegan, the remainder mostly salads and non-vegetarian
sandwiches. Convenient location outside the Berkeley Art Museum.
   • vegetarian friendly • vegan friendly • alcohol • tables • self-service
🚗 **From I-80,** take Ashby Ave east 2 miles to Telegraph Ave. Turn left onto Telegraph
under 1 mile to Durant Ave. Turn right onto Durant 1½ blocks to restaurant at
entrance to Berkeley Art Museum.

Cha-Ya Restaurant 🍴 &

1686 Shattuck Ave. ✆ 510-981-1213 ⏰ Lunch Tues-Sun 12-2, Dinner Daily 5-9:30
Vegan Japanese.
  • vegan • alcohol • counter • tables • wait staff • take-out
🚌 **From I-80**, take University Ave east 2 miles to Shattuck Ave. Turn left onto Shattuck 5 blocks to restaurant past Virginia St.

Herbivore 🍴

2451 Shattuck Ave. ✆ 510-665-1675 ⏰ M-Th, Sun 9am-10pm, F-Sat 9am-12am
Vegan soups, salads, sandwiches and noodles.
  • vegan • alcohol • tables • wait staff
🚌 **From I-80**, take Ashby Ave exit onto Ashby 1½ miles to Adeline St. Turn left onto Adeline ½ mile to Shattuck Ave. Turn left onto Shattuck ⅓ mile to restaurant on right at Haste St.

Raw Energy Organic Juice Cafe 🍴

2050 Addison St. ✆ 510-665-9464 ⏰ M-F 7:30-7:30, Sat 11-4
Raw, vegan.
  • vegan • organic focus • fresh juice • tables • self-service • take-out
🚌 **From I-80,** take University Ave east about 2 miles to Milvia St. Turn right onto Milvia 1 bock to Addison St. Turn left onto Addison to restaurant.

Razan's Organic Kitchen 🍴

2119 Kittredge St. ✆ 510-486-0449 ⏰ Daily 10-10
  • vegetarian friendly • organic focus • fresh juice • tables • self-service • take-out
🚌 **From I-80**, take University Ave east 2 miles to Shattuck Ave. Turn right onto Shattuck 4 blocks to restaurant at Kittredge St.

Smart Alec's 🍴

2355 Telegraph Ave. ✆ 510-704-4000 ⏰ Daily 11-9
Healthy fast food: vegan soups, salads, vegetarian, poultry or dolphin-safe tuna sandwiches.
  • vegetarian friendly • counter • wait staff
🚌 **From I-80**, take Ashby Ave east 2 miles to Telegraph Ave. Turn left onto Telegraph under 1 mile to restaurant 1 block south of UC Berkeley.

Udupi Palace 🍴

1901 University Ave. ✆ 510-843-6600 ⏰ Daily 11:30-10
North and South Indian vegetarian. Buffet available at lunch.
  • vegetarian • vegan friendly • tables • self-service • wait staff
🚌 **From I-80**, take University Ave east about 2 miles to restaurant on left at MLK Jr Way.

Vegi Food Restaurant 🍴

2083 Vine St. ✆ 510-548-5244 ⏰ M 5-9, Tues-F 11:30-3, 5-9, Sat-Sun 11:30-9
Chinese vegan.
  • vegan • tables • wait staff
🚌 **From I-80**, take University Ave east 2 miles to MKL Jr Blvd. Turn left onto MLK about ½ mile to Vine St. Turn right onto Vine 4 blocks to restaurant on right at Shattuck Ave.

Whole Foods Market 🛒 🍴 &

3000 Telegraph Ave. ✆ 510-649-1333 ⏰ Daily 8-10
  • organic produce • vegetarian friendly • salad bar • cafe • self-service • take-out,
🚌 **From I- 80**, take Ashby Ave east 2 miles to store at Telegraph Ave.

BOLINAS

Bolinas People's Store 🛒 &

14 Wharf Rd. ✆ 415-868-1433 ⏰ Daily 8:30-6:30
Sit outside and enjoy the homemade sandwiches, soups and vegetarian tamales.
  • organic produce • deli • take-out • co-op
🚌 **From Hwy 1**, take Olema Bolinas Rd (left from 1N, veer right from 1S) about 2 miles to store (where it turns into Wharf Rd).

BOULDER CREEK

New Leaf Community Market 🛍 🍴

13159 Hwy. 9 🕐 831-338-7211 ⏱ Daily 9-9
• organic produce • vegetarian friendly • cafe • deli • counter • table • self-service • take-out
🍎 Store is on Hwy 9 (aka Central Ave) south of Big Basin Way on west side.

BURLINGAME

Earthbeam Natural Foods 🛍

1399 Broadway 🕐 650-347-2058 ⏱ M-Sat 9-7, Sun 10-6
• organic produce
🍎 From 101 (Bayshore Fwy), take exit 419B onto Broadway about ⅓ mile to store at Capuchino Ave.

Que se Raw se Raw 🍴

1160 Capuchino Ave. 🕐 650-348-7298 ⏱ M-Sat 12-4
Raw food to go.
• vegan • organic focus • take-out
🍎 From 101 (Bayshore Fwy), take exit 419B onto Broadway about ⅓ mile to Capuchino Ave. Turn left onto Capuchino to store on left.

CAMPBELL

Hobee's 🍴

1875 S. Bascom Ave., Unit 190 🕐 408-369-0575 ⏱ M-F 7-9, Sat-Sun 8-9
See the Mountain View location for description.
• vegetarian friendly • salad bar • alcohol • tables • wait staff • take-out
🍎 From I-280 or I-880, merge onto Rt 17S to Campbell Ave. Turn left onto E Campbell Ave (right from 17N) to first big intersection at S Bascom Ave. Turn right onto S Bascom to The Prunyard. Store is in back.

Whole Foods Market 🛍 🍴 ♿

1690 S. Bascom Ave. 🕐 408-371-5000 ⏱ Daily 8-10 Bakery & Juice bar from 7:30
• organic produce • vegetarian friendly • salad bar • cafe • self-service • take-out
🍎 From I-280 or I-880, merge onto Rt 17S to Hamilton Ave exit. Turn left onto Hamilton (right from 17N) 2 blocks to store in shopping center at S Bascom Ave.

CAPITOLA

Dharma's Natural Foods Restaurant 🍴

4250 Capitola Rd. 🕐 831-462-1717 ⏱ Daily 8-9
• vegetarian • vegan friendly • tables • self-service • take-out
🍎 Coming from north on Hwy 17S, take Hwy 1S toward Monterey. From Hwy 1, take 41st Ave exit. Turn toward the ocean onto 41st (right from 1S, left from 1N) ½ mile to Capitola Rd. Turn left onto Capitola to restaurant at 42nd Ave.

New Leaf Community Market 🛍 🍴 ♿

1210 41st Ave. 🕐 831-479-7987 ⏱ Daily 8-9
• organic produce • vegetarian friendly • fresh juice • cafe • tables • self-service • take-out
🍎 Coming from north on Hwy 17S, take Hwy 1S toward Monterey. From Hwy 1, take 41st Ave exit. Turn toward the ocean onto 41st (right from 1S, left from 1N) under 1 mile to store on left in Begonia Plaza (past Jade & Brommer St).

CARMEL

Cornucopia Community Market 🛍

26135 Carmel Rancho Blvd. 🕐 831-625-1454 ⏱ M-Sat 9-7, Sun 10-6
🍎 From Hwy 1, take Carmel Valley Rd east (inland) under ¼ mile to Carmel Rancho Blvd. Turn right on Carmel Rancho to store on left in Carmel Rancho Shopping Ctr.

Earthbound Farms 🛍 🍴

7250 Carmel Valley Rd. 🕐 831-625-6219 ⏱ M-Sat 8-6, Sun 10-5

Organic farm stand with picnic tables outside.
• organic produce • vegetarian friendly • fresh juice • salad bar • deli • tables • self-service

From Hwy 1, take Carmel Valley Rd east (inland) 3½ miles to store on right.

CHICO

Chico Natural Foods
818 Main St. ☎ 530-891-1713 ◷ Daily 7:30-10
Self-serve soup and outdoor seating.
• vegetarian friendly • deli • tables • self-service • take-out

From I-5, take Hwy 32 east (becomes 8th St in Chico) about ⅔ mile to store on at Main St.

CITRUS HEIGHTS

Elliott's Natural Foods
8063 Greenback Lane ☎ 916-726-3033 ◷ M-F 9-7, Sat 9-6, Sun 9-5
• organic produce

From I-80, take Greenback Ln east about 4 miles (past Arcadia Dr) to store on left in Greenback Square Shopping Ctr.

CONCORD

Harvest House
2395 Monument Blvd. ☎ 925-676-2305 ◷ M-F 10-8, Sat 9-7, Sun 10-7
From I-680N, take Monument Blvd exit right onto Monument about 1½ miles to Detroit Ave. U-turn at Detroit and go 1 block to store. **From I-680S,** take Concord Ave (becomes Galindo, then Monument) almost 3 miles (through downtown) to store 1 block past Detroit.

CUPERTINO

Hobee's
21267 Stevens Creek Blvd. ☎ 408-255-6010 ◷ M-F 6:30-9, Sat-Sun 7:30-9
See the Mountain View location for description.
• vegetarian friendly • salad bar • alcohol • tables • wait staff • take-out

From I-280 or Hwy 101, take Hwy 85 south to Stevens Creek Blvd exit. Turn left onto Stevens Creek 1 block to restaurant in The Oaks Shopping Ctr (across from De Anza College).

Whole Foods Market
20955 Stevens Creek Blvd. ☎ 408-257-7000 ◷ Daily 8-10
• organic produce • vegetarian friendly • salad bar • cafe • self-service • take-out

From I-280 or Hwy 101, take Hwy 85 south to Stevens Creek Blvd exit. Turn left onto Stevens Creek 1 mile to store between Stellling Rd & DeAnza Blvd.

DAVIS

Davis Food Co-op
620 G St. ☎ 530-758-2667 ◷ Daily 8-10
• organic produce • vegetarian friendly • deli • take-out • co-op

From I-80, take Richards Blvd exit Downtown right onto Richards continuing onto E St about ½ mile to 6th St. Turn right onto 6th 2 blocks to store on right at G St.

Delta Of Venus Cafe & Pub
122 B St. ☎ 530-753-8639 ◷ M-W 8:30am-10pm, F-Sun 7:30am-12am
Breakfast is vegetarian, meat appears later in the day on the Caribbean-style menu.
• vegetarian friendly • alcohol • counter • tables • wait staff

From I-80, take Richards Blvd exit toward Downtown right onto Richards under ½ mile to 1st St. Turn left onto 1st 3 bocks to B St. Turn right onto B ½ block to restaurant on right.

Natural Food Works/Farmer's Kitchen Cafe 🍴

620 4th St. ✆ 530-756-1862 ⏱ M-Sat 11-8

Seasonal menu featuring organic local produce. Wild and free-range meat and fish. Many items gluten- and casein-free.

• vegetarian friendly • vegan friendly • organic focus • tables • wait staff

🚗 **From I-80,** take Richards Blvd exit toward Downtown right onto Richards continuing onto E St about ¼ mile to 4th St. Turn right onto 4th to restaurant on right.

EL CERRITO

El Cerrito Natural Grocery 🛒

10367 San Pablo Ave. ✆ 510-526-1155 ⏱ Daily 9-8

• organic produce

🚗 **From I-80E,** take Central Ave exit toward El Cerrito right onto Central under ½ mile to San Pablo Ave. Turn left onto San Pablo about ⅓ mile to store before Stockton Ave. **From I-80W,** take Carlson Blvd exit left onto Carlson about ½ mile to Sutter Ave. Turn left onto Sutter 1 block to San Pablo. Turn right onto San Pablo under ¼ mile to store after Stockton.

EUREKA

Eureka Co-op 🛒

1036 5th St. ✆ 707-443-6027 ⏱ Daily 6-9

On-site bakery uses organic whole wheat flour and unrefined sweeteners in the breads, cereals, even the cakes.

• organic produce • vegetarian friendly • deli • bakery • take-out • co-op

🚗 At 5th St (aka Hwy 101N) & L St (huge fruit & vegetable mural on bldg).

Eureka Natural Foods 🛒   ♿

1450 Broadway St. ✆ 707-442-6325 ⏱ M-F 7-9, Sat 8-9, Sun 8-8

• organic produce • vegetarian friendly • fresh juice • deli • take-out

🚗 On Hwy 101 (aka Broadway St) between W 14th & 15th St.

FAIR OAKS

Sunflower Drive-In 🍴

10344 Fair Oaks Blvd. ✆ 916-967-4331 ⏱ M-Tues 10:30-4, Wed-Sat 10:30-8, Sun 11-4

Nutburgers and millet burgers, burritos and sandwiches, soups, salads and "fountain delights."

• vegetarian • vegan friendly • fresh juice • tables • self-service • take-out

🚗 **From US 50,** take Sunrise Blvd north (right from 50W, loop around right from 50E) 2-3 miles to California Ave. Turn right onto California, make second left onto Fair Oaks Blvd 2 blocks and turn right to continue on Fair Oaks under 1 block to restaurant.

FAIRFAX

Good Earth Natural & Organic Foods 🛒 🍴   ♿

1966 Sir Francis Drake Blvd. ✆ 415-454-0123 ⏱ Daily 9-8

• organic produce • vegetarian friendly • fresh juice • salad bar • deli • organic focus • bakery • tables • counter • self-service • take-out

🚗 **From Hwy 101,** take Central San Rafael exit west on 3rd St about 5 miles. Merge right onto Sir Francis Drake Blvd about 3 miles to store on NW corner at Claus Dr.

FELTON

New Leaf Community Market 🛒 🍴

6240 Hwy. 9 ✆ 831-335-7322 ⏱ Daily 9-9

• organic produce • vegetarian friendly • cafe • deli • counter • tables • self-service • take-out

🚗 Felton is about 6 miles north of Santa Cruz on Hwy 9. Store is on east side of 9 at Graham Hill & Covered Bridge Rd intersection.

FORT BRAGG

Cafe 1 🍴
753 N. Main St. ✆ 707-964-3309 ① M-Sat 7:30-2:30, Sun 8-2
· vegetarian friendly · vegan friendly · organic focus · counter · tables · wait staff
📷 On Hwy 1 between Spruce & Bush St on the west side.

Living Light Cuisine Cafe 🍴
301B N. Main St. ✆ 707-964-2420 ① M-Sat 8-6, Sun 10-4
Raw food. Part of Living Light Culinary Arts Center.
· vegan · organic focus · fresh juice · tables · self-service · take-out
📷 On Hwy 1 at Redwood St on west side.

FRESNO

New Stars Vegetarian Restaurant 🍴
1134 E. Champlain Drive, Ste. 108 ✆ 559-434-6363 ① M-Sat 11-9, Sun 12-9
Asian, Indian and Italian vegetarian fare.
· vegetarian · vegan friendly · tables · wait staff · take-out
📷 **From CA 41**, take exit 135 for Blackstone Ave/Friant Rd onto Friant about 1 mile to E Shepherd Ave. Turn right onto E Shepherd 1⅓ miles to E Champlain Dr. Turn left onto E Champlain ½ mile to restaurant on right.

Whole Foods Market 🛒 🍴   ♿
650 W. Shaw Ave. ✆ 559-241-0300 ① Daily 7-9
· organic produce · vegetarian friendly · salad bar · cafe · self-service · take-out
📷 **From Hwy 99**, take exit 140 east on Shaw Ave (loop around and right from 99S, loop around and left from 99N) over 4½ miles to store on left in Fig Garden Shopping Ctr.

GARBERVILLE

Chautauqua Natural Foods 🛒
436 Church St. ✆ 707-923-2452 ① M-Sat 10-6
📷 **From Hwy 101**, take Garberville exit onto Redwood Rd about ¼ mile to Church St. Turn onto Church (begins at Redwood) to store on right.

Wood Rose Cafe 🍴
911 Redwood Drive ✆ 707-923-3191 ① M-F 8-2:30, Sat-Sun 8-1
Healthy breakfasts, soups, salads, burritos and sandwiches.
· vegetarian friendly · organic focus · alcohol · counter · tables · wait staff
📷 **From Hwy 101**, take Garberville exit onto Redwood Rd to restaurant on east side.

GRASS VALLEY

Briar Patch Community Market 🛒
290 Sierra College Drive ✆ 530-272-5333 ① M-Sat 7-8, Sun 8-7
· organic produce · vegetarian friendly · deli · tables · self-service · co-op
📷 **From CA 49S/CA 20W**, take exit 183 left onto Brunswick Rd and make second left onto Nevada City Hwy over ½ mile to Sierra College Dr. Turn right onto Sierra College under ¼ mile to store on right. **From CA 49N/CA 20E**, take exit 182B left onto Idaho Maryland Rd and right onto E Main St almost 1 mile to Sierra College. Turn left onto Sierra College under ¼ mile to store.

Natural Valley Health Foods 🛒
562 Sutton Way ✆ 530-273-6525 ① M-F 9-6, Sat 9:30-5:30
📷 **From CA 49S/CA 20W**, take exit 183 left onto Brunswick Rd under ¼ mile to Sutton Way. Turn left onto Sutton then right to stay on Sutton about ½ mile to store on left. **From CA 49N/CA 20E**, take exit 182B right onto Idaho Maryland Rd almost 1 mile to Sutton Way. Turn left onto Sutton under ¼ mile to store on right.

GUERNEVILLE

Food for Humans 🛍
16385 First St. ✆ 707-869-3612 ⏲ Daily 10-8
• organic produce
🛍 Where River Rd merges with Hwy 116 in town, turn south onto Mill St to store straight ahead at 1st St.

HALF MOON BAY

Oasis Natural Foods 🛍 🍴
523 Main St. ✆ 650-726-7881 ⏲ Daily 10-6
Vegan soups, sandwiches and tea in the herb garden behind the store.
• organic produce • vegan • organic focus • cafe • tables • self-service • take-out
🛍 **From Hwy 1**, take Kelly Ave exit east 3 blocks to Main St. Turn right onto Main to store on left. **From I-280**, take Hwy 92 east about 8 miles to Half Moon Bay. Turn left at first light onto Main past 3 stop signs to store.

HEALDSBURG

Cafe Gratitude 🍴
2200 Healdsburg Ave. ✆ 415-824-4652 ⏲ Daily 10-10
Focus is on raw food.
• vegan • organic focus • fresh juice • alcohol • tables • wait staff • take-out
🛍 **From Hwy 101**, take Healdsburg Ave/West St exit north about ½ mile to restaurant on right corner in Olive Leaf Ctr.

JACKSON

Gold Trail Natural Foods 🛍 🍴
625 S. Hwy. 49 ✆ 209-223-1896 ⏲ M-F 10-6, Sat-Sun 10-5 Juice Bar M-F 11-3
• organic produce • fresh juice • tables • self-service
🛍 Central Sierra Nevada foothills. Store is on east side of Hwy 49 in Mother Lode Plaza.

LAKE TAHOE

Sprouts Natural Food Cafe 🍴
3125 Harrison Ave. ✆ 530-541-6969 ⏲ Daily 8-9
Soups, salads, sandwiches on 7-grain bread, rice bowls and such.
• vegetarian friendly • organic focus • tables • self-service
🛍 Just off Hwy 50 (aka Harrison Ave) on west side at about San Francisco Ave and across from S Lake Tahoe Recreation Area.

LOS GATOS

Hobee's 🍴
165 Los Gatos Saratoga Rd. ✆ 408-395-5600 ⏲ M-F 7-9, Sat-Sun 8-9
See Mountain View location for description..
• vegetarian friendly • salad bar • alcohol • tables • wait staff • take-out
🛍 **From I-880,** merge onto CA 17S about 6½ miles to Hwy 9 exit toward Los Gatos. Merge onto Hwy 9/Los Gatos Saratoga Rd under ¼ mile to restaurant on left at University Ave. **From Hwy 85N**, merge onto CA 17S and follow directions above. **From Hwy 85S**, take Winchester Blvd exit south on Winchester continuing onto N Santa Cruz Ave about 2¼ miles total to Hwy 9. Turn left onto Hwy 8 to restaurant on right.

Whole Foods Market 🛍 🍴
15980 Los Gatos Blvd. ✆ 408-358-4434 ⏲ Daily 8-10
• organic produce • vegetarian friendly • salad bar • cafe • self-service • take-out
🛍 **From Hwy 85**, take Bascom Ave exit toward Los Gatos Blvd south on Bascom (becomes Los Gatos) about 1½ miles to store on left in Cornerstone Plaza (before Blossom Hill Rd). **From I-880**, merge onto CA 17S about 5¼ miles to Lark Ave exit. Turn left onto Lark ⅓ mile to Los Gatos. Turn right onto Los Gatos almost 1 mile to store.

MENDOCINO

Corners of the Mouth 🏠
45015 Ukiah St. © 707-937-5345   Daily 8-8
• organic produce • co-op

🚗 **From Hwy 1N,** turn left onto Main St about ⅓ mile to Lansing St. Turn right onto Lansing 2 blocks to Ukiah St. Turn left onto Ukiah to store on left in red church. **From Hwy 1S,** turn right onto Little Lake Rd right 3 blocks to Lansing. Turn left onto Lansing 3 blocks to Ukiah. Turn left onto Ukiah to store.

Lu's Kitchen 🍴
45013 Ukiah St. © 707-937-4939 ◷ Tues-Sat 11:30-5:30 Daily in summer
• vegetarian • vegan friendly • organic focus • tables • self-service

🚗 **From Hwy 1N,** turn left onto Main St about ⅓ mile to Lansing St. Turn right onto Lansing 2 blocks to Ukiah St. Turn left onto Ukiah to restaurant on left. **From Hwy 1S,** turn right onto Little Lake Rd 3 blocks to Lansing. Turn left onto Lansing 3 blocks to Ukiah. Turn left onto Ukiah to restaurant.

The Raven's 🍴
Coast Hwy & Comptche Ukiah Rd. © 707-973-5615 ◷ Breakfast daily from 7:30 Dinner daily from 5:30
Located in the Stanford Inn B&B and open to the public for breakfast and dinner. Special 3-course vegan dinner nightly.
• vegetarian • vegan friendly • organic focus • alcohol • tables • wait staff

🚗 **From Hwy 1 south of town center,** go inland on Comptche Ukiah Rd to second drive on left to restaurant in The Stanford Inn.

MENLO PARK

Flea Street Cafe 🍴
3607 Alameda de las Pulgas © 50-854-1226 ◷ Tues-Sat 5:30-9:30, Sun 5:30-8
Upscale gourmet dinner fare. Compostable restaurant waste is saved for local organic farmers.
• vegetarian friendly • organic focus • alcohol • tables • wait staff

🚗 **From Hwy 101** (Bayshore Fwy), take Woodside Rd exit west on Woodside (past El Camino) almost 3 miles to Alameda de las Pulagas. Turn left onto Alameda 2 miles to restaurant on left between Valparaiso Ave & Sand Hill Rd. **From I-280,** take Sand Hill Rd exit east on Sand Hill about 1¾ miles to Santa Cruz Ave. Turn left onto Santa Cruz about ¼ mile and stay in left lane onto Alameda de las Pulgas about ⅓ mile to restaurant.

The JZ Cool Eatery 🍴
827 Santa Cruz Ave. © 650-325-3665 ◷ Lunch Tues-Sat 11-3 Dinner Tues-Th 5-9, F-Sat 5-10
Same owners as the Flea Street Cafe with same organic focus but a lunchtime menu and more casual vibe.
• vegetarian friendly • organic focus • alcohol • counter • tables • wait staff

🚗 **From Hwy 101** (Bayshore Fwy), take Willow Rd toward Menlo Park about 1¼ miles to Middlefield Rd. Turn right onto Middlefield ¾ mile to Ravenswood. Turn left onto Ravenswood Ave (becomes Menlo Ave) under 1 mile to Crane St. Turn right onto Crane 1 block to Santa Cruz Ave. Turn left onto Santa Cruz to restaurant on left. **From I-280,** take Sand Hill Rd exit east on Sand Hill about 1 mile to Santa Cruz. Turn left onto Santa Cruz over 2 miles to restaurant on right.

MILL VALLEY

Whole Foods Market 🏠 🍴
414 Miller Ave. © 415-381-1200 ◷ Daily 8-8
• organic produce • vegetarian friendly • salad bar • cafe • self-service • take-out

🚗 **From US 101N,** take Stinson Beach/Mill Valley exit onto Hwy 1N about ¾ mile to Altamonte Blvd. Merge straight onto Altamonte (becomes Miller Ave) about 1⅓ miles to store on left. **From 101S,** take E Blithedale Ave exit right onto E Blithedale ¾ mile to Camino Alto. Turn left onto Camino Alto ½ mile to Miller. Turn right onto Miller under ½ mile to store.

MILPITAS
Loving Hut ⑪
516 Barber Lane ✆ 408-943-0250 ⊙ M 11-2, Tues-F 11-2, 5:30-9, Sat-Sun 11-9
Asian influenced vegan chain with a green agenda.
  • vegan • tables • wait staff • take-out
🚙 **From I-880S**, take exit 8A right onto Tasman Dr under ¼ mile to Alder Dr. Turn left onto Alder and left onto Barber Ln ½ mile to restaurant on right. **From I-880N**, take Great Mall Pkwy exit onto Thomson St and left onto Great Mall across hwy (becomes Tasman) and follow directions above.

MONTEREY
Whole Foods Market 🛍 ⑪   ♿
800 Del Monte Center ✆ 831-333-1600 ⊙ Daily 8-9
  • organic produce • vegetarian friendly • salad bar • cafe • self-service • take-out
🚙 **From Hwy 1N**, take Monterey exit onto Monrus Ave under ¼ mile to store on right in Del Monte Shopping Ctr. **From IS**, take Soledad Dr toward Monrus Ave about ⅓ mile to Monrus. Turn right onto Monrus to store.

MOUNTAIN VIEW
Chaat Paradise ⑪
165 E. El Camino Real ✆ Daily 11:30-10 ⊙ Indian vegetarian.
  • vegetarian • vegan friendly • tables • wait staff • take-out
🚙 **From 101S (Bayshore Fwy)**, turn right onto CA 85S (signs for Cupertino/Santa Cruz) under 2 miles to Grant Rd exit. Merge onto Grant under ¼ mile to El Camino Real. Turn left onto El Camino Real to restaurant on right. **From US 101N**, take Hwy 237W 2½ miles to El Camino Real. Turn left onto El Camino Real to restaurant.

Garden Fresh Vegetarian Restaurant ⑪
1245 W. El Camino Real ✆ 650-254-1688 ⊙ Daily 11:30-9:30
Asian vegetarian. Brown rice served.
  • vegetarian • vegan friendly • tables • wait staff • take-out
🚙 **From Hwy 101 (Bayshore Fwy)**, take Shoreline Blvd exit toward Mtn View south on N Shoreline about 1¾ miles to El Camino Real. Turn left onto El Camino Real to restaurant on left. **From I-280**, take El Monte Rd exit toward Mtn View right onto El Monte (becomes El Monte Ave) under 3 miles to El Camino Real. Turn right onto El Camino about ½ mile to restaurant on right before Shoreline.

Hobee's ⑪
2312 Central Expwy. ✆ 650-968-6050 ⊙ M-F 7-2:30, Sat-Sun 7:30-2:30
This California chain caters to just about every taste from tofu and brown rice to bacon and fries.
  • vegetarian friendly • salad bar • tables • wait staff • take-out,
🚙 **From Hwy 101 (Bayshore Fwy)**, take Rengstorff Ave south (left from 101S, loop around right from 101N) about 1 mile to Central Expwy. Turn right onto Central to restaurant on right. **From I-280**, take Page Mill Rd/G3N (left from I-280S, right from I-280N) about 1⅓ miles to Foothills Expwy. Turn right onto Foothills 1⅓ miles to Arastradero Rd. Turn left onto Arastradero (becomes W. Charleston) about 1½ miles to restaurant on left.

MT. SHASTA
Berryvale Grocery 🛍 ⑪   ♿
305 S. Mt. Shasta Blvd. ✆ 530-926-1576 ⊙ M-Sat 8:30-7:30, Sun 10-6
  • organic produce • vegetarian friendly • fresh juice • cafe • deli • tables • self-service
  • take-out
🚙 **From I-5**, take Central Mt Shasta exit east about ¼ mile (across tracks) to light at Mt Shasta Blvd. Turn right onto Mt Shasta 2 blocks to store on right.

MURPHYS

Mineral 🍴

419 Main St. ℂ 209-728-9743 ⏱ Lunch M, F-Sun 11:30-3 Dinner M, Th-Sun 5-9
Upscale vegan dining with a tasting menu and a la carte dining at the Exhibition Bar.
Reservations recommended.
   • vegan • organic focus • alcohol • tables • wait staff
🍎 **From CA 4**, go west on Main St ½ mile to restaurant on south side at Algiers Rd.

NAPA

Ubuntu 🍴

1140 Main St. ℂ 707-251-5656 ⏱ Daily 11:30-2:30, 5:30-9
Restaurant/yoga center built on green principles. Eat at the communal table or experience
haute vegetarian dining with the 7-course tasting menu.
   • vegetarian • vegan friendly • organic focus • alcohol • counter • tables • wait staff
🍎 **From CA 29**, take the 1st St exit toward Downtown east on 1st to California
Blvd. Turn left onto California 1 block to W Clay St. Turn right onto W Clay about
½ mile to Franklin St. Turn left onto Franklin to Pearl St. Turn right onto Pearl 3
blocks to Main. Turn left onto Main to restaurant on left.

NEVADA CITY

California Organics 🛍 🍴   ♿

135 Argall Way ℂ 530-265-9392 ⏱ Store M-Sat 8-9, Sun 9-8 Restaurant M-Th 11-
8:30, F 11-9, Sat 9-9, Sun 9-4
Vegetarian, vegan, wild fish, organic poultry grain-fed bison and a green agenda. In-house
organic bakery. Music on weekends. Dine on the patio or in the formal dining room.
   •organic produce • vegetarian friendly • organic focus • fresh juice • salad bar • cafe •
   deli • bakery • tables • wait staff • take-out
🍎 **From Hwy 49,** take Gold Flat Rd east 1 block to Searls Ave. Turn right onto Seals
about ¼ mile to Argall Way. Turn left onto Argall to store on left.

NEWARK

Udupi Palace 🍴

5988 Newpark Mall Rd. ℂ 510-794-8400 ⏱ Daily 11:30-10
North and South Indian vegetarian. Buffet available at lunch.
   • vegetarian • vegan friendly • tables • self-service • wait staff
🍎 **From I-880,** take the Stephens Blvd exit toward Newark west on Stephens (right
from I-880S, left from I-880N) 1 block past hwy to Ballentine Dr. Turn right onto
Ballentine about ½ mile to end at Newpark Mall. Turn left into mall to restaurant.

OAKLAND

Barney's Gourmet Hamburgers 🍴

4162 Piedmont Ave. ℂ 510-655-7180 ℂ M-Th 11-9:30, F-Sat 11-10, Sun 11-9
See Shattuck Ave location in Berkeley for description.
   • vegetarian friendly • vegan friendly • alcohol • tables • wait staff
🍎 **From I-580E,** take Broadway exit left onto Piedmont Ave about ¾ mile to
restaurant on right. **From I-580W**, take exit 21A onto W MacArthur Blvd about ¾
mile to Piedmont. Turn right onto Piedmont about ½ mile to restaurant.

Barney's Gourmet Hamburgers 🍴

5819 College Ave. ℂ 510-601-0444 ⏱ M-Th 11-9:30, F-Sat 11-10, Sun 11-9
See Shattuck Ave location in Berkeley for description.
   •vegetarian friendly • vegan friendly • alcohol • tables • wait staff
🍎 **From I-580,** take Hwy 24E about ½ mile to Claremont Ave. Turn left onto
Claremont about ½ mile to Chabot Ave. Turn right onto Chabot 1 block to College
Ave. Turn right onto College to restaurant on right.

Cafe Gratitude 🍴

230 Bay Place ℭ 415-824-4652 ⊘ Daily 10-10
Focus is on raw food.
  • vegan • organic focus • fresh juice • alcohol • tables • wait staff • take-out

🚗 **From I-580E,** take Oakland Ave exit onto W Perry Pl and turn right onto Vernon Ave ½ mile to Bay Pl. Turn right onto Bay to restaurant on right inside Whole Foods. **From I-580W,** take Grand Ave exit right onto Grand about ¾ mile to Bay. Veer right onto Bay to restaurant.

Food Mill 🍴

3033 MacArthur Blvd. ℭ 510-482-3848 ⊘ M-F 8-7:30, Sat 8-6:30, Sun 9-5:30
🚗 **From I-580E,** take 35th St exit left onto 35th about ¼ mile to MacArthur Blvd. Turn left onto MacArthur 2½ blocks to store on left. **From I-580W,** take Coolidge Ave exit left onto Montana St and right onto Coolidge 3 blocks to MacArthur. Turn right onto MacArthur 1½ blocks to store on right.

Golden Lotus 🍴

1301 Franklin St. ℭ 510-893-0383 ⊘ Daily 10-9
Asian, mostly Vietnamese and predominantly vegan.
  • vegetarian • vegan friendly • tables • wait staff

🚗 **From I-880S,** take exit for Broadway/Alameda onto Union St and turn right onto 7th St 1 mile to Franklin Ave. Turn left onto Franklin St about ⅓ mile to restaurant on left at 13th St. **From I-880N,** take Broadway exit right at fork onto Broadway 3 blocks to 9th St. Turn right onto 9th 1 block to Franklin. Turn left onto Franklin 3 blocks to restaurant. **From I-980E,** take exit 1A right onto 11th St under ½ mile to Franklin. Turn left onto Franklin 2 blocks to restaurant. **From I-980W,** take 12th St exit left at fork onto Brush St, turn left onto 11th and follow directions above.

Manzanita Restaurant 🍴

4001 Linden St. ℭ 510-985-8386 ⊘ M-F 11-3, Sat-Sun 11-4
Daily macrobiotic menu and Sunday lunch buffet.
  vegan • organic focus • tables • wait staff • self-service • take-out

🚗 **From I-580E,** bear left onto MacArthur Blvd ½ mile to Market St. Turn left onto Market 3 blocks to 40th St. Turn left onto 40th under ¼ mile to restaurant at Linden St.

New World Vegetarian Cuisine 🍴

464 8th St. ℭ 510-238-8816 ⊘ M-Th, Sun 11-9, F-Sat 11-9:30
Extensive international vegan menu.
  • vegan • tables • wait staff • take-out

🚗 **From I-880S,** take exit for Broadway/Alameda onto Union St and turn right onto 7th St 1 mile to Broadway. Turn left onto Broadway and left onto 8th St to restaurant on right. **From I-880N,** take Broadway exit right at fork onto Broadway 2 blocks to 8th St. Turn left onto 8th to restaurant.

Whole Foods 🛍 🍴

230 Bay Place ℭ 10-834-9800 ⊘ Daily 8-10
  • organic produce • vegetarian friendly • salad bar • cafe • self-service • take-out

🚗 **From I-580E,** take Oakland Ave exit onto W Perry Pl and turn right onto Vernon Ave ½ mile to Bay Pl. Turn right onto Bay to store on right. **From I-580W,** take Grand Ave exit right onto Grand about ¾ mile to Bay. Veer right onto Bay to store.

PACIFICA

Good Health Natural Foods 🛍

80 W. Manor Drive ℭ 650-355-5936 ⊘ M-Th 9:30-8, F 9:30-7, Sat 9:30-6, Sun 12-6
  • organic produce

🚗 **From Hwy 1,** take Manor D exit west about 1 block to store on left.

PALO ALTO

Country Sun Natural Foods 🛍

440 S. California Ave. ℭ 650-324-9190 ⊘ M-Sat 9-8, Sat-Sun 9-7

• organic produce

🏠 **From Hwy 101 (Bayshore Fwy),** take Oregon Expwy exit and follow ramp onto Oregon about 2 miles to El Camino Real. Turn right onto El Camino Real ¼ mile to light at California Ave. Turn right onto California to store on left. **From I-280,** take Page Mill Rd exit toward Arastradero Rd (left from I-280S, right from I-280N) about 3 miles to El Camino Real. Turn left onto El Camino Real ¼ mile to light at California. Turn right onto California to store.

Hobee's 🍴

4224 El Camino Real ✆ 650-856-6124 ⏱ M 7-2:30, Tues-F 7-9, Sat 7:30-9, Sun 8-2:30
See the Mountain View location for description.
   • vegetarian friendly • salad bar • alcohol • tables • wait staff • take-out

🏠 **From Hwy 101S (Bayshore Fwy),** take San Antonio Rd South exit straight onto San Antonio about ⅓ mile to E Charleston Rd. Turn right onto E Charleston (becomes W Charleston) about 1½ miles to El Camino Real. Turn left onto El Camino Real to restaurant. **From 101N,** take Rengstorff Rd exit and follow ramp around and right onto Rengstorff to Charleston. Turn left onto Charleston and follow directions above. **From I-280,** take Page Mill Rd exit toward Arastradero Rd/Palo Alto (left from I-280S, right from I-280N) about 3 miles to El Camino Real. Turn right onto El Camino Real about 1½ miles to restaurant after W Charleston.

Hobee's 🍴

67 Town & Country Village ✆ 650-327-4111 ⏱ M-F 7-9, Sat-Sun 8-9
Near Stanford U. See the Mountain View location for description.
   • vegetarian friendly • salad bar • alcohol • tables • wait staff • take-out,

🏠 **From Hwy 101 (Bayshore Fwy),** take Embarcadero Rd west (right from 101S, loop around right from 101N) about 2¼ miles to El Camino Real. Turn right onto El Camino Real to restaurant in Town & Country Village (just north of Stanford stadium). **From I-280,** take Sand Hill Rd exit toward Palo Alto and follow Sand Hill Rd East ramp onto Sand Hill about 3½ miles to El Camino Real. Turn right on El Camino Real under 1 mile to restaurant.

Loving Hut 🍴

165 University Ave. ✆ 650-321-5588 ⏱ M-Sat 11-9
Vegan fast-food chain with a green agenda.
   • vegan • organic focus • tables • self-service • take-out

🏠 **From Hwy 101 (Bayshore Fwy),** take exit 403 toward Palo Alto onto University Ave 2 miles to restaurant on right after Emerson St.

Whole Foods Market 🛒🍴   ♿

774 Emerson St. ✆ 650-326-8676 ⏱ Daily 8-10
   • organic produce • vegetarian friendly • salad bar • cafe • self-service • take-out

🏠 **From US 101 (Bayshore Fwy),** take University Ave exit toward Stanford (right from 101S, loop around right from 101N) under 2 miles to Emerson St. Turn left onto Emerson to 3 blocks to Homer Ave. Turn right onto Homer to store on right. **From I-280,** take Page Mill Rd exit toward Arastradero Rd/Palo Alto (left from I-280S, right from I-280N) about 3 miles to El Camino Real. Turn left on El Camino Real about 1½ miles to University Ave exit. Turn right onto University 2 blocks to Emerson. Turn right onto Emerson and follow directions above.

PARADISE

Almond Street Natural Foods 🛒

5729 Almond St. ✆ 530-877-5164 ⏱ M-F 9-6, Sat 9-4, Sun 11-3
   • organic produce

🏠 **From Hwy 99N,** take Skyway Ave east about 10½ miles to Pearson Rd. Turn right onto Pearson 2 blocks to Almond St. Turn left onto Almond to store on left. **From Hwy 70N,** turn left onto CA 171 (Clark Rd) almost 11½ miles to Pearson Rd. Turn left onto Pearson 1 mile (past 2 stop signs) to Almond St. Turn right onto Almond to store on left.

Nature's Pantry 🛍️

6008D Clark Rd. ✆ 530-872-0549 ⏰ M-Th 9-6, F 9-4, Sun 11-4

🍎 **From Hwy 99S,** take Skyway Ave east about 11 miles to Elliot Rd. Turn right onto Elliot about 1 mile to Clark Rd. Turn left onto Clark, then right into Safeway Plaza to store. **From Hwy 70N,** turn left onto CA 191 (Clark Rd) about 12 miles (past Elliot) to store.

PETALUMA

Whole Foods Market 🛍️ 🍴　　　　　　　　　　　　　　♿

621 E. Washington St. ✆ 707-762-9352 ⏰ Daily 8-9
• organic produce • vegetarian friendly • salad bar • cafe • self-service • take-out

🍎 **From Hwy 101,** take E Washington St exit toward Central Petaluma (left from 101S, right from 101N) 4 blocks to store.

QUINCY

Quincy Natural Foods Co-op 🛍️

269 Main St. ✆ 530-283-3528 ⏰ M-Sat 9-8, Sun 9-7
• organic produce • deli • bakery • take-out • co-op

🍎 CA 70 & 89 meet up in Quincy. Store is on 70/89 (aka Main St) in downtown Quincy (next to post office).

REDWOOD CITY

Whole Foods Market 🛍️ 🍴

1250 Jefferson Ave. ✆ 650-367-1400 ⏰ Daily 8-10
• organic produce • vegetarian friendly • salad bar • cafe • self-service • take-out

🍎 **From US 101S (Bayshore Fwy),** take exit 409 onto Veterans Blvd about ¾ mile to Jefferson Ave. Turn right onto Jefferson over ½ mile to store on right after El Camino Real. **From US 101N,** take exit 408 onto Woodside Rd, turn right onto Veterans Blvd about ¾ mile to Jefferson and turn left onto Jefferson over ½ mile to store.

RICHMOND

Williams Natural Foods 🛍️

12249 San Pablo Ave. ✆ 510-232-1911 ⏰ M-F 9-7, Sat 9-6, Sun 11-6
• organic produce

🍎 **From I-80,** take San Pablo Ave exit south on San Pablo (sharp right from I-80N, left onto Barrett Ave and second right onto San Pablo from I-80S) to store between Barrett & McDonald Ave. **From I-580E,** take Marina Bay Pkwy exit left onto Marina Bay (becomes 23rd St) about ⅓ mile to Cutting Blvd. Turn right onto Cutting about 1½ miles to San Pablo. Turn left onto San Pablo about ⅔ mile to store.

SACRAMENTO

Elliott's Natural Foods 🛍️　　　　　　　　　　　　　　♿

3347 El Camino Ave. ✆ 916-481-3173 ⏰ M-Sat 9-6, Sun 11-4
• organic produce

🍎 **From I-80,** take Watt Ave south (right from I-80E, left from I-80W) about 2½ miles to El Camino Ave. Turn right onto El Camino to store at Yorktown Ave. **From US 50,** take Watt north about 3½ miles to El Camino. Turn left onto El Camino to store.

Sacramento Natural Foods Co-op 🛍️ 🍴　　　　　　　　♿

1900 Alhambra Blvd. ✆ 916-455-2667 ⏰ Daily 7-10
• organic produce • fresh juice • salad bar • cafe • deli • tables • self-service • take-out

🍎 **From US 50W,** take Stockton Blvd exit right onto Stockton 1 block to 34th St. Turn sharp left onto 34th 1 block to S St. Turn right onto S 2 blocks to store parking lot on left. **From US 50E,** take 34th St exit left onto 34th 3 blocks to S. Turn left onto S 2 blocks store parking. **From I-80E,** merge onto 50E and follow directions above. **From I-80 Bus W,** take P St exit and veer left onto 29th St about ¼ mile to S. Turn left onto S 2 blocks to store parking on right.

Whole Foods Market 🛒 🍴

4315 Arden Way ✆ 916-488-2800 ⏰ Daily 8-10
• organic produce • vegetarian friendly • salad bar • cafe • self-service • take-out
🍎 **From I-80**, take Watt Ave south (right from I-80E, left from I-80W) about 2½ miles to El Camino Ave. Turn left onto El Camino 1 mile to Eastern Way. Turn right onto Eastern 1 mile to Arden Way. Turn left onto Arden to store on left. **From US 50**, take Watt Ave north (right at fork from US 50W, loop around from US 50E) 1⅓-1¾ miles to Fair Oaks Blvd. Turn right onto Fair Oaks about 1 mile to Arden. Turn right onto Arden to store.

SAN FRANCISCO

Alive! Restaurant 🍴

1972 Lombard St. ✆ 415-923-1052 ⏰W-Sun 5-10
Primarily raw foods. Located in the marina.
• vegan • organic focus • alcohol • tables • wait staff • take-out
🍎 **From US 101S**, exit toward Lombard St onto Richardson Ave/101 (becomes Lombard St) 1 mile to restaurant on left at Webster St. **From US 101N** (Van Ness Ave), turn left onto Lombard ½ mile to restaurant right at Webster.

Ananda Fuara 🍴

1298 Market St ✆ 415-621-1994 ⏰ M-Tues, Th-Sat 8-8, Wed 8-3
Run by followers of Sri Chinmoy. Multicultural entrees, wraps, sandwiches, burgers and pizza.
• vegetarian • vegan friendly • tables • wait staff • take-out
🍎 **From US 101N**, take 9th St exit left onto 9th over ½ mile to Market St. Turn left onto Market to restaurant. **From I-80W**, take 9th St exit and follow split in road right to Harrison St. Turn left onto Harrison, make first right onto 9th and follow directions above.

Barney's Gourmet Hamburgers 🍴

3344 Steiner St. ✆ 415-563-0307 ⏰ M-Th 11-10, F-Sat 11-10:30, Sun 11-9
See Shattuck Ave location in Berkeley for description.
• vegetarian friendly • vegan friendly • alcohol • tables • wait staff
🍎 **From US 101S**, merge onto Marina Blvd (signs for Marina) ¾ mile to Scott St. Turn right onto Scott under ½ mile to Chestnut St. Turn left onto Chestnut 2 blocks to Steiner St. Turn right onto Steiner to restaurant on left. **From US 101N**, turn left onto Lombard St about ¾ mile to Steiner. Turn right onto Steiner 1 block to restaurant on right.

Barney's Gourmet Hamburgers 🍴

4138 24th St. ✆ 15-282-7770 ⏰ M-Th 11-9:30, F-Sat 11-10, Sun 11-9
See Shattuck Ave location in Berkeley for description.
• vegetarian friendly • vegan friendly • alcohol • tables • wait staff
🍎 **From US 101**, take Cesar Chavez exit west on Chavez to end at Noe St. Turn right onto Noe 5 blocks to 24th St. Turn left onto 24th to restaurant on right after Castro St. **From Golden Gate Bridge**, follow 101S east on Lombard St to Divisidero St. Turn right onto Divisidero 2 miles to Castro. Merge left onto Castro 1⅓ miles to 24th. Turn right onto 24th to restaurant.

Bok Choy Garden 🍴

1820 Clement St. ✆ 15-387-8111 ⏰ Tues-Th, Sun 11-9, F-Sat 11-9:30
Chinese vegan.
• vegan • tables • wait staff
🍎 **From US 101S**, take the CA 1 exit toward 19th Ave and merge onto CA 1S almost 1½ miles to Clement St. Turn right onto Clement about 5 blocks to restaurant on right at 19th Ave.

Buffalo Whole Food & Grain Co. 🛍
598 Castro St. ℰ 415-626-7038 ◷ M-Sat 9-8, Sun 10-8
🚍 **From US 101N**, merge onto Central Skyway to Fell St. Turn left onto Fell 7 blocks to Divisadero St. Turn left onto Divisadero (becomes Castro St) about 1 mile to store on right at 19th St. **From US 101S**, turn right onto Divisadero (becomes Castro) about 2¾ miles to store.

Cafe Gratitude 🍴
2400 Harrison St. ℰ 415-824-4652 ◷ Daily 10-10
Focus is on raw food.
• vegan • organic focus • fresh juice • alcohol • tables • wait staff • take-out
🚍 **From I-80**, take 9th St exit east to Harrison St. Turn left onto Harrison St 1 mile to restaurant on left at 20th St.

Cafe Gratitude 🍴
1336 9th Ave. ℰ 415-824-4652 ◷ Daily 10-10
Focus is on raw food.
• vegan • organic focus • fresh juice • alcohol • tables • wait staff • take-out
🚍 **From I-280,** take CA 1N/Juniper Serra Blvd (signs for 19th Ave) about 5 miles to Lincoln Way. Turn right onto Lincoln about ½ mile to 9th Ave. Turn right onto 9th to restaurant on left.

Daily Health 🛍 🍴
1235 9th Ave. ℰ 415-681-7675 ◷ M-F 10-8, Sat-Sun 12-5
• vegan • deli • tables • self-service • take-out
🚍 **From US 101S,** take the CA 1 exit toward 19th Ave and merge onto CA 1S 3 miles (through the SF Presidio and Golden Gate Park) to Lincoln Way. Turn left onto Lincoln about ½ mile to 9th Ave. Turn right onto 9th to store on right (1 block south of Golden Gate Park). **From CA 1 (19th Ave) heading north**, turn right onto Lincoln Way and follow directions above.

Enjoy 🍴
754 Kirkham St. ℰ 415-682-0826 ◷Tues-Sun 11-2:30, 5-9
Chinese vegetarian.
• vegetarian • vegan friendly • tables • wait staff
🚍 **From Golden Gate Bridge,** take CA 1S (Park Presidio Blvd) almost 5½ miles (through park) to Irving St. Turn right onto Irving 1 block to 20th St. Turn left onto 20th 1 block to Judah St. Turn left onto Judah 7 blocks (under ½ mile) to Funston Ave. Turn right onto Funston 1 block to Kirkham St. Turn left onto Kirkham 1 block to restaurant at 12th Ave.

Firefly 🍴
4288 24th St. ℰ 415-821-7652 ◷ Daily from 5:30
Upscale menu with mostly vegetarian appetizers and a mix of vegetarian, fish, free-range chicken and "drug-free" beef entrees.
• vegetarian friendly • organic focus • alcohol • tables • wait staff
🚍 **From US 101,** take Cesar Chavez exit west on Chavez to end at Noe St. Turn right onto Noe 5 blocks to 24th St. Turn left onto 24th 3 blocks to restaurant between Diamond & Douglass St. **From Golden Gate Bridge,** follow 101S east on Lombard St to Divisidero St. Turn right onto Divisadero 2 miles to Castro St. Merge left onto Castro 1⅓ miles to 24th. Turn right onto 24th 2 blocks to restaurant.

Golden Era Vegetarian Restaurant 🍴
572 O'Farrell St. ℰ 415- 673-3136 ◷ M, W-Sun 11-9
Vietnamese vegetarian. Brown rice available.
• vegan • tables • wait staff • take-out
🚍 **From I-80,** take 7th St exit toward US 101N/Downtown left onto 7th (becomes Leavenworth St) about 1 mile to restaurant on right at O'Farrell St.

Greens Restaurant 🍴

Fort Mason, Bldg. A ✆ 415-771-6222 ⏰ Lunch Tues-Sat 12-2:30 Brunch Sun 10:30-2 Dinner M-F 5:30-9:30, Sat (Prix Fixe Only) 5:30-9
Mediterranean, Mexican and Southwest influences. Overlooking the Golden Gate Bridge in the Fort Mason Center—home to nonprofit arts, cultural and environmental organizations.
• vegetarian • vegan friendly • organic focus • alcohol • tables • wait staff • take-out
🚗 **From US 101S (across Golden Gate Bridge),** take Marina Blvd exit and follow Marina 1½ miles to Buchanan St. Turn left into Fort Mason Ctr to restaurant. **From 101N,** merge onto I-280N toward Port of SF 3⅓ miles and merge onto King St (becomes The Embarcadero) 2¾ miles to Bay St. Turn left onto Bay to Buchanan. Turn right onto Buchanan, cross Marina Blvd and make sharp right into Fort Mason Ctr to restaurant.

Harvest Market 🛒

2285 Market St. ✆ 415-626-0805 ⏰ Daily 8:30-11
• organic produce • vegetarian friendly • salad bar • deli • self-service • take-out
🚗 **From US 101S,** merge onto Richardson Ave to Divisidero St. Turn right onto Divisidero 2 miles and merge onto Castro St almost ½ mile to 16th St. Turn left onto 16th 1 block to Market St. Turn left onto Market to store on right at Noe St. **From US 101N,** turn left onto Vermont St 1 block to 16th. Turn left onto 16th 1 ½ miles to Market. Make sharp right onto Market to store.

Harvest Market 🛒 🍴

191 8th St. ✆ 415-621-1000 ⏰ Daily 8:30-11
• organic produce • vegetarian friendly • salad bar • cafe • deli • tables • self-service • take- out
🚗 **From I-80E,** take exit toward 101N and merge left onto 7th St under ½ mile to Minna St. Turn left onto Minna 1 block to 8th St. Turn left onto 8th 1 block to store on right at Howard St. **From I-80W,** take exit 1C toward 9th St right at fork toward S 9th/Fell St. Turn left onto Harrison 1 block to 9th. Turn right onto 9th ⅓ mile to Natona Ave (1 block past Howard). Turn right onto Natona 1 block to store.

Herbivore 🍴

531 Divisadero St. ✆ 415-885-7133 ⏰ M-Th, Sun 9-10, F-Sat 9-11
Vegan soups, salads, sandwiches and noodles.
• vegan • alcohol • tables • wait staff
🚗 **From US 101N,** merge onto Central Skyway to Fell St. Turn left onto Fell 7 blocks restaurant at Divisadero St. **From US 101S,** turn right onto Divisadero 1¾ miles to restaurant at Fell.

Herbivore 🍴

983 Valencia St. ✆ 415-826-5657 ⏰ M-Th, Sun 9-10, F-Sat 9-11
Vegan soups, salads, sandwiches and noodles.
vegan • alcohol • tables • wait staff
🚗 **From US 101S (aka Van Ness Ave),** go west on 21st St 5 blocks to Valencia St. Turn right onto Valencia to restaurant between 21st & 20th St. **From 101N,** take C Chavez/Protrero Ave exit left onto Protrero and right onto Chavez Ave under 1 mile to Valencia. Turn right onto Valencia about ⅔ mile to restaurant.

Loving Hut 🍴

1365 Stockton St. ✆ 415-362-2199 ⏰ M-Th, Sun 10:30-8:30, F-Sat 10:30-9
Asian influenced vegan chain with a green agenda.
• vegan • tables • wait staff • take-out
🚗 **From I-80W,** take Fremont St exit right at fork and left onto Folsum St ⅓ mile to The Embarcadero. Turn left onto The Embarcadero about ¾ mile to Broadway. Turn left onto Broadway over ½ mile to Stockton St. Turn right onto Stockton to restaurant on left. **From I-280N,** continue onto The Embarcadero about 1½ miles to Broadway and follow directions above.

Lucky Creation 🍴

854 Washington St. ℂ 415-989-0818 ⊕ M-Tues, Th-Sun 11-9:30
Vegetarian Chinese.
• vegetarian • vegan friendly • tables • wait staff

🚗 **From I-80W,** exit onto Fremont St 1 mile continuing onto Front St 1 block to Pine St. Turn left onto Pine almost ½ mile to Grant St. Turn right onto Grant about ⅓ mile to Washington St. Turn left onto Washington 1 block to restaurant on right. **From I-80W,** take exit for US 101N on 7th St and turn right onto Folsom St about ¾ mile to 3rd St. Turn left onto 3rd almost ½ mile continuing onto Kearny St ½ mile to Washington. Turn left onto Washington about 3 blocks to restaurant.

Millennium 🍴

580 Geary St. ℂ 415-345-3900 ⊕ M-Th, Sun 5:30-9, F-Sat 5:30-10
Upscale gourmet menu and environmental approach including composting and recycling.
• vegan • organic focus • alcohol • tables • wait staff

🚗 **From US 101S (across Golden Gate Bridge),** follow 101S east on Lombard St to Van Ness Ave. Turn right onto Van Ness about 1 mile to Bush St. Turn left onto Bush 7 blocks (about ½ mile) to Mason St. Turn right onto Mason 3 blocks to Geary St. Turn right onto Geary 3 blocks to restaurant on right at Jones St in the Savoy Hotel. **From Bay Bridge,** take I-80W to 5th St exit. Turn right onto 5th about ½ mile to Ellis St ((2 blocks past Market S). Turn left onto Ellis 2 blocks to Taylor St. Turn right onto Taylor 2 bocks to Geary. Turn left onto Geary 2 blocks to restaurant.

Minako 🍴

2154 Mission St. ℂ 415-864-1888 ⊕ W-Sun 5:30-9
Organic Japanese food. Small place with a big vegan selection, fish and free-range chicken.
• vegetarian friendly • vegan friendly • organic focus • alcohol • tables • wait staff

🚗 **From I-80W,** take exit 1B onto US 101N ¾ mile to exit 434A. Merge onto Duboce Ave under ½ mile to Valencia St. Turn left onto Valencia 2 blocks to 14th St. Turn left onto 14th 2 blocks to Mission St. Turn right onto Mission 3½ blocks to restaurant on left between 17th & 18th. **From I-280N,** exit onto San Jose Ave 1⅓ miles to Brook St. Turn right onto Brook 1 block to Mission. Turn left onto Mission 1½ miles to restaurant on right between 18th & 17th.

New Ganges 🍴

775 Frederick St. ℂ 415-681-4355 ⊕ Daily 11-2, 5-10
Vegetarian Indian cuisine.
• vegetarian • vegan friendly • tables • wait staff

🚗 **From Bay Bridge or US 101N,** take Fell St exit west to Golden Gate Park. Take left fork in park onto Kezar Dr to Lincoln Way. Turn left onto Lincoln 2 blocks to Arguello Blvd. Turn right onto Arguello 1 block to Frederick St. Turn left onto Frederick to restaurant.

Other Avenues Food Store 🛍

3930 Judah St. ℂ 415-661-7475 ⊕ Daily 10-8
• organic produce • co-op

🚗 **From Golden Gate Bridge,** take 19th Ave exit about 5½ miles (through park) to Judah St. Turn right onto Judah about 1½ miles to store between 44th & 45th Ave. **From Bay Bridge,** take Fell St exit west to Golden Gate Park. When road enters park take left fork onto Kezar Dr to Lincoln Way. Merge right onto Lincoln about 2½ miles to 44th Ave. Turn left onto 44th 2 blocks to Judah. Turn right onto Judah to store.

Rainbow Grocery Cooperative 🛍 ♿

1745 Folsom St. ℂ 415-863-0620 ⊕ Daily 9-9
A vegetarian market with a social and environmental outlook.
• organic produce • co-op

🚗 **From I-80W,** take 9th St exit and follow split in road right to Harrison St. Turn left onto Harrison about ¼ mile to 14th St (1 block past fwy overpass). Turn right onto 14th 2 blocks to Folsom St. Turn right on Folsom to store on right. (Parking lot is 1 block further on 13th St.) **From US 101N,** take 9th St exit 1 block to Harrison. Turn left onto Harrison and follow directions above.

Real Food Co. 🛍

3060 Fillmore St. ℂ 415-567-6900 ⏲ Daily 8-9
• organic produce

🚗 **From US 101S (across Golden Gate Bridge),** follow 101S east on Lombard St to Fillmore St (4 blocks past Divisidero St). Turn right onto Fillmore 4 blocks to store at Filbert St.

Real Food Co. 🛍

2140 Polk St. ℂ 415-673-7420 ⏲ Daily 9-9
• organic produce

🚗 **From US 101S (across Golden Gate Bridge),** follow 101S east on Lombard St to Van Ness Ave. Turn right onto Van Ness 2 blocks to Filbert St. Turn left onto Filbert 1 block to Polk St. Turn right onto Polk about 4 blocks to store (just north of Broadway St).

Shangri-La Vegetarian Restaurant 🍴

2026 Irving St. ℂ 415-731-2548 ⏲ Daily 11:30-8:45 (closed sometimes on W)
Chinese vegan.

• vegan • organic focus • kosher • alcohol • tables • wait staff • take-out

🚗 **From Golden Gate Bridge,** take CA 1S (Park Presidio Blvd/19th Ave) 5½ miles (through park) to Irving St. Turn right onto Irving about 2 blocks to restaurant at 21st Ave. **From I-280N,** take CA 1N/19th Ave about 4 miles to Irving St. Turn left onto Irving to restaurant at 21st.

The Nature Stop 🛍

1336 Grant Ave. ℂ 415-398-3810 ⏲ M-F 9-9, Sat-Sun 10-9
• vegetarian friendly • deli • take-out

🚗 **From The Embarcadero,** go west on Broadway St ½ mile to Columbus Ave. Turn right onto Columbus and veer right onto Grant to store on right after Vallejo St.

The Plant Cafe 🍴

3352 Steiner St. ℂ 415-931-2777 ⏲ M-F 11-10, Sat-Sun 10-10
Vegetarian, vegan, fish and chicken.

• vegetarian friendly • vegan friendly • organic focus • fresh juice • alcohol • tables • self-service

🚗 **From US 101S,** merge onto Marina Blvd (signs for Marina) ¾ mile to Scott St. Turn right onto Scott under ½ mile to Chestnut St. Turn left onto Chestnut 2 blocks to Steiner St. Turn right onto Steiner to restaurant on left. **From US 101N,** turn left onto Lombard St about ¾ mile to Steiner. Turn right onto Steiner 1 block to restaurant on right at Chestnut.

The Usual Suspects Cafe 🍴

450 Broadway ℂ 415-434-4444 ⏲ Tues-Sat 5-10
Pizza, falafel, burgers, vegan pesto, cashew cheez, homemade seitan.

• vegetarian • vegan friendly • alcohol • organic focus • counter • tables • wait staff

🚗 **From 101 Fwy,** take Broadway east (left from 101 S, right from 101N) 1 mile to restaurant on north side at Montgomery St. **From I-80W or I-280N,** take The Embarcadero about 1 mile to Broadway. Turn left onto Broadway under ½ mile to restaurant.

Thom's Natural Foods 🛍

5843 Geary Blvd. ℂ 415-387-6367 ⏲ Daily 10-8

🚗 **From Golden Gate Bridge,** take CA 1S (Park Presidio Blvd) 4 miles to Geary Blvd. Turn right onto Geary ½ mile to store between 22nd & 23rd Ave.

Weird Fish 🍴

2193 Mission St. ℂ 415-863-4744 ⏲ M-Th, Sun 11:30-4, 5-10:30, F-Sat 11:30-4, 5-11
Small place with a funky vibe and a sustainable outlook. Vegetarian and seafood.

• vegetarian friendly • vegan friendly • alcohol • tables • wait staff

🚗 **From I-80W,** take exit 1B onto US 101N ¾ mile to exit 434A. Merge onto Duboce Ave under ½ mile to Valencia St. Turn left onto Valencia 2 blocks to 14th St. Turn left onto 14th 2 blocks to Mission St. Turn right onto Mission 4 blocks to restaurant on left at 18th St. **From I-280N,** exit onto San Jose Ave 1⅓ miles to Brook St. Turn right onto Brook 1 block to Mission. Turn left onto Mission 1½ miles to restaurant on right at 18th.

Whole Foods Market 🛒 🍴 &

1765 California St. © 415-674-0500 ⏰ Daily 8-10
• organic produce • vegetarian friendly • salad bar • cafe • self-service • take-out

🏠 **From US 101N**, take Mission St exit toward Van Ness Ave onto 101N (becomes Van Ness) 1⅓ miles to Pine St. Turn left onto Pine 1 block to Franklin St. Turn right onto Franklin 1 block to store at California St. **From US 101S (across Golden Gate Bridge),** follow 101S east on Lombard to Van Ness. Turn right onto Van Ness ¾ mile to California. Turn right onto California 1 block to store at Franklin.

Whole Foods Market 🛒 🍴

399 4th St. © 415-618-0066 ⏰ Daily 8-10
• organic produce • vegetarian friendly • salad bar • cafe • self-service • take-out

🏠 **From I-80W**, take 5th St exit on left toward Golden Gate Bridge right onto 5th 3 blocks to Folsum St. Turn right onto Folsum and next right onto 4th St 3 blocks to store on left. **From I-80E (or US 101N)**, take exit toward 101N onto 7th St across hwy to Folsum. Turn right onto Folsum under ¼ mile and follow directions above.

SAN JOSE

Di Lac Cuisine 🍴

1644 E. Capitol Expwy. © 408-238-8686 ⏰ Daily 9-9
"Vegetarian & Tofu" with an Asian orientation.
• vegetarian • vegan friendly • tables • wait staff

🏠 **From US 101 (Bayshore Fwy),** take Capitol Expwy exit and Capitol Expwy East ramp onto Capitol Expwy about ⅓ mile (less from 101N) to restaurant on right before Silver Creek/King Rd intersection.

Global Vegetarian Bistro 🍴

322 E. Santa Clara St. © 408-294-6021 ⏰ Daily 9-9
Asian vegetarian.
• vegetarian • vegan friendly • tables • wait staff

🏠 **From I-280,** take the 11th St exit left from I-280S, right from I-280N onto 11th 1 mile to E Santa Clara St. Turn left onto E Santa Clara under ¼ mile to restaurant on left after S 8th St. **From US 101N (Bayshore Fwy),** take I-280N and follow directions above. **From US 101S,** take the Santa Clara St exit right onto E Santa Clara about 1½ miles to restaurant.

Happy Bamboo Vegetarian Cafe 🍴

1711 Branham Lane, Ste. A9 © 408-694-0740 ⏰ Tues-Sun 11:30-9
Mostly vegan Thai plus sandwiches, Mexican and western specialties. Brown rice available.
• vegetarian • vegan friendly • tables • wait staff

🏠 **From CA Hwy 85N,** take exit toward Camden Ave right onto Branham Ln to restaurant on left in Branham Shopping Ctr. **From Hwy 85S,** take Camden Ave exit right onto Camden and right onto Branham to restaurant.

Hobee's 🍴

680 River Oaks Plaza, Ste. P © 408-232-0190 ⏰ M-F 6:30-2:30, Sat-Sun 8-2:30
See the Mountain View location for directions.
• vegetarian friendly • salad bar • tables • wait staff • take-out

🏠 **From I-880,** take Montague Expwy exit and Montague Expwy West ramp west on Montague about 1⅓ miles to restaurant in River Oaks Plaza. **From US 101 (Bayshore Fwy),** take Montague Expwy exit and Montague Expwy ramp east under 3 miles to restaurant.

Sogo Tofu 🛒

1610 S. De Anza Blvd. © 408-517-8958 ⏰ Daily 8-8
Tiny store with take-out Chinese vegetarian lunch.
• vegetarian • take-out

🏠 **From Hwy 85,** take DeAnza Blvd exit south on DeAnza (right from Hwy 85S, left from Hwy 85N) about ⅓ mile to store on left before Prospect Rd.

Tofoo Com Chay 🍴

388 E. Santa Clara 📞 408-286-6335 ⏰ M-F 9-9, Sat 9-6
Small vegetarian deli with a few tables and take-out.
• vegetarian • vegan friendly • tables • self-service • take-out
🍎 **From I-280,** take the 11th St exit left from I-280S, right from I-280N onto 11th 1 mile to E Santa Clara St. Turn left onto E Santa Clara under ¼ mile to restaurant on left after S 9th St. **From US 101N (Bayshore Fwy),** take I-280N and follow directions above. **From US 101S,** take the Santa Clara St exit right onto E Santa Clara about 1⅓ miles to restaurant on left.

Vegetarian House 🍴

520 E. Santa Clara St. 📞 408-292-3798 ⏰ M-F 11-2, 5-9, Sat-Sun 11-9
Asian emphasis with a smattering of Italian, Middleastern and Indian.
• vegan • organic focus • tables • wait staff • take-out
🍎 **From I-280,** take the 11th St exit left from I-280S, right from I-280N onto 11th 1 mile to E Santa Clara St. Turn right onto E Santa Clara to restaurant on right. **From US 101N (Bayshore Fwy),** take1-280N and follow directions above. **From US 101S,** take the Santa Clara St exit right onto E Santa Clara about 1 mile to restaurant on left after 12th St.

SAN MATEO

Que se Raw se Raw 🍴

407 N. San Mateo Drive 📞 650-347-4565 ⏰ W-F
Raw food delivered to the deli refrigerator in the lobby of the Vitality Center between noon and 1 pm Wednesday to Friday. Sometimes it lasts through Saturday.
• vegan • organic focus • take-out
🍎 **From Hwy 101S (Bayshore Fwy),** take exit 432 right onto E Poplar Ave under 1 mile to N San Mateo Dr. Turn right onto N San Mateo to restaurant on left. **From Hwy 101N,** take exit 417B onto Peninsula Ave under 1 mile to N Claremont St. Turn left onto N Claremont 4 blocks to E Bellevue Ave. Turn right onto E Bellevue under ¼ mile (over tracks) to N San Mateo. Turn right onto N San Mateo to restaurant on right before Poplar.

Whole Foods Market 🛍️🍴 ♿

1010 Park Place 📞 650-358-6900 ⏰ Daily 8-10
• organic produce • vegetarian friendly • salad bar • cafe • self-service • take-out
🍎 **From Hwy 101S (Bayshore Fwy),** take exit 414A for E Hillsdale Blvd toward Fraser City onto Franklin Pkwy under ¼ mile to Saratoga Dr. Turn right onto Saratoga 1 block to Park Pl. Turn right onto Park to store on right (across from San Mateo Fairgrounds & Bay Meadow Race Track.) **From Hwy 101N,** take exit 414A right at fork, left onto E Hillsdale and follow directions above.

SAN RAFAEL

Barney's Gourmet Hamburgers 🍴

1020 Court St. 📞 415-454-4594⏰ M-Th 11-8, F-Sun 11-9:30
See Shattuck Ave location in Berkeley for description.
• vegetarian friendly • vegan friendly • alcohol • tables • wait staff
🍎 **From Hwy 101N,** take Central San Rafael exit onto Irwin St and turn left onto 3rd St about ⅓ mile to Lootens Pl. Turn right onto Lootens 3 blocks to 5th Ave. Turn right onto 5th 1 block to Court St. Turn right onto Court to restaurant. **From Hwy 101S,** take Central San Rafael exit right onto Mission Ave about ⅓ mile to Court. Turn left onto Court to restaurant.

Cafe Gratitude 🍴

2200 4th St. ℰ 415-824-4652 ⏰ Daily 10-10
Focus is on raw food.
   • vegan • organic focus • fresh juice • alcohol • tables • wait staff • take-out
🚗 **From Hwy 101**, take Central San Rafael exit west on 3rd St (merge onto Irwin St and left from 101N, merge onto Hetherton St and right from 101S) about 1 mile, continue on 2nd St ⅓ mile and merge onto 4th St about ½ mile to restaurant on right.

Radiance Vegetarian Cuisine 🍴   ♿

1559 4th St. ℰ 415-258-9850 ⏰ Tues-Sat 11:30-2:30, 5:30-9:30
International nouveau California cuisine.
   • vegetarian • vegan friendly • organic focus • alcohol • tables • wait staff
🚗 **From Hwy 101**, take Central San Rafael exit west on 3rd St (merge onto Irwin St and left from 101N, merge onto Hetherton St and right from 101S) ½ mile to C St. Turn right onto C and left onto 4th St about ½ mile to restaurant on left.

Whole Foods Market 🛒 🍴   ♿

340 Third St. ℰ 415-451-6333 ⏰ Daily 8-9
   • organic produce • vegetarian friendly • salad bar • cafe • self-service • take-out
🚗 **From Hwy 101**, take Central San Rafael exit onto 2nd St (right from 101N, left from 101S). Get into left lane (2nd merges onto 3rd St) about ¼ mile to Union St. Turn left onto Union to store.

SAN RAMON

Whole Foods Market 🛒 🍴   ♿

100 Sunset Drive ℰ 925-355-9000 ⏰ Daily 8-9
   •organic produce • vegetarian friendly • salad bar • cafe • self-service • take-out
🚗 **From I-680**, take Bollinger Canyon Rd exit west on Bollinger Canyon (left over fwy from I-680S, right from I-680N) about ⅓ mile to Sunset Dr. Turn left onto Sunset to store.

SANTA CLARA

Dasaprakash 🍴

2636 Homestead Rd. ℰ 408-246-8292 ⏰ Lunch M-F 11:30-2:30 Dinner M-Th 5:30-9:30, F 5:30-10 Sat-Sun 11:30-10
South Indian vegetarian.
   • vegetarian • vegan friendly • tables • wait staff
🚗 **From US 101 (Bayshore Fwy)**, take San Tomas Expwy south (right from 101S, loop around right from 101N) about 3 miles to Homestead Rd. Turn right onto Homestead to restaurant. **From I-280**, take Saratoga Ave North exit toward Santa Clara (right from I-280N, left from I-280S) about 1 mile to San Tomas. Turn left onto San Tomas about 1 mile to Homestead. Turn left onto Homestead to restaurant.

SANTA CRUZ

Alfresco 🍴

1130 Pacific Ave. ℰ 831-429-1765 ⏰ Daily 11-6
Kiosk outside New Leaf Market. Soups, wraps, salads, hot bowls, daily specials. Serviceware is biodegradable.
   • vegetarian • vegan friendly • self-service • take-out
🚗 **From Hwy 17**, take Hwy 1 north (right) toward Half Moon Bay. **From Hwy 1N**, turn left onto Mission St ⅓ mile to Front St. Turn right onto Front under ½ mile to Cathcart St. Turn right onto Cathcart 1 block to Pacific Ave. Turn right onto Pacific 1 block to kiosk on right.

Food Bin & Herb Room 🛒

1130 Mission St. ℰ 831-423-5526 ⏰ Daily 9am-12am
   • organic produce
🚗 **From Hwy 17**, take Hwy 1 north (right) toward Half Moon Bay. **From Hwy 1** (aka Mission St in Santa Cruz) store is at Laurel St on north side.

La Vie 🍴

429 Front St. © 831-429-6746 ⏰ M-Th 9-9, F 9-11, Sat 10-11, Sun 10-9
Mostly vegan with raw food options, a few dishes with cheese and fish on occasion. Supports local farms and sustainable lifestyle. Dine in the tatami room, at the bar, at a community table, in the garden or on the patio.
· vegetarian · vegan friendly · organic focus · fresh juice · alcohol · counter · tables · wait staff

🚗 **From Hwy 17**, take Hwy 1 north (right) toward Half Moon Bay. **From Hwy 1N**, turn left onto Mission St ⅓ mile to Front St. Turn right onto Front under ½ mile to restaurant on right at Cathcart St.

Malabar 🍴

514 Front St. ©831-423-7906 ⏰ Daily 11:30-9
Asian vegetarian.
· vegan · tables · wait staff

🚗 **From Hwy 17**, take Hwy 1 north (right) toward Half Moon Bay. **From Hwy 1N**, turn left onto Mission St ⅓ mile to Front St. Turn right onto Front ⅓ mile to restaurant on left past Soquel Ave.

New Leaf Community Market 🛍 🍴

2351 Mission St. © 831-426-1306 ⏰ Daily 8-9
· organic produce · vegetarian friendly · cafe · deli · counter · tables · self-service · take-out

🚗 **From Hwy 17**, take Hwy 1 north (right) toward Half Moon Bay. **From Hwy 1 (aka Mission St in Santa Cruz)** go south (toward ocean) onto Swift St and immediately left onto MacPherson St to store on left in Mission Plaza.

New Leaf Community Market 🛍 🍴

1134 Pacific Ave. © 831-425-1793 ⏰ Daily 9-9
· organic produce · vegetarian friendly · cafe · deli · counter · tables · self-service · take-out

🚗 **From Hwy 17**, take Hwy 1 north (right) toward Half Moon Bay. **From Hwy 1N**, turn left onto Mission St ⅓ mile to Front St. Turn right onto Front under ½ mile to Cathcart St. Turn right onto Cathcart 1 block to Pacific Ave. Turn right onto Pacific 1 block to store on right at Soquel Ave.

Saturn Cafe 🍴   ♿

145 Laurel St. © 831-429-8505 ⏰ Daily 10am-3am
· vegetarian · vegan · friendly · alcohol · tables · wait staff

🚗 **From Hwy 17**, take Hwy 1 north (right) toward Half Moon Bay about 1 mile to Chestnut St. Merge onto Chestnut ½ mile to Laurel St. Turn left onto Laurel 4 blocks to restaurant .

Staff of Life Natural Foods Market 🛍 🍴   ♿

1305 Water St. © 831-423-8632 ⏰ M-Sat 8-9, Sun 9-9
· organic produce · vegetarian friendly · fresh juice · salad bar · deli · bakery · self-service · take-out

🚗 **From Hwy 17**, take Hwy 1 south (left) toward Monterey. **From Hwy 1**, take Morrisey Blvd exit south on Morrisey (left onto Fairmont and right from 1S, left at fork in ramp and left from 1N) about ½ mile to Water St. Turn right onto Water 1 block to Poplar Ave for store parking lot.

SANTA ROSA

East West Cafe 🍴   ♿

557 Summerfield Rd. © 707-546-6142 ⏰ M-F 10-9, Sat-Sun 8-9
· vegetarian friendly · vegan friendly · alcohol · tables · wait staff · take-out

🚗 **From Hwy 101**, take Hwy 12E about 1¾ miles to to Hoen Frontage Rd. Stay right onto Hoen Frontage (becomes Hoen Ave)1½ miles to end at Summerfield Rd. Turn left onto Summerfield under 1 mile to restaurant on left.

Govinda's Vegetarian Buffet ⑪

1899 Mendocino Ave. ✆ 707-544-2491 ⊘ M-F 11:30-2:30, 5-8
Lunch and dinner buffets run by the Hare Krishna and located in the Community Market.
  • vegetarian • vegan friendly • tables • self-service • take-out

🚗 **From Hwy 101,** take Steele Ln exit east (right from 101N, left from 101S) about ½ mile to Mendocino Ave. Turn right onto Mendocino and first right onto Clement St to restaurant on left corner (parking in back).

Santa Rosa Community Market ⑪   ♿

1899 Mendocino Ave. ✆ 707-546-1806 ⊘ M-Sat 8-9, Sun 10-8
Completely vegetarian, ecologically-oriented, worker-owned natural food store.
  • organic produce • vegetarian • salad bar • take-out

🚗 **From Hwy 101,** take Steele Ln exit east (right from 101N, left from 101S) about ½ mile to Mendocino Ave. Turn right onto Mendocino and first right onto Clement St to store on left corner (parking in back).

Whole Foods Market ⑪ ⑪   ♿

1181 Yulupa Ave. ✆ 707-575-7915 ⊘ Daily 8-9
  • organic produce • vegetarian friendly • salad bar • cafe • self-service • take-out

🚗 **From Hwy 101,** take Hwy 12E about 1¾ miles to Hoen Frontage Rd. Stay right onto Hoen Frontage (becomes Hoen Ave) almost 1 mile to Yulupa Ave. Turn left onto Yulupa to store.

SEBASTOPOL

East West Cafe ⑪   ♿

128 N. Main St. ✆ 707-829-2822 ⊘ M-Th 8-8, F-Sun 8-9
Over half the menu is vegetarian plus tofu can replace chicken in many of the entrees.
  • vegetarian friendly • alcohol • tables • wait staff

🚗 **From Hwy 101** south of Santa Rosa, take Hwy 12W about 8 miles into Sebastopol to Hwy 116 (Petaluma Ave). Turn right onto Petaluma/116W and left onto McKinley which ends after 2 blocks at Main St. Turn left onto Main to restaurant.

Slice of Life ⑪   ♿

6970 McKinley St. ✆ 707-829-6627 ⊘ Tues-Th 11-9, Fri 11-10, Sat 9-10, Sun 9-9
Italian and Mexican focus, all-day vegan breakfast, organic crust pizza (available by the slice), homemade desserts.
  • vegetarian • vegan friendly • organic focus • fresh juice • alcohol • tables • wait staff
  • take-out

🚗 **From Hwy 101** just south of Santa Rosa, take Hwy 12W about 8 miles into Sebastopol to Hwy 116 (Petaluma Ave). Turn right onto Petaluma/116W and left onto McKinley to restaurant across from Town Plaza.

Whole Foods Market ⑪ ⑪   ♿

6910 McKinley St. ✆ 707-829-9801 ⊘ Daily 8-9
  • organic produce • vegetarian friendly • salad bar • cafe • self-service • take-out

🚗 **From Hwy 101** just south of Santa Rosa, take Hwy 12W about 8 miles into Sebastopol to Hwy 116 (Petaluma Ave). Turn right onto Petaluma/116W and left onto McKinley to store.

STANFORD

The Cool Cafe ⑪   ♿

328 Lomalita Drive ✆ 650-725-4758 ⊘ W, F-Sun 11-5, Th 11-8
In the Cantor Center for Visual Arts at Stanford U overlooking the Rodin sculpture garden. Gourmet sandwiches, soups and salads at lunch, full-service dinner Thursdays.
  • vegetarian friendly • organic focus • alcohol • tables • self-service • wait staff

🚗 **From US 101 (Bayshore Fwy),** take Embarcadero Rd exit west on Embarcadero (becomes Galvez Dr) over 2 miles (past El Camino Real & Stanford U Hospital) to Campus Dr. Turn left onto Campus to Palm Dr. Turn left onto Palm into campus to Museum Way. Turn right onto Museum to restaurant straight ahead in Canter Arts Ctr.
From I-280, take Sand Hill Rd exit toward Menlo Park east on Sand Hill about 1¾ miles

to Santa Cruz Ave. Turn right onto Santa Cruz and left onto Junipero Serra about ½ mile (past golf course) to Campus Dr. Turn left onto Campus and follow directions above.

SUNNYVALE

Bhavika's Chatpat ⍟

1053 E. El Camino Real © 408-551-0917 ⊘ Tues-Sun 11-9
Vegetarian Indian with a variety of burgers and chaat. Small, unassuming and affordable.
　· vegetarian · vegan friendly · tables · self-service · take-out

🚗 **From US 101 (Bayshore Fwy)**, take Lawrence Expwy exit south about 2½ miles to El Camino Real ramp. Turn right onto El Camino under ½ mile to restaurant on right in strip mall before Henderson Ave. **From I-280**, take Lawrence Expwy north about 1¾ miles to El Camino. Turn left onto El Camino ½ mile to restaurant.

Hobee's ⍟

800 Ahwanee Ave. © 408-524-3580 ⊘ M 7-2:30, Tues-F 7-9, Sat 8-9, Sun 8-2:30
Ssee the Mountain View site location for description.
　· vegetarian friendly · salad bar · alcohol · tables · wait staff · take-out

🚗 **From US 101 (Bayshore Fwy)**, take N Matilda Ave exit toward Sunnyvale south (right) about ⅓ mile to restaurant at Ahwanee Ave.

Komala Vilas ⍟

1020 E. El Camino Real © 408-733-7400 ⊘ M, W-Sun 11:30-2:30, 5-9:30
South Indian vegetarian. Table service at lunch, pick-up counter orders at night.
　· vegetarian · vegan friendly · tables · self-service · wait staff · take-out

🚗 **From US 101 (Bayshore Fwy)**, take Lawrence Expwy exit south about 2½ miles to El Camino Real ramp. Turn right onto El Camino about ½ mile to restaurant on left past Henderson Ave. **From I-280**, take Lawrence Expwy north about 1¾ miles to El Camino. Turn left onto El Camino ½ mile to restaurant.

Merit Vegetarian ⍟

548 Lawrence Expwy. © 408-245-8988 ⊘ Daily 11-9
Vegan Vietnamese with lots of tofu and mock meat options.
　· vegan · tables · wait staff

🚗 **From US 101 (Bayshore Fwy)**, take Lawrence Expwy exit south about ½ mile to restaurant on left.

Saravana Bhavan ⍟

1305 S. Mary Ave. © 408-616-7755 © Tues-Th 11:30-2, 5:30-10, F 11:30-2:30, 5:30-10:30 Sat -Sun 11-3, 5:30-10
South Indian vegetarian. Part of an international chain.
　· vegetarian · vegan friendly · tables · wait staff

🚗 **From I-280**, take CA 85 N to Fremont Ave toward Los Almos. Turn right onto W Fremont ½ mile to S Mary Ave. Turn right onto S Mary to restaurant on right.

Udupi Palace ⍟

976 E. El Camino Real © 408-830-9600 ⊘ Daily 11:30-10
North and South Indian vegetarian. Buffet available at lunch.
　· vegetarian · vegan friendly · tables · self-service · wait staff

🚗 **From US 101 (Bayshore Fwy)**, take Lawrence Expwy exit south about 2½ miles to El Camino Real ramp. Turn right onto El Camino about ⅔ mile to restaurant on left. **From I-280**, take N Wolfe Rd north (left from 1-280S, right from I-180N) about 1½ miles to E Fremont Ave. Turn right onto E Fremont and right onto El Camino to restaurant on right.

TAHOE CITY

New Moon Natural Foods 🛍 ⍟　　　　　　　　　　　　　　 ♿

505 W. Lake Blvd. © 530-583-7426 ⊘ Daily 10-6
　·organic produce · deli · counter · self-service · take-out

🚗 **From I-80**, take exit 185 onto Hwy 89S 13 miles to Tahoe City. Turn right at (only) light onto W Lake Blvd (no street sign) 1 mile to Granlibakken Rd. Turn right onto Granlibakken to store lot on left.

TRUCKEE

New Moon Natural Foods 🛍   ♿

11357 Donner Pass Rd. ✆ 530-587-7426 ⏱ M-Sat 9-7, Sun 10-6
• organic produce

🍎 **From I-80E**, take exit 186 toward Central Truckee right onto Donner Pass Rd about ½ mile to store in Donner Plaza. **From I-80W**, take exit 188 toward Lake Tahoe right onto Hwy 89 (Truckee Byp) under ¼ mile to Donner Pass. Turn left onto Donner Pass over 1 mile to store.

UKIAH

Ukiah Natural Foods 🛍

721 S. State St. ✆ 707-462-4778 ⏱ M-F 8-8, Sat 8-6, Sun 10-6
• organic produce • co-op

🍎 **From Hwy 101**, take Gobbi St exit west (left from 101S, loop around right from 101N) about ½ mile to S State St. Turn left onto State to store on SW corner.

VALLEY SPRINGS

Health Habit 🛍   ♿

1906 Vista del Lago ✆ 209-772-3000 ⏱ M-Sat 10-6, Sun 11-5
• organic produce

🍎 **From CA Hwy 12 and 26 intersecton,** go south 2 miles south on Hwy 26 to store on east side in Vista del Largo in Terrace Shopping Ctr.

WALNUT CREEK

Whole Foods Market 🛍 🍴   ♿

1333 E. Newell Ave. ✆ 925-274-9700 ⏱ Daily 8-10
•organic produce • vegetarian friendly • salad bar • cafe • self-service • take-out

🍎 **From I-680**, take S Main St exit north toward Walnut Creek to Newell Ave. Turn right onto Newell a few blocks to store

WILLITS

Mariposa Market 🛍

600 S. Main St. ✆ 707-459-9630 ⏱ M-F 9:30-6:30, Sat 10-6, Sun 11-4
• organic produce • vegetarian friendly • deli • take-out

🍎 Store is on west side of Hwy 101 as you go through town..

YOUNTVILLE

French Laundry 🍴

6640 Washington St. ✆ 707-944-2380 ⏱ Lunch F-Sun 11-1 Dinner daily 5:30-9:15
5-course prix fixe vegetarian tasting menu at dinner. Reserve at least 2 months ahead.
• vegetarian friendly • alcohol • tables • wait staff

🍎 **Take Hwy 29 (St Helena Hwy)** to Yountville. Turn east onto Madison St (right from 29N, left from 29S) 1 block to Washington St. Turn right onto Washington about 3 blocks to restaurant.

YUBA CITY

Sunflower Natural Foods Market 🛍 🍴

726 Sutter St. ✆ 530-671-9511 ⏱ M-Sat 10-6 Deli M-F 10-2:30, Sat 10-3
• vegetarian friendly • deli • tables • self-service • take-out

🍎 **From CA 20E,** take Colusa Ave right about ¼ mile to Sutter St. Turn right onto Sutter to store on right. **From CA 20W,** take Sutter St ramp toward Garden Hwy left onto Sutter ¼ mile to store.

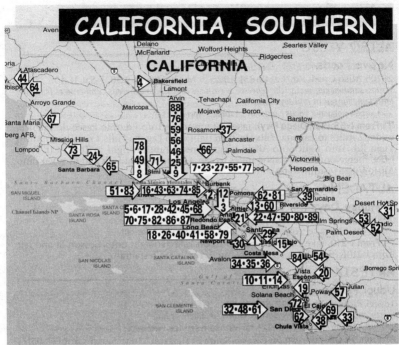

CALIFORNIA, SOUTHERN

1. Aliso Viego	30. Irvine	60. Rowland Heights
2. Altadena	31. Joshua Tree	61. San Diego
3. Artesia	32. La Jolla	62. San Dimas
4. Bakersfield	33. La Mesa	63. San Gabriel
5. Beverly Hills	34. Laguna Beach	64. San Luis Obispo
6. Brentwood	35. Laguna Niguel	65. Santa Barbara
7. Burbank	36. Laguna Woods	66. Santa Clarita
8. Camarillo	37. Lancaster	67. Santa Maria
9. Canoga Park	38. Lemon Grove	68. Santa Monica
10. Cardiff	39. Loma Linda	69. Santee
11. Carlsbad	40. Lomita	70. Sherman Oaks
12. Cerritos	41. Long Beach	71. Simi Valley
13. Chino Hills	42. Los Angeles	72. Solana Beach
14. Corona Del Mar	43. Monterey Park	73. Solvang
15. Costa Mesa	44. Morro Bay	74. South El Monte
16. Covina	45. North Hollywood	75. Studio City
17. Culver City	46. Northridge	76. Tarzana
18. El Segundo	47. Norwalk	77. Thousand Oaks
19. Encinitas	48. Ocean Beach	78. Topanga
20. Escondido	49. Ojai	79. Torrance
21. Fountain Valley	50. Orange	80. Tustin
22. Fullerton	51. Oxnard	81. Upland
23. Glendale	52. Palm Desert	82. Venice
24. Goleta	53. Palm Springs	83. Ventura
25. Granada Hills	54. Palomar Mt.	84. Vista
26. Hermosa Beach	55. Pasadena	85. West Covina
27. Highland Park	56. Porter Ranch	86. West Hollywood
28. Hollywood	57. Poway	87. Westwood
29. Huntington Beach	58. Redondo Beach	88. Woodland Hills
	59. Reseda	

ALISO VIEJO

Native Foods 🍴

26705 Aliso Creek Rd. ℂ 949-831-1926 ⏰ M-Th, Sun 11-9:30, F-Sat 11-10
Wraps, sandwiches, pizza (the "cheese" is cashews and sunflower seeds) and entrees featuring tofu, tempeh, seitan and soy chicken.
• vegan • organic focus • alcohol • tables • wait staff

🚗 **From I-5S (San Diego Fwy)**, take exit toward El Toro Rd onto Paseo de Valencia under 2 miles to Laguna Hills Dr. Turn right onto Laguna Hills 1½ miles to Alisio Viejo Rd. Turn right onto Alisio Viejo to restaurant on right in Town Ctr. **From I-5N**, merge onto Hwy 73N 4 miles to exit 4. Keep right at fork and turn left onto Alisio Viego ½ mile to restaurant.

ALTADENA

O Happy Days 🛍 🍴

2283 Lake Ave. ℂ 626-797-0383 ⏰ M-F 11-6:30, Sat 11-6
• organic produce • vegan • deli • tables • self-serve • take-out

🚗 **From I-210,** take Lake Ave exit north on Lake (straight onto Corson St and left from I-210E, right from I-210W) about 2¼ miles to restaurant.

ARTESIA

Udupi Palace 🍴

18635 Pioneer Blvd. ℂ 62-860-1950 ⏰ Tues-Sun 11:30-9:45
North and South Indian vegetarian. Buffet available at lunch.
• vegetarian • vegan friendly • tables • self-service • wait staff

🚗 **From I-605,** take exit 5B east on South St (left from I-605S, right from I-605N) about 1 mile to Pioneer Blvd. Turn left onto Pioneer under ¼ mile to restaurant on left after 187th St.

BAKERSFIELD

Cone's Health Foods 🛍

1002 Wible Rd. ℂ 661-832-5669 ⏰ M-F 9-7, Sat 10-6, Sun 11-6

🚗 **From CA 99N,** take Ming Ave exit right onto Ming 1 block to Wible Rd. Turn right onto Wible about ⅓ mile to store. **From CA 99S**, take CA 58E exit onto Stockdale Hwy toward Brundage Ln ⅓ mile to Wible. Turn right onto Wible about ⅔ mile to store.

Elaine's Cafe & Market 🛍 🍴   ♿

1717 20th St. ℂ 661-869-2233 ⏰ M-Th 10-7, F 10-2, Sun 11-2
Nondairy ice cream is a specialty. Self-service veggie burger bar on Sunday.
• vegan • tables • self-service • wait staff • take-out

🚗 **From CA 99,** take exit 26 (26A from CA 99N) east on Hwy 178E/24th St (left from CA 99S, right from CA 99N) over 1 mile (becomes 23rd St) to H St. Turn right onto H 3 blocks to 20th St. Turn right onto 20th 1 block to restaurant on left at G St.

Lassen's Natural Foods 🛍 🍴

4308 California Ave. ℂ 661-324-6990 ⏰ M-Sat 9-9
• organic produce • vegetarian friendly • fresh juice • deli • tables • self-service • take-out,

🚗 **From CA 99**, take exit 5 west on California Ave (right from CA 99S, left from CA 99N) ½-¾ mile to store on right.

BEVERLY HILLS

Whole Foods Market 🛍 🍴   ♿

239 N. Crescent Drive ℂ 310-274-3360 ⏰ Daily 7-10
• organic produce • vegetarian friendly • salad bar • cafe • self-service • take-out

🚗 **From I-405 (San Diego Fwy),** take Santa Monica Blvd east (right from I-405N, left from I-405S) about 3 miles to Crescent Blvd. Turn right onto Crescent about 2 blocks to store on right between Santa Monica & Wilshire Blvd.

BRENTWOOD

A Votre Sante

13016 San Vicente Blvd. © 310-451-1813 ⏰ M 11-10, Tues-F 8:30-10, Sat 9-10, Sun 9-9
A natural foods restaurant offering vegetarian dishes, organic poultry and salmon.
  • vegetarian friendly • alcohol • tables • wait staff

From I-405N (San Diego Fwy), take Wilshire Blvd exit toward Westwood onto Wilshire under 1 mile to San Vicente Blvd. Turn right onto San Vicente 2 miles to restaurant on left before 26th St. **From I-405S**, take exit 55C onto Wilshire Blvd W and follow directions above.

Barney's Gourmet Hamburgers

11660 San Vincente Blvd. © 310-447-6000 ⏰Daily 11-10
The attraction for vegetarians is the garden burgers and tofu burgers with various toppings and plenty of salad choices.
  • vegetarian friendly • vegan friendly • alcohol • tables • wait staff,

From I-405N (San Diego Fwy), take Wilshire Blvd W exit toward Westwood onto Wilshire under 1 mile to San Vicente Blvd. Turn right onto San Vicente about ½ mile to restaurant on left after Darlington Ave. **From I-405S**, take exit 55C onto Wilshire Blvd W and follow directions above.

BURBANK

Full o' Life

2515 W. Magnolia Blvd. © 818-845-8343 ⏰ Store M-Th 8-8, F 8-4, Sun 9:30-6 Cafe M-F 11-3:30, Sun 11-3
  • organic produce • fresh juice • cafe • vegetarian friendly • tables • wait staff

From I-5S, take exit 16B right onto W Burbank Blvd about ¼ mile to N Victory Pl. Turn left onto N Victory ½ mile to W Magnolia. Turn right onto W Magnolia 1 mile to store on right after N Buena Vista St. **From I-5N**, merge onto CA 134W/Ventura Fwy. **From CA 134W**, take exit 3 right onto S Buena Vista about 1⅓ miles to W Magnolia. Turn left onto W Magnolia to store. **From CA 134E**, take Pass Ave exit left onto Pass 1 mile to W Magnolia. Turn right onto W Magnolia 1 mile to store on left. **From US 101**, exit onto CA 134E and follow directions above.

CAMARILLO

Lassen's Natural Foods

2207 Pickwick Drive © 805-482-3287 ⏰ M-Sat 9-8
  • organic produce • vegetarian friendly • deli • take-out

From 101S (Ventura Fwy), take Carmen Dr exit left onto Ventura Blvd about ¾ mile to light at Arneil Rd. Turn left onto Arneil under ½ mile to light at Pickwick Dr. Turn left onto Pickwick and right into Ponderosa N Shopping Ctr to store. **From 101N**, take Lewis Rd exit left onto Daily Dr about ¼ mile to light at Arneill. Turn right onto Arneill about ⅓ mile to light at Pickwick and follow directions above.

CANOGA PARK

Follow Your Heart Natural Foods

21825 Sherman Way © 818-348-3240 ⏰ Daily 8-9
  • organic produce • vegetarian • vegan friendly • cafe • counter • tables • self-service • take-out

From 101 (Ventura Fwy), take Topanga Canyon Blvd exit north (right from 101N, left from 101S) about 2 miles to Sherman Way. Turn right onto Sherman to store.

Call Ahead

We suggest you call first if possible before visiting a location. Stores and restaurants have a habit of moving (and closing), and hours, services, etc. change more often than you might expect.

CARDIFF

Ki's Restaurant ♿

2591 South Coast Hwy. 101 ✆ 760-436-5236 ⊙ M-F 8-8:30, Sat-Sun 8-9
Breakfast and lunch are self-serve. Full-service dinner starts at 5.
  • vegetarian friendly • organic focus • fresh juice • alcohol • tables • self-service • wait staff
🍽 **From I-5,** take Lomas Santa Fe Dr west about 2 miles to Hwy 101. Turn right onto 101 about 1½ miles to restaurant on "restaurant row."

CARLSBAD

Cilantro Live #2 🍽

300 Carlsbad Village Dr. ✆ 760-585-0136 ⊙ Tues-Sun 11:30-8:30
Focus is raw food.
  • vegan • organic focus • fresh juice • salad bar • tables • wait staff • take-out
🍽 **From I-5 (San Diego Fwy),** take exit 50 west on Carlsbad Village Dr/Elm Ave (right from I-5S, left from I-5N) over ½ mile to Carlsbad Blvd. Turn right onto Carlsbad Blvd to restaurant across from rail station.

Jimbo's Naturally 🛍 🍽

1923 Calle Barcelona ✆ 760-334-7755 ⊙ Daily 8-9
  • organic produce • vegetarian friendly • fresh juice • salad bar • deli • bakery • tables • self-service • takeout
🍽 **From I-5,** take exit 43 east on Leucadia Blvd about 1½ miles to Calle Barcelona. Turn left onto Calle Barcelona about ⅓ mile to store on right.

CERRITOS

That's Amore! Italian Pizza Kitchen 🍽 ♿

13349 Artesia Blvd. ✆ 562-926-2112 ⊙ M-Sat 11-9, Sun 1-7
Vegetarian Italian with numerous vegan options for pizza, pasta, subs, even vegan cannoli.
  • vegetarian • vegan friendly • alcohol • tables • wait staff
🍽 **From I-5S (Santa Ana Fwy),** take exit 119 right onto Firestone Blvd and left onto Carmenita Rd about 1⅓ miles to Artesia Blvd. Turn left onto Artesia to restaurant on right. **From I-5N,** take exit 113C onto Hwy 91W under 3½ miles to exit 20. Turn right onto Carmenita over ½ mile to Artesia. Turn left onto Artesia to restaurant.

Vegi Wokery 🍽

11329 183rd St. ✆562-809-3928 ⊙ M-Sat 11:30-2:30, 4:30-9
Chinese vegetarian. Brown "rice" is a 7- grain mix including barley, oats and buckwheat.
  • vegetarian • vegan friendly • tables • wait staff • take-out
🍽 **From I-605,** take South St exit west (right from I-605S, left from I-605N) 1 block to Studebaker Rd Turn right on Studebaker ½ mile to 183rd St. Turn right onto 183rd about ½ mile to restaurant.

CHINO HILLS

Veggie & Tea House 🍽

14670 Pipeline ✆ 909-606-6067 ⊙ Daily 11-8
Many of the vegetables are grown on their 400 acre organic farm. Brown rice available.
  • vegetarian • vegan friendly • organic focus • tables • wait staff • take-out
🍽 **From CA 71 (Chino Valley Fwy),** take exit 8 for Ramona Ave west on CA 142/ Chino Valley Pkwy (right from 71S, left from 71N) under ½ mile to Pipeline. Turn right onto Pipeline under ½ mile to restaurant on left.

CORONA DEL MAR

Zinc Cafe & Market 🍽

3222 E. Coast Hwy. ✆ 949-719-9462 ⊙ Cafe Daily 7-5, Market M, Sun 7-6, Tues-Sat 7-6
Breakfast, soups, salads, extensive sandwich menu, pizzettes, hot entrees.
  • vegetarian • alcohol • tables • self-service • take-out
🍽 On US Hwy 1 between Larkspur & Marguerite Ave.

COSTA MESA

Mother's Market & Kitchen

225 E. 17th St. ✆ 949-631-4741 ⊙ Daily 8-10 Restaurant & juice bar close at 9:30
· organic produce · vegetarian · vegan friendly · fresh juice · salad bar · deli · bakery
· counter · tables · wait staff · take-out

🚗 **From I-405 (San Diego Fwy),** take CA 55S (becomes Newport Blvd) toward Newport Beach about 5 miles to 17th St. Turn left onto 17th 1 block to store on right after Orange Ave.

Native Foods

2937 Bristol St. ✆ 714-751-2151 ⊙Daily 11-10
See Aliseo Viejo location for description.
· vegan · organic focus · alcohol · tables · wait staff

🚗 **From I-405S (San Diego Fwy),** turn right onto Bristol St ½ mile to restaurant on right in The Camp. **From I-405N,** take exit 9A left at fork and follow signs for Hwy 55S about ½ mile. Take fork right and continue straight to Baker St. Turn right onto Baker ⅓ mile to Bristol. Turn left onto Bristol to restaurant.

COVINA

Covina Tasty

1063 N. Citrus Ave. ✆ 626-332-8816 ⊙ Daily 11-11
Vegan burgers, "steak" and "fish" sandwiches, "chicken" nuggets, onion rings, fries, salads in a former Tastee Freeze.
· vegetarian · vegan friendly · tables · self-service · take-out

🚗 **From I-210 (Foothills Fwy),** take exit 41 toward Covina south on Citrus Ave (right from I-210E, left onto E Baseline Rd and left onto Citrus from I-210W) about 1½ miles to restaurant on right after W Covina Blvd. **From I-10** (San Bernadino Fwy), take exit 37A toward Covina north on Citrus (left from I-10E, right from I-10W) 2 miles to restaurant on left.

CULVER CITY

Leaf Cuisine

11938 W. Washington Blvd. ✆ 310-390-6005 ⊙ -Sat 8-9, Sun 10-9
Raw foods menu.
· vegan · organic focus · fresh juice · kosher · tables · self-service · take-out

🚗 **From I-405S (San Diego Fwy),** take exit 5 for Washington Blvd right onto Sawtelle Blvd to Washington. Turn left onto Washington about ½ mile to restaurant after Atlantic Ave. **From I-405N,** take Washington Blvd exit left onto Sepulveda Blvd ⅓ mile to Washington. Turn left onto Washington about ¾ mile to restaurant.

M. Cafe de Chaya

9343 Culver Blvd. ✆ 310-838-4300 ⊙ Daily 8-9
Macrobiotic, mostly vegan with a few fish offerings.
· vegetarian friendly · vegan friendly · alcohol · tables · self-service · take-out

🚗 **From I-10E (Santa Monica Fwy),** take exit 6 toward Culver City onto Exposition Blvd and turn right onto Venice Blvd 1 block to Culver Blvd. Turn left onto Culver to restaurant on right. **From I-10W,** take exit 6 left onto Robertson Blvd, left onto National Blvd and right onto Venice ⅓ mile to Culver. Turn left onto Culver to restaurant.

Rainbow Acres

13208 W. Washington Blvd. ✆ 10-306-8330 ⊙ M-F 7-9, Sat 8-8, Sun 9-8
· vegetarian friendly · deli · tables · self-service · take-out

🚗 **From I-405S (San Diego Fwy),** take Venice Blvd exit onto Matteson Ave to Sawtelle Blvd. Turn left onto Sawtell and right onto Washington Pl (becomes Washington Blvd) 1¾ miles to store on left after Tivoli Ave. **From I-405N,** take Washington Blvd exit left onto Sepulveda Blvd ⅓ mile to Washington Pl. Turn right onto Washington Pl (becomes Washington Blvd) 2 miles to store.

Tender Greens 🍴

9523 Culver Blvd. ✆ 310-842-8300 ⏰ M-Th, Sun 11:30-9, F-Sat 11:30-10
A relaxed cafe with local produce, artisanal breads and for carnivores hormone-free beef and chicken and line-caught Pacific tuna.
  • vegetarian friendly • organic focus • alcohol • tables • self-service
🍎 **From I-10E (Santa Monica Fwy),** take exit 6 toward Culver City onto Exposition Blvd and turn right onto Venice Blvd ⅓ mile to Bagley Ave. Turn left onto Bagley 1 block to Culver Blvd. Turn right onto Culver 1 block to restaurant on right. **From I-10W,** take exit 5 right onto National Blvd under ½ mile to Bagley. Turn right onto Bagley ½ mile to Culver. Turn right onto Culver to restaurant.

EL SEGUNDO

The Veggie Grill 🍴

720 Allied Way ✆ 310-535-0025 ⏰ Daily 11-10
Salads, sandwiches, burgers.
  • vegan • alcohol • tables • self-service • take-out
🍎 **From I-105,** take exit 1B onto Hwy 1S/Sepulveda Blvd ½ miles to S Hughes Way. Turn left onto S Hughes ⅓ mile to S Allied Way. Turn right onto Allied to restaurant in Plaza El Segundo. **From I-405S,** merge onto I-105W and follow directions above. **From I-405N** (San Diego Fwy), take exit 43 left onto Rosecrans Ave (signs for El Segundo) about ½ miles to Sepulveda. Turn left onto Sepulveda and u-turn back onto Sepulveda going north at N Valley Dr ½ mile to S Hughes. Turn right onto S Hughes under ¼ mile to S Allied. Turn right onto Allied to restaurant.

ENCINITAS

Henry's Marketplace 🛍

1327 Encinitas Blvd. ✆ 760-633-4747 ⏰ Daily 7-10
  • organic produce • vegetarian friendly • deli • take-out
🍎 **From I-5,** take Encinitas Blvd exit east toward Encinitas (left from I-5S, right from I-5N) about 1¾ miles to store.

Swami's Cafe 🍴

1163 S. Coast Hwy. 101 ✆ 60-944-0612 ⏰ Daily 7-5
Casual wholefoods breakfast and lunch place on the highway.
  • vegetarian friendly • vegan friendly • fresh juice • counter • tables • self-service
🍎 **From I-5,** take Encinitas Blvd exit west (right from I-5S, left from I-5N) ⅓ mile to 1st St (Hwy 101). Turn left onto 1st about ¾ mile to restaurant on left at K St.

The Roxy 🍴

517 S. Coast Hwy. 101 ✆ 760-436-5001 ⏰ M-Sat 11-10, Sun 11-9
Started as vegetarian with a Mediterranean influence but now serves chicken and seafood.
  • vegetarian friendly • vegan friendly • fresh juice • alcohol • tables • wait staff
🍎 **From I-5,** take Encinitas Blvd exit west (right from I-5S, left from I-5N) ⅓ mile to 1st St (Hwy 101). Turn left onto 1st under ¼ mile to restaurant on left after D St.

ESCONDIDO

Henry's Marketplace 🛍

510 W. 13th Ave. ✆ 760-745-2141 ⏰ Daily 7-10
  • organic produce • vegetarian friendly • deli • take-out
🍎 **From I-15N,** take Centre City Pkwy exit 1 mile and merge onto S Centre City Pkwy about 1⅔ miles to W 13th Ave. Turn left onto W 13th to store. **From I-15S,** take CA 78E under 1 mile to Centre City Pkwy S ramp, merge onto N Centre City Pkwy about 1⅔ miles to W 13th and turn right onto W 13th to store.

Jimbo's Naturally 🛍 🍴   ♿

1633 S. Centre City Pkwy. ✆ 760-489-7755 ⏰ Daily 8-9
  • organic produce • vegetarian friendly • fresh juice • deli • tables • self-service • take-out
🍎 **From I-15N,** take Centre City Pwky exit 1 mile and merge onto S Centre City

Pkwy about 2½ miles to store on left. **From I-15S,** merge onto CA 78E toward Ramona under 1 mile to Centre City Pkwy S ramp and merge onto N Centre City Pkwy almost 2 miles to store on right.

FOUNTAIN VALLEY

Au Lac

16563 Brookhurst St. ℰ 714-418-0658 ⏲ Tues-Th 11:30-9:30, F-Sun 11:30-10
Vegan Chinese and Vietnamese plus a daily selection of raw foods.
 • vegan • tables • wait staff

📌 **From I-405S (San Diego Fwy),** take Warner Ave East exit right onto Warner ¾ mile to Brookhurst St. Turn left onto Brookhurst about ⅓ mile to restaurant at Heil Ave. **From I-405N,** take exit 14 onto Brookhurst St North ramp. Merge onto Brookhurst about 1 mile to restaurant.

FULLERTON

Rutabegorz

211 N. Pomona Ave. ℰ 714-738-9339 ⏲ M-Th 11-9, F-Sat 11-10
Daily vegetarian soup, many vegetarian Mexican options, wraps (with whole wheat tortillas), all-vegetable stews, sandwiches, salads and smoothies.
 • vegetarian friendly • alcohol • tables • wait staff • take-out

📌 **From CA 91,** take Harbor Blvd exit north (left from 91E, right from 91W) about 1 mile (past several lights and under railroad crossing) to light at Commonwealth Ave. Turn right onto Commonwealth 1 block to Pomona Ave. Turn left onto Pomona 1½ blocks to restaurant on right.

GLENDALE

Glendale Adventist Medical Center ⓘ

1509 Wilson Terrace ℰ 818-409-8095 ⏲ Daily 6am-9pm
Vegetarian cafeteria in the Seventh-day Adventist tradition.
 • vegetarian • tables • self-service

📌 **From Ventura Fwy (CA 134),** take Harvey Dr exit north (right from 134W, left from 134E), make first left onto Wilson Terrace and follow signs to hospital parking. Cafeteria is on the ground floor across from main auditorium and conference rooms.

Whole Foods Market ⓘ

331 N. Glendale Ave. ℰ 818-548-3695 ⏲ Daily 7-10
 • organic produce • vegetarian friendly • salad bar • cafe • self-service • take-out

📌 **From Ventura Fwy,** take exit 8 south on N Glendale Ave (right from Ventura Fwy E, right onto Montery Rd and right from Ventura Fwy W) under ½ mile to store on right.

GOLETA

Lassen's Natural Foods

5154 Hollister Ave. ℰ 805-683-7696 ⏲ M-Sat 9-8
 • organic produce

📌 **From Hwy 101,** take Rt 217 (Ward Memorial Blvd) south (right from 101S, left from 101N) about ½ mile to Hollister Ave. Turn right onto Hollister to store.

GRANADA HILLS

Vegetable Delight ⓘ

17823 Chatsworth St. ℰ 818-360-3997 ⏲ Tues-Sun 11:30-9:30
Chinese vegan with many faux meat items.
 • vegan • alcohol • tables • wait staff • take-out

📌 **From I-5,** take CA 118W about 3¾ miles to Bilboa St exit. Turn left onto Bilboa about 1 mile to Chatsworth St. Turn right onto Chatsworth over 1 mile to restaurant between White Oak & Zelzah Ave.

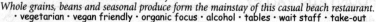

HERMOSA BEACH

The Spot 🍽

110 2nd St. © 310-376-2355 ⏲ Daily 11-10
Whole grains, beans and seasonal produce form the mainstay of this casual beach restaurant.
· vegetarian · vegan friendly · organic focus · alcohol · tables · wait staff · take-out

🚗 **From the beach,** go inland 1 block to Hermosa Ave and at 2nd St go inland 1 block to restaurant on right. **From I-405S** (San Diego Fwy), take exit 42B right onto Inglewood Ave over 2 miles to 190th St. Turn right into 190th continuing onto Anita St then Herondo St about 2 miles total to Hermosa Ave. Turn right onto Hermosa Ave 3 blocks to 2nd St. Turn right onto 2nd to restaurant. **From I-405N,** take exit 40 toward Redondo Beach onto Artesia Blvd 1 mile to CA 1 (Pacific Coast Hwy). Turn left onto CA 1 1¼ miles to 2nd. Turn right onto 2nd under ½ mile to restaurant on left.

HIGHLAND PARK

Cinnamon Vegetarian Restaurant 🍽

5511 N. Figuero St © 323-982-9480 ⏲ M-Th 9-8:30, F-Sat 9-9, Sun 9-8
Mexican vegetarian fare plus soups, salads, sandwiches and veggie burgers.
· vegetarian · vegan friendly · fresh juice · counter · tables · wait staff

🚗 **From CA 110N (Pasadena Fwy),** take exit 28A left onto S Ave 5 2⅓ mile to N Figueroa St. Turn right onto N Figueroa about 4 blocks to restaurant on left after N Ave 55. **From 110S,** take exit 28B onto S Ave 59 almost ½ mile to N Figueroa. Turn left onto N Figueroa 2 blocks to restaurant on right past N Ave 56.

HOLLYWOOD

M. Cafe de Chaya 🍽

7119 Melrose Ave. © 323-525-0588 ⏲ M-Sat 9-10, Sun 9-9
Macrobiotic, mostly vegan with a few fish offerings.
· vegetarian friendly · vegan friendly · alcohol · tables · self-service · take-out

🚗 **From US 101S (Hollywood Fwy),** take exit 9C toward Highland Ave onto Cahuenga Blvd continuing onto N Highland for 2¼ miles total to Melrose Ave. Turn right onto Melrose under ½ mile to restaurant on right after N La Brea Ave. **From US 101N,** take exit 7 toward Western Ave left onto Santa Monica Blvd about 2¼ miles to N La Brea. Turn right onto N La Brea ½ mile to Melrose. Turn left onto Melrose to restaurant.

Nite Moon Cafe 🍽

6322 De Longpre Ave. © 323-988-4052 ⏲ M-Th 11-9, F 11-4:30, Sat 10:30-2:30
In the Golden Bridge Yoga Center. Soups, salads, sandwiches, homemade baked goods.
· vegetarian · vegan friendly · fresh juice · tables · self-service

🚗 **From US 101S (Hollywood Fwy),** take exit 9A right onto Vine St over ½ mile to De Longpre Ave (first left after Sunset Blvd). Turn left onto De Longpre to restaurant on left. **From US 101N,** take exit 8A onto W Sunset 1 mile to Vine. Turn left onto Vine and first left onto De Longpre to restaurant.

Paru's 🍽

5140 W. Sunset Blvd. © 323-661-7600 ⏲ M-F 4-11 Sat-Sun 1-10
Southern Indian vegetarian.
· vegetarian · vegan friendly · alcohol · tables · wait staff

🚗 **From US 101 (Hollywood Fwy),** take Sunset Blvd exit east (right from 101S, left from 101W) about ¾ mile to restaurant on south side between Western & Normandie Ave.

Truly A Vegan Restaurant 🍽

5907 Hollywood Blvd. © 323-466-7533 ⏲ Daily 11-9:30
Mixed menu including Thai, burgers, wraps, noodle dishes, curries, veggie meat entrees and more.
· vegan · tables · wait staff

🚗 **From US 101 (Hollywood Fwy),** take Hollywood Blvd exit west (left from 101S, right from 101W) to restaurant on north side after Bronson Ave.

HUNTINGTON BEACH

Mother's Market & Kitchen 🛍️ 🍴   ♿

19770 Beach Blvd. © 714-963-6667 ⏱ Daily 8-10 Restaurant & juice bar close at 9:30
  • organic produce • vegetarian • vegan friendly • fresh juice • salad bar • deli • bakery
  • counter • tables • wait staff • take-out

🚗 **From Hwy 1S (Pacific Coast Hwy),** turn left onto Seapoint Ave about 1 mile to
Garfield Ave. Turn right onto Garfield 1¾ miles to Beach Blvd. Turn right onto
Beach about ¾ mile to store after E Utica Ave. **From Hwy 1N,** go north on Beach
about 2 miles to store (before E Utica). **From I-405S** (San Diego Fwy), take Beach
Blvd exit and follow Center St ramp toward Huntington Beach. Merge onto Beach
almost 4 miles to store after E Utica. **From I-405N,** take Harbor Blvd exit left onto
Harbor about 1 mile to Adams Ave. Turn right onto Adams 4 miles to Beach. Turn
left onto Beach ¼ mile to store (before E Utica).

IRVINE

Mother's Market & Kitchen 🛍️ 🍴   ♿

2963 Michelson Drive © 949-752-6667 ⏱ Daily 8-10 Restaurant & juice bar close at 9:30
  • organic produce • vegetarian • vegan friendly • fresh juice • salad bar • deli • bakery
  • counter • tables • wait staff • take-out

🚗 **From I-405 (San Diego Fwy),** take exit 7 south on Jamboree Rd (right from
I-405S, left from I-405N) to first left onto Michelson Dr to store in Park Place Ctr.

The Veggie Grill 🍴

4213 Campus Drive © 949-509-0003 ⏱ Daily 11-10
Salads, sandwiches, burgers.
  • vegan • alcohol • tables • self-service • take-out

🚗 **From I-405,** take exit 5 south on Culver Dr (right from I-405S, left from
I-405N) about 1½ miles to Campus Dr. Turn right onto Campus almost 1 mile to
restaurant on right in UC Irvine University Center.

The Veggie Grill 🍴

81 Fortune Drive © 949-727-9900 ⏱ Daily 11-10
Salads, sandwiches, burgers.
  • vegan • alcohol • tables • self-service • take-out

🚗 **From I-405S (San Diego Fwy),** take exit 1C left onto Irvine Ctr Dr, right onto
Enterprise Dr and left onto Fortune Dr to restaurant on right in Irvine Spectrum
Ctr. **From I-405N or I-5N** (Santa Ana Fwy), take exit 1 toward Irvine Ctr Dr and
turn right onto Fortune to restaurant. **From I-5S,** take exit 94 left at fork and merge
onto Fortune ½ mile to restaurant on left.

The Wheel of Life 🍴

14370 Culver Drive © 949-551-8222 ⏱ M, W-Th, 11-3, 4:30-9:30, F 11-3, 4:30-10,
Sat 11-3:30, 4:30-10, Sun 11-3:30, 4:30-9:30
Vegan Thai.
  • vegan • tables • wait staff

🚗 **From I-5 (Santa Ana Fwy),** take exit 99 west onto Culver Dr (right from I-5S, left
onto Trabuco Rd and left onto Culver from I-5N) under ½ mile to restaurant on
left between Scottsdale & Walnut Dr.

**For listing changes, updates and travel resources,
go to HealthyHighways.com**

JOSHUA TREE

Joshua Tree Health Food Store 🛍️

61693 29 Palms Hwy. ✆ 760-366-7489 ⊕ M-Sat 9-6
 • organic produce

🚗 **From Hwy 62 (29 Palms Hwy)**, store is on south side after Outpost Rd.

LA JOLLA

Che Cafe Collective 🍴

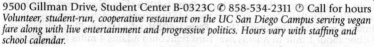

9500 Gillman Drive, Student Center B-0323C ✆ 858-534-2311 ⊕ Call for hours
Volunteer, student-run, cooperative restaurant on the UC San Diego Campus serving vegan fare along with live entertainment and progressive politics. Hours vary with staffing and school calendar.
 • vegan • organic focus • tables • self-service • co-op

🚗 **From I-5**, take La Jolla Village Dr exit west past Villa La Jolla Dr (and gas station) to off-ramp on right onto Gillman Dr. Turn right at stop sign onto Gillman and left at next stop sign onto Scholar's Dr (info booth on right.) Cafe is in mural-covered bldg on left. (Continue up hill for parking.)

Lean and Green 🍴

7825 Fay Ave. ✆ 858-459-5326 ⊕ M-W 8-7, Th-F 8-6, Sat 9-3
Healthy fast food with an environmental outlook. Seating is all outdoors with heat lamps for chilly weather.
 • vegetarian friendly • vegan friendly • organic focus • fresh juice • tables • self-service • take-out

🚗 **From I-5S**, take exit 28 right onto La Jolla Village Dr about ¾ mile to Torrey Pines Rd. Turn left onto Torrey Pines 2¾ mile to Prospect Pl. Turn right onto Prospect ½ mile to Prospect Ave. Merge left onto Prospect about 6 blocks to Fay Ave. Turn left onto Fay to restaurant on left in the Merrill Lynch Bldg. **From I-5N**, take exit 26A and merge onto La Jolla Pkwy 1¾ miles to Torrey Pines. Continue on Torrey Pines 1 miles to Prospect Pl and follow directions above.

Whole Foods Market 🛍️

8825 Villa La Jolla Drive ✆ 858-642-6700 ⊕ Daily 7-10
 • organic produce • vegetarian friendly • fresh juice • salad bar • deli • take-out

🚗 **From I-5S**, take exit 28 right onto La Jolla Village Dr and turn left at light onto Villa La Jolla Dr to store on left past next light in shopping plaza at Nobel Dr. **From I-5N**, take exit 28A left at light back across interstate ⅓ mile to store.

LA MESA

Henry's Marketplace 🛍️

4630 Palm Ave. ✆ 619-460-7722 ⊕ Daily 7-10
 • organic produce • vegetarian friendly • deli • take-out

🚗 **From I-8E**, take Spring St exit toward Downtown right onto Spring about ⅓ mile to La Mesa Blvd. Turn left onto La Mesa 1 block to Palm Ave. Turn right onto Palm 2 blocks to store. **From I-8W**, take El Cajon Blvd exit toward Spring past Spring to Baltimore Dr. Turn left onto Baltimore and follow onto University Ave about ¼ mile to Spring. Turn right onto Spring 2 blocks to La Mesa and follow directions above.

LAGUNA BEACH

The Stand 🍴

238 Thalia St. ✆ 949-494-8101 ⊕ Daily 7-7
Thirty years on the beach serving healthy, vegan whole wheat burritos, tamales, sandwiches, salads and beans-brown rice-and-vegetables in a variety of ways.
 • vegan • organic focus • counter • self-service • take-out

🚗 **From I-405 or I-5**, take Rt 133 (Laguna Canyon Rd) south (toward beach) 8-10 miles to Pacific Coast Hwy (Hwy 1). Turn left onto 1 about ⅔ mile to Thalia St. Turn left onto Thalia to restaurant on right.

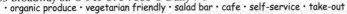

Whole Foods Market ♿

283 Broadway St. ℂ 949-376-7888 ⊘ Daily 7-9
· organic produce · vegetarian friendly · salad bar · cafe · self-service · take-out
🍎 **From I-405 or I-5,** take Rt 133 (Laguna Canyon Rd) south (toward beach) 8-10 miles to store on left 1 block before the beach.

Zinc Cafe & Market

350 Ocean Ave. ℂ 949-494-6302 ⊘ Market M-F 7-6, Sat-Sun 7-5, Cafe daily 7-4
See Corona del Mar location for description.
· vegetarian · alcohol · counter · tables · self-service · take-out
🍎 **From I-405 or I-5,** take Rt 133 (Laguna Canyon Rd) south (toward beach) 8-10 miles. Where Rt 133 becomes Broadway St turn left onto Forest Ave and right onto Ocean Ave to restaurant on right.

LAGUNA NIGUEL_____

Henry's Marketplace

27271 La Paz Rd. ℂ 949-349-1994 ⊘ Daily 7-10
· organic produce · vegetarian friendly · deli · take-out
🍎 **From I-5S,** take Alicia Pkwy exit right onto Alicia Pkwy about 1⅔ miles to Moulton Pkwy. Turn left onto Moulton about ½ mile to La Paz Rd. Turn right onto La Paz about ¾ mile to store. **From I-5N,** merge onto CA 73N toward Long Beach almost 3 miles to La Paz exit. Follow exit ¾ mile and turn left onto La Paz about ½ mile to store.

LAGUNA WOODS_____

Mother's Market & Kitchen ♿

24165 Paseo de Valencia ℂ 949-768-6667 ⊘ Daily 8-10 Restaurant & juice bar close at 9:30
· organic produce · vegetarian · vegan friendly · fresh juice · salad bar · deli · bakery · tables · wait staff · take-out
🍎 **From I-5S,** take El Toro Rd exit right onto Paseo de Valencia about ⅓ mile to store. **From I-5N,** take El Toro exit left onto El Toro about ½ mile to Paseo de Valencia. Turn left onto Paseo de Valencia to store.

LANCASTER_____

The Whole Wheatery

44264 10th St. W. ℂ 661-945-0773 ⊘ M-F 9-7, Sat 9-6, Sun 11-5 Cafe M-Sat 10:30-4, Sun 11-4
· organic produce · vegetarian friendly · fresh juice · deli · cafe · bakery · alcohol · tables · wait staff · take-out
🍎 **From CA 14,** take Ave K exit right onto K about ½ mile to 10th St. Turn left onto 10th under 1 mile store on right in bright orange strip mall. **From 138E,** take Ave I exit left onto W Ave I about ¼ mile to 20th St W. Turn right onto 20th 1 mile to W Ave J. Turn left onto J 1 mile to 10th St. Turn right onto 10th to store on left.

LEMON GROVE_____

Cilantro Live!

7822 Broadway ℂ 619-433-0680 ⊘ Tues-Sat 12-8
Focus is raw food.
· vegan · organic focus · fresh juice · salad bar · tables · wait staff · take-out
🍎 **From I-8W,** merge onto CA 94W. **From CA 94,** take exit 8 right onto Lemon Grove Ave and veer left onto North Ave 1 block to Grove St. Turn right onto Grove 2 blocks to Broadway. Turn right onto Broadway to restaurant on right. **From I-8E,** take exit 11 onto Spring St about 1½ miles to Broadway. Turn right onto Broadway about 1½ miles to restaurant (before Lemon Grove).

Henry's Marketplace 🛍️

3205 Lemon Grove Ave. ✆ 619-667-8686 ⏰ Daily 7-10
· organic produce · vegetarian friendly · deli · take-out
🍎 **From I-805,** take CA 94E about 4½ miles to Lemon Grove Ave. Turn right onto Lemon Grove about ¼ mile to store.

LOMA LINDA

Loma Linda Market 🛍️

11161 Anderson St. ✆ 909-558-4565 ⏰ M-Th 7-7, F 7-3, Sun 8-6
A completely vegetarian market.
🍎 **From I-10,** take Anderson St exit and follow Anderson south (right from I-10E, left from I-10W) about 1 mile (past Loma Linda University Medical Ctr) to store at Prospect St (behind bank & post office).

LOMITA

House of Vege 🍴

2439 Pacific Coast Hwy. ✆ 310-530-1180 ⏰ M-F 11-3, 5-9, Sat- Sun 11-9
Chinese vegetarian featuring faux meat and offering brown rice.
· vegetarian · vegan friendly · tables · wait staff · take-out
🍎 **From I-110,** take CA 1/Pacific Coast Hwy exit west (right from I-110S, left from I-110N) about 2½ miles to restaurant between Pennsylvania Ave & Airport Dr.

LONG BEACH ♿

Whole Foods Market 🛍️ 🍴

6550 E. Pacific Coast Hwy. ✆ 562-598-8687 ⏰ Daily 7-10
· organic produce · vegetarian friendly · salad bar · cafe · self-service · take-out
🍎 **From I-605S or I-405,** take CA 22W towards Long Beach about 1 mile to Studebaker Rd exit. Turn right onto Studebaker 1⅓ miles to Westminster. Turn right onto Westminster (becomes 2nd St) about ½ mile to Pacific Coast Hwy. Turn left onto PCH to store.

Zephyr Vegetarian Cafe 🍴

340 E. 4th St. ✆ 562-435-7113 ⏰ Tues-Sat 12-9, Sun 11-4
Mostly vegan with a raw foods focus.
· vegetarian · vegan friendly · organic focus · alcohol · tables · self-service · take-out
🍎 **From I-710S (Long Beach Fwy),** merge onto Shoreline Hwy and take ramp onto W 6th St 1 mile to Elm St. Turn right onto Elm to first right onto E 4th St to restaurant on left. **From Ocean Blvd** go north (inland) on Long Beach Blvd 4 blocks to 4th. Turn right onto E 4th to restaurant on right.

LOS ANGELES

Brite Spot Family Restaurant 🍴

1918 Sunset Blvd. ✆ 213-484-9800 ⏰ M-Tues 6am-10:30pm, W-Sun 6am-4am
1950s diner ambience and menu but for nonmeaters there is veggie meatloaf, tofu scramble, sloppy tofu mess, tofu-veggie saute and more.
· vegetarian friendly · vegan friendly · tables · wait staff · take-out
🍎 **From US 101 (Hollywood Fwy),** take exit 4A north on Alvarado St (left from US 101S, right from 101N) ½ mile to W Sunset Blvd. Turn right onto W Sunset 1 block to restaurant on right.

California Vegan 🍴

7300 Sunset Blvd. Unit A ✆ 323-874-9079 ⏰ Daily 11-10:30
Thai vegan with brown rice plus wraps, burgers and a few other surprises.
· vegan · organic focus · alcohol · tables · self-service
🍎 **From US 101S (Hollywood Fwy),** take exit 9C toward Highland Ave onto Cahuenga Blvd continuing onto N Highland for 1¼ miles total to W Sunset Blvd. Turn right

onto W Sunset over ½ mile to restaurant on left after N Fuller. **From US 101N**, take W Sunset 2⅓ miles to restaurant.

Cru

1521 Griffith Park Blvd. © 323-667-1551 ⊙ M, W-Sun 5:30-10
Raw and vegan cuisine.
• vegan • organic focus • tables • wait staff • take-out

From US 101S (Hollywood Fwy), take exit 5A left onto N Benton Way ½ mile to W Sunset Blvd. Turn left onto W Sunset under 1 mile to Griffith Park Blvd. Take right fork onto Griffith Park to restaurant on right. **From US 101N**, take exit 5A, merge right onto N Rampart Blvd ½ mile to W Sunset and follow directions above.

Erewhon Natural Foods Market

7660 Beverly Blvd. © 323-937-0777 ©M-Sat 8-10, Sun 9-9
• organic produce • vegetarian friendly • fresh juice • salad bar • deli • tables • self-service • take-out

From US 101N (Hollywood Fwy), take exit 6B toward Normandie Ave left onto Melrose Ave, left onto Normandie and right onto Beverly Blvd 3¼ miles to restaurant on right between La Brea & Fairfax Ave. **From US 101S**, take Highland Ave/Hollywood Bowl exit south on Cahuenga Blvd (becomes Highland) about 2 ½ miles to Beverly. Turn right onto Beverly 1 mile to store on right.

Fatty's

1627 Colorado Blvd. © 323-254-8804 ⊙ W-Sat 5-10, Sun 5-9
Tapas, artisanal cheese fondues, vegan soups, specialty pizzas, chef specials and more.
• vegetarian • vegan friendly • alcohol • tables • wait staff

From I-5, take CA 2N toward Glendale about 3¼ miles to Broadway/Colorado Blvd exit. Turn right onto Colorado about 1½ miles to restaurant between Vincent & Townsend Ave. **From CA 134W**, merge onto Colorado Blvd toward Eagle Rock under 1½ miles to restaurant. **From CA 134E**, take Harvey Dr exit right onto Harvey and left onto E Wilson (becomes W Broadway, then Colorado) about 1¾ miles to restaurant.

Go Veggie

5462 S. Centinela Ave. © 310-577-0167 ⊙ M-F 10-6:30, Sat 10:30-5
Vegetarian and vegan items sold by the pound.
• vegetarian • vegan friendly • tables • self-service • take-out

From I-405 (San Diego Fwy), take Jefferson Blvd exit west on Jefferson (exit 50A right from I-405S, left from I-405N) about ¾ mile to S Centinela Ave. Turn right onto S Centinela 2 blocks to restaurant on right after Beatrice St.

Govinda's

3764 Watseka Ave. © 310-836-1269 ⊙ M-Sat 11-3, 5-8:30
Lunch and dinner buffets run by the Hari Krishna temple at very affordable prices.
• vegetarian • vegan friendly • salad bar • tables • self-service

From I-10E (Santa Monica Fwy), take exit 4 toward Overland Ave left onto National Blvd about ¼ mile and turn left to stay on National ½ mile to Exposition Blvd. Merge straight onto Exposition about ¼ mile to Watseka Ave. Turn right onto Watseka about ¼ mile to restaurant. **From I-10W**, take exit 6 onto Robertson Blvd 1 block to National. Turn left onto National 1 block to Venice Blvd. Turn left onto Venice over ½ mile to Watseka. Turn right onto Watseka to restaurant.

Green Leaves Vegan

1769 Hillhurst Ave. © 323-664-2345 ⊙ Daily 11am-12am
Thai with faux meats plus sandwiches, wraps, salads and beyond. BYOB.
• vegan • tables • wait staff

From I-5 (Santa Ana Fwy), take exit 141 onto Los Feliz Blvd toward Hollywood 1¾ miles to Hillhurst Ave. Turn left onto Hillhurst about ½ mile to restaurant on right. **From I-5N**, take exit 141A left onto Los Feliz 1⅓ miles to Hillhurst and follow directions above.

Inaka 🍴

131 S. La Brea Ave. ✆ 323-936-9353 ⏰ Tues-F 12-2:30, 6-9:45, Sat 5:30-9:45, Sun 5-9
Macrobiotic fare in a simple setting.
  • vegetarian friendly • vegan friendly • tables • wait staff

🚗 **From I-10 (Santa Monica Fwy)**, take exit 8 north on S La Brea Ave (left from I-10W, right from I-10E) 2¾-3 miles to restaurant on left between W 2nd & W 1st St. **From US 101N** (Hollywood Fwy), take exit 7 left onto Santa Monica Blvd 2 miles to Highland Ave. Turn left onto Highland ½ mile to Melrose Ave. Turn right onto Melrose 5 blocks to N La Brea. Turn left onto N LaBrea ¾ mile to restaurant on right after W 1st St. **From US 101S**, take exit 9C toward Highland south on Cahuenga Blvd (becomes Highland) about 2¼ miles to Melrose and follow directions above.

Mao's Kitchen 🍴

7315 Melrose Ave. ✆ 310-581-8305 ⏰ M-Th, Sun 11:30-10:30, F-Sat 11:30am-3am
Tofu, meat, chicken or fish as well as vegetable stock in any dish. Brown rice and vegan sauces available. BYOB.
  • vegetarian friendly • vegan friendly • tables • wait staff • take-out

🚗 **From 101S (Hollywood Fwy)**, take 9C toward Highland Ave onto Cahuenga Blvd S (becomes N Highland) 2¼ miles to Melrose Ave. Turn right onto Melrose over ½ mile to restaurant on right after N Poinsetta Pl. **From US 101N**, take exit 7 left onto Santa Monica Blvd 2¼ miles to N La Brea Ave. Turn left onto N La Brea ½ mile to Melrose. Turn right onto Melrose ⅓ mile to restaurant.

Mr. Wisdom Hari Krishna Restaurant & Specialty Health Food Store 🛒 🍴

3526 W. Slauson Ave. ✆ 323-295-1517 ⏰ M-F 10-7, Sat 10-6
  • vegan • organic focus • fresh juice • salad bar • cafe • counter • tables • self-service
  • take-out

🚗 **From I-405N (San Diego Fwy)**, take exit 48 right onto La Tijera Blvd 1⅓ miles to W Slauson Blvd. Turn right onto W Slauson about 1¾ miles to store on right a few blocks before Crenshaw Blvd. **From I-405S**, take Slauson Ave exit, merge onto CA 90E and turn right onto Slauson about 3 miles to store.

Nature Mart 🛒

2080 Hillhurst Ave. ✆ 323-660-0052 ⏰ Daily 7-10
  • organic produce

🚗 **From I-5 (Santa Ana Fwy)**, take exit 141 onto Los Feliz Blvd toward Hollywood 1¾ miles to Hillhurst Ave. Turn left onto Hillhurst 2 blocks to store on left. **From I-5N**, take exit 141A left onto Los Feliz 1⅓ miles to Hillhurst and follow directions above.

Rahel Veggie Cuisine 🍴

1047 S. Fairfax Ave. ✆ 323-937-8401 ⏰ M-Th, Sun 11-10, F-Sat 11-11
Billed as the only vegan Ethiopian restaurant in America.
  • vegan • tables • wait staff • take-out

🚗 **From I-10E (Santa Monica Fwy)**, take exit 7A onto S La Cienega Blvd almost 2 miles to N Pico Blvd. Turn right onto N Pico about ½ mile to S Fairfax Ave. Turn left onto S Fairfax under ½ mile to restaurant. **From I-10W**, take exit 7A right onto Venice Blvd ⅓ mile to S Fairfax. Turn left onto S Fairfax under 1 mile to restaurant.

Sante La Brea 🍴   ♿

345 N. La Brea Ave. ✆ 323-857-0412 ⏰ M-F 10-10, Sat 8-10, Sun 8-9
Will alter dishes to make vegan or add fish or free-range chicken on request.
  • vegetarian friendly • vegan friendly • organic focus • alcohol • bakery • tables • wait
  staff • take-out

🚗 **From I-10 (Santa Monica Fwy)**, take exit 8 north on S La Brea Ave (right from I-10W, loop around right from I-10E) 3-3½ miles to restaurant on left after Beverly Blvd. **From US 101N**, take exit 7 left onto Santa Monica Blvd 2¼ miles to N La Brea. Turn left onto N La Brea 1 mile to restaurant on right. **From US 101S** (Hollywood Fwy), take exit 7C south on Cahuenga Blvd (becomes Highland Ave) 1¾ miles to Santa Monica. Turn right onto Santa Monica 4 blocks to N La Brea. Turn left onto N La Brea 1 mile to restaurant.

Shojin Natural & Organic 🍴
333 S. Alameda St. ℂ 213-617-0305 ⏰ W-Sun 12-9
Japanese menu in the Buddhist tradition.
· vegan · organic focus · tables · wait staff

🍎 In downtown LA. **From 101 Fwy,** take Alameda St exit south about ¾ mile (past 3rd St) to Little Tokyo Shopping Ctr on right. Restaurant is on 3rd fl. **From 110 (Harbor) Fwy,** take 4th St exit east 1⅓ miles to Alameda 1 block to restaurant on left. **From 10 (Santa Monica) Fwy,** take Alameda St exit north 1⅓ miles (past 4th St) to restaurant on left.

Tantawan Vegan 🍴
1311 N. Glendale Blvd., Ste. A ℂ 213-484-9383 ⏰ Daily 11-10:30
Thai vegan menu.
· vegan · organic focus · tables · wait staff · take-out

🍎 **From 101 (Hollywood Fwy),** take Alvarado St exit (4A from 101S, 4B from 101N) north on Alvarado almost 1 mile to Glendale Blvd. Turn sharp right onto Glendale Blvd ⅓ mile to restaurant on right between Montana & Reservoir St. **From I-5,** take Glendale Fwy/CA 2S exit south about 1¼ miles and veer left onto Glendale Blvd ⅓ mile to restaurant after Montana.

The Vegan Joint 🍴
14038 National Blvd. ℂ 310-559-1357 ⏰ M, W-Th, Sun 11-9, F-Sat 11-10
A homey place serving all-day breakfast, lunch and dinner. Varied menu with a Thai slant.
· vegan · organic focus · tables · wait staff

🍎 **From I-405 (San Diego Fwy),** merge onto I-10E (Santa Monica Fwy). **From I-10E,** take exit 4 toward Overland Ave and turn left onto National Blvd ⅓ mile to restaurant on corner between Overland & Motor Ave. **From I-10W,** take exit 5 left then right onto National 1/5 mile to restaurant after Motor.

Tierra Cafe 🍴
818 Wilshire Blvd. #D ℂ 213-629-1402 ⏰ M-F 9-3
Vegetarian fast-food in a food court in downtown LA.
· vegetarian · vegan friendly · organic focus · fresh juice · counter · tables · self-service · take-out

🍎 **From Harbor Fwy S**, take 4th St exit toward Wilshire Blvd/6th St left at fork and take 6th St exit onto S Beaudry Ave to Wilshire. Turn left onto Wilshire about 3 blocks to restaurant on right after S Figueroa St. **From Harbor Fwy N**, take 4th St/3rd St exit and take exit 23A onto W 6th 3 blocks to S Flower St. Turn right onto S Flower 1 block to Wilshire. Turn right onto Wilshire 1 block to restaurant on left.

Vegan Express 🍴   ♿
3217 Cahuenga Blvd. W. ℂ 323-851-8837 ⏰ M-Th, Sun 11-9, F-Sat 11-10
Vegan fast foods with an Asian orientation plus sandwiches, wraps and veggie meat dinners. Breakfast includes unusual burritos and wheat-free pancakes. Dessert includes raw selections.
· vegan · tables · self-service · take-out

🍎 **From US 101N (Hollywood Fwy),** take exit toward Barham Blvd/Burbank onto Cahuenga Blvd about ½ mile to Barham. Turn left onto Barham and right onto Cahuenga to restaurant. **From US 101S,** take exit toward Barham left onto Cahuenga to restaurant just off fwy.

Vegan Glory 🍴
8393 Beverly Blvd. ℂ 323-653-4900 ⏰ Daily 11-10
Vegan Thai plus burgers, wraps and salads. Brown rice served.
· vegan · organic focus · alcohol · counter · tables · wait staff · take-out

🍎 **From US 101N (Hollywood Fwy),** take exit 6B (Melrose Ave) toward Normandie Ave left onto Melrose, left onto Normandie and right onto Beverly Blvd 4¼ miles to restaurant on right between Fairfax & La Cienega Ave. **From 101S,** merge onto CA 170 and bear right onto N Highland Ave 1 mile to Santa Monica Blvd. Turn right onto Santa Monica ⅓ mile to La Brea. Turn left onto Brea 1 mile to Beverly. Turn right onto Beverly 1¾ mile to restaurant.

Vegisoul ⏚

1436 W. Jefferson Blvd. ©323-731-8344 ⊙ Tues-Sat 11-9, Sun 11-7
Mostly vegan soulfood. Cooking done in distilled water.
   • vegetarian • vegan friendly • organic focus • counter • tables • self-service • take-out
🍎 **From I-10 (Santa Monica Fwy),** take exit 11/Western Ave and follow signs for S
Normandie Ave. Turn south onto S Normandie (right from I-10E, left from I-10W) under
1 mile to W Jefferson Blvd. Turn left onto W Jefferson to restaurant on right. **From I-110S**
(Harbor Fwy), merge onto I-10W and follow directions above. **From I-110N,** take exit 20B
for 37th St toward Exhibition Blvd and merge onto S Hope St ⅓ mile to Jefferson. Turn
left onto W Jefferson 1⅓ miles to restaurant on left after Vermont Ave.

Whole Foods Market 🛍 ⏚ &

11737 San Vincente Blvd. © 310-826-4433 ⊙ Daily 7-10:30
   • organic produce • vegetarian friendly • salad bar • cafe • self-service • take-out
🍎 Located in Brentwood section of LA. **From I-405 (San Diego Fwy),** take Wilshire
Blvd west about ½ mile to San Vincente Blvd. Turn right onto San Vincente about
½ mile to store.

Whole Foods Market 🛍 ⏚ &

6350 W. 3rd St. © 323-964-6800 ⊙ Daily 7-11
   • organic produce • vegetarian friendly • salad bar • cafe • self-service • take-out
🍎 **From US 101 (Hollywood Fwy),** take Highland Ave/Hollywood Bowl exit south
on Cahuenga Blvd (becomes Highland) about 1 mile to Hollywood Blvd. Turn
right onto Hollywood about 1⅓ miles to Fairfax Ave. Turn left onto Fairfax 2 miles
to E 3rd St. Turn left onto 3rd to store.

Whole Foods Market 🛍 ⏚ &

11666 National Blvd. © 310-996-8840 ⊙ Daily 7-10
   • organic produce • vegetarian friendly • salad bar • cafe • self-service • take-out
🍎 **From I-10 (Santa Monica Fwy),** take exit 4 (Overland Ave) onto National Blvd 1⅓
miles to store at S Barrington Ave. **From I-10E,** take exit 2A left onto Pico Blvd about
½ mile to Barrington. Turn right onto Barrington ¾ mile to store at National.

MONTEREY PARK

Happy Family 3 ⏚

111 N. Atlantic Blvd. © 626-282-8986 ⊙ M-F 11:30-2:45, 5-8:45, Sat-Sun 11:30--8:45
Chinese vegetarian.
   • vegetarian • vegan friendly • tables • wait staff • take-out
🍎 **From I-10 (San Bernadino Fwy),** take exit 23B onto S Garfield Ave about 1 mile
to W Garvey Ave. Turn right onto W Garvey about ½ mile to restaurant on right
at Atlantic Ave.

MORRO BAY

Sunshine Health Foods/Shine Cafe 🛍 ⏚ ⏚

415 Morro Bay Blvd. © 805-772-7873 ⊙ M-F 9-6, Sat 10-5, Sun 10-4
   • organic produce • vegetarian • vegan friendly • organic focus • tables • self-service •
   take-out
🍎 **From Hwy 1N,** exit onto Morro Bay Blvd 1 mile to store on right between Napa
and Monterey Ave. **From Hwy 1S,** take exit 179A south onto Main St ½ mile to
Morro Bay Blvd. Turn left onto Morro Bay to store on left after Monterey.

NORTH HOLLYWOOD

Leonor's Mexican Restaurant ⏚

11403 Victory Blvd. © 818-980-9011 ⊙ Daily 10-9
Vegan Mexican cuisine featuring soy-based meat and cheese.
   • vegan • tables • wait staff
🍎 **From Hollywood Fwy,** take exit 8B east on Victory Blvd 1½ miles to restaurant
on left before Tijunga Ave.

NORTHRIDGE

Cafe Graikos 🍴

19346 Rinaldi St. ✆ 18-831-1187 ⏱ M-Th, Sun 11-9:30, F-Sat 11-10
Greek with more vegetarian and vegan options than usual.
 • vegetarian friendly • vegan friendly • alcohol • tables • wait staff

🚍 **From I-405 (San Diego Fwy),** take Hwy 118 exit toward Simi Valley west on Hwy 118W (right from I-405S, left from I-405N) about 4½ mile to exit 37 for Tampa Ave. Turn right onto Tampa 1 block to Rinaldi St. Turn right onto Rinaldi to restaurant on right.

NORWALK

Our Daily Bread 🛒 🍴

12201 Firestone Blvd. ✆ 562-863-6897 ⏱ M, W, Th 10-4:30, Tues 10-7, F 10-2
A Seventh-day Adventist-run bookstore, grocery and vegan lunch counter.
 • vegan • tables • self-service • take-out

🚍 **From I-5S (Santa Ana Fwy),** take San Antonio Dr/Norwalk Blvd exit left onto Union St and right onto San Antonio under ¼ mile to Firestone Blvd. Turn left onto Firestone to store. **From I-5N**, take Firestone Blvd exit on left toward CA 42 about ¾ mile to store.

OCEAN BEACH

Ranchos 🍴   ♿

1830 Sunset Cliffs Blvd. ✆ 619-226-7619 ⏱ M-F 10-10, Sat-Sun 8-10
Mexican with an emphasis on "natural cooking" and more interesting vegetarian options than usual. Whole wheat tortillas and brown rice available. A Certified Green Restaurant.
 • vegetarian friendly • alcohol • tables • wait staff • take-out

🚍 **From I-8W,** follow to end and merge onto Sunset Cliffs Blvd about 1 mile to restaurant at Narragansett Ave (3 blocks from ocean). **From I-5**, exit onto I-8W and follow directions above.

OJAI

Rainbow Bridge Natural Food Store 🛒 🍴

211 E. Matilija St. ✆ 805-646-4017, 805-646-6623 ⏱ Daily 8-9
 • vegetarian friendly • organic produce • deli • tables • self service • take-out

🚍 **From CA 33,** continue west on CA 150/Ojai Ave to S Signal St. Turn left onto S Signal 1 block to E Matilija St. Turn right onto E Matilija to store on right.

The Farmer and the Cook 🛒 🍴   ♿

339 W. El Roblar Drive ✆ 805-640-9608 ⏱ Tues-F 8-8, Sat 8-9, Sun 9-9
Proprietors' organic farm furnishes the vegetables and herbs sold at the store and used in the food. Baking done with spelt rather than wheat.
 • organic produce • vegetarian • vegan friendly • organic focus • fresh juice • salad bar
 • cafe • deli • bakery • tables • self-service • take-out

🚍 **From CA 33/CA 150 intersection**, go northwest on 33/Maricopa Hwy ¾ mile to El Roblar Dr. Turn left onto El Roblar ½ mile to store on left at Encinal Ave.

ORANGE

Rutabegorz 🍴   ♿

264 N. Glassell St. ✆ 714-633-3260 ⏱ M-Sat 11-9
See Fullerton location for description. Note no alcohol at this locale.
 • vegetarian friendly • tables • wait staff • take-out

🚍 **From I-5 (Santa Ana Fwy),** take State College Ave/CA 57N to Chapman Ave exit. Turn right (east) onto Chapman about 1½ miles to traffic circle at S Glassell St. Turn left onto Glassell 1½ blocks to restaurant on left.

OXNARD

Lassen's Natural Foods 🛍

3471 Saviors Rd. ✆ 805-486-8266 ⏱ M-Sat 9-7
• organic produce

🚗 **From US 101N (Ventura Fwy)**, take Vineyard Ave exit toward Oxnard left onto Vineyard and left again onto Oxnard Rd (becomes Saviers Rd) 4 miles to store on right. **From 101S,** take Oxnard Ave exit right and follow directions above.

PALM DESERT

Native Foods 🍴

73-890 El Paseo ✆ 760-836-9396 ⏱ M-Sat 11-9:30
See Aliseo Viejo location for description.
• vegan • organic focus • alcohol • tables • wait staff

🚗 **From I-10,** take exit 131 south on Monterey Ave (right from I-10E, left from I-10W) about 6 miles to Hwy 111. Turn left onto 111 about 1 mile to Portola Ave. Turn right onto Portola and make first right onto El Paseo restaurant on right.

PALM SPRINGS

Native Foods 🍴

1775 E. Palm Canyon Drive ✆ 760-416-0070 ⏱ M-Sat 11:30-9:30
See Aliseo Viejo location for description.
• vegan • organic focus • alcohol • tables • wait staff

🚗 **From I-10,** take Palm Dr exit toward Desert Hot Springs south on N Gene Autry Trail (right from I-10E, left from I-10W) 6 miles to E Palm Canyon Dr. Turn right onto Palm Canyon 2 miles to restaurant on left in Smoke Tree Village.

Nature's RX 🛍 🍴

555 S. Sunrise Way ✆ 760-323-9487 ⏱ Daily 10-6
Cafe Totonaca inside the market serves breakfast and lunch.
• organic produce • vegetarian • vegan friendly • fresh juice • cafe • self-service • take-out

🚗 **From I-10,** take Palm Dr exit toward Desert Hot Springs south on N Gene Autry Trail (right from I-10E, left from I-10W) about 4½ miles to E Ramon Rd. Turn right onto E Ramon 2 miles to S Sunrise Way. Turn left onto S Sunrise to store on left.

Palm Greens Cafe 🍴 ♿

611 S. Palm Canyon Drive ✆ 760-864-9900 ⏱ M-Th 9-3 F-Sun 9-8
• vegetarian • vegan friendly • fresh juice • tables • self service

🚗 **From I-10,** take exit 120 south on N Indian Canyon Dr (right from I-10E, left from I-10W) 4 miles to Vista Chino. Turn right onto Vista Chino and left onto N Palm Canyon Dr 2¼ miles to store on right in strip mall after E Ramon St.

PALOMAR MT.

Mother's Kitchen 🍴 ♿

33120 Canfield Rd. ✆ 760-742-4233 ⏱ Th-F 11-4, Sat-Sun 8:30-5
• vegetarian • alcohol • tables • self-service

🚗 **From Hwy 76,** go northeast up mountain on S7/S Grade Rd (left from Hwy 76E, right from Hwy 76W) about 6¾ miles to Canfield Rd. Turn left onto Canfield to restaurant on left after State Park Rd.

PASADENA

Orean's: The Health Express 🍴

817 N. Lake Ave. ✆ 626-794-0861 ⏱ Daily 9:30-9
Vegan fast food. There is even a drive-through window. Outdoor tables only.
• vegan • tables • self-service • take-out

🚗 **From I-210,** take Lake Ave exit north on Lake (straight onto Corson St then left from I-210E, right from I-210W) about ½ mile to restaurant.

Whole Foods Market 🛒 🍴   ♿

3751 E. Foothills Blvd. ✆ 626-351-5994 ⏱ Daily 7-10
  • organic produce • vegetarian friendly • salad bar • cafe • self-service • take-out

🚗 **From I-210,** take Rosemead Blvd North exit onto Rosemead (loop around right from I-210E, right from I-210W) about ⅓ mile to store on NE corner at Foothills Blvd.

PORTER RANCH

Whole Foods Market 🛒 🍴   ♿

19340 Rinaldi St. ✆ 818-363-3933 ⏱ Daily 8-10
  • organic produce • vegetarian friendly • salad bar • cafe • self-service • take-out

🚗 **From I-5 (Golden State Fwy),** take CA 118W to Tampa Ave exit. Turn right onto Tampa to store in shopping center on right before Rinaldi St.

POWAY

Henry's Marketplace 🛒

13536 Poway Rd. ✆ 858-486-7851 ⏱ Daily 7-10
  • organic produce • vegetarian friendly • deli • take-out

🚗 **From I-15,** take Rancho Pensaquitos Blvd/Poway Rd east on Poway (merge right from I-15N, left from I-15S) about 4¼ miles to store on left.

REDONDO BEACH

The Green Temple 🍴

1700 S. Catalina Ave. ✆ 310-944-4525 ⏱ Tues-Th, 11-3:30, 5-8:30, F-Sat 11-3:30, 5-9:30, Sun 9-8:30
Mostly vegan and an eclectic "funky" decor.
  • vegetarian • vegan friendly • organic focus • tables • wait staff

🚗 **From Hwy 1,** take Ave H west 1 block to S Catalina. Turn left onto Catalina 1 block to store. **From I-405S** (San Diego Fwy), take Rt 107S (Hawthorne Blvd) about 3½ miles to Torrance Blvd. Turn right onto Torrance 2 miles to S Catalina Ave. Turn left onto Catalina about 1⅓ miles to store. **From I-405N**, take Artesia Blvd/CA 91W exit right about ⅔ mile to Hawthorne. Turn left onto Hawthorne about 2½ miles to Torrance and follow directions above.

Whole Foods Market 🛒 🍴   ♿

405 N. Pacific Coast Hwy. ✆ 310-376-6931 ⏱ Daily 8-9
  • organic produce • vegetarian friendly • salad bar • cafe • self-service • take-out

🚗 **On Hwy 1 (Pacific Coast Hwy)** on east side at Camelian St. **From I-405S** (San Diego Fwy), take Rt 107S (Hawthorne Blvd) about 2 miles to 190th St. Turn right onto 190th about 2 miles to Hwy 1. Turn left onto Hwy 1½ mile to store on right. **From I-405N**, take Western Ave exit left onto Western and right onto 190th about 4 miles to Hwy 1. Turn left onto Hwy 1 ½ mile to store.

RESEDA

Vinh Loi Tofu 🍴

18625 Sherman Way ✆ 818-996-9779 ⏱ Daily 7-7
Largely vegan Vietnamese food. Tofu, soymilk and custard made onsite using traditional methods. Just a few small tables
  • vegetarian • vegan friendly • tables • self-service • take-out

🚗 **From the Ventura Fwy,** take exit 23 north on Reseda Blvd (left from Fwy S, right from Fwy N) 2 miles to Sherman Way. Turn left onto Sherman 2 blocks to restaurant on right after Amigo Ave.

ROWLAND HEIGHTS

Happy Family Restaurant 🍴

18425 E. Colima Rd. © 626-965-9923 ⏱ M-F 11:30-2:45, 5-9, Sat-Sun 11:30-9:20
Chinese vegetarian.
  · vegetarian · vegan friendly · tables · wait staff · take-out

🚗 **From US 60E,** take Fullerton Rd exit and take Fullerton Rd S ramp onto Fullerton about ¼ mile to Colima Rd. Turn left onto Colima past first block to restaurant. **From US 60W,** take Fullerton Rd exit left onto Fullerton ½ mile to Colima and follow directions above.

SAN DIEGO

Cilantro Live! 🍴

3807 5th Ave. © 619-325-1949 ⏱ Daily 11:30-10
Focus is raw food.
  · vegan · organic focus · fresh juice · salad bar · tables · wait staff · take-out

🚗 **From I-5S (San Diego Fwy),** take Washington St east 1½ miles to 4th Ave. Turn right onto 4th 2 blocks to Robinson Ave. Turn left onto Robinson 1 block to 5th Ave. Turn left onto 5th to restaurant on right. **From I-5N,** take exit 16B right onto 6th Ave 1½ miles to Evans Pl. Turn left onto Evans 1 block to 5th. Turn right onto 5th 1 block to restaurant on right past Robinson.

Henry's Marketplace 🛍

1260 Garnet Ave. © 858-270-8200 ⏱ Daily 7-10
  · organic produce · vegetarian friendly · deli · take-out

🚗 **From I-5,** take exit 23 (23A from I-5N) west on Garnet Ave (merge onto Mission Bay Dr and right from I-5S, merge onto Mission Bay and left from I-5N) about 1¾ miles to store on right.

Henry's Marketplace 🛍

4175 Park Blvd. © 619-291-8287 ⏱ Daily 7-11
  · organic produce · vegetarian friendly · deli · take-out

🚗 **From I-805,** take El Cajon Blvd exit west on El Cajon (right from I-805S, left from I-805N) about 1¼ miles to Park Blvd. Turn left onto Park to store.

Henry's Marketplace 🛍

3315 Rosecrans St. © 619-523-3640 ⏱ Daily 7-10
  · organic produce · vegetarian friendly · deli · take-out,

🚗 **From I-5S,** merge onto CA 209S toward Rosencrans St about 1 mile to store on left. **From I-5N,** exit onto Pacific Coast Hwy 1⅓ miles to exit on left onto Barnett Ave. Take Barnett about ¾ mile to Lytton St. Veer right onto Lytton under ¼ mile to Rosencrans. Turn right onto Rosencrans almost ½ mile to store on right.

Henry's Marketplace 🛍

4439 Genesee Ave. © 858-268-2400 ⏱ Daily 7-10
  · organic produce · vegetarian friendly · deli · take-out

🚗 **From I-805,** take Balboa Ave West/CA 274W about 1 mile to Genessee Ave. Turn right onto Genessee about ⅓ mile to store.

Henry's Marketplace 🛍

3358 Governor Drive © 858-457-5006 ⏱ Daily 7-10
  · organic produce · vegetarian friendly · deli · take-out

🚗 **From I-805,** merge onto CA 52W about 1⅔ miles to Genessee Ave exit. Follow Genessee Ave North ramp onto Genessee about ½ mile to Governor Dr. Turn left onto Governor about ½ mile to store. **From I-5N,** merge onto CA 52E toward San Clemente almost 1 mile to Regents Rd exit. Take left fork off ramp onto Regents about ¾ mile to Governor. Turn right onto Governor abut ¼ mile to store. **From I-5S,** take Genessee Ave exit and follow Genessee Ave East ramp onto Genessee about 3 miles to Governor. Turn right onto Governor about ½ mile to store.

Jimbo's Naturally

12853 El Camino Real © 858-793-7755 ⏰ Daily 8-9
- organic produce · vegetarian friendly · fresh juice · salad bar · deli · bakery · tables
- self-service · take-out

From I-5, take Del Mar Heights Rd exit east on Del Mar (left from I-5S, right from I-5N) about ¾ mile to El Camino Real. Turn right onto El Camino Real to store on left in Del Mar Highlands Town Ctr.

Jimbo's Naturally

10511 4S Commons Drive © 58-432-7755 ⏰ Daily 8-9
- organic produce · vegetarian friendly · fresh juice · salad bar · deli · bakery · tables
- self-service · take-out

From I-15S, take Rancho Bernardo Rd exit right onto Rancho Bernardo almost 2 miles to Dove Canyon Rd. Turn left onto Dove Canyon 1 block to S Common Dr. Turn right onto S Common to store. **From I-15N,** take exit 22 left onto Camino del Norte 2⅓ miles to Dove Canyon. Turn right onto Dove Canyon 1 block to S Common. Turn left onto S Common to store.

Jyoti Bihanga Restaurant

3351 Adams Ave. © 619-282-4116 ⏰ M-Tues, Th-F 11-9, Wed 11-3, Sat 12-9, Sun sporadically 9-1
Run by disciples of Sri Chinmoy. Salads, sandwiches, wraps and internationally-inspired hot entrees. Buffet two or three Sundays a month.
- vegetarian · vegan friendly · tables · wait staff

From I-805N, take El Cajon Blvd exit right onto El Cajon about ½ mile to 35th St. Turn left onto 35th to second light (Adams Ave). Turn left onto Adams ¼ mile to restaurant at Felton St. **From I-805S,** take Adams Ave exit (first exit past Fwy 8) and turn right at stop sign onto Ohio St to light at Adams. Turn right onto Adams about ½ mile to restaurant at Felton.

Krishna Cafe

1030 Grand Ave. © 858-483-2500, 272-8263 ⏰ F 6-8
Inexpensive Indian buffet dinner in a peaceful temple setting.
- vegetarian · vegan friendly · tables · self-service

From I-5S (San Diego Fwy), take exit 23 toward State Hwy 274/Balboa Ave/ Garnet Ave onto Mission Bay Dr, turn right onto Garnet Ave and follow onto Balboa 1 mile to Grand Ave. Veer right onto Grand 1 mile to restaurant on right. **From I-5N,** take exit 22 toward Grand onto Mission Bay and turn left onto Grand 2 miles to restaurant on right after Dawes St.

Nature's Express

2949 5th Ave. © 619-550-1818 ⏰ Daily 10-7 Drive-through 11-10
Healthier fast food with vegan burgers, dogs, fries and shakes.
- vegan, organic focus, fresh juice, tables, self-service

From I-5S (San Diego Fwy), take exit 16 onto CA 123N ⅓ mile to exit 1B onto Quince Dr 1 block to 6th Ave. Turn left onto 6th 1 block to Palm St. Turn right onto Palm 1 block to 5th Ave. Turn right onto 5th to restaurant on right at Quince St (across from park). **From I-5N,** take exit 16B right onto 6th Ave under 1 mile to Palm. Turn left onto Palm and right onto 5th to restaurant.

Ocean Beach People's Organic Food Co-op

4765 Voltaire St. © 619-224-1387 ⏰ Daily 8-9
- organic produce · vegetarian · vegan friendly · organic focus · salad bar · cafe · deli
- bakery · counter · tables · self-service · take-out · co-op

From I-5, merge onto I-8W about 3⅓ miles to end where it becomes Sunset Cliffs Blvd. Continue onto Sunset Cliffs about ⅔ mile to Voltaire St. Turn left onto Voltaire to store on right.

Ranchos North Park 🍴   ♿

3910 30th St. ✆ 619-574-1288 ⏰ M-F 10-10, Sat-Sun 8-10
See Ocean Beach location for description.

• vegetarian friendly • alcohol • tables • wait staff • take-out

🍎 **From I-805S,** take North Park Way exit toward University Ave right onto Boundary Ave and left onto University about ⅓ mile to restaurant at 30th St. **From I-805N,** take University Ave exit and veer left onto Wabash Ave and left onto University about ½ mile to restaurant.

Sipz Fuzion Cafe 🍴

5501 Clairemont Mesa Blvd. ✆ 58-279-3747 ⏰ Daily 11-9
Soups, salads and bowls of Thai, Vietnamese, Chinese and Italian fare. Mostly vegan including all desserts. Emphasis on affordability.

• vegetarian • vegan friendly • alcohol • tables • wait staff

🍎 **From I-805,** take exit 22 west on Clairemont Mesa Blvd ½-¾ mile to restaurant on left.

Spread 🍴

2879 University Ave. ✆ 619-543-0406 ⏰ Tues-Sat 6-10
A casual place with an upscale menu that changes daily.

• vegetarian • vegan friendly • organic focus • alcohol • tables • wait staff

🍎 **From I-805,** take exit 15 west on University Ave (merge onto Wabash Ave and left from I-805N, merge onto Boundary St and left from I-805S) ½-¾ mile to restaurant on left after 30th St.

Veg N Out 🍴

3442 30th St., North Park ✆ 619-546-8411 ✆ M-F 11-9, Sat 12-10, Sun 12-4
Deli atmosphere with burgers, soy dogs, sandwiches, sides, kids' specials and similar fare.

• vegetarian • vegan friendly • tables • self-service • take-out

🍎 **From I-805,** take exit 15 west on University (merge onto Wabash Ave and left from I-805N, merge onto Boundary St and left from I-805S) about ½ mile to 30th St. Turn left onto 30th ½ mile to restaurant on right after Myrtle Ave.

Vegan Zone 🍴

859 Hornblend St. ✆ 858-272-1913 ⏰ Tues-Sun 11:30-3:30, 4:30-9:30
Asian orientation plus wraps, breakfast burritos, vegan pancakes and other untraditional fare.

• vegan • alcohol • tables • wait staff • take-out

🍎 **From the beach,** restaurant is about 2 blocks inland on Hornblend. **From I-5S,** take exit 23 toward Bilboa Ave/Garnet Ave onto Mission Bay Dr ¼ mile to Garnet. Turn right onto Garnet (becomes Balboa, then Grand Ave) about 2 miles to Bayard St. Turn right onto Bayard 2 blocks back to Hornblend St. Turn left onto Hornblend to restaurant on left. **From I-5N,** take Grand Ave/Garnet Ave exit onto Mission Bay to Grand. Turn left onto Grand 2⅓ miles to Bayard and follow directions above.

Whole Foods Market 🛍️   ♿

711 University Ave. ✆ 619-294-2800 ⏰ Daily 8-10
• organic produce • vegetarian friendly • salad bar • cafe • self-service • take-out

🍎 **From I-805S,** merge onto CA 163S (Cabrillo Fwy) toward Downtown about 4 miles to University Ave exit and take 6th Ave south about ½ mile to University Ave. Turn left onto University 1 block to store. **From I-8,** merge onto CA 163S and follow directions above. **From I-5N,** merge onto CA 163N toward Escondido about 1¾ miles to Robinson Ave. Turn left onto Robinson 2 blocks to 7th Ave. Turn right onto 7th 1 block to store at University.

SAN DIMAS

Veggie & Tea House 🍴

641 Arrow Hwy. ✆ 909-592-6323 ⏰ Daily 11-8
See Chino Hills location for description.

• vegetarian • vegan friendly • organic focus • tables • wait staff • take-out

🍎 **From I-210,** take CA 57S about 1¼ miles to Arrow Hwy. Turn left onto Arrow about ⅓ mile to restaurant.

SAN GABRIEL

Gourmet Vegetarian
140 W. Valley Blvd. #222 © 626-280-5998 ⊕ M-F 11-3, 5-9, Sat-Sun 11-9
Chinese vegetarian. Brown rice available.
• vegetarian • vegan friendly • tables • wait staff

From I-10 (San Bernadino Fwy), take exit 25A toward San Gabriel north on Del Mar Ave ½-1 mile to W Valley Blvd. Turn left onto W Valley to restaurant on left in Focus Plaza on 2nd floor.

Tea Shaker Restaurant
7258 N. Rosemead Blvd. © 626-287-5850⊕ M-Th, Sun 11-10, F-Sat 11-11
Vegan with an eclectic Asian influence.
• vegan • tables • wait staff

From I-10 (San Bernadino Fwy), take CA 19N/Rosemead Blvd exit toward Pasadena north on Rosemead about 4 miles to restaurant. **From I-210,** take Rosemead exit south on Rosemead about 1¼ miles to restaurant.

SAN LUIS OBISPO

Evos Fresh & Healthy
3973 S. Higuera St. ⊕ Daily 11-10
Healthy fast-food concept with soyburgers, veggie patties, whole wheat wraps, organic greens, vegan chili, veggie corn dogs, natural meat, "airfriesTM", smoothies and such.
• vegetarian friendly • tables • self-service • take-out

From Hwy 101, take exit 200 east on Los Osos Valley Rd (right from Hwy 101N, left from Hwy 101S) ⅓-½ mile to Higuera St. Turn left onto Higuera ⅓ mile to restaurant on right.

Natural Foods Co-op
745 Francis St. © 805-544-7928 ⊕ M-Sat 9-6
• organic produce • co-op

From Hwy 101, take Marsh St exit east ½ mile to Broad St. Turn right onto Broad about ¾ mile to Francis St. Turn left onto Francis to store at corner.

New Frontiers
896 Foothill Blvd. © 805-785-0194 ⊕ M-F 8-9, Sat 8-8, Sun 9-8
• organic produce • vegetarian friendly • fresh juice • salad bar • cafe • deli • bakery • tables • self-service • take-out

From Hwy 101N, take exit 203C right onto California Blvd about ½ mile Foothill Blvd. Turn left onto Foothill to store on right after N Santa Rosa Blvd. **From Hwy 101S,** take California Blvd exit right and follow directions above.

SANTA BARBARA

Lazy Acres
302 Meigs Rd. © 805-564-4410 © Daily 7-10
• organic produce • vegetarian friendly • deli • bakery • tables • self-service • take-out

From Hwy 101, take Carrillo St west (becomes Meigs Rd) about 2 miles to store on left.

Sojourner Cafe
134 E. Canon Perdido © 805-965-7922 ⊕ M-Sat 11-11, Sun 11-10
Mostly vegetarian/vegan wholefoods with a smattering of fish and poultry.
• vegetarian friendly • vegan friendly • organic focus • alcohol • tables • wait staff

From Hwy 101N, take Garden St toward Downtown (right) about ½ mile to E Canon Perdido. Turn left onto E Canon Perdido under 2 blocks to restaurant. **From Hwy 101S,** take W Carillo St toward Downtown (left) about ½ mile to Anacapa St. Turn right onto Anacapa 1 block and left onto E Canon Perdido to restaurant.

SANTA CLARITA

Lassen's Natural Foods 🛒

26861 Bouquet Canyon Rd. ✆ 661-263-6935 ⊘ M-Sat 9-8
• organic produce

🚗 **From I-5 (Golden State Pkwy),** go east on Magic Mt Pkwy (sharp left from I-5S, right from I-5N) about 2 miles to Valencia Blvd. Turn left onto Valencia about 1 mile and bear left onto Bouquet Canyon Rd about 1½ miles to store.

Whole Foods Market 🛒 🍴

24130 Valencia Blvd. ✆ 661-260-2377 ⊘ Daily 7-10
• organic produce • vegetarian friendly • salad bar • cafe • self-service • take-out

🍎 **From I-5 (Golden State Pkwy),** take exit 169 east on Valencia Blvd (left from I-5S, right from I-5N) about 1¼ miles to store on right.

SANTA MARIA

Lassen's Natural Foods 🛒 🍴

1790 S Broadway ✆ 805-925-3432 ⊘ M-Sat 9-8
•organic produce • vegetarian friendly • fresh juice • deli • tables • self-service • take-out

🍎 **From Hwy 101,** take Bettaravia Rd exit west toward Sisquoc (left from 101N, right from 101S) about 1 mile to Broadway. Turn right onto Broadway about ½ mile to store on right.

SANTA MONICA

Barney's Gourmet Hamburgers 🍴

225 26th St. ✆ 310-899-0133 ⊘ Daily 11-8
See Brentwood location for description.
• vegetarian friendly • vegan friendly • alcohol • tables • wait staff

🚗 **From I-405N (San Diego Fwy),** take exit 55B onto Wilshire Blvd W under 1 mile to San Vicente Blvd. Turn right onto San Vicente 2 miles to S 26th St. Turn left onto S 26th to restaurant on left. **From I-405S,** take exit 55C onto Wilshire Blvd W and follow directions above.

California Vegan 🍴

12113 Santa Monica Blvd. #207 ✆ 310-207-4798 ⊘ Daily 11-10:30
Thai vegan with brown rice plus wraps, burgers and a few other surprises.
• vegan • organic focus • alcohol • tables • self-service

🚗 **From I-10W (Santa Monica Fwy),** merge onto I-405N (San Diego Fwy). **From I-405,** take exit 55A west on Santa Monica Blvd (merge onto Cotner St then left from I-405N, merge onto Beloit Ave then right from I-405S) about 1 mile to restaurant on right after S Bundy Dr. **From I-10E,** take exit 1B left onto 20th St ½ mile to Santa Monica. Turn right onto Santa Monica 1¼ miles to restaurant on left after Wellesley Ave.

Chandni 🍴

1909 Wilshire Blvd. ✆ 310-828-7060 ⊘ M-F 10:30-2:30, 5-10, Sat-Sun 11-3, 5-10
Vegetarian Indian cuisine.
• vegetarian • vegan friendly • alcohol • tables • wait staff

🚗 **From I-10W,** take Cloverfield Blvd exit right onto Cloverfield about ¼ mile to Olympic Blvd. Turn left onto Olympic about ¼ mile to 20th St. Turn right onto 20th ⅔ mile to Wilshire Blvd. Turn left onto Wilshire to restaurant. **From Ocean Ave,** go inland on Wilshire about 1⅓ miles to restaurant.

Co-opportunity 🛒

1525 Broadway ✆ 310-451-8902⊘ Daily 7-10
• organic produce • vegetarian friendly • fresh juice • deli • take-out • co-op

🚗 **From I-10W (Santa Monica Fwy),** take exit 2 north on Cloverfield Blvd ½ mile to Broadway. Turn left onto Broadway over ½ mile to store at 16th St. **From Santa Monica Pier,** go inland on Colorado Blvd about 1 mile to 14th St. Turn left onto 14th 1 block to Broadway. Turn right onto Broadway 2 blocks to store.

Euphoria Loves Rawvolution Cafe ⫼

2301 Main St. ✆ 310-392-9501 ⏲ Daily 10-9
Raw foods in an eco-friendly establishment.

• vegetarian • vegan friendly • organic focus • tables • wait staff • take-out

🚗 **From I-10W (Santa Monica Fwy),** take exit 1A left onto 4th St ⅓ mile to Pico Blvd. Turn right onto Pico 2 blocks to Main St. Turn left onto Main 4 blocks to restaurant on left at Strand St.

Juliano's Raw ⫼

609 Broadway ✆ 310-587-1552 ⏲ M-Th, Sun 10-10, F-Sat 10-11
Raw "living" foods. A Certified Organic Restaurant including the paint on the walls.

• vegan • organic focus • alcohol • counter • tables • wait staff

🚗 **From I-10W (Santa Monica Fwy),** take exit 1A right at fork onto 5th St 2 blocks to Broadway. Turn right onto Broadway to restaurant after 6th St. **From Santa Monica Pier,** take Colorado Ave under ½ mile to 6th St. Turn left onto 6th 1 block to restaurant at Broadway.

One Life Natural Foods ⬚ ⫼

3001 Main St. ✆ 310-392-4501 ⏲ Daily 8-9

• organic produce • vegetarian friendly • deli • tables • self-serve • take-out

🚗 **From I-10W (Santa Monica Fwy),** take exit 1A left onto 4th St ⅓ mile to Pico Blvd. Turn right onto Pico 2 blocks to Main St. Turn left onto Main about 1 mile to store on left at Pier Ave. **From the beach on Pacific Ave,** turn inland at Pier Ave 1 block to store at Main.

Real Food Daily ⫼

514 Santa Monica Blvd. ✆ 10-451-7544 ⏲ M-Sat 11:30-10 Sun 10-3
Macrobiotic principles applied to globally-inspired dishes.

• vegan • organic focus • fresh juice • alcohol • bakery • kosher • counter • tables • wait staff • take-out

🚗 **From I-10W (Santa Monica Fwy),** take exit 1A right onto 4th St 3 blocks to Santa Monica Blvd. Turn right onto Santa Monica to restaurant on left. **From Ocean Ave,** go inland on Santa Monica about 3 blocks to restaurant.

Whole Foods Market ⬚ ⫼

2201 Wilshire Blvd. ✆ 310-315-0662 ⏲ Daily 7-10

• organic produce • vegetarian friendly • salad bar • cafe • self-service • take-out

🚗 **From I-10W,** take Cloverfield Blvd exit right onto Cloverfield and right onto 26th St about 1 mile to Wilshire Blvd. Turn left onto Wilshire about ⅓ mile to store on right between 24th & 23rd St. **From Ocean Ave,** go inland on Wilshire over 1 ½ miles to store on left.

Wild Oats Market ⬚ ⫼

500 Wilshire Blvd. ✆ 310-395-4510 ⏲ Daily 8-9

• organic produce • vegetarian friendly • salad bar • cafe • self-service • take-out

🚗 **From I-10W (Santa Monica Fwy),** take exit 1A right at fork onto 5th St about ⅔ mile to Wilshire Blvd. Turn right onto Wilshire to store. **From Ocean Ave,** go inland on Wilshire about 4 blocks to store.

Wild Oats Market ⬚ ⫼

1425 Montana Ave. ✆ 310-576-4707 ⏲ Daily 8-9

• organic produce • vegetarian friendly • salad bar • cafe • self-service • take-out

🚗 **From I-10W (Santa Monica Fwy),** take exit 2 north on Cloverdale Blvd about ¼ mile to Olympic Blvd. Turn left onto Olympic almost ¾ mile to 14th St. Turn right onto 14th 1¼ miles to Montana Ave. Turn right onto Montana to store. **From Ocean Ave,** go inland on Montana about 1 mile to store.

SANTEE

Henry's Marketplace 🗔
9751 Mission Gorge Rd. © 619-258-4060 ⊘ Daily 7-10
 • organic produce • vegetarian friendly • deli • take-out

🛏 **From I-15 (or I-805),** take CA 52E about 7¾ miles (11 miles from I-805) to Mission Gorge Rd exit. Turn left onto Mission Gorge about 1⅓ miles to store.

SHERMAN OAKS

Barney's Gourmet Hamburgers 🍴
14006 Riverside Drive 24 A © 818-808-0680 ⊘ M-F 11-9, Sat 11-7, Sun 11-6
See Brentwood location for description.
 • vegetarian friendly • vegan friendly • alcohol • tables • wait staff

🛏 **From US 101 (Ventura Fwy),** take exit 16 north on Woodman Ave (left from 101S, right from 101N) 1 block to Riverside Ave. Turn left onto Riverside to restaurant on left in Fashion Sq.

Leaf Cuisine 🍴
14318 Ventura Blvd. © 818-907-8779 ⊘ M-Sat 11-9, Sun 11-4
Raw foods menu.
 • vegan • organic focus • fresh juice • kosher • tables • self-service • take-out

🛏 **From I-405N (San Diego Fwy),** take exit 63A for Ventura Blvd left onto Sepulveda Blvd under ¼ mile to Ventura. Turn right onto Ventura about 1¼ miles to restaurant on right. **From I-405S,** merge onto US 101S. **From US 101** (Ventura Fwy), take exit 17 south on Van Nuys Blvd (right from 101S, left from 101N) about ½ mile to Ventura. Turn left onto Ventura under ¼ mile to restaurant on right after Beverly Glen Blvd.

Whole Foods 🗔 🍴   ♿
4520 Sepulveda Blvd. © 818-382-3700 ⊘ Daily 7-10
 • organic produce • vegetarian friendly • salad bar • cafe • self-service • take-out

🛏 **From I-405N,** take Ventura Blvd/Sherman Oaks exit to Sepulveda Blvd. Merge left onto Sepulveda to store. **From I-405S,** take Valley Vista Blvd/Sepulveda Blvd exit. Merge left onto Sepulveda to store. **From US 101** (Hollywood Fwy), take Sepulveda Blvd exit south about ½ mile (past Sherman Oaks Galleria & Ventura Blvd) to store.

Whole Foods Market 🗔 🍴   ♿
12905 Riverside Drive © 818-762-5548 ⊘ Daily 7-10
 • organic produce • vegetarian friendly • salad bar • cafe • self-service • take-out

🛏 **From US 101 (Hollywood Fwy/Ventura Fwy),** take Coldwater Canyon Ave north 1 block to store on left at Riverside Dr.

SIMI VALLEY

Lassen's Natural Foods 🗔
2955-A4 Cochran St. © 805-526-9287 ⊘ M-F 9-8, Sat. 9-6
 • organic produce

🛏 **From CA 118W (Ronald Reagan Fwy),** take Sycamore Dr exit right onto Sycamore 2 blocks to Racine St. Turn left onto Racine, make first left onto Galena Ave and left onto Cochran to store on right. **From CA 118E,** take Tapo Canyon Rd exit left onto Tapo Canyon and right onto Cochran to store.

SOLANA BEACH

Zinc Cafe & Market 🍴
132 S. Cedros Ave. © 858-793-5436 ⊘ Daily 7-5
Breakfast, soups, salads, extensive sandwich menu, pizzettes and hot entrees.
 • vegetarian, alcohol, counter, tables, self-service, take-out

🛏 **From I-5 (San Diego Fwy),** take Lomas Santa Fe Dr exit toward Solana Beach west onto Lomas Santa Fe (right from I-5S, left from I-5N) 1 mile to S Cedros Ave. Turn left onto S Cedros to restaurant on left. **From the waterfront,** turn inland on Lomas Santa Fe 1 block to S Cedros. Turn right onto S Cedros to restaurant on left.

SOLVANG

New Frontiers 🏠 🍴

1984 Old Mission Dr. ℂ 805-693-1746 ⏱ M-Sat 8-8, Sun 10-7
• organic produce • vegetarian friendly • fresh juice • salad bar • cafe • deli • bakery • tables • self-service • take-out

🚗 **From US 101,** go east on CA 246 (left from 101S, right from 101N) 4 miles to Old Mill/Alamo Pintado Rd. Turn left onto Old Mill/Alamo Pintado 1 bock to Mission Dr. Turn right onto Mission to store on left.

SOUTH EL MONTE

Veggie-Life Restaurant 🍴

9324 E. Garvey Ave. #8 ℂ 626-443-8687 ⏱ Tues-Sun 9-9
Vegetarian Vietnamese menu.
• vegan • tables • wait staff

🚗 **From I-10,** take CA 19/Rosemead Blvd exit south on Rosemead about ⅔ mile to Garvey Ave. Turn left onto Garvey about ¼ mile to restaurant.

STUDIO CITY

Good Earth Restaurant & Bakery 🍴   ♿

12345 Ventura Blvd. ℂ 818-506-7400 ⏱ Daily 8:30-10
A natural foods restaurant with vegetarian choices, fish and poultry.
• vegetarian friendly • fresh juice • alcohol • bakery • tables • wait staff

🚗 **From US 101S (Ventura Fwy),** take exit 14 toward Studio City left onto Laurel Canyon Dr about ¾ mile to Ventura Blvd. Turn right onto Ventura under ½ mile to restaurant on right. **From US 101N** (Hollywood Fwy), take exit 12B toward Ventura Blvd left onto Universal Pl and make first right onto Ventura about 2¼ miles to restaurant.

Hugo's Restaurant 🍴   ♿

12851 Riverside Drive ℂ 818-284-4256 ⏱ M-F 7:30am-10pm, Sat-Sun 8-10
Imaginative menu with vegan, vegetarian and gluten-free choices.
• vegetarian friendly • vegan friendly • alcohol • tables • wait staff • take-out

🚗 **From US 101 (Ventura Fwy),** take exit 15 north on Coldwater Canyon (right from US 101N, left from US 101S) 1 block to Riverside Dr. Turn right onto Riverside to restaurant.

Leonor's Mexican Restaurant 🍴

12445 Moorpark St. ℂ 818-762-0660 ⏱ Daily 10-10
Vegan Mexican cuisine featuring soy-based meat and cheese.
• vegan • tables • wait staff

🚗 **From US 101(Ventura Fwy),** take exit 14 south on Laurel Canyon Blvd (left from US 101N, right from US 101S) about ¼ mile to Moorpark St. Turn right onto Moorpark about ½ mile to restaurant on right.

Vegan Plate 🍴

11943 Ventura Blvd. ℂ 818-506-9015 ⏱ Daily 11-10
Vegan Thai.
• vegan • tables • wait staff • take-out

🚗 **From US 101S (Ventura Fwy),** take exit 14 left onto Laurel Canyon Blvd about ¾ mile to Ventura Blvd. Turn left onto Ventura 1½ blocks to restaurant on left after Radford Ave. **From US 101N** (Hollywood Fwy), take exit 12B toward Ventura Blvd left onto Universal Pl and make first right onto Ventura about 1½ miles to restaurant on right.

TARZANA

Garden Wok 🍴
6117 Reseda Blvd. © 818-881-8886 ⏰ Tues-Sat 11:30-9:30, Sun 4-9:30
Family-run vegetarian Chinese restaurant.
• vegetarian • vegan friendly • wait staff • take-out • tables

🚇 **From US 101 (Ventura Fwy),** take exit 23 north on Reseda Blvd (left from US 101S, right from US 101N) about ½ mile to restaurant on left 1 block past tracks.

Madeleine Bistro 🍴
18621 Ventura Blvd. © 818-758-6971 ⏰ W-Sun 11:30-2, 5-9
Vegan gourmet.
• vegan • organic focus • fresh juice • alcohol • tables • wait staff • take-out

🚇 **From US 101 (Ventura Fwy),** take Reseda Blvd south (right from US 101S, left from US 101N) ⅓ mile to Ventura Blvd. Turn right onto Ventura under ¼ mile to restaurant on right.

THOUSAND OAKS

Lassen's Natural Foods 🛒 🍴
2857 E. Thousand Oaks Blvd. © 805-495-2609 ⏰ M-Sat 8-9
• organic produce • vegetarian friendly • deli • tables • self-service • take-out

🚇 **From US 101 (Ventura Fwy),** take exit 41 north on Hampshire Rd (right from 101N, left from 101 S) about ¼ mile to Thousand Oaks Blvd. Turn left onto Thousand Oaks, right onto Skyline Dr and left into Skyline Plaza to store.

Whole Foods Market 🛒 🍴
740 N. Moorpark Rd. © 805-777-4730 ⏰ Daily 8-10
• organic produce • vegetarian friendly • salad bar • cafe • self-service • take-out

🚇 **From US 101 (Ventura Fwy),** take exit 44 north on Moorpark Rd (left from 101S, right from 101N) about ¾ mile to store on right.

TOPANGA

Inn of the Seventh Ray 🍴   ♿
128 Old Topanga Canyon Rd. © 310-455-1311 ⏰ Lunch M-F 11:30-3, Sat 10:30-3, Sun 9:30-3 Dinner Daily 5:30-10
Vegetarian, vegan, raw foods, wild fish and hormone-free poultry.
• vegetarian friendly • organic focus • alcohol • tables • wait staff

🚇 **From US 101 (Ventura Fwy),** take Topanga Canyon Blvd south (CA 27S) about 8 miles (past light at Topanga School Rd, sign for restaurant on right). Turn right and cross bridge to restaurant on right. **From I-10,** go west to end and turn right onto Pacific Coast Hwy almost 6 miles to Topanga Canyon Blvd. Turn right onto Topanga Canyon 4¼ miles. Turn left after Topanga Canyon Post Office onto Old Topanga Canyon Rd to restaurant on right.

TORRANCE

Casa de Tree 🍴
2543 Pacific Coast Hwy., Ste. E © 310-784-0455 ⏰ Tues-F 11:30-2, 5:30-8, Sat 11:30-8, Sun 11:30-7
Vegan bakery serving wholesome soups, salads, sandwiches, pasta (including whole wheat, spelt and rice) and brown rice sushi.
• vegan • organic focus • bakery • tables • self-service • wait staff • take-out

🚇 **From CA 1 (Pacific Coast Hwy),** restaurant is south of Cranshaw Blvd at Airport Dr on north side in Rolling Hills Plaza. **From I-110 (Harbor Fwy),** take exit 4 west on Hwy 1 (right from I-110S, left from I-110N) almost 3 miles to restaurant on right. **From I-405N (San Diego Fwy),** take I-110S and follow directions above. **From I-405S,** take exit 39 right onto Cranshaw 5 miles to Hwy 1 and turn left ⅓ mile to restaurant on left.

Whole Foods Market 🛍 🍴   🚹
2655 Pacific Coast Hwy. ✆ 310-257-8700 ⏰ Daily 7-10
• organic produce • vegetarian friendly • salad bar • cafe • self-service • take-out

🍎 **Store is on Hwy 1 (Pacific Coast Hwy)** at Cranshaw Blvd. **From I-110 (Harbor Fwy),** take exit 4 west on Hwy 1 (right from I-110S, left from I-110N) almost 3 miles to store. **From I-405N (San Diego Fwy),** take I-110S and follow directions above. **From I-405S,** take exit 39 right onto Cranshaw 5 miles to Hwy 1 and turn left to store on left.

TUSTIN

Rutabegorz 🍴   🚹
158 W. Main St. ✆ 714-731-9807 ⏰ M-Sat 11-9, Sun 11-8
See Fullerton location for menu description.
• vegetarian friendly • tables • wait staff • take-out

🍎 **From I-5S,** take Newport Ave exit left onto Newport, left at first light onto El Camino Real and left at second light onto Main St 1 block to restaurant on left. **From I-5N,** take Red Hill Ave exit right onto Red Hill and left onto El Camino Real almost 1 mile to Main. Turn left onto Main 1 block to restaurant.

Whole Foods Market 🛍 🍴   🚹
2847 Park Ave. ✆ 714-731-3400 ⏰ Daily 7-10
• organic produce • vegetarian friendly • salad bar • cafe • self-service • take-out

🍎 **From I-5 (Santa Ana Fwy),** take Jamboree Rd exit southwest on Jamboree (left from I-5N, right from I-5N) about 1¾ miles and take exit toward Warner Ave to merge onto Valencia South Loop Rd. At end continue right onto Park Ave to store on left in The District at Tustin Legacy. **From I-405,** take exit 7 northeast on Jamboree about 1½ miles to Barranca Pkwy. Turn left onto Barranca, right onto District Dr and right onto Park to store.

UPLAND

Veggie Era 🍴
903-B W. Foothill Blvd. ✆ 909-982-3882 ⏰ Tues-Sat 11-9, Sun 4-9
Chinese-Indonesian vegan menu.
• vegan • tables • self-service • wait staff • take-out

🍎 **From I-10,** take Mountain Ave exit north (left from I-10E, right from I-10W) about 1⅓ miles to Foothill Blvd. Turn right onto Foothill under ½ mile (past light) to restaurant on left in Upland Square.

VENICE

Seed 🍴
1604 Pacific Ave. ✆ 310-396-1604 ⏰ Daily 10-9
Macrobiotic and vegan.
• vegan • organic focus • tables • self-service • take-out

🍎 **From I-10 W (Santa Monica Fwy),** take exit 1A left onto 4th St ⅓ mile to Pico Blvd. Turn left onto Pico under ¼ mile to Ocean Ave. Turn left onto Ocean (becomes Pacific Ave) about 1¾ miles to Windward Ave. Turn left onto Windward to restaurant on right. **From Hwy 1N (Lincoln Blvd),** turn left onto Venice Blvd about 1 mile to Venice Way. Veer right onto Venice Way about ⅓ mile to Pacific Ave. Turn right onto Pacific and right onto Winward to restaurant.

VENTURA

Lassen's Natural Foods 🛍 🍴
4071 E. Main St. ✆ 805-644-6990 ⏰ M-Sat. 9-8
• organic produce • vegetarian friendly • deli • tables • self-service • take-out

🍎 **From US 101N (Ventura Fwy),** take Telephone Rd exit left onto Telephone and turn right onto Main St under ½ mile to store on right. **From US 101S,** take Main St exit and turn right onto Main about ⅓ mile to store on left.

VISTA

Frazier Farms Market 🛍 🍴

225 Vista Village Drive © 760-758-7175 ⏲ Daily 8-9
  • organic produce • vegetarian friendly • fresh juice • salad bar • deli • bakery • tables
  • self-service • take-out

🚗 **From I-5 (San Diego Fwy),** take exit 51B toward Vista Way east on Hwy 78 almost 6 miles to exit 6B. Turn left onto Vista Village Dr 1 block to store on right.

WEST COVINA

One World Vegetarian Cuisine 🍴 ♿

178 S. Glendora Ave. © 626-917-2727 ⏲ M-Sat 11-9, Sun 3-8
Eclectic Asian fusion menu.
  • vegetarian • vegan friendly • organic focus • fresh juice • tables • wait staff

🚗 **From I-10 (San Bernadino Fwy),** take exit 35 south on S Vincent Ave (right from I-10E, left from I-10W), left onto Lakes Dr, right onto State St and left onto S Glendora Ave to restaurant on right (behind movie theater).

WEST HOLLYWOOD

Real Food Daily 🍴

414 N. La Cienega Blvd. © 310-289-9910 ⏲ M-Th 11:30-10, F-Sat 11:30-11, Sun 10-3
See Santa Monica location for description. A bonus is the valet parking in the evening.
  • vegan • organic focus • fresh juice • alcohol • bakery • kosher • counter • tables •
  wait staff • take-out

🚗 **From I-10 (Santa Monica Fwy),** take La Cienega Blvd north about 3 miles to restaurant on right 1½ blocks past the Beverly Center between Beverly Blvd & Melrose Ave.

Hugo's Restaurant 🍴 ♿

8401 Santa Monica Blvd. © 323-654-3993 ⏲ M-F 7:30am-10pm, Sat-Sun 8-10
Imaginative menu with vegan, vegetarian and gluten-free choices.
  • vegetarian friendly • vegan friendly • alcohol • tables • wait staff • take-out

🚗 **From US 101N (Hollywood Fwy),** take exit 7 left onto Santa Monica Blvd 4 miles to restaurant on right after N Kings Rd (about 2 blocks before La Cienega). **From 101S,** take exit 9C (Highland Ave) onto Cahuenga Ave (becomes N Highland) about 1¾ miles to Santa Monica. Turn right onto Santa Monica 2 miles to restaurant.

Whole Foods Market 🛍 🍴 ♿

7871 Santa Monica Blvd. © 323-848-4200 ⏲ Daily 8-11
  • organic produce • vegetarian friendly • salad bar • cafe • self-service • take-out

🚗 **From US 101N (Hollywood Fwy),** take exit 7 left onto Santa Monica Blvd 3 miles to store on right at S Fairfax Ave. **From 101S,** take exit 9C (Highland Ave) onto Cahuenga Ave (becomes N Highland) about 1¾ miles to Santa Monica. Turn right onto Santa Monica 1⅓ miles to store.

WESTWOOD

Good Earth Restaurant & Bakery 🍴

1037 Broxton Ave. © 310-209-1351 ⏲ M-F 10-9, Sat-Sun 9-9
See Studio City location for description.
  • vegetarian friendly • fresh juice • alcohol • bakery • tables • wait staff

🚗 **From I-405 (San Diego Fwy),** take Wilshire Blvd exit toward UCLA east on Wilshire about ½ mile to Gayley Ave. Turn left onto Gayley ⅓ mile to Weyburn Ave. Turn right onto Weyburn 1 block to Broxton Ave. Turn right onto Broxton to restaurant on right.

Native Foods 🍴

1110 ½ Gayley Ave. 🕿 310-209-1055 🕐 Daily 11-10
See Aliseo Viejo location for description.
 • vegan • organic focus • counter • tables • self-service
🛍 **From I-405 (San Diego Fwy)**, take Wilshire Blvd exit toward UCLA east on Wilshire about ½ mile to Gayley Ave. Turn left onto Gayley to restaurant on right in Westwood Village.

Whole Foods Market 🛍 🍴   ♿

1050 S. Gayley Ave. 🕿 310-824-0858 🕐 Daily 7-10
 • organic produce • vegetarian friendly • salad bar • cafe • self-service • take-out
🛍 **From I-405 (San Diego Fwy)**, take Wilshire Blvd exit toward UCLA east on Wilshire about ½ mile to Gayley Ave. Turn left onto Gayley about ¼ mile to store.

WOODLAND HILLS

Whole Foods Market 🛍 🍴   ♿

21347 Ventura Blvd. 🕿 818-610-0000 🕐 Daily 7-10
 • organic produce • vegetarian friendly • salad bar • cafe • self-service • take-out
🛍 **From 101N (Ventura Fwy)**, take Canoga Ave exit left to Ventura Blvd. Turn left onto Ventura to store. **From 101S**, take Ventura Blvd exit and bear right onto Ventura under 1 mile to store.

YORBA LINDA

Henry's Marketplace 🛍

17482 Yorba Linda Blvd. 🕿 714-572-3535 🕐 Daily 7-10
 • organic produce • vegetarian friendly • deli • take-out
🛍 **From CA 91**, take N Tustin Ave exit north (right from 91W, left from 91E) about ⅓ mile to E La Palma Ave. Turn right onto E Palma ¾ mile to N Richfield Rd. Turn left onto N Richfield 2 miles to Yorba Linda Blvd. Turn left onto Yorba Linda to store.

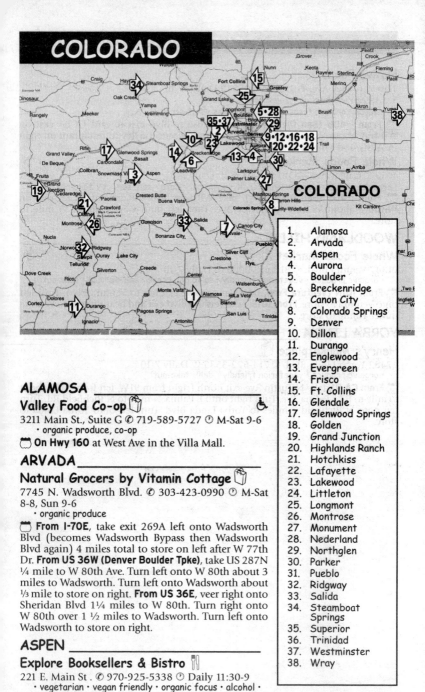

COLORADO

1.	Alamosa
2.	Arvada
3.	Aspen
4.	Aurora
5.	Boulder
6.	Breckenridge
7.	Canon City
8.	Colorado Springs
9.	Denver
10.	Dillon
11.	Durango
12.	Englewood
13.	Evergreen
14.	Frisco
15.	Ft. Collins
16.	Glendale
17.	Glenwood Springs
18.	Golden
19.	Grand Junction
20.	Highlands Ranch
21.	Hotchkiss
22.	Lafayette
23.	Lakewood
24.	Littleton
25.	Longmont
26.	Montrose
27.	Monument
28.	Nederland
29.	Northglen
30.	Parker
31.	Pueblo
32.	Ridgway
33.	Salida
34.	Steamboat Springs
35.	Superior
36.	Trinidad
37.	Westminster
38.	Wray

ALAMOSA

Valley Food Co-op

3211 Main St., Suite G ℰ 719-589-5727 ⏱ M-Sat 9-6
 • organic produce, co-op

🏠 **On Hwy 160** at West Ave in the Villa Mall.

ARVADA

Natural Grocers by Vitamin Cottage

7745 N. Wadsworth Blvd. ℰ 303-423-0990 ⏱ M-Sat
8-8, Sun 9-6
 • organic produce

🏠 **From I-70E**, take exit 269A left onto Wadsworth
Blvd (becomes Wadsworth Bypass then Wadsworth
Blvd again) 4 miles total to store on left after W 77th
Dr. **From US 36W (Denver Boulder Tpke)**, take US 287N
¼ mile to W 80th Ave. Turn left onto W 80th about 3
miles to Wadsworth. Turn left onto Wadsworth about
⅓ mile to store on right. **From US 36E**, veer right onto
Sheridan Blvd 1¼ miles to W 80th. Turn right onto
W 80th over 1 ½ miles to Wadsworth. Turn left onto
Wadsworth to store on right.

ASPEN

Explore Booksellers & Bistro

221 E. Main St . ℰ 970-925-5338 ⏱ Daily 11:30-9
 • vegetarian • vegan friendly • organic focus • alcohol •
tables • wait staff

🏠 Take Hwy 82 into Aspen, where it become Main St. Store is 1 block past park in
Victorian house with small sign in front yard.

Mountain Natural's 🛍️ 🍴

316B Aspen Airport Business Center © 970-925-5502 ⏲ M-F 7:30-6, Sat 10-4
· organic produce · vegetarian friendly · deli · counter · self-service · take-out

🍎 **From Hwy 82,** store is across from Aspen airport.

AURORA

Masalaa 🍴

3140 S. Parker Rd. © 303-755-6272 ⏲ M-Th 11:30-2, 5:30-9:30, F 11:30-2. 5:30-10
Sat 12-3, 5:30-10, Sun 12-3, 5:30-9:30
Indian vegetarian with a daily lunch buffet.
· vegetarian · vegan friendly · alcohol · tables · self-service · wait staff

🍎 **From I-225,** take exit 4 northwest on S Parker Rd (left from I-225N, merge right
from I-225S) about ½ mile to restaurant on right after S Peoria St.

Natural Grocers by Vitamin Cottage 🛍️

15192 E. Hampden Ave. © 303-680-2344 ⏲ M-F 9-8:04, Sat 9-7:04, Sun 11-6:06
· organic produce

🍎 **From I-225,** take exit 4 southeast on S Parker Rd (merge right from I-225N,
loop around right from I-225S) 1-1⅓ miles to E Hampden Ave. Veer left onto E
Hampden about 1 mile to store on right before S Chambers Rd.

BOULDER

Ideal Market 🛍️

1275 Alpine Ave. © 303-443-1354 ⏲ Daily 7:30-10
· organic produce · vegetarian friendly · salad bar · deli · bakery · take-out

🍎 **From Hwy 36W,** take Canyon Blvd exit left onto Canyon Blvd 1 mile to Broadway
St. Turn right onto Broadway ¾ mile to Alpine Ave. Turn right onto Alpine to store
on left. **From N Foothills Hwy,** veer right onto Broadway under 3 miles to Alpine.
Turn left onto Alpine to store.

Leaf 🍴

2010 16th St. © 303-442-1485 ⏲ M-Th, Sun 11-9, F-Sat 11-10
Pan-global menu. From 3 to 6 is vegan happy hour.
· vegetarian · vegan friendly · organic focus · alcohol · tables · wait staff

🍎 **From Hwy 36W,** take Canyon Blvd exit left onto Canyon Blvd under 1 mile to
16th St. Turn right onto 16th 2 blocks to restaurant on right at Pearl St.

Natural Grocers by Vitamin Cottage 🛍️

2355 30th St. © 303-402-1400 ⏲ M-Sat 9-8, Sun 11-6
· organic produce

🍎 **From Hwy 36,** turn east (right from 36W, left from 28thS) onto Pearl St 1 block
to 30th St. Turn right onto 30th to store on left.

Organic Orbit Eco Food Cafe 🍴

1200 Yarmouth Ave. © 303-440-8348 ⏲ W-Sat Lunch 11-4 Happy Hour 5-6 Dinner
6-9-10
Organic, local and live food options. Built using green principles and materials.
· vegetarian · vegan friendly · organic focus · fresh juice · alcohol · tables ·
wait staff · take-out

🍎 **From US 36S/N Foothills Hwy,** turn right onto Broadway St ½ mile to Yarmouth
Ave. Turn left onto Yarmouth to restaurant. **From US 36W/Denver Boulder Tpke**,
turn left onto Yarmouth ½ mile to restaurant at Broadway.

Scotch Corner Pub 🍴

1800 Broadway St., Ste. 150 © 303-545-2000 ⏲ M-Sat 11-11, Sun 12-9
*Vegetarian versions of classic Scottish dishes (like veggie bangers) cooked in a meat-free
kitchen. Live music.*
· vegetarian friendly · alcohol · counter · tables · wait staff

🍎 **From Hwy 36W,** take Canyon Blvd exit left onto Canyon Blvd 1 mile to restaurant
on right at Broadway St.

South Side Walnut Cafe ¶

673 S. Broadway St. © 720-304-8118 ⊘ Daily 7-3
- vegetarian friendly • vegan friendly • counter • tables • wait staff

🚗 **From US 36W (Foothills Pkwy),** take Foothills Pkwy/Hwy 1559N exit right at first fork, left at second fork (toward Table Mesa Dr) and turn left onto S Boulder Rd continuing on Table Mesa about 1 mile to S Broadway St. Turn left onto S Broadway under ¼ mile to restaurant on left. **From US 36E (Boulder Denver Tpke),** turn left onto Table Mesa and follow directions above.

Sunflower ¶ &

1701 Pearl St. © 303-440-0220 ⊘ Tues-Th 11-19, F 11-10, Sat 10-10, Sun 10-9
Upscale dining with vegetarian/vegan dishes, fish, free-range poultry and exotic meats.
- vegetarian friendly • vegan friendly • organic focus • fresh juice • alcohol • tables • wait staff

🚗 **From Hwy 36W,** turn left onto Canyon Blvd ¾ mile to 17th St. Turn right onto 17th 2 blocks to restaurant. From Foothills Pkwy, take Pearl St ramp west onto Pearl Pkwy (becomes Pearl St) about ⅓ mile to 28th St. Turn left onto 28th ⅓ mile to Canyon. Turn right onto Canyon ¾ mile to 17th. Turn right onto 17th 2 blocks to restaurant.

The Kitchen ¶

1039 Pearl St. © 303-544-5973 ⊘ M-F 8:30-2, 5:30-9:30, Sat-Sun 9-2, 5:30-10:30
Upscale, eco-friendly restaurant.
- vegetarian friendly • organic focus • alcohol • tables • wait staff

🚗 **From Hwy 36W,** turn left onto Canyon Blvd 1⅓ miles to 9th St. Turn right onto 9th 3 blocks to Pearl St. Turn right onto Pearl 2 blocks to restaurant on left.

Turley's ¶

2805 Pearl St. © 303-442-2800 ⊘ M-Th 6:30am-9pm, F-Sat 6:30-10, Sun 7-9
A casual place with options for vegetarians and meat-eaters, the health-conscious and the not-so health-conscious.
- vegetarian friendly • counter • tables • wait staff • take-out

🚗 **From Hwy 36,** turn east (right from 36W, left from 28thS) onto Pearl St to restaurant on left. **From Foothills Pkwy,** take Pearl St ramp west onto Pearl Pkwy (becomes Pearl St) under ½ mile to store on right after 29th St.

V.B. Burgers ¶

3267 28th St. © 303-440-2400 ⊘ Daily 11-9
Organic, vegan fast food: burgers, baked fries, salad, soup, chili and shakes.
- vegan • organic focus • tables • self-service • take-out

🚗 **Restaurant is on Hwy 36 (28th St in town)** between Valmont Rd & Diagonal Hwy on the west side. **From Foothills Pkwy north of town**, merge onto CO 119 (Diagonal Hwy) ¾ mile to 28th St. Turn left onto 28th to restaurant on right. **From Foothills Pkwy south of town**, turn left onto Valmont ¾ mile to 28th. Turn right onto 28th under ½ mile to restaurant on left.

Walnut Cafe ¶ &

3073 Walnut St. © 303-447-2315 ⊘ Daily 7-4
- vegetarian friendly • vegan friendly • tables • wait staff

🚗 **From Hwy 36,** take Arapahoe Ave exit east (right from 36W, left from 36E) ¼ mile to 30th St. Turn left onto 30th ⅓ mile to Walnut St. Turn right onto Walnut to store (just west of Crossroads Mall). **From Foothills Pkwy,** take Pearl St ramp west onto Pearl Pkwy (becomes Pearl St) about ⅓ mile to 30th. Turn left onto 30th ¼ mile to Walnut. Turn left onto Walnut to store.

Whole Foods Market 🛒 ¶ &

2905 Pearl St. © 303-545-6611 ⊘ Daily 7:30-10
- organic produce • vegetarian friendly • salad bar • cafe • self-service • take-out

🚗 **From Hwy 36,** turn east (right from 36W, left from 28thS) onto Pearl to store on left between 28th & 30th St. **From Foothills Pkwy,** take Pearl St ramp west onto Pearl Pkwy (becomes Pearl St) about ⅓ mile to store on right.

Wild Oats Market 🛍 🍴 &

2584 Baseline Rd. ✆ 303-499-7636 ⏲ Daily 7:30-9
· organic produce · vegetarian friendly · salad bar · cafe · self-service · take-out

🍎 **From Hwy 36**, take Baseline Rd west (right from 36E, left under overpass from 36W) and turn left just before Broadway (Hwy 93) into Basemar Ctr to store in center of strip mall.

Wild Oats Market 🛍 🍴 &

1651 Broadway St ✆ 303-442-0909 ⏲ Daily 7:30-10
· organic produce · vegetarian friendly · salad bar · cafe · self-service · take-out

🍎 **From Hwy 36,** take Arapahoe Ave west about 10 blocks (1 mile) to store on SW corner at Broadway. **From Hwy 93 heading north**, 93 becomes Broadway in city limits. Go about 4 miles to store on SW corner at Arapahoe.

BRECKENRIDGE _____

Amazing Grace Natural Foods 🛍

213 Lincoln Ave. ✆ 970-453-1445 ⏲ M-Sat 7-3
· organic produce · vegetarian friendly · deli · take-out

🍎 **From I-70,** take Hwy 9S about 10 miles to Breckenridge. Turn left at third light onto French St 2 blocks to store at Lincoln Ave.

CANON CITY _____

Mother Nature's Health Foods 🛍

915 Main St. ✆ 719-275-9367 ⏲ M-F 9-6, Sat. 9-5:30
· organic produce

🍎 **From Hwy 50,** go north on 9th St 1 block to store at Main St intersection.

COLORADO SPRINGS _____

Mountain Mama Natural Foods 🛍

1625-A W. Uintah St. ✆ 719-633-4139 ⏲ M-Sat 8-7, Sun 11-5
· organic produce · vegetarian friendly · deli · take-out

🍎 **From I-25,** take exit 143 west on Uintah St (right from I-25S, left from I-25N) about ½ mile to store on left.

Natural Grocers by Vitamin Cottage 🛍

1780 E. Woodmen Rd. ⏲ M-F 9-8, Sat 9-7, Sun 10-6
· organic produce

🍎 **From I-25,** take exit 149 east on Woodmen Rd (left from I-25S, right from I-25N) about 1 mile to store on right.

Natural Grocers by Vitamin Cottage 🛍

1825 S. Nevada Ave. ✆ 719-634-9200 ⏲ M-F 9-8, Sat 10-7, Sun 11-6
· organic produce

🍎 **From I-25,** take exit 140 (140B from I-25S) south on S Nevada Rd (left from I-25N, right from I-25S) about ½ mile to store on left after E St Elmo Ave.

Sammy's Organics 🛍 🍴

830 Arcturus Drive ✆ 719-471-3348 ⏲ M-F 7-8, Sat 9-7, Sun 11-5
· organic produce · vegetarian friendly · organic focus · deli · tables · self-service · take-out

🍎 **From I-24,** take exit 141 (US 24W/Cimmaron St) left onto Cimmaron ⅓ mile to S 8th St. Turn left onto S 8th 1½ miles to Arcturus Dr. Turn right onto Arcturus to store on right.

Sammy's Organics 🛍

1837 N. Circle Drive ✆ 19-630-1793 ⏲ M-Sat 9-7, Sun 11-5
· organic produce

🍎 **From I-25,** take exit 145 east on Fillmore St (right fromI-25N, left from I-25S) about 4 miles (through residential area, becomes N Circle Dr) to Constitution Ave. Turn left at Constitution into store lot.

Urban Farm at Colorado College ⑪ &

1090 N. Cascade St. ("Q"-McHugh Commons) ✆ 719-389-7000 ⊕ Daily 11am-12am
*"Planet-friendly" campus eatery is over 80% organic and additive-free. Menu includes nutri-
tional analysis with items keyed for organic, non-dairy, wheat-free and vegan.*
　　• organic focus • vegetarian friendly • vegan friendly • alcohol • counter • tables • self-service
⑪ **From I-25**, take exit 143 east on Uintah St (left from I-25S, right from I-25N)
about ½ mile to N Cascade Ave. Turn right onto N Cascade to Colorado College
campus. Restaurant is in the "Q"-McHugh Commons (across from soccer field).

Whole Foods Market 🛍 ⑪

7635 N. Academy Blvd. ✆ 719-531-9999 ⊕ M-F, Sun 8-9, Sat 7-9
　　• organic produce • vegetarian friendly • salad bar • cafe • self-service • take-out
🍎 **From I-25S**, take exit 150 left onto N Academy Blvd 1 mile to store in shopping
center on left. **From I-25N**, take exit 149 right at fork onto E Woodmen Rd 1 mile
to N Academy. Turn left onto N Academy about ¾ mile to store in shopping center
on right.

Wild Oats Market 🛍 ⑪

3180 New Center Point ✆ 719-622-1099 ⊕ Daily 8-9
　　• organic produce • vegetarian friendly • salad bar • cafe • self-service • take-out
🍎 **From US 24S**, turn right onto Constitution Ave 3 miles to New Center Point.
Turn right onto Nwe Center over ½ mile to traffic circle. Take second exit to
continue on New Center about ¼ mile to store on left. **From US 24N**, continue on
Powers Blvd about 2½ miles to S Carefree Circle. Turn right onto S Carefree and at
traffic circle take third exit onto New Center Point to store on left.

DENVER

City O' City ⑪ &

206 E. 13th Ave. ✆ 303-831-6443 ⊕ M-F 7am-2am, Sat-Sun 8 am-2am
Eco-friendly coffeehouse/bar serving pizza, wraps, salads and other light fare.
　　• vegetarian • vegan friendly • alcohol • tables • wait staff
⑪ **From I-25**, take exit 210A east on W Colfax Ave (left from I-25S, right at fork
from I-25N) over 1½ miles to Grant St. Turn right onto Grant 2 blocks to E 13th
Ave. Turn right onto E 13th to restaurant on left.

Govinda's Buffet ⑪ &

1400 Cherry St. ✆ 303-333-5461 ⊕ M-F 11:30-2:30, 5-8, Sat 5-8
Vegetarian Indian lunch and dinner buffet. Bhakti yoga center next door.
　　• vegetarian • vegan friendly • organic focus • tables • serve-service • take-out
⑪ **From I-25**, take exit 204 north on Colorado Blvd (right from I-25N, left from
I-25S) ⅓ mile to 14th St. Turn right onto 14th 6 blocks to restaurant at Cherry
St. **From I-70**, take exit 276B south on Colorado (right from 70E, left from 70W)
about 3 miles to 14th. Turn left onto 14th 6 blocks to restaurant.

Mercury Cafe ⑪

2199 California St. ✆ 303-294-9281 ⊕ Tues-F 5:30-11, Sat-Sun 9-3, 5:30-11 Desserts
& drinks until 1:30am
*Menu ranges from Tofu Rancheros to bacon and eggs, tofu "chops" to steak. Whole-grain,
naturally-sweetened baked goods, late night desserts.*
　　• vegetarian friendly • vegan friendly • organic focus • tables • wait staff
⑪ **From I-25S**, take exit 213 (38th St/Park Ave) south on Park about 1 mile where
it becomes 22nd St. Follow 22nd ¾ mile to restaurant on right at California St.
From I-25N, take exit 210A east on W Colfax Ave 1 mile to Stout St. Turn left
onto Stout about 1 mile to 22nd. Turn right onto 22nd 1 block to restaurant on
right at California. **From I-70W**, take exit 275B left onto Brighton Blvd (becomes
Broadway) about 2⅓ miles to 22nd. Turn left onto 22nd 3 blocks to restaurant on
right at California.

Natural Grocers by Vitamin Cottage 🛍

5231 Leetsdale Drive ✆ 303-399-0164 ⏰ M-Sat 9-8:04, Sun 10-6:06
• organic produce

🍎 **From I-25S**, take exit 203 left onto E Evans Ave about 1¼ miles to S Monaco Pkwy. Turn left onto S Monaco 1¾ miles to Leetsdale Dr. Turn left onto Leetsdale under 1 mile to store on right past S Hudson St. **From I-25N**, take exit 205 right at fork onto E Hampden Ave under ½ mile to S Monaco. Turn left onto Monaco about 3½ miles and follow directions above.

Natural Grocers by Vitamin Cottage 🛍

2033 S. Colorado Blvd. ✆ 303-756-8400 ⏰ M-F 9-8, Sat 9-7, Sun 11-6
• organic produce

🍎 **From I-25**, take exit 204 south on S Colorado Ave (right from I-25S, left from I-25N) to store on right just off hwy.

Natural Grocers by Vitamin Cottage 🛍

2375 15th St. ✆ 303-455-3172 ⏰ -F 9-8, Sat 9-7, Sun 11-6
• organic produce

🍎 **From I-25N**, take exit 211 onto Water St continuing on Platte St about ½ mile to 15th St. Turn right onto 15th to store on left. **From I-25S**, take exit 212 right onto 20th St and left onto Central St under ½ mile to 15th. Turn left onto 15th to store.

Natural Grocers by Vitamin Cottage 🛍

7690 N. Academy Blvd. ✆ 719-577-2500 ⏰ M-F 9-7, Sat 9-8, Sun 10-6
• organic produce

🍎 **From I-225S**, take exit 9 right onto E 6th Ave continuing onto E Lowry Blvd 3 miles total to traffic circle. Take second exit, continue on E Lowry ½ mile to traffic circle and take second exit to continue on E Lowry ⅓ mile to traffic circle. Take first exit onto N Rampart Way and take next right onto E Academy to store on right. **From I-225N**, take exit 9 left onto E Alameda Ave 3¾ miles to E Fairmont Dr. Turn right onto E Fairmont under ½ mile to traffic circle. Take second exit onto N Rampart and follow directions above.

Porter Adventist Hospital Cafeteria 🍴 ♿

2525 S. Downing St. ✆ 303-778-2425 ⏰ Daily 6:45-10, 11-1:30, 4:30-6:30, 7-11
All-vegetarian cafeteria.
• vegetarian • tables, self-service

🍎 **From I-25S**, take exit 206B toward Washington St/Emerson St left onto Bechtel Blvd about ½ mile to Downing St. Turn right onto Downing 1¼ miles to Porter hospital on right. Cafeteria is 2nd door on right from main entrance. **From I-25N**, take exit 206A left onto Downing and follow directions above.

WaterCourse Foods 🍴

837 E. 17th Ave. ✆ 303-832-7313 ⏰ M-Th 7am-9pm, F 7-10, Sat 8-10, Sun 8-9
A broad menu including biscuits & gravy, Seitan Philly, portabella Reuben and many other seitan, tempeh and tofu variations.
• vegetarian • vegan friendly • organic focus • tables • wait staff

🍎 **From I-25**, take exit 210A east on W Colfax Ave (right from I-25N, left from I-25S) about 2 miles Clarkson St. Turn left onto Clarkson 2 blocks to E 17th Ave. Turn right onto 17th to restaurant on left between Clarkson & Emerson St.

Whole Foods Market 🛍 🍴 ♿

2375 E. 1st Ave. ✆ 720-941-4100 ⏰ Daily 7-10
• organic produce • vegetarian friendly • salad bar • cafe • self-service • take-out

🍎 **From I-25S**, take exit 212A south on Speer Blvd (becomes 1st Ave) about 4 miles to store at University Blvd. **From I-25N**, take exit 205A north on University Blvd about 2 miles to store at 1st.

Whole Foods Market 🛒 🍴

1111 S. Washington St. ✆ 303-733-6201 ⏰ Daily 7:30-10
• organic produce • vegetarian friendly • salad bar • cafe • self-service • take-out

🚗 **From I-25S**, take exit 206B toward Washington St and follow ramp along Buchtel Blvd ½ mile to E Mississippi. Turn right onto Mississippi to store 2 blocks east of interstate at S Washington. **From I-25N**, take exit 207A (Lincoln St) toward Broadway right onto E Ohio Ave ⅓ mile to Washington. Turn right onto Washington about ⅓ mile (past third intersection) to store.

Whole Foods Market 🛒 🍴

7400 E. Hampden Ave. ✆ 303-488-2000 ⏰ Daily 8-10
• organic produce • vegetarian friendly • salad bar • cafe • self-service • take-out

🚗 **From I-25**, take exit 201 east on E Hampden Ave (left from I-25S, right from I-25N) 1 mile to store in shopping plaza on right.

Wild Oats Market 🛒 🍴

900 E.11th Ave. ✆ 303-832-7701 ⏰ Daily 7:30-10
• organic produce, vegetarian friendly, salad bar, cafe, self-service, take-out

🚗 **From I-25**, take exit 210A east on W Colfax Ave (right from I-25N, left from I-25S) about 2½ miles to Emerson St. Turn right onto Emerson 4 blocks to store on SE corner at 11th Ave.

DILLON

Natural Grocers by Vitamin Cottage 🛒

761 Anemone Trail ✆ 970-262-1100 ⏰ M-F 9-8, Sat 9-7, Sun 11-6
• organic produce

🚗 **From I-70**, take exit 205 onto US 6E (right from I-70E, left from I-70W) ⅓ mile to Anemone Trail. Turn right onto Anemone to store on right.

DURANGO

Durango Natural Foods 🛒

575 E. 8th Ave. ✆ 970-247-8129 ⏰ Daily 8-8
• organic produce • vegetarian friendly • deli • take-out • co-op

🚗 **From US 550**, turn east onto 6th St (right from 550N, left from 550S) ⅔ mile to store on right at 8th Ave. **From US 160E**, merge onto US 550N under ¼ mile to 6th St and follow directions above. **From east of Durango on US 160W**, turn right onto Rt 3 (becomes 8th Ave) about 2½ miles to store on left at 6th St.

Local Wild Life 🍴

845 E. 3rd Ave. ✆ 970-247-8395 ⏰ Tues, F 11:11-2:22, W 6-8
The twice-a-week "educational" lunch under the auspices of Turtle Lake Refuge is a 4-course raw foods meal prepared with local produce. Weekly Wednesday dinner and lecture.
• vegan • organic focus • tables • wait staff

🚗 From US 550 (Main Ave in town), turn east onto 9th St 2 blocks to E 3rd Ave. Turn right onto E 3rd to restaurant in the Rocky Mt Retreat Bldg (at the back).

Nature's Oasis 🛒 🍴

1123 Camino Del Rio ✆ 970-247-1988 ⏰ M-Sat 8-8, Sun 8-7
• organic produce • vegetarian friendly • fresh juice • deli • tables • self-service • take-out

🚗 **On US 550** at about 11th St.

ENGLEWOOD

Natural Grocers by Vitamin Cottage 🛒

9670 E. Arapahoe Rd. ✆ 303-790-0488 ⏰ M-F 9-8, Sat 9-7, Sun 11-6
• organic produce

🚗 **From I-25**, take exit 197 east on Arapahoe (left from I-25S, right from 1-25N) under ½ mile to store on right.

EVERGREEN
Natural Grocers by Vitamin Cottage 🛍️
1291 Bergen Pkwy. ✆ 303-679-9800 ⏰ M-F 9-8, Sat 10-7, Sun 11-6
• organic produce

🚗 **From I-70W**, take exit 252 onto Evergreen Pkwy/CO 74 almost 2 miles to Bergen Pkwy. Turn left onto Bergen ⅓ mile to store on right. **From I-70E**, take exit 251 right onto Mount Vernon Rd/CO 40 ½ mile to Evergreen Pkwy. Turn right onto Evergreen and follow directions above.

Whispering Weeds Organic Bakery & Cafe 🍴
27972 Meadow Drive ✆ 303-567-0140/303-670-0672 ⏰ M-Sat 8:30-4:30
• vegetarian friendly • organic focus • fresh juice • bakery • counter • tables • wait staff • take-out

🚗 **From I-70W**, take exit 252 onto Evergreen Pkwy/CO 74 almost 6½ miles to Douglas Park Rd. Turn left onto Douglas Park and left onto Meadow Dr ¾ mile to restaurant on right. **From I-70E**, take exit 252 and follow directions above.

FRISCO
Alpine Natural Foods 🛍️🍴   ♿
301 W. Main St. ✆ 970-668-5535 ⏰ M-Sat 8-8, Sun 9-7
• organic produce • vegetarian friendly • deli • tables • self-service • take-out

🚗 **From I-70**, take exit 201 toward Frisco east on Main St (left from I-70W, right from I-70E) about ⅓ mile to store at Creekside Dr.

FT. COLLINS
Fort Collins Food Co-op 🛍️
250 E. Mountain Ave. ✆ 970-484-7448 ⏰ M-F 8:30-8, Sat 8:30-7, Sun 11-7
• organic produce • vegetarian friendly • deli • co-op • take-out

🚗 **From I-25**, take exit 269B west on Mulberry St about 3½ miles to College Ave. Turn right onto College 4 blocks to Mountain Ave. Turn right onto Mountain 1 block to store on left.

Natural Grocers by Vitamin Cottage 🛍️
4318 S. College Ave. ✆ 970-266-9919 ⏰ M-Sat 9-8 Sun 11-6
• organic produce

🚗 **From I-25**, take exit 265 west on E Harmony Rd 4½ miles to S College Ave. Turn right onto S College ⅓ mile to store on right.

Whole Foods Market 🛍️🍴
2201 S. College Ave. ✆ 970-267-9200 ⏰ Daily 8-10
• organic produce • vegetarian friendly • salad bar • cafe • self-service • take-out

🚗 **From I-25S**, take exit 269B onto E Mulberry St under 4 miles to S College Ave. Turn left onto S College 1½ miles to store on right. **From I-25N**, take exit 268 left onto E Prospect Rd 4 miles to S College. Turn left onto S College ½ mile to store.

GLENDALE
Wild Oats Market 🛍️🍴   ♿
870 S. Colorado Blvd. ✆ 303-691-0101 ⏰ Daily 7:30-10
• organic produce • vegetarian friendly • salad bar • cafe • self-service • take-out

🚗 **From I-25**, take exit 204 north on Colorado Blvd about 15 blocks to store on east side between Kentucky & Ohio Ave.

GLENWOOD SPRINGS
Good Health Grocery 🛍️
722 Cooper Ave. ✆ 970-945-0235 ⏰ M-Sat 9-7, Sun 9-6
• organic produce • vegetarian friendly • deli • take-out

🚗 **From I-70**, take exit 116 toward Glenwood Springs south on CO 82 (Grand Ave) about ¼ mile to 8th Ave. Turn left onto 8th to store on right at Cooper Ave.

Natural Grocers by Vitamin Cottage 🛍

100 W. Meadows Drive ✆ 970-945-7000 ⏲ M-F 9-8, Sat 9-7, Sun 11-6
• organic produce

🛍 Store about 10 miles south of I-70 exit 116 just off CO 82. **From CO 82**, turn southwest onto Diamond A Ranch Rd (right from CO 82E, left from CO 82W) and take second exit off traffic circle continuing on Diamond A Ranch to Mt Meadows Cir. Turn right onto Mt Meadows to store on right.

GOLDEN

Wild Oats Market 🛍 🍴   ♿

14357 W. Colfax Ave. ✆ 303-277-1339 ⏲ Daily 7:30-10
• organic produce, vegetarian friendly, salad bar, cafe, self-service, take-out

🛍 **From I-70**, take exit 263 onto Denver West Marriott Blvd (left from 70W, right from 70E) about ¼ mile to Cole Blvd. Turn right onto Cole to store.

GRAND JUNCTION

Appleseed Health Foods 🛍   ♿

2830 North Ave. ✆ 970-243-5541 ⏲ M-F 9-6, Sat 9-5:30

🛍 **From I-70E**, take exit 26 toward Grand Junction onto US 6E about 7 miles to store between 28¼ & 28½ Rd. **From I-70W**, take exit 37 toward Clifton/Grand Junction onto Bus 70W about 3½ miles. Continue on US 6W over 1½ miles to store.

Natural Grocers by Vitamin Cottage 🛍

2464 U.S. Hwy. 6 & 50 ✆ 970-263-7750 ⏲ M-F 9-8, Sat 9-7, Sun 11-6
• organic produce

🛍 **From I-70**, take exit 26 onto US 30/US 60 (merge from I-70E, left from I-70W) about 3⅓ miles to store on left past 24½ Rd.

HIGHLANDS RANCH

Natural Grocers by Vitamin Cottage 🛍

9567 S. University Blvd., Ste. E ✆ 303-346-7670 ⏲ M-F 9-8, Sat 9-7, Sun 11-6
• organic produce

🛍 **From I-25**, take exit 193 west on Lincoln Ave (left from I-25N, right from I-25S) about 6½ miles (becomes University Blvd) to store on left.

Whole Foods Market 🛍 🍴   ♿

9366 S. Colorado Blvd. ✆ 303-470-6003 ⏲ Daily 8-9
• organic produce, vegetarian friendly • salad bar • cafe • self-service • take-out

🛍 **From I-25**, take exit 193 west on Lincoln Ave (left from I-25N, right from I-25S) about 6½ miles (becomes University Blvd) to S Colorado Blvd. Turn right onto S Colorado to store on right.

HOTCHKISS

Hardin's Natural Foods 🛍

31424 Hwy. 92 ✆ 970-872-3019 ⏲ M-Sat 9-6, Sun 12-5
Fresh sandwiches daily. Also a seasonal wine tasting room featuring Colorado wines.
• organic produce

🛍 CO 92 and CO 133 intersect in Hotchkiss. Store is on CO 92 3⅓ miles west of CO 133 on north side.

LAFAYETTE

Natural Grocers by Vitamin Cottage 🛍

100 W. South Boulder Rd. ✆ 303-926-1600 ⏲ M-F 9-8, Sat 9-7, Sun 11-6
• organic produce

🛍 **From CO 287**, go east on W S Boulder Rd (right from US/CO 287N, left from CO 287S) under ½ mile to store on right before S Public Rd.

LAKEWOOD

Natural Grocers by Vitamin Cottage 🛍

3333 S. Wadsworth Blvd. ✆ 303-989-4866 ⏰ M-F 9-8:00, Sat 9-7:00, Sun 11-6:00
• organic produce

🚗 **From US 285**, take Wadsworth Blvd exit north on Wadsworth (left from US 285N, right from US 285S) 2 blocks to store on left in Mission Trace Shopping Ctr.

Natural Grocers by Vitamin Cottage 🛍

12612 W. Alameda Pkwy. ✆ 303-986-5700 ⏰ M-F 9-8, Sat 9-7, Sun 11-6
• organic produce

🚗 **From I-70E**, take exit 261 onto US 6E 2¼ miles to Union Blvd exit. Turn right onto Union about ½ mile to W Alameda Pkwy. Turn right onto W Alameda ½ mile to store on left. **From I-70W**, take exit 262 left onto W Colfax Ave and right onto Indiana Ave about ½ mile to US 6E. Turn left onto US 6E about 1½ miles to Union exit and follow directions above.

Natural Grocers by Vitamin Cottage 🛍

9030 W. Colfax Ave. ✆ 303-232-6266 ⏰ M-F 9-8, Sat 9-7, Sun 11-6
• organic produce

🚗 **From I-70E**, take exit 261 onto US 6E 3½ miles to Kipling St exit. Go north on Kipling about 1 mile to W Colfax Ave. Turn right onto W Colfax over ½ mile to store on right after Garrison St. **From I-70W**, take exit 267 left onto Kipling St about 3 miles to W Colfax Ave. Turn left onto W Colfax and follow directions above.

Whole Foods Market 🛍 🍴

444 S. Wadsworth Blvd. ✆ 303-935-5000 ⏰ Daily 7:30-10
• organic produce • vegetarian friendly • salad bar • cafe • self-service • take-out

🚗 **From I-25**, take exit 209B onto US 6W about 3½ miles to Wadsworth Blvd/Hwy 121S exit. Merge onto Wadsworth heading south about 1⅓ miles to store on left.

LITTLETON

Natural Grocers by Vitamin Cottage 🛍

11550 W. Meadows Drive ✆ 303-948-9944 ✆ M-F 9-8, Sat 9-7, Sun 11-6
• organic produce

🚗 **From Hwy 470**, go east on W Ken Caryl Ave (right from Hwy 460W, left from Hwy 470E) about 1 mile to S Simms St. Turn left onto S Simms and make first right onto W Meadow Dr to store on right.

Whole Foods Market 🛍 🍴   ♿

5910 S. University Blvd. ✆ 303-798-9699 ⏰ Daily 8-9
• organic produce • vegetarian friendly • salad bar • cafe • self-service • take-out

🚗 **From I-25**, take exit 199 west (towards mountains) on Belleview Ave (right from I-25S, left from I-25N) 3 miles to University Blvd. Turn left onto University 1 mile to Orchard Dr (second light). Turn left onto Orchard to store on SE corner.

LONGMONT

Natural Grocers by Vitamin Cottage 🛍

1739 N. Main St. ✆ 303-684-8200 ⏰ M-F 9-8, Sat 9-7, Sun 11-6
• organic produce

🚗 On US 287 north of 17th Ave on west side.

MONTROSE

Green Market Natural Foods & Vitamins 🛍 🍴

1541 Oxbow Drive ✆ 970-240-3434 ⏰ M-F 9-7, Sat 9-6, Sun 11-5
• organic produce • vegetarian friendly • fresh juice • cafe • counter • tables • self-service • take-out

🚗 CO 50 and CO 550 intersect in Montrose. Store is 2½ miles south of this intersection on the east side of CO 50/550 between Ogden & Otter Rd.

MONUMENT

Natural Grocers by Vitamin Cottage 🗂
655 Hwy. 105 ✆ 719-487-0448 ⏰ M-F 9-8, Sat 9-7, Sun 11-6
• organic produce

🍎 **From I-25,** take exit 161 toward Monument onto Hwy 105 ½ mile to store on left before Beacon Lite Rd.

NEDERLAND

Mountain People's Co-op 🗂   ♿
30 E. First St. ✆ 303-258-7500 ⏰ Daily 8-8
• organic produce, vegetarian friendly, deli, bakery, take-out, co-op

🍎 Nederland is about 17 miles west of Boulder on Hwy 119S (which ends in Nederland). **From 119,** take roundabout onto S Bridge St 1 block to 1st St. Turn left onto 1st to store (along Boulder Creek).

NORTHGLEN

Natural Grocers by Vitamin Cottage 🗂
11465 Washington St. ✆ 303-280-1900 ⏰ M-F 9-8, Sat 9-7, Sun 11-6
• organic produce

🍎 **From I-25,** take exit 223 onto E 120th Ave (merge right from I-25N, left from I-25S) under 1 mile to Washington St. Turn right onto Washington over ½ mile to store on right after E 114th Ct.

PARKER

Natural Grocers by Vitamin Cottage 🗂
11402 S. Parker Rd. ✆ 303-805-1285 ⏰ M-F 9-8, Sat 9-7, Sun 11-6
• organic produce

🍎 **From I-25,** take exit 194 onto Hwy E 470 N (right from I-25N, left from I-25S) about 5 miles to exit 5. Merge right onto S Parker Rd about 3¼ miles to store on left.

PUEBLO

Natural Grocers by Vitamin Cottage 🗂
101 W. 29th St. ✆ 719-542-2411 ⏰ M-F 9-8, Sat 9-7, Sun 11-6
• organic produce

🍎 **From I-25,** take exit 100B east on W 29th St (left from I-25S, right from I-25N) about ⅓ mile to store on left before Dillon Dr.

RIDGWAY

Season's Harvest 🗂 🍴
521 Clinton St. ✆ 970-626-9719 ⏰ M-F 10-6, Sat-Sun 10-5
• organic produce • vegetarian friendly • fresh juice • deli • tables • self-service • take-out

🍎 **From 550/62 intersection,** go west on Sherman under ½ mile to N Lena St. Turn right onto N Lena 1 block to Clinton. Turn left onto Clinton to store on right.

SALIDA

Simple Foods Market 🗂
1548 G St., #4 ✆ 719-539-7144 ⏰ M-Sat 9-7, Sun 10-6
• organic produce

🍎 Salida is about 4 miles east of US 285 on US 50. **From US 50** (aka E Rainbow Blvd), store is 1 block north on G St.

STEAMBOAT SPRINGS
Bamboo Market 🛍 🍴
1110 Yampa St., Ste. 100 © 970-879-9992 ⏰ M-F 8-8 Deli until 4, Sat-Sun 9-6 Deli until 3
• organic produce • vegetarian friendly • fresh juice • deli • tables • self-service • take-out
🚪 **From US 40 (Lincoln Ave)**, turn south (toward the river) onto 12th St 1 block to Yampa St. Turn left onto Yampa 1 block to store on left.

SUPERIOR
Wild Oats Market 🛍 🍴
303 Marshall Rd. © 720-274-1415 ⏰ Daily 7:30-10
• organic produce • vegetarian friendly • salad bar • cafe • self-service • take-out
🚪 **From Hwy 36**, exit onto S McCaslin Blvd (left from Hwy 36W, right from Hwy 36E) and make first right onto Marshall Rd to store on right after 1st Ave.

TRINIDAD
The Natural Food Store 🛍
316 Prospect St. © 27219-846-7577 ⏰ M-F 10-5, Sat 10-2
• organic produce
🚪 **From I-25S**, take exit 14B onto E Colorado Ave and turn left onto Arizona Ave 2 blocks to Pine St. Turn right onto Pine ⅓ mile to Prospect St. Turn left onto Prospect ⅓ mile to store on left. **From I-25N**, take exit 13B right onto Main St and left onto Hwy 12 under ½ mile (across hwy) to Prospect. Turn left onto Prospect to store.

WESTMINSTER
Wild Oats Market 🛍 🍴
9229 N. Sheridan Blvd. © 303-650-2333 ⏰ Daily 8-9
• organic produce • vegetarian friendly • salad bar • cafe • self-service • take-out
🚪 **From US 36**, take Sheridan Blvd exit north on Sheridan (right coming from Denver, left coming from Boulder) ⅓-½ mile to second light (93rd Ave). Turn left onto 93rd to store in shopping center.

WRAY
Strawberry Patch 🛍
421 Main St. © 970-332-4064 ⏰ M-F 10-5:30
• organic produce, fresh juice, take-out
🚪 **From Hwy 34**, turn south onto Main St about 1½ blocks to store on west side (across from theater).

CONNECTICUT

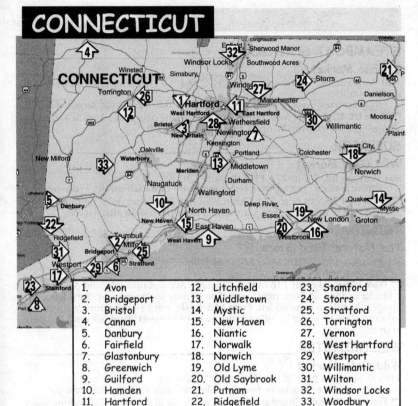

1. Avon	12. Litchfield	23. Stamford
2. Bridgeport	13. Middletown	24. Storrs
3. Bristol	14. Mystic	25. Stratford
4. Cannan	15. New Haven	26. Torrington
5. Danbury	16. Niantic	27. Vernon
6. Fairfield	17. Norwalk	28. West Hartford
7. Glastonbury	18. Norwich	29. Westport
8. Greenwich	19. Old Lyme	30. Willimantic
9. Guilford	20. Old Saybrook	31. Wilton
10. Hamden	21. Putnam	32. Windsor Locks
11. Hartford	22. Ridgefield	33. Woodbury

AVON

Garden of Light Pure Foods Market

395 W. Main St. ℂ 860-409-2196 ⏱ M-F 9-8, Sat 9-6:30, Sun 11-5

Hot soup and a microwave so customers can heat deli foods from their Glastonbury store.

· organic produce · vegetarian friendly · deli · take-out

🛍 Avon is 11 miles west of Hartford on Rt 44. Store is on 44 (aka Main St) just east of Rt 167 (across from Simsbury Commons Mall).

BRIDGEPORT

Bloodroot 🍴

85 Ferris St. ℂ 03-576-9168 ⏱ Lunch Tues, Th-Sun 11:30-2:30 Dinner Tues-Th 6-9, F-Sat 6-10

Collectively run with a feminist bookstore on site.

· vegetarian · vegan friendly · organic focus · alcohol · tables · self-service · take-out

🛍 **From NY**, take I-95 to exit 24. Go straight past intersection and turn right onto Black Rock Tpke/Brewster St. At fourth light turn left onto Fairfield Ave. At next light turn right onto Ellsworth St 2 blocks to Thurston St. Turn left onto Thurston and right onto Harbor Ave 3 blocks to Ferris St. Turn left onto Ferris to restaurant. **From New Haven**, take I-95 to exit 25. Turn left onto Fairfield Ave. At third light turn left onto Ellsworth and follow directions above.

BRISTOL

Super Natural Market & Deli 🛍 🍴

430 N. Main St. ℂ 60-582-1663 ⏱ M-F 8-6, Sat 9-5

• vegetarian friendly • deli • tables • self-service • take-out

From I-84, take exit 33 toward Bristol onto Rt 72W (becomes Memorial Blvd, then School Rd) about 3 miles to Main St. Turn right onto Main about ¾ mile to store.

CANNAN

Health Food Junction
35 Church St. © 860-824-8466 ① M-F 9:30-5, Sat 9:30-4

US 7 and US 44 intersect in Canaan. Store is on US 44 (aka Church St) west of Railroad St and south of Main St.

DANBURY

Chamomile Natural Foods
58-60 Newtown Rd. (Rte. 6) © 203-792-8952 ① M-W, F 9:30-6:30, Th 9:30-7:30, Sat 10-5:30, Sun 10-3
• organic produce

From I-84, take exit 8 (US 6E/Newtown Rd) onto 6E about ½ mile to store on right in Rt 6 Plaza.

FAIRFIELD

Mrs. Green's Natural Market
1916 Post Rd. © 203-255-4333 ① M,W, F-Sat 9-7, Tues, Th 9-8, Sun 10-6
• organic produce, vegetarian friendly, deli, tables, self-service, take-out

From I-95, take exit 21 south on Mill Plain Rd (right from I-95N, left from I-95S) about ¼ mile to Post Rd (aka US 1). Turn right onto Post Rd under ¼ mile to store on right.

GLASTONBURY

Garden of Light Pure Foods Market
2836 Main St. © 860-657-9131 ① M-F 9-8, Sat 9-6:30, Sun 11-5
• organic produce • vegetarian friendly • deli • tables • self-service • take-out

From I-91, take exit 25 toward Glastonbury onto Rt 3N across bridge almost 2 miles to Main St Glastonbury exit. Turn left onto Glastonbury Blvd and right onto Main to store in plaza on left at light.

GREENWICH

Whole Foods Market   &
90 E. Putnam Ave. © 203-661-0631 ① Daily 8-10
• organic produce • vegetarian friendly • deli • bakery • take-out

From I-95, take exit 4 toward Cos Cob north on Indian Field Rd about ⅔ mile to end. Turn left onto Rt 1 (E Putnam Ave) 1 mile to store on left.

GUILFORD

Foodworks
1055 Boston Post Rd. © 203-458-9778 ① Tues-W, F 9:30-7, M, Th 9:30-7:30, Sat 10-7, Sun 11-6
• organic produce • vegetarian friendly • fresh juice • deli • tables • self-service • take-out

From I-95, take exit 58 toward Guilford south on Rt 77 (right from I-95N, left from I-95S) ½ mile to store on right at Rt 1 (Boston Post Rd).

Shoreline Diner   &
345 Boston Post Rd. © 203-458-7380 ① Daily 7am-12am
A traditional diner with a surprising repertoire of vegetarian entrees beyond salads and a veggie burger. Check out the (highly touted) vegan chocolate cake.
• vegetarian friendly • alcohol • counter • tables • wait staff • take-out

From I-95, take exit 59 toward Guilford right onto Goose Ln and take first left onto Boston Post Rd (US 1) about ⅓ mile to restaurant on left.

HAMDEN

Thyme & Season 🍴

3040 Whitney Ave. ℗ 203-407-8128 ⏰ M-F 9-7:30, Sat 9-7, Sun 11-5
• organic produce • vegetarian friendly • deli • take-out

🍎 **From I-91**, take exit 10 onto Rt 40N about 3 miles to Rt 10N. Take 10N (aka Whitney Ave) about ¼ mile to store on left.

HARTFORD

Alchemy Juice Bar Cafe 🍴

203 New Britain Ave. ℗ 860-246-5700 ⏰ Tues-Th, Sat 11:30-8:30, F 11:30-10:30, Sun 10-6
• vegetarian • vegan friendly • organic focus • fresh juice • tables • self-service • wait staff • take-out

🍎 **From I-84E**, take exit 48A/B for Capitol St/Asylum toward Capitol Ave. Turn right onto Capitol and left onto Broad St 1⅓ miles to New Britain Ave. Turn right onto New Britain to restaurant on left. **From I-84W**, take exit 48 toward Asylum St onto Spring St to Garden St. Veer left onto Garden, right onto Asylum, left onto Broad and follow directions above.

Lion's Den Vegetarian Restaurant 🍴

3347 Main St. ℗ 860-241-0220 ⏰ Daily 8:30am-11pm
A small place with a daily plate of homemade vegetarian West Indian food.
• vegetarian • vegan friendly, tables, self-service, take-out

🍎 **From I-84E**, take exit 49 for High St/Ann St left at fork, left onto Pleasant St, left onto N Chapel St, right onto Ann and left onto Main 2 miles to restaurant on left after Tower Ave. **From I-84W**, take exit 50 toward Main, merge onto Morgan St, turn right onto Main and follow directions above. **From I-91N**, take exit 33 left onto Jennings Rd continuing onto Boce Barlow Way about ¾ mile to end at Windsor St. Turn right onto Windsor and continue right onto Main ½ mile to restaurant on left. **From I-91S**, take exit 34 toward N Main St right onto Windsor Ave continuing onto Main about ½ mile to restaurant on right after Rosemont St.

LITCHFIELD

Amazing Grains 🍴

383 Torrington Rd. ℗ 860-567-4435 ⏰ M-F 8:30-7, Sat 8-6, Sunday 10-4
Organic and local produce seasonally.

🍎 Store is on US 202 (aka Torrington Rd in town) on west side.

MIDDLETOWN

It's Only Natural Market 🍴 ♿

575 Main St. ℗ 860-346-1786 ⏰ M-F 9-7, Sat 9-6, Sun 11-4
• organic produce

🍎 **From I-91**, take exit 22S toward Middletown/Old Saybrook onto Rt 9S about 5½ miles to Main St (exit 16). At top of ramp turn left onto Main 2 blocks store on right at Liberty St.

It's Only Natural Restaurant 🍴 ♿

386 Main St. ℗ 860-346-9210 ⏰ M-Th 11-9, F-Sat 11-10, Sun 11-3
• vegetarian • vegan friendly • alcohol • tables • wait staff

🍎 **From I-91**, take exit 22S toward Middletown/Old Saybrook onto Rt 9S about 5½ miles to Washington St (exit 15). Turn right onto Washington 2 blocks to Main St. Turn left onto Main 1 block to restaurant on left.

MYSTIC

Puritan & Genesta Natural Foods 🍴 🍴

2 Holmes St. ℗ 860-536-3537 ⏰ M-F 8-8, Sat 9-8, Sun 10-6
Soups, sandwiches and hot entrees on weekdays.
• organic produce, vegetarian friendly, deli, tables, self-service, take-out

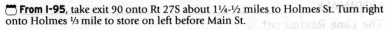

◯ **From I-95**, take exit 90 onto Rt 27S about 1¼-½ miles to Holmes St. Turn right onto Holmes ⅓ mile to store on left before Main St.

NEW HAVEN

Ahimsa 🍴
1227 Chapel St. ℂ 203-786-4774 ⏱ Lunch Tues-Sat 11:30-2:30, Brunch Sun 11-3 Juice Bar Tues-Sun 11-5 Tapas Tues-Wed, Sun 4-10, Th-Sat 4-12 Dinner Tues-Sun 5-10
Lunch buffet, Sunday champagne brunch, juice and smoothies throughout the day, and at night full dinner in the restaurant or light fare in the adjoining tapas bar.
· vegan · organic focus · fresh juice · alcohol · kosher · tables · self-service · wait staff
◯ **From I-95**, take exit 47 toward Downtown New Haven onto CT 34W about 1 mile to York St. Turn right onto York 3 blocks to Chapel St. Turn left onto Chapel 2 blocks to restaurant. **From I-91S**, take exit 1 for CT 34W and follow directions above.

Claire's Corner Copia 🍴   ♿
1000 Chapel St. ℂ 203-562-3888 ⏱ M-Th 8am-9pm, F 8-10, Sat 9-10, Sun 9-9
Eclectic menu with an Italian/Mexican slant. Organic gardens supply summer heirloom vegetables and herbs.
· vegetarian · vegan friendly · organic focus · kosher · tables · self-service
◯ **From I-95**, take exit 47 toward Downtown New Haven onto CT 34W about ⅔ mile to exit 1. Follow exit to light at Church St. Turn right onto Church to third light (Chapel St). Turn left onto Chapel to restaurant at second light on left at College St. **From I-91S**, take exit 3 onto Trumbull St about 4 blocks to Temple St. Turn left onto Temple ½ mile to Chapel. Turn right onto Chapel 1 block to restaurant.

Edge of the Woods Market 🛍 🍴   ♿
379 Whalley Ave. ℂ 203-787-1055 ⏱ M-F 8:30-7:30, Sat 9-6:30, Sun 9-6
· organic produce · vegetarian · vegan friendly · fresh juice · cafe · deli · bakery · self-service · take-out
◯ **From I-95**, take exit 47 toward Downtown New Haven onto CA 34W (Frontage Rd) past Yale New Haven Medical Ctr to Howe St (second light). Turn right onto Howe 5 blocks to Whalley Ave. Turn left onto Whalley to store in Market Square Shopping Ctr. **From I-91S**, take exit 3 onto Trumbull St about 4 blocks to Temple St. Turn left onto Temple 2 blocks to Grove St. Turn right onto Grove (becomes Tower Pkwy, then Whalley Ave) about 1¼ miles to store.

Thali Too 🍴   ♿ 📷
65 Broadway ℂ 203-776-1600 ⏱ M-Sat 11:30-9:40, Sun 11:30-8:40
Indian vegetarian with a rice bar where you mix and match rice or noodles, topping and sauce. Plus a build-your-own lassi bar.
· vegetarian · vegan friendly · alcohol · tables · wait staff
◯ **From I-95N**, take exit 47 on left onto CT 34 about 1 mile to York St. Turn right onto York under ½ mile to Elm St. Turn left onto Elm and veer right onto Broadway) to restaurant on right. **From I-91S**, take exit 1 onto CT 34W and follow directions above.

NIANTIC

Natural Food Store 🛍
374 Main St. ℂ 60-739-9916 ⏱ M-F 9:30-6, Sat-Sun 10-5
· organic produce
◯ **From I-95N**, take exit 72 onto Rocky Neck Connecter under 1 mile to CT 156/W Main St. Turn left onto W Main about 2¾ miles to store on right between Lake Ave & State Rd. **From I-95S**, take exit 74 toward Niantic right onto CT 161/Flanders Rd 3 miles (becomes Pennsylvania Ave) to CT-156/Main St. Turn left onto Main ⅓ mile to store on left after State.

NORWALK

The Lime Restaurant 🍴

168 Main Ave. ℂ 203-846-9240 ⏱ M-Sat 11-4, 5-10, Sun 4:30-9:30
Ample vegetarian choices including all the soups and sauces.
  • vegetarian friendly • alcohol • tables • wait staff

🍴 **From I-95**, take exit 15 onto Rt 7N about 1½ miles to exit 2. Turn left onto Rt 123⅓ mile to Main St. Turn right onto Main 2 blocks to restaurant on left.

NORWICH

Ginger Root Health Food Store 🍂

205 W. Thames St. ℂ 860-889-8720 ⏱ M-F 9-7, Sat 9-5:30

🍴 **From I-395N**, take exit 79A onto Hwy 2AE ⅓ mile to Hwy 32. Turn left onto Hwy 32/Norwich 2½ miles to store on left after Dunham St. **From I-395S**, take exit 81 toward Norwich onto Hwy 2E/32S. Follow 32S 4 miles to store on right after Geer Ave.

OLD LYME

The Grist Mill 🍂

19 Halls Rd. ℂ 860-434-2990 ⏱ M-Th, Sat 9:30-6, F 9:30-5:30, Sun 12-4

🍴 **From I-95N**, take exit 70 left onto US 1/Neck Rd under ¼ mile to Halls Rd. Turn right onto Halls about ½ mile to store in Old Lyme Shopping Ctr. From I-95S, take exit 70 straight off ramp onto US 1/Halls Rd to store just off hwy in Old Lyme Shopping Ctr.

OLD SAYBROOK

Foodworks 2 🍂

17 Main St. ℂ 860-395-0770 ⏱ M-F 9:30-6, Sat 10-6, Sun 11-5
  • organic produce

🍴 **From I-95N**, take exit 67 right onto Middlesex Tpke about ½ mile to Main St (Boston Post Rd is straight ahead). Veer left onto Main to store on right. **From I-95S**, take exit 68 toward Old Saybrook left onto Springbook Rd/US 1 (becomes Boston Post Rd) about 1⅓ miles to Main St. Veer left onto Main store.

PUTNAM

Harvest Moon Health Foods 🍂

554 Liberty Hwy. (Rte. 21) ℂ 860-928-2352 ⏱ M-W 10-7, Th-Sat 10-5
Organic produce seasonally.

🍴 **From I-395**, take exit 97 toward Woodstock east on CT 44/Providence Pike (right from I-395N, left from I-395S) under 1 mile to Converse Rd/CT 21. Turn right onto Rt 21 under ¼ mile to store on right.

RIDGEFIELD

Nature's Temptations 🍂 🍴

32 Prospect St. ℂ 203-438-5443 ⏱ M-F 9:30-7, Sat 9-5, Sun 10-3
  • organic produce • vegetarian friendly • fresh juice • salad bar • deli • bakery • tables
  • self-service • take-out

🍴 **From I-84**, take exit 3 onto Rte 7S 5 miles to CT 35/Danbury Ridgefield Rd. Merge onto CT 35 3 miles to Prospect St. Turn left onto Prospect almost 2 blocks to store on right.

STAMFORD

Mrs. Green's Natural Market 🍂 🍴

950 High Ridge Rd. ℂ 203-329-1313 ⏱ M, W, F 9-8, Tues, Th 9-9, Sat 9-7, Sun 10-6
  • organic produce • vegetarian friendly • tables • self-service • take-out

🍴 **From Merritt Pkwy**, take exit 35 toward Stamford/Bus District right onto High Ridge Rd/CT 137 about ½ mile to store.

STORRS

Champlion's General Store 🛍️

2 Old Mill Court ℂ 860-429-1144 ⏰ M-Sat 9-5

🍎 **From US 44 (Hartford Providence Tpke)**, turn south onto CT 32/Stafford Rd (left from 44E, right from 44W) 2 miles to Rt 275. Turn right onto Rt 275/S Eaglesville Rd and veer right onto Old Mill Ct to store on right.

STRATFORD

Nature's Way Natural Foods 🛍️

922 Barnum Ave. Cutoff ℂ 203-377-3652 ⏰ M-Sat 9-9, Sun 9-5
• organic produce

🍎 **From I-95**, take exit 32 (W Broad St toward Stafford). **From I-95N**, enter roundabout and take 1st St exit onto W Broad to Main St. Turn left onto Main about ²/₃ mile to Barnum Ave Cutoff. Turn right onto Barnum Cutoff to store on left. **From I-95S**, turn right off exit onto Linden Ave about ¼ mile to Main. Turn left onto Main about ¹/₃ mile to Barnum Ave Cutoff. Turn right onto Barnum Cutoff to store.

TORRINGTON

The Good Life 🛍️

43 Daycoeton Place ℂ 860-482-0111 ⏰ M-W, F 9-5:30, Th 9-6:30, Sat 9-5
• organic produce

🍎 **From CT 8**, take exit 44 for State Hwy 4 toward Torrington/US-202 onto E Main St/US 202 (right from CT 8S, left from CT 8N) about ½ mile to Daycoeton Pl. Turn right onto Daycoeton 1 block to store on left (behind bank & library).

VERNON

Nature's Grocer 🛍️ 🍴

81 East St. ℂ 860-870-0020 ⏰ M-F 9-7, Sat 9-4
On site gluten-free bakery.
• vegetarian friendly • deli • bakery • tables • self-service • take-out

🍎 **From I-84**, take exit 67 toward Rockville north on CT 31/Reservoir (left from I-84E, right from I-84W) under ½ mile to CT 30/Hartford Tpke. Turn right onto Hartford Tpke 1 block to East St. Turn left onto East to store on right.

WEST HARTFORD

Whole Foods Market 🛍️ 🍴 ♿

340 N. Main St. ℂ 860-523-7174 ⏰ Daily 8-10
• organic produce • vegetarian friendly • salad bar • cafe • self-service • take-out

🍎 **From I-84E**, take exit 41 left onto S Main St (becomes N Main) about 3½ mile to store on right. **From I-84W**, take exit 50 onto US 44W 4¹/₃ miles to N Main. Turn left onto Main to store on left. **From I-91**, take exit 32B onto Trumbull St, turn right onto US 44 and follow directions above.

Whole Foods Market 🛍️ 🍴

50 Raymond Rd. ℂ 860-523-8500 ⏰ Daily 8-10
• organic produce • vegetarian friendly • salad bar • cafe • self-service • take-out

🍎 **From I-84**, take exit 43 left onto Park Rd and make first right onto Raymond Rd ½ mile to store on right.

WESTPORT

Fountain of Youth 🛍️ 🍴

1789 Post Rd. E. ℂ 203-259-9378 ⏰ Sat 9-7, Sun 10-5
• organic produce • vegetarian friendly • fresh juice • salad bar • counter • tables • self-service • take-out

🍎 **From I-95S**, take exit 19 onto Pease Ave and merge west on Rt 1 (Boston Post Rd) about ½ mile to store on right. **From I-95N**, take exit 19 left onto Center St, left onto Rt 1 and follow directions above.

Organic Market 🛍 🍴

285 Post Rd. E. ℰ 203-227-9007 ⏱ -Sat 9-6, Sun 11-5
· organic produce · vegetarian friendly · fresh juice · deli · tables · self-service · take-out

🚗 **From I-95**, take exit 17 toward Westport/Saugatuck left onto 136/Saugatuck Ave (becomes Riverside Ave) about 1 mile to Sylvan Rd S. Turn left onto Sylvan about ⅓ mile to US 1/Post Rd. Turn left onto Post Rd about ¼ mile to store on left.

Whole Foods Market 🛍 🍴   ♿

399 Post Rd. W. ℰ 203-227-6858 ⏱ M-Sat 8-10, Sun 8-9
· organic produce · vegetarian friendly · salad bar · cafe · self-service · take-out

🚗 **From I-95**, take exit 17 toward Westport/Saugatuck left onto 136/Saugatuck Ave (becomes Riverside Ave) about 1 mile to Sylvan Rd S. Turn left onto Sylvan about ⅓ mile to US 1/Post Rd. Turn left onto Post Rd under ½ mile to store on left.

WILLIMANTIC

Willimantic Food Co-op 🛍

91 Valley St. ℰ 860-456-3611 ⏱ M-F 9-8, Sat 9-6, Sun 10-5
· organic produce · co-op

🚗 **From Rt 66E or Rt 6E**, take exit for Willimantic onto CT 32/Main St 2 miles to Church St. Turn left onto Church 1 block to Valley St. Turn right onto Valley to store on left. **From Rt 66W or Rt 6W**, take Boston Post Rd about 2¼ miles to Jillson Sq. Turn right onto Jillson 1 block to Valley. Turn left onto Valley to store on right.

WILTON

Wilton Organic Gourmet 🛍 🍴

33 Danbury Rd. ℰ 203-762-9711 ⏱ M-Sat 8-6:30
· organic produce · vegetarian friendly · deli · counter · self-service · take-out

🚗 **From I-95**, take exit 15 onto Rt 7N (becomes Main Ave, then Danbury Rd) almost 5 miles to store on left. **From Merritt Pkwy**, take exit 40B (Main Ave N/Rt 7N) right onto Main Ave (becomes Danbury Rd) about 1½ miles to store.

WINDSOR LOCKS

Fresh City 🍴

Bradley International Airport, Terminal A ℰ 860-292-1580 ⏱ Daily 5-9 depending on flight schedule
A fast-food alternative featuring wraps, stir fries, noodle dishes, soups and salads with the option to add tofu to most dishes.
· vegetarian friendly · fresh juice · tables · self-service · take-out

🚗 Inside terminal A at Bradley International Airport.

WOODBURY

Good News Cafe 🍴

694 Main St. S. ℰ 203-266-4663 ⏱ M, W-Sat 11:30-10, Sun 12-10
Gourmet menu with vegetarian entrees beyond pasta.
· vegetarian friendly · organic focus · alcohol · tables · wait staff · take-out

From I-84E, take exit 15 toward Southbury left onto Rt 6/Main St N almost 4 miles to restaurant. **From 84W**, take exit 17 toward Waterbury/Middlebury onto Rt 64 7½ miles to Main. Turn left onto Main to restaurant.

New Morning Natural & Organic 🛍 🍴

738 Main St. S. ℰ 203-263-4868 ⏱ M-Sat 8-7, Sun 10-5
· organic produce · vegetarian friendly · fresh juice · deli · tables · self-service · take-out

From I-84E, take exit 15 toward Southbury left onto Rt 6/Main St N 3½-4 miles to store on left in strip mall. **From 84W**, take exit 17 toward Waterbury/Middlebury onto Rt 64 7½ miles to Main. Turn left onto Main to store on right.

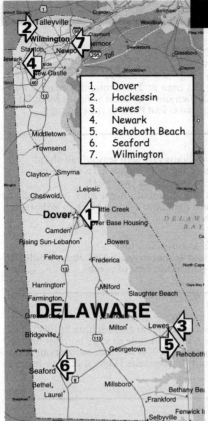

1. Dover
2. Hockessin
3. Lewes
4. Newark
5. Rehoboth Beach
6. Seaford
7. Wilmington

DOVER

Good News Natural Foods

739 S. Governors Ave. ℡ 302-730-1910 ⏰ M-F 10-6, Sat 10-5
• organic produce

🛒 **From Rt 1S**, take exit 98 right onto Hwy 8 toward Downtown Dover 2 miles to S Governors Ave. Turn left onto S Governors 1 mile to store on left between Hope & Dover St. **From Rt 1N/US 113N**, take exit 95 onto S Bay Rd about 2½ miles to E Lockerman St. Turn left onto E Lockerman under 1 mile to S Governors. Turn left onto S Governors about ½ mile to store. **From US 13S (aka S State St)**, turn right onto South St 1 block to S Governors. Turn left onto S Governors 3 blocks to store. **From US 13N**, merge left onto S Governors to store on right after Dover.

HOCKESSIN

Harvest Market

7417 Lancaster Pike ℡ 302-234-6779 ℡ M-F 9-7, Sat 10-7
There is a case with grab-and-go prepared foods.
• organic produce

🛒 **From I-95S**, take exit 5A-B toward Newport onto DE 141N about 2⅓ miles to exit 6 (Rt 2/Kirkwood Hwy toward Newport). Merge onto 2W about ⅔ mile to 41N. Take 41 N about 5 miles into Hockessin to Yorklyn Rd. Turn left onto Yorklyn 1 block to store at Old Lancaster Pike. **From I-95N**, take the I-295 exit (5A) toward NJ/NY. Merge onto 141N toward Newport and follow directions above.

LEWES

Good For You Natural Foods Market

28841 Lewes Georgetown Hwy (Rte. 9) ℡ 302-684-8330 ⏰ M-Sat 10-6, Sun 12-5
Market has a 1-acre farm and while not yet certified practices all the qualifying organic rules.
• organic produce

🛒 **From Rt 1S/Coastal Hwy**, turn right onto Nassau Park Rd, left onto Nassau Commons Blvd and right onto Rt 9 under 2 miles to store on right. **From Rt 1N**, turn left onto Rt 9 3½ miles to store.

NEWARK

Nature's Way Health Foods

620 Newark Shopping Center ℡ 302-737-7986 ⏰ M-Sat 10-5
Specializes in wheat- and gluten-free products.

🛒 **From I-95**, take exit 3 (3B from 95N) onto Rt 273W toward Newark 4 miles (4-lane hwy becomes 2-lane past Rt 2, then one-way street) to Newark Shopping Ctr and turn right to store on left.

Newark Natural Foods Cooperative 🛍 ♿

280 E. Main St. ✆ 302-368-5894 ⏱ M-Sat 9-8, Sun 9-5
• organic produce • vegetarian friendly • deli • take-out • co-op

🚗 **From I-95**, take exit 3 (3B from 95N) onto Rt 273W toward Newark 4 miles (4-lane hwy becomes 2-lane past Rt 2, then one-way street which is Main St). At second light (Tyre Ave) turn right into Market East Plaza to store on right.

REHOBOTH BEACH

Planet X Cafe 🍴

35 Wilmington Ave. ✆ 302-226-1928 ⏱ hours vary with season; call ahead
Two creative vegan and three vegetarian entrees on the mainly fish and poultry menu.
• vegetarian friendly • vegan friendly • alcohol • tables • wait staff

🚗 **Take Rt 1 to Rehoboth Beach**. Exit onto Rehoboth Ave/1 Alt E over 1 mile to restaurant just past the boardwalk. Turn right onto 1st St 1 block to Wilmington Ave. Turn right onto Wilmington to restaurant on right.

Rainbow Earth Foods 🛍

220 Rehoboth Ave. ✆ 302-227-3177 ⏱ M-F 9-6, Sun 10-5
🚗 **Take Rt 1 to Rehoboth Beach**. Exit onto Rehoboth Ave/1 Alt E about 1 mile into town. Store is across from fire station (2½ blocks west of ocean).

SEAFORD

Open Cupboard Natural Foods 🛍

202 High St. ✆ 302-629-6147 ⏱ M-F 10-5:30, Sat-Sun 10-5
🚗 **From Rt 20**, go south on N Market St (right from Rt 20E, left from Rt 20W) under ½ mile to High St. Turn left onto High under ¼ mile to store on right between Pearl & Conwell St. **From US 13S**, merge onto Rt 20W and follow directions above. **From US 13N**, turn left onto Middleford Rd (becomes High) about 1½ miles to store on right.

WILMINGTON

Country Health Food Store 🛍

2199 Kirkwood Hwy. ✆ 302-995-6620 ⏱ M, Tues, Sat 9:15-7, W-F 9:15-8, Sun 9:15-4
🚗 **From I-95S**, take exit 5A-B toward Newport onto DE 141N about 2⅔ miles to exit 6 (Kirkwood Hwy). Follow exit 6A toward Kirkwood about ⅔ mile to store (near Elsmere border). **From I-95N**, merge onto I-295N toward NJ Tpke. Merge almost immediately onto 141N about 3¼ miles to exit 6 and follow directions above.

Lucky's Coffee Shop & Restaurant 🍴

4003 Concord Pike ✆ 302-477-0240 ⏱ Daily 6am-10pm
A typical diner/coffee shop with a surprising vegetarian selection including falafel, hummus plate, Asian dumplings, sesame noodles, lasagna and entree salads.
• vegetarian friendly • tables • wait staff

🚗 **From I-95**, take exit 8 (8B from I-95S) toward W Chester onto US 202N/ Concord Pike 2¼ miles to restaurant on right before Silverside Rd.

Magpie Tea Garden 🛍 🍴

1715 Delaware Ave. ✆ 302-654-2911 ⏱ M 9-5, Tues-Sat 9-7
• organic produce • vegetarian friendly • fresh juice • deli • tables • self-service • take-out

🚗 **From I-95S**, take exit 7B toward Hwy 52N/Delaware Ave, merge onto Jackson St and turn right onto Delaware/Pennsylvania Ave ½ mile to N Clayton St. Turn right onto N Clayton 3 blocks to Delaware Ave. Turn left onto Delaware 1 block to store on left after N Dupont St. **From I-95N**, take exit 7 toward Hwy 52N/Delaware Ave, merge onto Adams St, turn left onto Delaware and follow directions above.

DISTRICT OF COLUMBIA

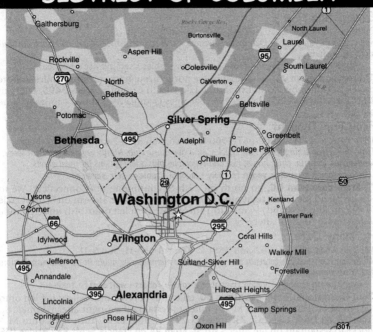

Amma Vegetarian Kitchen 🍴

3291-A M St. N.W. ℗ 202-625-6625 ⏱ Lunch M-Th, 11:30-2:30, F-Sun 11:30-3:30 Dinner M-Th, Sun 5:30-10, F-Sat 5:30-10:30

South Indian vegetarian fare.

· vegetarian · vegan friendly · alcohol · tables · wait staff · take-out

🍽 In Georgetown. **From downtown DC**, take 15th St NW north (slight jog left onto I St) to M St. Turn left onto M 1¼ miles to restaurant on right after Potomac St. **From VA on I-66**, take exit 73 onto US 29N ½ mile to M. Turn right onto M 4 blocks to restaurant on left after 33rd St. **From VA on Francis Scott Key Bridge (US 29)**, turn right onto M and follow directions above.

Amsterdam Falafel Shop 🍴

2425 18th St. N.W. ℗ 202-234-1969 ⏱ M, Sun 11am-12 am, Tues 11am-2:30am, W 11am-3am, Th 11am-3:30am, F-Sat 11am-4am

Top-it-yourself falafel and Dutch-style fries (with mayo or malt vinegar).

· vegetarian · vegan friendly · tables · self-service · take-out

🍽 In Adams Morgan. **From downtown DC**, go north on 17th St continuing onto Connecticut Ave to Columbia Rd NW. Turn right onto Columbia ⅓ mile to Belmont Rd NW. Turn right onto Belmont 1 block to 18th St NW. Turn left onto 18th to restaurant on right.

Asylum 🍴

2471 18th St. N.W. ℗ 202-319-9353 ⏱ M-Th 5pm-2am, F 5pm-3am, Sat 10am-3am, Sun 10am-2am

A "biker bar" offering "veganized" versions of pub food and a vegan weekend brunch. Table service on weekends while on weekdays service style varies.

· vegetarian friendly · vegan friendly · alcohol · counter · tables · self-service · wait staff

🍽 In Adams Morgan. **From downtown DC**, go north on 17th St continuing onto Connecticut Ave to Columbia Rd NW. Turn right onto Columbia ½ mile to 18th St NW. Turn right onto 18th to restaurant on left.

Everlasting Life 🥡 🍴
2928 Georgia Ave. © 202-232-1700 ⏱ M-Sat 9-9, Sun 11-7
Source of Life Juice Bar & Deli inside the store serves southern-style vegan food from the Soul Vegetarian chain.
   • organic produce • vegan • fresh juice • deli • tables • self-service • take-out
🍎 **From downtown DC**, take Georgia Ave north through town about 2 miles to store on left at Columbia Rd in Everlasting Life Health Complex. **From I-495**, take exit 30 (Colesville Rd/US 29) onto 29S (becomes Georgia Ave) about 4 miles to store on right.

Food For Thought 🍴
1811 14th St. N.W. © 202-667-7960 ⏱ M-Th, Sun 8pm-2am, F-Sat 7pm-3am
Tiny smoke-free dining spot in the Black Cat, a live music club. Mostly vegetarian/vegan soups, sandwiches, lasagna, chili, brown rice and vegetables plus a few options for meat-eaters.
   • vegetarian friendly • vegan friendly • alcohol • tables • self-service
🍎 **From downtown DC**, go north on 17th St continuing on Connecticut Ave to Rhode Island Ave. Turn right onto Rhode Island (take the 3rd exit on Scotts Circle to stay on Rhode Island) ½ mile to 14th St NW. Turn left onto 14th under ½ mile to restaurant on right after S St NW.

Harmony Cafe 🍴
3287-½ M St. N.W. © 202-338-3881 ⏱ M-Sat 11:30-11, Sun 5-11
While not exclusively vegetarian every dish on the menu can be made in a vegetarian version including wanton soup.
   • vegetarian friendly • vegan friendly • alcohol • tables • wait staff • take-out
🍎 In Georgetown. **From downtown DC**, take 15th St NW north (slight jog left onto I St) to M St. Turn left onto M 1¼ miles to restaurant on right after Potomac St. **From VA on I-66**, take exit 73 onto US 29N ½ mile to M. Turn right onto M 4 blocks to restaurant on left after 33rd St. **From VA on Francis Scott Key Bridge (US 29)**, turn right onto M and follow directions above.

Indian Delight 🍴
1100 Pennsylvania Ave. N.W. © 202-371-2295 ⏱ Daily 10-7
Indian vegetarian fast-food in the old Post Office Pavilion.
   • vegetarian • vegan friendly • tables • self-service
🍎 **From the National Mall**, go north on 12th St NW to Pennsylvania Ave NW. Turn right onto Pennsylvania 1 block to restaurant on right. **From I-395N**, take the 12th St exit left at fork, continue straight to Constitution Ave, turn right then left onto 12th St and follow directions above. **From New York Ave NE,** go south on 6th St NW about ¾ mile to Pennsylvania. Turn right onto Pennsylvania 3½ blocks to restaurant on left after 10th St NW.

Java Green 🍴
1020 19th St. N.W. © 202-775-8899 ⏱ M-F 8-8:30, Sat 11-6:30
Vegetarian and mostly vegan Korean-American dishes. Vegan brunch on Saturday.
   • vegetarian • vegan friendly • fresh juice • tables • self-service
🍎 **From downtown DC**, take Constitution Ave west to 23rd St NW. Turn right onto 23rd ¾ mile to Washington Circle. Take the third exit onto New Hampshire Ave NW 1 block to L St NW. Turn right onto L 3 blocks to 19th St NW. Turn right onto 19th to restaurant on right.

Juice Joint Cafe 🍴
1025 Vermont Ave. N.W. © 202-347-6783 ⏱ M-F 7:30-4
Vegetarian, fish and poultry.
   • vegetarian friendly • vegan friendly • fresh juice • tables • self-service
🍎 **From downtown DC**, take Constitution Ave east to 15th St NW. Turn left onto 15th ¾ mile and merge onto Vermont Ave NW 1 block to restaurant.

Nirvana

1810 K St. N.W. ✆ 202-223-5043 ⏰ M-F 11:30-3, 5-9, F 11:30-3, 5-10, Sat 12-3, 5-10
Indian vegetarian with lunch buffet featuring a different region of India each day.
· vegetarian · vegan friendly · tables · self-service · wait staff

🚗 **From downtown DC/Constitution Ave**, go north on 17th St NW about ½ mile to I St NW. Turn left onto I 3 blocks to 20th St NW. Turn right onto 20th 1 block to K St NW. Turn right onto K 2 blocks to restaurant on right between 19th & 18th St NW.

Nora

2132 Florida Ave. N.W. ✆ 202-462-5143 ⏰ M-Th 6-10, F-Sat 5:30-10:30
Always a vegetarian entree on the daily menu plus a 4-course vegetarian tasting menu. Reservations required.
· vegetarian friendly · organic focus · alcohol · tables · wait staff

🚗 **From downtown DC**, go northwest on Massachusetts Ave to Florida Ave (third light past Dupont Circle). Turn right onto Florida 1 block to restaurant on right at R St NW. **From Sheridan Circle**, go southeast on Mass Ave to first light and turn left onto Florida 1 block to restaurant.

Pumpernickel's Bagelry & Catering

5504 Connecticut Ave., N.W. ✆ 202-244-9505 ✆ M-Sat 7-8, Sun 8-4
Special vegan take-out breakfast and lunch menus and vegan pizza by the slice.
· vegetarian friendly · vegan friendly · tables · self-service · take-out

🚗 **From I-495**, take exit 33 toward Chevy Chase south on Connecticut Ave/MD 185S (merge right from I-495E, left from I-495W) about 2½ miles to Chevy Chase Circle. Take the fourth exit off Chevy Chase Circle continuing onto Connecticut under ½ mile to restaurant on right after Morrison St NW.

Secrets of Nature's Health Food

3923 S. Capitol St. S.W. ✆ 202-562-0041 ⏰ M-Sat 8-6
· vegetarian · vegan friendly · tables · wait staff

🚗 **From I-295** take exit 2 toward Malcolm X Ave onto S Capitol St SW about 1 mile to restaurant on right. **From I-295N**, take exit 1 onto Laboratory Rd SE and loop around right onto Overlook Ave SW almost ½ mile to Magazine Rd SW. Turn right onto Magazine (across hwy) and continue on Chesapeake St SW ½ mile to S Capitol St SE. Turn left onto S Capitol under ¼ mile to restaurant on left past Atlantic St.

Seneb Co-op

6224 Third St. N.W. ✆ 202-723-5566 ⏰ M-Sat 10-8
· organic produce · vegetarian · vegan friendly · cafe · tables · self-service · take-out
· co-op

🚗 **From I-495W** (Capitol Beltway), take exit 30B toward Silver Spring unto US 20S/Colesville Rd about 1½ miles to Georgia Ave NW. Turn left onto Georgia about 1 mile to Sheridan St NW. Turn left onto Sheridan over ½ mile to 3rd St NW. Turn right onto 3rd to store on right. **From I-495E**, take exit 31B, veer right onto Georgia Ave about 2½ miles to Sheridan and follow directions above.

Soul Vegetarian Cafe

2606 Georgia Ave. N.W. ✆ 202-328-7685 ⏰ M-Sat 11-9, Sun 11-3
Healthy, vegan, southern-style soul food. Homemade soy cheese and "ice-kream."
· vegan · tables · self-service · take-out

🚗 **From downtown DC**, take Georgia Ave north through town about 1½ miles to restaurant on left after Euclid St (across from Howard U). **From I-495**, take exit 30 (Colesville Rd) onto 29S (becomes Georgia Ave) about 5 miles to restaurant on right 1 block past Fairmont St.

Sticky Fingers Bakery

1370 Park Rd. N.W. ✆ 202-299-9700 ⏰ M-Th 7-7, F 7-9, Sat 8-9, Sun 9-6
Vegan baked goods and cafe.
· vegan · bakery · tables · self-service · take-out

🚗 **From downtown DC/Constitution Ave**, go north on 14th St NW about 2⅔ miles to Park Rd. Turn right onto Park to restaurant on right.

Taberna Del Alabardero 🍴

1776 I St., N.W. ✆ 202-429-2200 ⏰ M-F 11:30-2:30, 5:30-10, Sat 2:30-10:30
Upscale Spanish restaurant with separate vegetarian lunch and dinner menus.
• vegetarian friendly • vegan friendly • alcohol • tables • wait staff

🚗 **From downtown DC/Constitution Ave**, go north on 17th St NW about ½ mile to I St NW. Turn left onto I 1 block to 18th. Entrance is on 18th between I & H St.

Teaism 🍴

800 Connecticut Ave. N.W. ✆ 202-835-2233 ⏰ M-F 7:30-5:30
• vegetarian friendly • tables • self-service • take-out

🚗 **From downtown DC/Constitution Ave**, go north on 15th St NW over ½ mile to Eye St/I St NW. Turn left onto Eye 3 blocks to Connecticut Ave NW. Turn left onto Connecticut 1 block and turn right onto H St to restaurant on right between Connecticut & 17th St.

Teaism 🍴

2009 R St. N.W. ✆ 202-667-3827 ⏰ M-Th 8-10, F 8-11, Sat 9-11, Sun 9-10
• vegetarian friendly • tables • self-service

🚗 **From downtown DC/Constitution Ave**, go north on 17th St NW about ¾ mile continuing on Connecticut Ave under ½ mile to Dupont Circle. Continue to follow Connecticut about 3 blocks to R St NW. Veer right onto 20th St NW and left onto R to restaurant on right.

Teaism 🍴

400 8th St. N.W. ✆ 202-638-6010 ⏰ M-F 7:30-10, Sat-Sun 9:30-9
• vegetarian friendly • alcohol • tables • self-service

🚗 **From I-395S**, take exit toward 6th St SW/L'Enfant Promenade left onto 3rd St NW 2 blocks to Indiana Ave/D St NW. Turn right onto D under ½ mile to restaurant on left at 8th St NW. **From I-395N**, take D St NW exit left onto D ½ mile to restaurant.

Vegetate 🍴

1414 9th St. N.W. ✆ 202-232-4585 ⏰ Tues-Th 6-10, F-Sat 6-11, Sun 5-9
Innovative menu offering "bites," "small plates" and "large plates."
• vegetarian • vegan friendly • alcohol • tables • wait staff

🚗 **From downtown DC (Independence Ave)**, go north on 7th St SW (through the National Mall) to Constitution Ave. Turn right onto Constitution 1 block to 6th St NW. Turn left onto 6th under 1 mile to NY Ave NW. Turn right onto NY 2 blocks to 9th St NW. Turn right onto 9th 4½ blocks (past Washington Convention Ctr) to restaurant on left between O & P St NW.

Washington Deli 🍴

1990 K St. N.W. ✆ 202-331-3344 ⏰ M-F 6-5, Sat 10-3
Special vegan take-out breakfast and lunch menus. Seating in the mall.
• vegetarian friendly • vegan friendly • tables • self-service • take-out

🚗 **From downtown DC/Constitution Ave**, go north on 14th St almost 1½ miles to K St NW. Turn left onto K about ¾ mile to restaurant on left. Entrance is on 20th St.

Wellness Cafe 🍴

325 Pennsylvania Ave. ✆ 202-543-2266 ⏰ M-F 9-7, Sat 11-7
Hot food is vegan but sandwiches include meat and fish. A few tables but primarily take-out.
• vegetarian friendly • vegan friendly • organic focus • fresh juice • tables • self-service • take-out

🚗 **From downtown DC/Constitution Ave**, go south on 7th St through the National Mall to Independence Ave SW. Turn right onto Independence 1 mile and merge onto Pennsylvania Ave SE to restaurant after 3rd St SE across from Library of Congress.

Whole Foods Market

1440 P St. N.W. © 202-332-4300 ⊙ Daily 8-10
· organic produce · vegetarian friendly · salad bar · cafe · self-service · take-out

From White House, take 15th St north (becomes VT Ave) under ¾ mile to 14th St intersection. Take 14th 3 blocks to P St. Turn left onto P to store on left (a few blocks west of Logan Circle). **From I-395**, take 14th St bridge and follow 14th 1¼ miles to P. Turn left onto P to store.

Whole Foods Market

4530 40th St. N.W. (Tenley Circle) © 202-237-5800 ⊙ M-Sat 8-10, Sun 8-9
· organic produce · vegetarian friendly · salad bar · cafe · self-service · take-out

From I-495 (Capitol Beltway), take exit 39 (MD 190E) toward Washington onto River Rd NW about 4¾ miles to Chesapeake St. Turn left onto Chesapeake 2 blocks to Wisconsin Ave. Turn right onto Wisconsin 1 block to Brandywine St. Turn left onto Brandywine 1 block to 40th St. Turn right onto 40th to store. **From downtown DC**, go NW on Wisconsin (about 3 miles starting at M St in Georgetown) to Brandywine. Turn right onto Brandywine and right onto 40th to store.

Whole Foods Market

2323 Wisconsin Ave. N.W. © 202-333-5393 ⊙ Daily 8-10
· organic produce · vegetarian friendly · salad bar · cafe · self-service · take-out

From I-495 (Capitol Beltway), take exit 39 (MD-190E) toward Washington onto River Rd NW about 5 miles to Wisconsin Ave NW. Turn right onto Wisconsin about 2 miles to store on left after Calvert St NW (2 blocks south of National Cathedral).

Yes! Organic Market

1825 Columbia Rd. N.W. © 202-462-5150 ⊙ M-Sat 8-9, Sun 9-8
· organic produce · vegetarian friendly · fresh juice · deli · take-out

From I-495 (Capitol Beltway), take exit 33 south on Connecticut Ave about 6 miles to Calvert St. Turn left onto Calvert to Columbia Rd. Turn right onto Columbia to store on right. **From downtown DC**, take Connecticut north 1 mile to fork at Columbia Rd. Veer right onto Columbia almost ½ mile to store on left.

Yes! Organic Market

3425 Connecticut Ave. N.W. © 202-363-1559 ⊙ M-Sat 8-9, Sun 8-8
· organic produce · vegetarian friendly · fresh juice · deli · take-out

From I-495 (Capitol Beltway), take exit 33 south on Connecticut Ave about 5 miles to store on left. **From downtown DC**, go north on Connecticut Ave almost 2½ miles to store on right.

Yes! Organic Market

3809 12th St. N.E. © 202-832-7715 ⊙ M-Sat 8-9, Sun 8-8
· organic produce

From MD 295, exit onto 50W 1 mile to S Dakota Ave. Turn right onto S Dakota NE 2¼ miles to Michigan Ave NE. Turn left onto Michigan about ½ mile to Quincy St NE. Turn left onto Quincy 1 block and right onto 12th St to store on left. **From I-395S**, turn right onto NY Ave NW/US 50/US 1 about ½ mile to NE Capitol St. Turn left onto NE Capitol 1⅓ miles to Michigan Ave NE. Turn right onto Michigan 1¼ miles to Perry St NE. Turn right onto Perry 1 block to NE 12th. Turn left onto 12th 1 block to store on right at Quincy.

Yes! Organic Market

658 Pennsylvania Ave. S.E. © 202-546-9850 ⊙ M-Sat 8-9, Sun 8-7
· organic produce · vegetarian friendly · deli · take-out

From I-295N, continue on DC 295N to exit 5B. Merge onto Pennsylvania Ave over 1 mile to store on right. **From 295S**, take exit 5 onto Pennsylvania Ave SE to Michigan Ave SE, U-turn back onto Pennsylvania and follow directions above.

FLORIDA

1.	Altamonte Springs	45.	Miami
2.	Atlantic Beach	46.	Miami Beach
3.	Aventura	47.	Miramar
4.	Belleaire Bluffs	48.	Mount Dora
5.	Big Pine Key	49.	Naples
6.	Blue Mountain Beach	50.	New Smyrna Beach
7.	Boca Raton	51.	North Miami
8.	Bonita Springs	52.	North Miami Beach
9.	Boynton Beach	53.	Ocala
10.	Bradenton	54.	Opa Locka
11.	Brandon	55.	Orange City
12.	Brooksville	56.	Orange Park
13.	Cape Canaveral	57.	Orlando
14.	Cape Coral	58.	Ormond Beach
15.	Clearwater	59.	Osprey
16.	Cocoa	60.	Oviedo
17.	Cocoa Beach	61.	Palm Beach Gardens
18.	Coconut Grove	62.	Palm Coast
19.	Coral Gables	63.	Palm Harbor
20.	Coral Springs	64.	Pembroke Pines
21.	Crystal River	65.	Pensacola
22.	Daytona Beach	66.	Pinecrest
23.	Deerfield Beach	67.	Plant City
24.	Delray Beach	68.	Plantation
25.	Dover	69.	Port Charlotte
26.	Englewood	70.	Port Orange
27.	Fernandina Beach	71.	Port Saint Lucie
28.	Fort Lauderdale	72.	Rockledge
29.	Fort Myers	73.	Sarasota
30.	Fort Pierce	74.	South Daytona
31.	Gainesville	75.	Spring Hill
32.	Holiday	76.	St. Augustine
33.	Hollywood	77.	St. Cloud
34.	Inverness	78.	St. Petersburg
35.	Jacksonville	79.	Stuart
36.	Key West	80.	Sunrise
37.	Kissimmee	81.	Tallahassee
38.	Lake Helen	82.	Tampa
39.	Lake Worth	83.	Temple Terrace
40.	Lakeland	84.	Venice
41.	Lantana	85.	West Palm Beach
42.	Largo	86.	Winter Haven
43.	Lauderhill	87.	Winter Park
44.	Melbourne	88.	Yulee

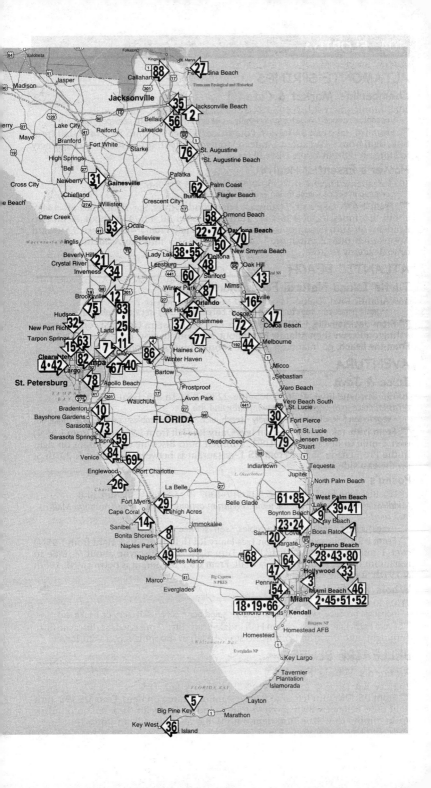

ALTAMONTE SPRINGS

Chamberlin's Market & Cafe 🛍 🍴 &

1086 Montgomery Rd. © 407-774-8866 ⏱ M-Sat 9-8:30, Sun 11-5:30
· organic produce · vegetarian friendly · bakery · tables · self-service · take-out

🛍 **From I-4**, take exit 94 toward Longwood/Winter Spr onto SR 434W (left from I-4E, right from I-4W) about 1 mile to Montgomery Rd. Turn left onto Montgomery to store on right in Winn-Dixie Plaza.

Hoover's Essential Health 🛍

1035 Academy Drive © 407-869-0000 ⏱ M-Th 8-8, F 8-6:30, Sun 8-7
· organic produce · vegetarian friendly · deli · take-out

🛍 **From I-4W**, take exit 94 toward Longwood/Winter Spr right onto SR 434W about 3¼ miles to SR 436/438. Turn right onto SR 436/438 about ¾ mile to Academy St. Turn left onto Academy to store on left. **From I-4E**, take exit 92 toward Apopka left onto E Altamonte Dr/SR 436/438 2¾ miles to Academy. Turn left onto Academy to store.

ATLANTIC BEACH

Turtle Island Natural Foods Market 🛍 🍴

363 Atlantic Blvd. © 904-247-6400 ⏱ M-Sat 10-8, Sun 11-2
· organic produce · vegetarian friendly · cafe · deli · self-service · take-out

🛍 **From Jacksonville, I-10E or I-95**, take exit 353B east on Union St continuing on Arlington Expwy then Atlantic Blvd about 16½ mile to store on left after 1A/3rd St. **From the beach**, go inland on Atlantic about 4 blocks to store on right.

AVENTURA

Juice & Java 🍴

20335 Biscayne Blvd. #L26 © 305-466-2233 ⏱ M-Th 8-9, F-Sat 8-8
A casual place with vegetarian, vegan, poulty and fish.
· vegetarian friendly · vegan friendly · fresh juice · counter · tables · self-service · take-out

🛍 **From I-95**, take exit 16 east on Ives Dairy Rd (left from I-95S, right from I-95N) over 1 mile to Biscayne Blvd/US 1. Turn left onto Biscayne to restaurant on right in the Promenade Shops. **From US 1**, restaurant is between NE 203rd & 207th St on the east side.

Pasha's 🍴

19501 Biscayne Blvd., #1433 © 305-917-4007 ⏱ M-Sat 9-9:30, Sun 10-8
Middleastern with more than the usual vegetarian options. Located in the Aventura Mall food court.
· vegetarian friendly · alcohol · tables · self-service

🛍 **From I-95**, take exit 16 east on Ives Dairy Rd (left from I-95S, right from I-95N) over 1 mile to Biscayne Blvd/US 1. Turn right onto Biscayne about ½ mile to restaurant on left in the Aventura Mall. **From US 1**, restaurant is between NE 195th & 197th St on the east side.

Whole Foods Market 🛍 🍴 &

21105 Biscayne Blvd. ⏱ Daily 8-10
· organic produce · vegetarian friendly · salad bar · cafe · self-service · take-out

🛍 **From I-95**, take exit 18 east on Hallandale Beach Blvd 2 miles to US1/Biscayne Blvd. Turn right onto Biscayne 1½ miles to store on left in shopping center with Target.

BELLEAIRE BLUFFS

Richard's Whole Foods 🛍

2927 W. Bay Drive © 727-584-9199 ⏱ M-Sat 9-6, Sun 11-5

🛍 **From US 19N**, turn left onto Bay Dr 2 miles to store on right. **From US 19S**, turn right onto Belleview Blvd about ¼ mile to Indian Rocks Rd. Turn left onto Indian Rocks 2 miles to W Bay. Turn right onto W Bay about ¼ mile to store.

BIG PINE KEY

Good Food Conspiracy 🛍 🍴

U.S. Hwy. 1, MM 30.2 ℂ 305-872-3945 🕐 M-Sat 9:30-7, Sun 11-5
• organic produce • vegetarian friendly • fresh juice • cafe • tables • self-service • take-out
🍎 On US 1 traveling through the FL keys at mile marker 30.2

BLUE MOUNTAIN BEACH

For the Health of It 🛍

2219 Scenic Hwy. 30 A ℂ 850-267-0558 🕐 M-Sat 9:30-5:30
• organic produce • fresh juice
🍎 Blue Mountain Beach is on the Emerald Coast Pkwy (SR 30) between Panama City
and Destin. Store is on this road about 2 miles west of US 331 on the south side.

BOCA RATON

Eilat Cafe 🍴   ♿

6853 S.W. 18th St. ℂ 561-368-6880 🕐 M-Th, Sun 12-9
*The kosher menu is a mix of Middleastern vegetarian, pasta, pizza and fish. Dine inside or
on the outdoor lakefront boardwalk.*
• vegetarian friendly • kosher • alcohol • tables • wait staff
🚗 From I-95, take exit 44 west on Palmetto Park Rd 2 miles to Powerline Rd. Turn
left onto Powerline 1 mile to S.W. 18th St (3rd light). Turn left onto 18th to first
left into Wharfside at Boca Pointe. Turn right in plaza to restaurant on left.

Organically Fresh 🛍 🍴

21338 St. Andrews Blvd. ℂ 561-362-0770 🕐 M-F 8:30-6 Sat 10-4
• vegetarian friendly • organic focus • deli • tables • self-service • take-out
🚗 From I-95, take exit 45 west on Glades Rd 1 mile to St Andrews. Turn left onto
St Andrews ½ mile to store in Town Square strip mall.

Pine Garden 🍴

1668 N. Federal Hwy. ℂ 561-395-7534 🕐 M-Sat 11:30-10, Sun 3-10
*This otherwise typical Chinese restaurant has an extensive, separate vegetarian menu. Ask if
it doesn't come automatically.*
• vegetarian friendly • vegan friendly • alcohol • tables • wait staff • take-out
🚗 From I-95, take exit 45 east on Glades Rd 2½ miles to US 1. Turn left onto US
1/N Federal Hwy under ½ mile to restaurant on right.

Whole Foods Market 🛍 🍴   ♿

1400 Glades Rd. ℂ 561-447-0000 🕐 Daily 8-10
• organic produce • vegetarian friendly • salad bar • cafe • self-service • take-out
🚗 From I-95, take exit 45 east on Glades Rd about ½ mile to store on right in
University Commons Shopping Ctr.

BONITA SPRINGS

For Goodness Sake 🛍 🍴

9118 Bonita Beach Rd. ℂ 239-992-5838 🕐 M-F 9:30-6:30, Sat 10-6, Sun 12-4 Cafe
M-Sat 10-4
• organic produce • vegetarian friendly • fresh juice • cafe • tables • self-service • take-out
🚗 From I-75, take exit 116 toward Bonita Springs/Gulf Beaches west on Bonita
Beach Rd 3 miles to store on right in Sunshine Plaza.

BOYNTON BEACH

Nutrition Cottage 🛍

1815 S. Federal Hwy. ℂ 561-734-4626 🕐 M-Sat 10-5:30
🚗 From I-95, take exit 56 east on Woolbright Rd (left from I-95S, right from
I-95N) about 1 mile to US 1/S Federal Hwy. Turn right onto US 1 to store on right
in Sunshine Square.

BRADENTON

Good Earth Natural Foods 🛍
6717 Manatee Ave. W. ✆ 941-795-0478 ① M-F 9-7, Sat 9-5:30
• organic produce
🍎 **From I-75 exit 220 or US 41**, take SR 64W (becomes Manatee Ave) to store on left in Northwest Promenade (10 miles from I-75, 1½ miles past 41).

Good Earth Natural Foods 🛍
3110 53rd Ave. E. ✆ 941-756-4372 ① M-F 9-7, Sat 9-5:30
• organic produce*
🍎 **From I-75**, take exit 217 onto SR 70W about 4 miles to store on left in Cedar Plaza. **From US 41 or 301**, take 70E to store on right after US 301.

Good Earth Natural Foods 🛍
5153 14th St. W. ✆ 941-753-8902 ① M-F 9-7, Sat 9-5:30
• organic produce
🍎 On US 41 (14th St) north of SR 70 on east side in Plaza South.

Richard's Whole Foods 🛍
2601-B Manatee Ave. ✆ 41-749-0892 ① M-Sat 9-7, Sun 11-5
🍎 **From I-75 exit 220, US 41 or US 301**, take FL 64W (Manatee Ave) to store (about 1½ miles west of 301).

BRANDON

Chuck's Natural Food Marketplace & Purple Plate Cafe 🛍 🍴
114 N. Kings Ave. ✆ 813-657-2555 ① M-F 9-8, Sat 9-6, Sun 12-6 Cafe M-F 9-6, Sat-Sun 9-3
• organic produce • vegetarian friendly • fresh juice • deli • tables • self-service • take-out
🍎 **From I-75**, take exit 257 toward Brandon onto FL 60E about 2¾ miles to N Kings Ave. Turn left onto N Kings to store.

BROOKSVILLE

Brooksville Natural Foods 🛍
1254 Broad St. S. ✆ 352-796-9798 ① M-F 9-7, Sat 9-6, Sun 12-4
• organic produce
🍎 **From I-75**, take exit 301 toward Brooksville west on SR 50/Cortez Blvd (right from I-75S, left from I-75N) 10½ miles to Broad St. Turn right onto Broad to store on left. **From Rt 589**, take Cortez/SR 50 inland (merge right from Rt 589N, left from Rt 589S) 5½ miles to Broad. Turn left onto Broad to store.

CAPE CANAVERAL

Sunseed Food Co-op Inc. 🛍   ♿
6615 N. Atlantic Ave., Ste. B ✆ 321-784-0930 ① M-W, Sat 10-6, Th-F 10-7
• organic produce
🍎 **From I-95**, take exit 205 for Cape Canaveral east on SR 528E (Beeline Expressway) about 12½ miles (across intercoastal). When road becomes A1A continue south about 2½ miles (becomes N Atlantic Ave) to store on west side. **From Orlando**, take 528 east and follow directions above.

CAPE CORAL

Back to Nature 🛍
1217 SE 47th Terrace ✆ 239-549-7667 ① M-F 9-6, Sat 9-5
🍎 **From I-75**, take exit 131 toward Cape Coral west on Daniels Pkwy (becomes Cypress Lake Dr) about 6 miles to Summerlin Rd. Turn right onto Summerlin ¾ mile to College Pkwy. Turn left onto College 1 mile (over bridge) to Vincennes Blvd. Turn right onto Vincennes and right onto 47th Terrace to store on right in strip mall.

Mother Earth Natural Foods

1631 Del Prado Blvd. ✆ 239-574-6333 ⏰ M, W, F 9-6, Tues, Th 9-6:30, Sat 9-5:30

🛒 **From I-75**, take exit 136 toward Ft Myers west on Colonial Blvd (becomes Veteran's Memorial Pkwy/884W) about 9 miles (across Mid-Point Bridge). Take first exit off bridge right onto Del Prado Blvd under 1 mile to store on right in Publix shopping ctr (past Coralwood Mall). **From US Hwy 41**, take Colonial Blvd west and follow directions above.

CLEARWATER

Nature's Food Patch Natural Market & Cafe ♿

1225 Cleveland St. ✆ 727-443-6703 ⏰ M-Sat 9-9, Sun 11-8 Cafe M-Sat 9-8, Sun 11-7
· organic produce · vegetarian friendly · fresh juice · salad bar · cafe · deli · bakery · counter · tables · self-service · take-out

🛒 **From I-275 exit 39 or I-4**, take Rt 60W (Gulf-to-Bay Blvd) about 14 miles (across water) to light at Highland Ave. Take right fork toward Downtown/Beaches and continue on 60W (becomes Cleveland St) under 1 mile to store on left at Missouri Ave in Cleveland Shopping Plaza.

COCOA

Gardner's Cottage ♿

902 Florida Ave. ✆ 321-631-2030 ⏰ M-F 11-2:30
Eat at one of the vintage tables in the 1925 cottage or outside in the herb and flower garden.
· vegetarian · vegan friendly · fresh juice · cafe · counter · tables · wait staff · take-out

🛒 **From I-95**, take exit 201 toward Cocoa Beach east on US 520 almost 4 miles to light at US 1. Turn right onto US 1 to first light (Rosa L Jones Dr). Turn left onto Rosa Jones to next light and turn right onto Florida Ave to store on left in yellow cottage just before corner.

COCOA BEACH

The New Habit

3 N. Atlantic Ave. ✆ 321-784-6646 ⏰ Daily 11-5
A variety of vegetarian and healthier choices along with conventional chips and soda.
· vegetarian friendly · tables · self-service · take-out

🛒 **From I-95**, take exit 201 toward Cocoa Beach east on SR 520 almost 11½ miles (over intercoastal) to A1A (aka Atlantic Ave). Turn right onto Atlantic 2¾ miles to restaurant on NE corner at Minuteman Cswy (1 block from Ocean).

COCONUT GROVE

Coconut Grove Organic Farmer's Market

3300 Grand Ave. ✆ 305-238-7747 ⏰ Sat 10:30-7
Come for lunch, fresh produce or to stock up on prepared raw and vegan foods.
· organic produce · vegan · tables · self-service · take-out

🛒 **From US 1S**, turn left onto SW 32nd Ave over ½ mile to Grand Ave. Turn right onto Grand 1 block to market on right. **From US 1N**, turn right onto Grand under 1 mile to market on left at Margaret St.

CORAL GABLES

Whole Foods Market

6701 Red Rd. ✆ 305-421-9421 ⏰ Daily 8-10
· organic produce · vegetarian friendly · salad bar · cafe · self-service · take-out

🛒 **From US 1** (S Dixie Hwy), go south on SW 57th Ave/Red Rd (left from US 1S, right from US 1N) to store on left.

CORAL SPRINGS

Whole Foods Market 🛍 🍴

810 University Drive © 954-753-8000 ⏱ Daily 8-10
• organic produce • vegetarian friendly • salad bar • cafe • self-service • take-out

🍎 **From I-95**, take exit 36 west on Atlantic Blvd/Rt 814W about 7⅔ miles to University Dr. Turn right onto University (Rt 817N) to first light and turn left into Atlantic Crossings Shopping Ctr to store. **From FL Tpke**, take Atlantic Blvd west about 3 miles to University and follow directions above.

CRYSTAL RIVER

Huffman's Heritage Whole Foods, Inc. 🛍

430 S.E. Kings Bay Drive © 352-795-2233 ⏱ M-F 9-6, Sat 9-4
• organic produce • vegetarian friendly • fresh juice • salad bar • deli • self-service • take-out

🍎 **From Rt 44W**, turn left onto US 19S under ½ mile to Kings Bay Dr. Turn right onto Kings Bay to store on left at Cutler Spur Blvd.

DAYTONA BEACH

Dancing Avocado Kitchen 🍴

110 S. Beach St. © 386-947-2022 ⏱ M-Sat 8-4
Nachos, sandwiches, quesadillas, burritos and salads with attention to unrefined ingredients. Outdoor deck overlooking the intercoastal.
• vegetarian friendly • fresh juice • alcohol • tables • wait staff • take-out

🍎 **From I-95**, take exit 261A toward Daytona Beach east on W International Speedway/US 92E about 5⅓ miles to Beach St (before bridge across intercoastal). Turn right onto Beach to restaurant on right.

Nature's Table 🍴

1700 W. International Speedway Blvd. © 386-252-2424 ⏱ M-Sat 10-8:30, Sun 11-6
Healthier fast food in mall food court.
• vegetarian friendly • tables • self-service • take-out

🍎 **From I-95**, take exit 261A toward Daytona Beach east on W International Speedway/US 92E about 2½ miles to Volusia Mall on left. Enter mall and make first right to food court on left (before Sears Auto Ctr).

DEERFIELD BEACH

Pizza Fusion 🍴

196 N. Federal Hwy. © 954-427-5353 ⏱ Daily 11-10
Organic crust pizza with vegetarian and meat toppings. Soy cheese and 7-grain and gluten-free crusts available. Also sandwiches and organic salads.
• vegetarian friendly • organic focus • alcohol • tables • self-service • take-out

🍎 **From I-95**, take exit 42 (42A from I-95N) east on W Hillsboro Blvd (left from I-95S, right from I-95N) about 1½ miles to US 1. Turn left onto US 1 block to restaurant on right.

DELRAY BEACH

Kebob Mediterranean Grill 🍴

676 S. Federal Hwy. © 561-276-5582 ⏱ M-Th, Sun 11-10, F-Sat 11-11
Middleastern cuisine with more than the usual vegetarian options.
• vegetarian friendly • alcohol • tables • wait staff

🍎 **From I-95**, take exit 51 east on Linton Blvd about ¾ mile to Federal Hwy. Turn north and enter Plaza at Delray on west side (sign says Regal 18) to restaurant left of movie theater.

Nutrition Cottage 🛍 🍴

407 E. Atlantic Ave. © 561-272-8571 ⏱ M-Th 9-6, F-Sat 9-10, Sun 11-5
• organic producem • vegetarian friendly, fresh juice, counter, self-service • take-out

🍎 **From I-95**, take exit 52 east on Atlantic Ave about 1½ miles to store on north side after 4th Ave.

DOVER

Souther's Natural Food Co-op 🛍

14750 Dr. M L King Jr. Blvd. ℰ 813-659-0349 ⏰ M-F 9-6, Sun 1-6
• organic produce

🛍 **From I-4**, take exit 14 south on Branch Forbes Rd (right from I-4E, left from I-4W) 1½ miles to Dr MLK Jr Blvd. Turn left onto MLK 1½ miles to store on right past Bethlehem Rd.

ENGLEWOOD

Richard's Whole Foods 🛍

471 S. Indiana Ave. ℰ 941-473-0278 ⏰ M-Sat 9-6, Sun 11-5

🛍 **From US 41/Tamiami Trail,** go south on Englewood Rd 7 miles (becomes Indiana Ave) or on River Rd and onto Indiana about 8¼ miles to store on left.

FERNANDINA BEACH

Nassau Health Foods 🛍

833 T.J. Courson Rd. ℰ 904-277-3158 ⏰ M-F 9-7, Sat 9-6
• organic produce

🛍 **From I-95S**, take exit 280 toward Hilliard left onto US 17 7 miles to A1A/Buccaneer Trail. Turn left onto A1A (becomes S 8th St) 9½ miles to TJ Courson Rd. Turn right onto TJ Courson to store on left. **From I-95N**, take exit 373 toward Fernanda Beach right onto A1A/Buccaneer Trail 11½ miles to TJ Courson and follow directions above.

FORT LAUDERDALE

Cafe Emunah 🍽

3558 N. Ocean Blvd. ℰ 954-561-6411 ⏰ M-Th, Sun 11-10 , Sat 1 hour after sundown-1 am
A "kabbalistic lifestyle lounge and tea bar." Fish predominates but vegetarians and vegans are well accommodated. Beer and wine on the house.
• vegetarian friendly • vegan friendly • alcohol • kosher • tables • wait staff

🍽 **From I-95**, take exit 31 (31A from I-95N) east on W Oakland Park Blvd (turn left then bear right onto NW Oakland Park St, then left onto W Oakland Park Blvd from I-95S, merge right from I-95N) 3 miles to N Ocean Blvd/A1A. Turn left onto N Ocean ⅓ mile to restaurant on right after NE 34th St.

Pizza Fusion 🍽

1013 N. Federal Hwy. ℰ 954-358-5353 ⏰ M-Th, Sun 11-10, Sat 11-11
See Deerfield Beach location for description.
• vegetarian friendly • organic focus • alcohol • tables • self-service • take-out

🍽 **From I-95,** take exit 29 (29A from I-95N) east on Sunrise Blvd (left from I-95S, right from I-95N) about 2 miles to restaurant on left at NE 10th St.

Sublime 🍽   ♿

1431 N. Federal Hwy. ℰ 954-539-9000 ⏰ Tues-Sun 5:30-10
Upscale restaurant serving vegan wholefoods. Profits go to organizations that support animal welfare and vegan lifestyles.
• vegan, organic focus, fresh juice, alcohol, tables, wait staff

🍽 **From I-95S,** take exit 31 left onto Oakland Park Blvd about 2½ miles to US 1/ North Federal Hwy. Turn right onto Federal 1½ miles to restaurant on right. **From I-95N**, take exit 29A right onto Sunrise Blvd almost 3 miles to Federal. Turn left onto Federal about ½ mile to restaurant on left.   ♿

Whole Foods Market 🛍 🍽

2000 N. Federal Hwy. ℰ 954-565-5655 ⏰ Daily 8-10
• organic produce • vegetarian friendly • salad bar • cafe • self-service • take-out

🛍 **From I-95S,** take exit 31 left onto Oakland Park Blvd about 2½ miles to US 1/ North Federal Hwy. Turn right onto Federal 1 mile to store on left. **From I-95N,** take exit 29A right onto Sunrise Blvd almost 3 miles to Federal. Turn left onto Federal 1 mile to store on right.

FORT MYERS

Ada's Natural Food Market 🛍️ 🍴

4650 S. Cleveland Ave. ℂ 239-939-9600 ⏰ M-Sat 8-8, Sun 8-6
• organic produce • vegetarian friendly • deli • tables • self-service • take-out

🍎 **From I-75**, take exit 136 toward Ft Myers west on Hwy 884/Colonial Blvd 4½ miles to Cleveland Ave. Turn left onto Cleveland to store on right in Burlington Coat Plaza.

Mother Earth Natural Foods 🛍️

4600 Summerlin Rd. ℂ 239-939-0990 ⏰ M, W, F 9-6, Tues, Th 9-6:30, Sat 9-5:30
• organic produce

🍎 **From I-75**, take 136 toward Ft Myers west on Hwy 884/Colonial Blvd 5¼ miles to Summerlin Rd. Turn left onto Summerlin to store on right in Colonial Crossing Shopping Ctr.

Mother Earth Natural Foods 🛍️   ♿

15271-7 McGregor Blvd. ℂ 239-489-3377 ⏰ M, W, F 9-6, Tues, Th 9-6:30, Sat 9-5:30
• organic produce

🍎 **From I-75**, take exit 131 west on Daniels Pkwy about 7½ miles (past US 41 becomes Cypress Lake Dr) to McGregor Blvd. Turn left onto McGregor about 4 miles to store on left in McGregor Point.

Mother Earth Natural Foods 🛍️

6520 S. Tamiami Trail ℂ 239-454-8009 ⏰ M, W, F 9-6, Tues, Th 9-6:30, Sat 9-5:30
• organic produce

🍎 **From I-75**, take exit 131 west on Daniels Pkwy almost 5 miles to US 41 (Tamiami Trail). Turn left onto Tamiami about 1½ miles to Island Park Rd. Turn right onto Island Park and left to store in Island Park Shopping Ctr.

FORT PIERCE

Nutrition World 🛍️

2501 S. Federal Hwy. ℂ 772-464-3598 ⏰ M-F 9-7, Sat 9-6, Sun 11-6
• fresh juice

🍎 **From I-95**, take exit 129 toward Fort Pierce east on Okeechobee Rd (left from I-95S, merge right from I-95N) about 1½ miles to Virginia St. Turn right onto Virginia 2½ miles to Federal Hwy/US 1. Turn right onto US 1 to store on right in Sabal Palm Shopping Ctr.

GAINESVILLE

Book Lover's Cafe 🍴   ♿

505 N.W. 13th St. ℂ 352-374-4241 ⏰ Daily 10-9
A rotating menu of various international cuisines. Located in Books, Inc.
• vegetarian • vegan friendly • tables • wait staff

🍎 **From I-75**, take exit 384 toward Gainesville onto FL 24E (Archer Rd) about 3¼ miles to 13th St (FL 25N/US 441N). Turn left onto 13th about 1 mile to restaurant on right at 5th Ave.

Mother Earth Market East 🛍️

521 N.W. 13th St. ℂ 352-378-5224 ⏰ M-Sat 9-9 Sun 11-7
• organic produce

🍎 **From I-75**, take exit 384 toward Gainesville onto FL 24E (Archer Rd) about 3¼ miles to 13th St (FL 25N/US 441N). Turn left onto 13th about 1 mile to store on right.

Mother Earth Market West 🛍️

1237 N.W. 76th Blvd. ℂ 352-331-5224 ⏰ M-Sat 8-8, Sun 10-6
• organic produce

🍎 **From I-75**, take exit 387 toward Newberry onto SR 26W/Newberry Rd about ¼ mile to 76th Blvd. Turn right onto 76th about ¼ mile to end. Store is on right in strip mall.

The Jones Eastside Eatery ¶

401 N.E. 23 Ave. © 352-373-6777 ⊕ Daily 8-3
A popular local breakfast/lunch place with options for vegetarians, vegans and the bacon-and-grits crowd.
  • vegetarian friendly • alcohol • tables • wait staff

From I-75, take exit 387 toward Newberry east on NW 8th Ave/Newberry Rd continuing on W University Ave 5 miles total to NW 13th St. Turn left onto NW 13th 1½ miles to NW 23rd Ave. Turn right onto NW 23rd 1 mile to store on right after Main St.

Top Restaurant ¶

30 N. Main St. © 352-337-1188 ⊕ Tues-Sat 5pm-2am, Sun 11:30am-2:30pm
About half the menu is vegetarian with interesting tempeh and tofu creations.
  • vegetarian friendly • alcohol • tables • wait staff

From I-75, take exit 384 toward Gainesville onto FL 24E (Archer Rd) about 3¼ miles to 13th St (FL 25N/US 441N). Turn left onto 13th about ¾ mile to University Dr. Turn right onto University under 1 mile to Main St. Turn left onto Main 1 block to restaurant on left.

HOLIDAY

Judy's Natural Foods ¶

1922 U.S. 19 N. © 727-943-0020 ⊕ M-F 9-6, Sat 9-5, Sun 10-4 Cafe M-F 11-3
  • organic produce • vegetarian friendly • fresh juice • tables • wait staff • take-out

From US 19, store is at intersection with Mile Stretch Rd.

HOLLYWOOD

Gourmet Greenhouse Restaurant ¶

5809 Hollywood Blvd. © 954-989-6400 ⊕ Tues-Sat 11-3
Part of the Center for Human Development, a non-denominational spiritual and healing center. Many raw items.
  • vegan • tables • wait staff

From FL Tpke, take exit 49 and merge onto Hollywood Blvd about 1¼ miles to restaurant on left at N 58th St (in Ctr for Human Development).

Sara's Kosher Vegetarian Restaurant ¶

3944 46th Ave. © 954-986-1770 ⊕ M-Th, Sun 9:30-10, F 9-3, Sat opens 1 hour after sundown-1am
Kosher vegetarian and fish.
  • vegetarian • tables • wait staff

From FL Tpke S, take exit 53 left onto Orange Dr ½ mile to S State Rd 7. Turn right onto SR 7 almost 1½ miles to Stirling Rd. Turn left onto Stirling 1 mile to N 46th Ave. Turn right onto N 46th 1 block to restaurant on right. From FL Tpke N, take exit 53 right onto Griffin Rd ½ mile to S State Rd 7. Turn right onto SR 7 1 mile to Stirling and follow directions above.

INVERNESS

Inverness Natural Foods ¶

1856 Hwy. 44 W. © 352-726-4483 ⊕ M-F 9-6, Sat 9-4:30
Small produce selection.

Store is on Rt 44 1⅓ miles west of Rt 45 intersection on south side after tracks.

Rutabaga's Etc. ¶

299 S. Croft Ave. © 352-344-0096 ⊕ M-F, Sat 9-5
  • organic produce • vegan • fresh juice • deli • tables • self-service • take-out

From Hwy 44, go north on Croft Ave (left from 44E, right from 44W) under ¼ mile to store.

JACKSONVILLE

Good Earth Market 🛍

10950 San Jose Blvd. ✆ 904-260-9547 ⏰ M-Sat 9-7, Sun 12-5

🚗 **From I-295**, take exit 5B onto San Jose Blvd/FL 13S 1 block to store (across from Wal-Mart).

Grass Roots 🛍

2007 Park St. ✆ 904-384-4474 ⏰ M-Sat 9-8, Sun 12-5
  • organic produce • fresh juice

🚗 **From I-95S**, take Forest St exit right at fork and left onto Forest ⅓ mile to first left (Park St.) Turn left onto Park ¾ mile to Margaret St. Turn right onto Margaret and left back onto Park to store on right after Margaret. **From I-95N**, take exit 351A left onto Park 3 blocks to Margaret and follow directions above. **From I-10E**, take exit 352 left onto Stockton St 5 blocks to College St. Turn left onto College 4 blocks to Margaret. Turn right onto Margaret 3 blocks to Park. Turn right onto park to store on right.

Native Sun Natural Foods Market 🛍 🍴

11030 Baymeadows Rd. ✆ 904-260-2791 ⏰ M-Sat 8-8
An all-organic supermarket. Hot food from 11 to 7.
  • organic produce • vegetarian friendly • organic focus • fresh juice • deli • tables • self-service • take-out

🚗 **From I-95S**, take exit 344 left onto Hwy 202E/J Turner Butler Blvd 4⅓ miles to exit for S Johns Bluff Rd. Follow ¾ mile and merge onto SR 9A S about 2 miles to Baymeadows Rd exit. Turn right off ramp and make U-turn at first light to store on right. **From I-95N**, take exit 337 onto SR 9A N over 4 miles to Baymeadows Rd exit. Turn left off exit to store on left (U-turn at first light to access).

Native Sun Natural Foods Market 🛍 🍴

10000 San Jose Blvd. ✆ 904-260-6950 ⏰ M-Sat 8-8
An all-organic supermarket. No hot food at this location.
  • organic produce • vegetarian friendly • organic focus • fresh juice • deli • tables • self-service • take-out

🚗 **From I-95S**, take exit 341 right onto Baymeadows Road about 2⅓ miles to end at San Jose Blvd. Turn left onto San Jose about 1½ miles (5 lights) to store on right. **From I-95N**, take exit 337 onto I-295N toward Orange Park. Take I-295N 5 miles to exit 5A and merge right onto San Jose Blvd/SR 13N) about 1 mile (6 lights) to store on left.

Natural Food Products Shoppe 🛍

4343 Colonial Ave. ✆ 904-384-4642 ⏰ M-F 9-6, Sat 9-1
Three vegetarian sandwiches made fresh to go.
  • fresh juice • vegetarian • take-out

🚗 **From I-295S**, merge onto I-10E. **From I-10E**, take exit 358 right onto Cassat Ave 2½ miles to San Juan Ave. Turn left onto San Juan 1 mile to Euclid St. Turn right onto Euclid 3 blocks to Colonial St. Turn right onto Colonial to store on right. **From I-95N**, merge onto I-10W and exit onto 17S/Roosevelt Blvd about 3½ miles to San Juan. Turn left onto San Juan 3 blocks to Euclid and follow directions above. **From I-295N**, take exit 17 right onto Wilson Blvd almost 2 miles to Blanding Blvd. Turn left onto Blanding 1 mile to San Juan. Turn right onto San Juan about ½ mile (5 blocks) to Euclid and follow directions above.

Southern Nutrition Center 🛍

4345 University Blvd. S. ✆ 904-737-3312 ⏰ M-Sat 9-6

🚗 **From I-95S**, take exit 346B toward Bowden Rd straight onto University 4 blocks (about ¾ mile) to store on right in shopping center. **From I-95N**, take exit 345 toward University Blvd/SR 109 right onto Bowden to light at Spring Park Rd. Turn left onto Spring Park under ½ mile to next light at University. Turn right onto University 4 blocks to store.

KEY WEST

Blue Heaven 🍴
729 Thomas St. © 305-296-8666 ⏲ M-Sat 8-10:30, Sun 8-2, 5-10:30
Tropical food in a great outdoor setting with a rope swing and chickens in the yard.
• vegetarian friendly • alcohol • tables • wait staff

🚶 **Take US 1 to where it becomes Truman Ave.** Turn right onto Thomas St about 2 blocks to restaurant on right across from Truman Annex.

Sugar Apple Veggie Deli & Juice Bar 🛍️ 🍴
917 Simonton St. © 305-292-0043 ⏲ M-Sat 10-6 Cafe M-Sat 11-4
• vegan • fresh juice • deli • tables • self-service • take-out

🚶 **Take US 1 south almost to end of Truman Ave.** Turn right onto Center St 1 block to Olivia St. Turn right onto Olivia 1 block to Simonton St. Turn right onto Simonton to store.

The Cafe 🍴
509 Southard St. © 305-296-5515 ⏲ -Sat 11-10
Vegetarian with the exception of tuna.
• vegetarian friendly • alcohol • counter • tables • wait staff

🚶 **Take US 1 south to almost to end of Truman Ave.** Turn right onto Simonton St 4 blocks to Southard St. Turn left onto Southard 1½ blocks restaurant on right.

KISSIMMEE

Chamberlin's Market & Cafe 🛍️ 🍴   ♿
1114 N. John Young Pkwy. © 407-846-7454 ⏲ M-Sat 9-8:30, Sun 11-5:30
• organic produce • vegetarian friendly • fresh juice • cafe • bakery • tables • self-service • take-out

🚶 **From FL TpkeS**, take exit 249 right onto Osceola Pkwy 2½ miles to N John Young. Turn left onto N John Young almost 3 miles to store. **From FL TpkeN**, take exit 242 left onto US 192W 6⅓ miles to N John Young. Turn left onto N John Young to store.

The Organic Place 🛍️ 🍴
1246 S. John Young Pkwy. © 407-944-9095 ⏲ M-F 9-7, Sat 9-6
• organic produce • vegetarian friendly • fresh juice • cafe • tables • self-service • take-out

🚶 **From FL Tpke S**, take exit 249 and follow right fork for Kissimmee onto E Osceola Pkwy 1½ miles to S Orange Blossom Trail. Turn left onto S Orange Blossom 2⅓ miles to W Vine St. Turn right onto W Vine under 1 mile to N John Young Pkwy. Turn left onto N John Young 1¾ miles to store on right past Clay St. **From FL Tpke N**, take exit 242 toward Kissimee left onto US 441 about 6⅓ miles to N John Young. Turn left onto N John Young 1¾ miles to store.

LAKE HELEN

Trading Center 🛍️
140 E. Michigan Ave. © 386-228-2905 ⏲ M-F 10-6, Sat 11-4
🚶 **From I-4**, take exit 116 toward Lake Helen east on W Main about 1 mile to S Lakeview Dr. Turn right onto S Lakeview 2 blocks to E Michigan Ave. Turn left onto E Michigan to store on left.

LAKE WORTH

The Grateful Garden 🛍️ 🍴
332 N. Dixie Hwy. © 561-667-8775 ⏲ Tues-W 11-9, Th-Sat 11-12, Sun 10-4
• organic produce • vegetarian friendly • organic focus • cafe • tables • co-op

🚶 **From I-95**, take exit 63 for Lake Worth east on 6th Ave S (left from I-95S, right from I-95N) over ½ mile to US 1/Dixie Hwy. Turn left onto US about ¾ mile to store on right at 4th Ave N.

LAKELAND

Anthony's Health Hut 🛍 🍴

5329 S. Florida Ave. ✆ 863-644-5330 ⏰ M-F 9-6, Sat 9-5 Food service ½ hour after opening to ½ hour before closing
· vegetarian friendly · fresh juice · tables · self-service · take-out

🏠 **From I-4**, take exit 27 toward Lakeland onto FL 570 E (loop around right from I-4E, onto Frontage Rd and right from I-4W) about 6½ miles to exit 7. Turn right onto S Florida Ave almost 2 miles to store.

Chamberlin's Market & Cafe 🛍 🍴   ♿

1531 U.S. Hwy. 98 S. ✆ 863-687-8413 ⏰ M-Sat 9-8:30, Sun 11-5:30
· organic produce · vegetarian friendly · fresh juice · cafe · bakery · tables · self-service · take-out

🏠 **From I-4E**, take exit 28 toward US 92/Lakeland onto Rt 546E about 4½ miles (becomes 92E/98E) until 98 heads south. Continue south on 98 2½ miles to store between N & S Crystal Lake Dr. **From I-4W**, take exit 38 and follow US 98E onto 92E then back onto 98E for 9 miles to store.

Grassroot Organic Restaurant 🍴

1212 S. Florida Ave. ✆ 863-603-7668 ⏰ Tues-Sat 11-9
Raw foods available.
· vegetarian · vegan friendly · organic focus · tables · wait staff

🏠 **From I-4E**, take exit 31 onto Kathleen Rd 2¹⁄₃ miles to Lake Wire Dr. Turn right onto Lake Wire continuing on Sikes Blvd ½ mile total to W Lime St. Turn left onto W Lime 3 blocks to S Florida Ave. Turn right onto S Florida about 1 mile to restaurant on left at Belmar St. **From I-4W**, take exit 32 toward Lakeland left onto US 98/SR 700/35/N Florida Ave continuing on S Florida 4¼ miles total to restaurant.

LARGO

Crunchy Mama 🛍

12788 Indian Rocks Rd., Ste. 8 ✆ 727-593-1800 ⏰ M-Tues, Th 10-5, W 10-7, Sat 10-2
· organic produce · co-op

🏠 **From US 19**, take Umberton Rd/SR 688 west (towards beach) 3¹⁄₃ miles to Indian Rocks Rd. Turn right onto Indian Rocks over ½ mile to store on left.

LAUDERHILL

Woodlands Pure Vegetarian 🍴

4816 N. University Drive ✆ 954-749-3221 ⏰ M-F 11:30-3, 5-10, Sat-Sun 11:30-10
Vegetarian Indian with a weekday buffet lunch option.
· vegetarian · vegan friendly · tables · self-serve · wait staff · take-out

🏠 **From FL Tpke**, take exit 62 and follow right fork onto 870W/W Commercial Blvd 3 miles to N University Dr. Turn left onto N University about ½ mile to restaurant on left in University Shoppes.

MELBOURNE

Nature's Market 🛍

461 N. Harbor City Blvd. ✆ 321-254-8688 ⏰ M-Sat 9-7
Juice bar serves sandwiches and smoothies.
· organic produce · fresh juice · take-out

🏠 **From I-95**, take exit 183 toward Melbourne onto SR 518E almost 5 miles to N Harbor City Blvd (US 1). Turn right onto Harbor City about 1 mile to store (about 1 mile north of airport).

Paradise Health & Nutrition 🛍

4270 Minton Rd. ✆ 321-722-1440 ⏰ M-Sat 8-7
· organic produce

🏠 **From I-95**, take exit 176 toward Palm Bay west on Palm Bay Rd (right from I-95S, left from I-95N) under 1 mile to Minton Rd. Turn right onto Minton to store on left.

Paradise Health & Nutrition 🛍

7777 N. Wickham Rd. ✆ 321-242-6040 ⏰ M-Sat 8-7

🚗 **From I-95**, take exit 191 east on N Wickham Rd/SR 404 (left from I-95S, right from I-95N) about 1½ miles to store on right.

Wild Oats Market 🛍 🍴

1135 W. New Haven Ave. ✆ 321-674-5002 ⏰ M-Sat 8-9, Sun 10-8
• organic produce • vegetarian friendly • salad bar • cafe • self-service • take-out

🚗 **From I-95**, take exit 180 toward Melbourne onto US 192E/New Haven Ave (left from I-95S, right from I-95N) about 4 miles (past Melbourne Square Mall) to store on right (past Toys R Us, under Office Depot Sign). **From 192W**, store is after intersection of New Haven & Dairy Rd.

MIAMI

Beehive Natural Foods & Deli 🛍 🍴   ♿

5750 S.W. 40th St. ✆ 305-666-3360 ⏰ M-Sat 9-7
• vegetarian • fresh juice • deli • counter • self-service • take-out

🚗 **From S Dixie Hwy/US 1**, go west on Bird Rd (aka SW 40th St) about 2⅓ miles to store on left at SW 58th Ave. **From 826 (Palmetto Expwy)**, go east on Bird Rd 2 miles to store on right.

Canela Cafe 🍴

5132 Biscayne Blvd. ✆ 305-756-3930 ⏰ M-Sat 12-11:30
Latin food with a vegetarian tapas section on the menu.
• vegetarian friendly • alcohol • tables • wait staff

🚗 **From I-95S**, take exit 6A left onto NW 62nd Ave 1 mile and continue on NW 61st Ave ½ mile to Biscayne Blvd. Turn right onto Biscayne about ¾ mile to restaurant on right between NE 52nd & NE 51st St. **From I-95N**, merge onto I-195E. **From I-195** take exit 2B and go north on Biscayne Blvd (merge onto NE 36th St and right from I-195E, merge onto NE 38th St and right from I-195W) about 1 mile to restaurant on left after NE 51st.

Garden of Eatin' 🍴

136 N.W. 62nd St. ✆ 305-754-8050 ⏰ M-Sat 12-8
• vegan • fresh juice • tables • wait staff

🚗 In Little Haiti. **From I-95**, take exit 6A west on NW 62nd Ave (left from I-95S, merge onto 5th Rd and right from I-95N) about ½ mile to restaurant on right between NW 1st Pl & NW 1st Ave (between yellow bldgs at end of parking lot).

Granny Feelgoods 🛍 🍴

25 W. Flagler St. ✆ 305-377-9600 ⏰ M-F 7-4
A small natural food store and casual eatery in the heart of downtown Miami.
• vegetarian friendly • fresh juice • counter • tables • wait staff

🚗 **From I-95S**, take exit 3B for NW 8th St onto NW 3rd Ct and turn right onto NW 1st St, left onto NW River Dr and left onto Flagler under ½ mile to store on left at Miami Ave. **From I-95N**, take exit 2B right onto NW 2nd St, right onto NW 2nd Ave and left onto Flagler under ¼ mile to store on left. **From I-375E** or MacArthur Cswy, take exit 2 for Biscayne Blvd south on Biscayne almost 1 mile to Flagler. Turn right onto Flagler under ½ mile to store on right after Miami Ave.

Hale's Health Foods 🛍

16427 N.W. 67th Ave. ✆ 305-821-5331 ⏰ M-F 9:30-6:30, Sat 10-6

🚗 **From Palmetto Expwy (826)**, take NW 67th Ave south 2 blocks to store on east side.

Lifefood Gourmet
377 S.W. 15th Rd. © 786-523-9669 ◷ Th-Sun 12-9
Raw foods.
 • vegan • organic focus • tables • wait staff
🍎 **From I-95S**, take exit 1B for US 41 onto NW 3rd Ct continuing on SW 4th Ave over ½ mile total to SW 15th Rd/Broadway. Turn left onto SW 15th to restaurant on left in bldg with brown canopy on 2nd fl. **From US 1N/S Dixie Hwy**, continue on Brickell Ave about 1 mile to Coral Way/SE 13th St. Turn left onto Coral Way across hwy, past Publix & Walgreens. Turn right after Walgreens onto SW 15th to restaurant on right.

Om Garden
379 S.W. 15th Rd. © 305-856-4433 ◷ M-Sat 11:30-10
Raw and cooked foods, vegan pizzas and sandwiches.
 • vegan • fresh juice • tables • wait staff
🍎 **From I-95S**, take exit 1B for US 41 onto NW 3rd Ct continuing on SW 4th Ave over ½ mile total to SW 15th Rd/Broadway. Turn left onto SW 15th to restaurant on left. **From US 1N/S Dixie Hwy**, continue on Brickell Ave about 1 mile to Coral Way/SE 13th St. Turn left onto Coral Way across hwy, past Publix & Walgreens. Turn right after Walgreens onto SW 15th to restaurant on right.

Pasha's
1414 Brickell Ave. © 305-416-5116 ◷ Daily 8-11
See Aventura location for description.
 • vegetarian friendly • alcohol • tables • self-service
🍎 In Miami financial district on US 1 just south of SE 14th St on west side.

Pasha's
3801 N. Miami Ave. © 305-573-0201 ◷ M-F 9-4
See Aventura location for description.
 • vegetarian friendly • alcohol • tables • self-service
🍎 In the Miami design district. **From I-95**, merge onto I-195E (exit 4 from I-95S, 4A-B from I-95N). **From I-195E** take exit 2B onto NE 36th St. under ½ mile to N Miami Ave. Turn right onto N Miami to restaurant on right. **From I-195W**, take exit 2B toward Biscayne Blvd onto NE 36th and follow directions above.

Prana Health Food and Vegetarian Restaurant
7293 N.W. 36th St. © 305-594-6966 ◷ M-Sat 11-4
One-price, all-you-can-eat, 90% vegan buffet.
 • vegetarian • vegan friendly • fresh juice • tables • self-service
🍎 **From Palmetto Expwy (SR 826)**, go east on NW 36th St (right from SR 836N, left from SR 826S) about ⅓ mile to restaurant on left toward back of the Airport Shopping Ctr. **From the Dolphin Expwy**, go north on Palmetto Expwy and follow directions above.

The Honey Tree
5138 Biscayne Blvd. © 305-759-1696 ◷ M-F 9-7
Vegetarian and vegan entrees, soups, salads and empanadas.
 • vegetarian • vegan friendly • fresh juice • deli • counter • tables • self-service • take-out
🍎 **From I-95,** take exit 4 onto I-195E toward Miami Beach to Biscayne Blvd (exit 2B). Loop around right onto NE 36th St and right onto Biscayne (US 1N) almost 1 mile to store at 51st St on west side. **From I-195W** (across intercoastal), take exit 2B onto NE 38th St to Biscayne. Turn right onto Biscayne and follow directions above.

The Lost and Found Saloon
185 N.W. 36th St. © 305-576-1008 ◷ M-Th, Sun 11-10, F-Sat 11-12
Vegetarian choices include triple bean burgers, pinon and pepita crusted tofu and a tofu melt in an urban bar setting.
 • vegetarian friendly • alcohol • counter • tables • wait staff • take-out

🍴 In the Miami design district. **From I-95,** merge onto I-195E (exit 4 from I-95S, 4A-B from I-95N). **From I-195E** take exit 2A right onto N Miami Ave 1 block to NW 36th St. Turn right onto NW 36th about 1½ blocks to restaurant on right between NW 1st & NW 2nd Ave. **From I-195W,** take exit 2B toward Biscayne Blvd onto NW 38th St to Biscayne. Turn left onto Biscayne to NW 36th. Turn right onto NW 36th over ½ mile to restaurant.

Vegetarian Restaurant 🍴
107th Ave. ✆ 305-553-0078 🕐 M-Sat 10-6
Soup, whole wheat pizza, empanadas, wraps, sandwiches and a daily full-meal special.
   • vegan • fresh juice • counter • tables • self-service • take-out
🚗 **From FL Tpke,** take exit 21 east on US 44/SW 8th St 1 mile to SW 107th St. Turn left onto SW 107th under ½ mile to restaurant on right in Holiday Shopping Plaza.

MIAMI BEACH

Apple A Day Natural Food Market 🛒
1534 Alton Rd. ✆ 305-538-4569 🕐 M-Sat 8-11, Sun 8-10
   • organic produce • vegetarian • vegan friendly • fresh juice • deli • tables • self-service • take-out
🚗 **From I-95S,** take exit 4 onto I-195E toward Miami Beach across Julia Tuttle Causeway over 4 miles to Miami Beach. Bear right (towards Convention Center) onto Alton Rd about 2¼ miles to 15th St (1 block past Lincoln Rd). Turn right onto 15th to store on left just past corner in small shopping plaza. **From 836E, I-95S exit 5 or I-95N,** take exit 2D toward Miami Beach onto I-395E across MacArthur Causeway 3 miles to Miami Beach. Merge left onto Alton about ¾ mile to 15th St. Turn left onto 15th to store.

Books & Books Cafe 🍴
927 Lincoln Rd. ✆ 305-695-8898 🕐 M-Th, Sun 10-11, F-Sat 10-12
Outdoor dining on Lincoln Road.
   • vegetarian friendly • alcohol • tables • wait staff
🚗 **From I-95S,** take exit 4 onto I-195E toward Miami Beach across Julia Tuttle Causeway over 4 miles to Miami Beach. Bear right (towards Convention Center) onto Alton Rd about 2 miles to 17th St. Turn left onto 17th 2 blocks to Michigan Ave. Turn right onto Michigan 2 blocks to Lincoln Rd. Turn left onto Lincoln ½ block to restaurant on left. **From 836E, I-95S exit 5 or I-95N,** take exit 2D toward Miami Beach onto I-395E across MacArthur Causeway 3 miles to Miami Beach. Merge left onto Alton about ¾ mile to 16th St. Turn right onto 16th 2 blocks to Michigan. Turn left onto Michigan 2 blocks Lincoln Rd. Turn right onto Lincoln to restaurant. Note: Lincoln Rd is closed to traffic; park elsewhere and walk.

Front Porch Cafe 🍴
1420 Ocean Drive ✆ 305-531-8300 🕐 M-Th 7-8, F-Sun 7-9
Sit across from the ocean and watch the South Beach scene.
   • vegetarian friendly • alcohol • tables • wait staff
🚗 **From 836E, I-95S exit 5 or I-95N,** take exit 2D toward Miami Beach onto I-395E across MacArthur Causeway about 3 miles to Miami Beach. Merge onto 5th St to end at Ocean Dr. Turn left onto Ocean about 10 blocks to restaurant on left between 14th & 15th St.

Go-Go 🍴
926 Alton Rd. ✆ 305-673-3137 🕐 M-F 11-10, Sat 12-6
Soup, salads and go-go pies (empanadas).
   • vegetarian friendly • alcohol • tables • self-service • take-out
🚗 **From 836E, I-95S exit 5 or I-95N,** take exit 2D toward Miami Beach onto I-395E across MacArthur Causeway 3 miles to Miami Beach. Stay in left lane after causeway and take Alton Rd exit onto Alton 4 blocks to restaurant on left between 9th & 10th St in small shopping strip with laundermat. **From I-95S,** take exit 4 onto I-195E toward Miami Beach across Julia Tuttle Causeway over 4 miles to Miami Beach. Bear right (towards Convention Center) onto Alton Rd about 2½ miles to restaurant on right between 10th & 9th.

Gourmet Carrot 🍴
959 West St. © 305-534-4211 ⏱ M-Th, Sun 11:30-10:30, F 11:30-3
 • vegetarian friendly • vegan friendly • fresh juice • alcohol • kosher • counter • tables
 • wait staff

🚗 **From I-95S**, take exit 4 onto I-195E toward Miami Beach across Julia Tuttle Causeway over 4 miles to Miami Beach. Bear right (towards Convention Center) onto Alton Rd about 2¾ miles to 10th St. Turn right onto 10th 1 block to West. Turn left onto West to restaurant on left. **From 836E, I-95S exit 5 or I-95N**, take exit 2D toward Miami Beach onto I-395E across MacArthur Causeway 3 miles to Miami Beach. Merge left onto Alton to 9th St. Turn left onto 9th 1 block to West St. Turn right onto West to restaurant on right.

Indomania 🍴
131 26th St. © 305-535-6332 ⏱ Tues-Th 6-10, F-Sat 6-11
Their vegetarian rijsttafel (rice with spicy accoutrements) is a rare find in the U.S.
 • vegetarian friendly • alcohol • tables • wait staff

🚗 **From I-95**, take exit 4 (4A-B from I-95N) onto I-195E toward Miami Beach across Julia Tuttle Causeway over 4 miles and bear left onto Arthur Godfrey Rd about ¾ mile to Indian Creek Dr. Turn right onto Indian Creek under 1 mile to 26th St. Turn left onto 26th 1½ blocks to restaurant on left between Collins & the boardwalk.

Juice & Java 🍴
1346 Washington Ave. © 305-531-6675 ⏱ M-F 9-9, Sat 10-9, Sun 11-6
A casual place for breakfast, salads, hot and cold sandwiches, wraps.
 • vegetarian friendly • vegan friendly • fresh juice • tables • self service

🚗 **From I-95S**, take exit 4 onto I-195E toward Miami Beach across Julia Tuttle Causeway over 4 miles to Miami Beach. Bear right (towards Convention Center) onto Alton Rd about 2 miles to 17th St. Turn left onto 17th ½ mile to Washington St. Turn right onto Washington ½ mile to restaurant on right between 14th & 13th St. **From 836E, I-95S exit 5 or I-95N**, take exit 2D toward Miami Beach onto I-395E across MacArthur Causeway 3 miles to Miami Beach. Merge onto 5th St to Washington. Turn left onto Washington ¾ mile to restaurant on left between 13th & 14th.

Pasha's 🍴
900 Lincoln Rd. © 305-673-3919 ⏱ M-Th, Sun 8am-12am, F-Sat 8am-1am
See Aventura location for description. This location on trendy Lincoln Road offers one of the best priced meals in South Beach.
 • vegetarian friendly • alcohol • tables • self-service • wait staff

🚗 **From I-95S**, take exit 4 onto I-195E toward Miami Beach across Julia Tuttle Causeway over 4 miles to Miami Beach. Bear right (towards Convention Center) onto Alton Rd about 2 miles to 17th St. Turn left onto 17th 3 blocks to Jefferson Ave. Turn right onto Jefferson 2 blocks to restaurant on right at far corner of Lincoln Rd. **From 836E, I-95S exit 5 or I-95N**, take exit 2D toward Miami Beach onto I-395E across MacArthur Causeway 3 miles to Miami Beach. Merge left onto Alton about ¾ mile to 16th St. Turn right onto 16th 3 blocks to Jefferson. Turn left onto Jefferson 2 blocks to restaurant on right corner at Lincoln Rd. Note: Lincoln Rd is closed to traffic; park elsewhere and walk.

Whole Foods Market 🛍🍴 ♿
1020 Alton Rd. © 305-532-1707 ⏱ Daily 8-12
 • organic produce • vegetarian friendly • salad bar • cafe • self-service • take-out

🚗 **From 836E, I-95S exit 5 or I-95N**, take exit 2D toward Miami Beach onto I-395E across MacArthur Causeway 3 miles to Miami Beach. Stay in left lane after causeway and take Alton Rd exit onto Alton 5 blocks to store on left at 10th St. **From I-95S**, take exit 4 onto I-195E toward Miami Beach across Julia Tuttle Causeway over 4miles to Miami Beach. Bear right (towards Convention Center) onto Alton Rd about 2½ miles to store on right at 10th St.

MIRAMAR

Vegetarian Delight Juice Bar 🍴

6060 Miramar Pkwy., #4 ✆ 954-241-7402 ⏰ Daily 11-9
Daily plate of homemade West Indian vegetarian food. One small table and a couple of counter stools.
 • vegan • juice bar • counter • tables • self-service • take-out

🍎 **From I-95**, take exit 18 onto FL 858W (Hallandale Beach Blvd, becomes Miramar Pkwy) about 2½ miles to store on left. **From FL Tpke**, take exit 49 towards Hollywood onto FL 820E (Hollywood Blvd) about ⅓ mile to US 441/FL 7. Turn right onto 441S/7S 1¾ miles to Miramar Pkwy. Turn right onto Miramar to store.

MOUNT DORA

5th Avenue Cafe 🍴

116 E. 5th Ave. ✆ 352-383-0090 ⏰ Tues 11:30-3, W-F 11:30-3:30, 5-9, Sat-Sun 10-3, 5-9
Upscale menu with vegetarian, natural meat and poultry selections.
 • vegetarian friendly • organic focus • alcohol • tables • wait staff

🍎 **From US 441/FL 46 intersection**, take FL 46 west (E 1st Ave, right onto N Highland, left onto E 5th Ave) about 1½ m miles to restaurant on left before N Donnelly St. **Coming from the lake on FL 46E**, restaurant is on right after N Donnelly.

Health Basket 🛍 🍴

18834 US Hwy. 441 ✆ 352-735-1166 ⏰ M-F 9-7, Sat 10-5, Sun 12-5
 • fresh juice • vegetarian friendly • cafe • counter • tables • self-service • take-out

🍎 **FromUS 441/FL 46 intersection**, take US 441 N about 2½ N miles to store past N Donnelly St. Coming from the lake on FL 46E, turn left onto N Donnelly about 1½ miles to US 441. Turn left onto 441 to store.

NAPLES

Food & Thought 🛍 🍴

2132 Tamiami Trail N. ✆ 239-213-2222 ⏰ Store M-Sat 9-8 Restaurant M-Sat 9-7:30
 • organic produce • vegetarian friendly • organic focus • tables • self-service • take-out

🍎 **From I-95**, take exit 101 toward Naples west on Golden Gate Pkwy (right from I-95S, left from I-95N) about 4 miles to US 41/Tamiami Trail. Turn right onto Tamiami to store on right.

For Goodness Sake 🛍 🍴

2464 Vanderbilt Beach Rd. # 528 ✆ 239-597-0120 ⏰ M-Sat 10-6 Cafe closes at 4
 • organic produce • vegetarian friendly • fresh juice • cafe • tables • self-service • take-out

🍎 **From I-75S**, take exit 111 toward Naples Park right onto Immokalee Rd about 1¾ miles to Airport Pulling Rd. Turn left onto Airport Pulling 2 miles to Vanderbilt Beach Rd. Turn left onto Vanderbilt Beach to store on right in Naples Walk Plaza. **From I-75N**, take exit 107 toward Naples left onto Pine Ridge Rd 2 miles to Airport Pulling. Turn right onto Airport Pulling about 2¼ mile to Vanderbilt Beach. Turn right onto Vanderbilt Beach to store.

For Goodness Sake 🛍

7211 Radio Rd. ✆ 239-353-7778 ⏰ M-F 10-6, Sat 10-5, Sun 10-4
 • organic produce

🍎 **From I-75S**, take exit 105 left onto Golden Gate Pkwy 1 mile to Santa Barbara Blvd. Turn right onto Santa Barbara under 1½ miles to Radio Rd. Turn right onto Radio under ¼ mile to store on right in Publix Plaza. **From I-75N**, take exit 101 toward Naples left onto SR 84½ mile to Davis Blvd/SR 84. Turn right onto Davis about ½ mile to Radio. Turn right onto Radio 1½ miles to store.

Nature's Garden

2089 9th St. N., Naples Plaza © 239-643-4959 ⊕ M-Sat 9-9, Sun 10-8
• organic produce • vegetarian friendly • fresh juice • cafe • deli • bakery • tables •
self-service • take-out

From I-75, take exit 105 west on Golden Gate Pkwy (right from I-75S, left from I-75N) 4 miles to US 41/9th St. Turn right onto 9th to store on left in Naples Plaza.

SunSplash Market

850 Neapolitan Way © 239-434-7221 ⊕ M-Sat 8-8, Sun 10-6
• vegetarian friendly • cafe • tables • self-service • take-out

From I-75, take exit 107 west on Pine Ridge Rd (896W) about 4 miles to 9th St/Tamiami Trail. Turn left onto 9th ½ mile to Neapolitan Way. Turn right onto Neapolitan to store on left in Neapolitan Way Shopping Ctr.

NEW SMYRNA BEACH

Heath's Natural Foods

600 E. 3rd Ave. © 386-423-5126 ⊕ M-Sat 8:30-7
• organic produce • fresh juice • bakery

From I-95, take exit 249 (249A from I-95S) toward Deland/New Smyrna Beach east on SR 44E 5½ miles (over intercoastal, 44E becomes A1A then E 3rd Ave) to store on left 1 block after light at Peninsula Ave at S Cooper St.

NORTH MIAMI

Here Comes the Sun

2188 N.E. 123rd St. © 305-893-5711 ⊕ M-Sat 11-8:30
• vegetarian friendly • alcohol • tables • self-service

From Biscayne Blvd, take the 123rd St Cswy about ½ mile to store in shopping strip on right. **From Miami Beach**, take the 96th St/Kane Concourse 2 miles (across the intercoastal) to store on left.

Julio's Natural Foods Restaurant

1602 N.E. Miami Gardens Drive © 305-947-4744 ⊕ M-Sat 10-10, Sun 10-5
• vegetarian friendly • vegan friendly • organic focus • fresh juice • tables • wait staff

From I-95, take exit 14 towards N Miami Beach/Aventura east on NE 183rd St/NE Miami Gardens Dr (left off NE 6th Ave from I-95S, left from left fork from I-95N) about 1¼ miles to restaurant on right in Sky Lakes Mall. **From Biscayne Blvd,** go west on NE Miami Gardens Dr under 1½ miles to restaurant on left.

Sara's Kosher Vegetarian Restaurant

2214 N.E. 123rd St. © 305-891-3312 ⊕ M-Th, Sun 7am-10pm, F 7am-2:30pm, Sat 8:30pm-12am
Kosher vegetarian and fish.
• vegetarian friendly • kosher • alcohol • tables • wait staff

From Biscayne Blvd, take the 123rd St Cswy about ½ mile to restaurant in shopping strip on right. **From Miami Beach**, take the 96th St/Kane Concourse 2 miles (across the intercoastal) to restaurant on left.

NORTH MIAMI BEACH

Pasha's

14871 Biscayne Blvd. © 786-923-2323 ⊕ Daily 8-11
See Aventura location for description.
• vegetarian friendly • alcohol • tables • self-service

On US 1 (aka Biscayne Blvd) between 146th & 151st St on east side.

Shing Wang Vegetarian Icee & Tea House

237 N.E. 167th St. © 305-654-4008 ⊕ M, W-Sun 11:30-9:30
Tofu and vegetable dishes plus mix-and-match mock meats, sauces, rice and noodles.

• vegetarian • alcohol • tables • self-service

From I-95, take exit 12 (12B from I-95N) onto NW 167th St/SR 826E toward N Miami Beach/Hospital/Sunny Isles about 1¼ miles to NE 3rd Ave. U-turn back onto NW 167th to restaurant in shopping strip on right between NE 3rd & NE 2nd Ave. **From US 1/Biscayne Blvd,** go west (inland) on NE 163rd St/N Miami Beach Blvd 2¾ miles to restaurant.

Vegetarian Restaurant by Hakin &
73 N.E. 167th St. ✆ 305-405-6346 ⏰ M-Th 7:30-9, F 7:30-3, Sun 7:30-5
Raw and vegan with a Caribbean slant.

• vegan • fresh juice • tables • wait staff • take-out

From I-95, take exit 12 (12B from I-95N) onto NW 167th St/SR 826E toward N Miami Beach/Hospital/Sunny Isles about 1 mile to NE 1st Ave. U-turn back onto NW 167th to restaurant in shopping strip on right between NE 1st & N Miami Ave. **From US 1/Biscayne Blvd**, go west (inland) on NE 163rd St/N Miami Beach Blvd about 2¾ miles to restaurant.

OCALA

B-Healthy
8449 S.W. Hwy. 200, Ste. 139 ✆ 352-854-4577 ⏰ M-F 8:30-6:30, Sat 9-6
From I-75S, take exit 341 toward Dunnellon left onto Hwy 484/135th St continuing onto 135th about 6¾ miles to US 301. Turn right onto US 301 4½ miles to SE 180th St. Turn right onto SE 180th under 1 mile to Hwy 209. Turn left onto Hwy 209 about ¾ mile to Hwy 200. Turn right onto Hwy 200 to store. **From I-75N**, take exit 329 toward Wildwood and merge right onto SR 44 3½ miles to S Main St/US 301.Turn left onto S Main 7 miles to CR 202. Turn left onto CR 202 1 mile to Hwy 209. Turn right onto HWY 201 ⅓ mile to Hwy 200. Turn left onto Hwy 200 to store.

Mother Earth Market
1917 E. Silver Springs Blvd. ✆ 352-351-5224 ⏰ M-Sat 9-8, Sun 10-6
• organic produce
From I-75, take exit 352 onto SR 40E/Silver Springs Blvd (left from I-75S, right from I-75N) about 5 miles to store on left in Ocala Ctr.

OPA LOCKA

Abundant Energy Sources, Inc.
2131 N.W. 139th St., #23 ✆ 305-685-0517 ⏰ M-Sat 10-6
From I-95, take exit 10B west on Opa Locka Blvd (right from I-95S, merge onto NW 6th Ave and left from I-95N) about 1⅓ miles to NW 19th Ave. Turn right onto NW 19th 1 block to NW 139th St. Turn left onto NW 139th 2½ blocks to store on right. **From FL Tpke**, take I-95S exit and follow directions above.

ORANGE CITY

Debbie's Health
862 Saxon Blvd. ✆ 386-775-7002 ⏰ M-F 8-8, Sat 9-8, Sun 11-6
• organic produce
From I-4, take exit 11AB toward Orange City west on Saxon Blvd about ¼ miles to store in Orange City Marketplace.

ORANGE PARK

The Granary Whole Foods, Inc.
1738 Kingsley Ave. ✆ 904-269-7222 ⏰ M-Sat 9-6
• organic produce
From I-295, take exit 10 toward Orange Park onto US 17S about 2½ miles to Kingsley Ave. Turn right onto Kingsley (stay in left lane after tracks) 2 miles to store on left.

ORLANDO

Chamberlin's Market 🛍   ♿

7600 Dr. Phillips Blvd. ✆ 407-352-2130 ⏰ M-Sat 9-8:30, Sun 11-5:30
  • organic produce

🍎 **From I-4**, take exit 74A west on Sand Lake/FL 482W 1 mile to Dr Phillips Blvd. Turn right on Dr Phillips then left into Marketplace Ctr to store.

Dandelion Communitea Cafe 🍴   ♿

618 N. Thornton Ave. ✆ 407-362-1864 ⏰ M 11-5, Tues-Sat 11-10, Sun 11-6
Certified Green Restaurant.

  • vegetarian • vegan friendly • organic focus • alcohol • tables • wait staff • take-out

🍎 **From I-4**, take exit 84 for State Hwy 50 W/US-92/US-17 S east on E Colonial Dr (merge onto N Hughey Ave then left from I-4W, merge onto N Garland Ave and right from I-4E) about 1 mile to N Thornton Ave. Turn right onto N Thornton to restaurant on right.

Ethos Vegan Kitchen 🍴   ♿

1235 N. Orange Ave. #101 ✆ 407-228-3898 ⏰ M-Sat 11-10, Sun 10-3
  • vegan • alcohol • bakery • tables • self-service • take-out

🍎 **From I-4W**, take exit 85 east on Princeton St (left from I-4W, right from I-4E) under ¼ mile to N Orange Ave. Turn right onto N Orange over ½ mile to restaurant on left after Virginia Dr.

Garden Cafe 🍴

810 W. Colonial Drive ✆ 407-999-9799 ⏰ Tues-F 11-10, Sat-Sun 12-10
Chinese vegetarian (mostly vegan) plus a few western choices with cheese optional. Home-made vegetable stock, brown rice available.

  • vegetarian • vegan friendly • tables • wait staff • take-out

🍎 **From I-4E**, take Amelia St exit (83B) toward US 17/92/Colonial Dr/SR 50. Follow N Garland Ave about ¼ mile and turn left onto W Colonial about ½ mile to restaurant (next to Burger King). **From I-4W**, take Ivanhoe Blvd/US 17/92/Colonial Dr/SR 50 exit (84) and take left fork on ramp, then right fork to W Colonial. Turn right onto W Colonial and follow directions above.

Infusion Tea 🍴

1600 Edgewater Drive ✆ 407-999-5255 ⏰ M-Sat 8-10, Sun 11-5, Summer M-W 8-9, Th-F 8-10, Sat 8:30-10, Sun 11-5
A tea shop and cafe serving soups, sandwiches, salads, seasonal specialties. Nice kids' menu.

  • vegetarian • vegan friendly • organic focus • tables • wait staff

🍎 **From I-4W,** take exit 84 for State Hwy 50 W/US-92/US-17 S and merge onto S Colonial Dr to Edgewater Dr. Turn right onto Edgewater 1 mile to restaurant on left after Guernsey St. **From I-4E**, take exit 84 onto S Ivanhoe Blvd and veer left onto Lakeview St under ½ mile to Edgewater. Turn right onto Edgewater under ½ mile to restaurant.

Infusion Tea 🍴

652 E. Central Blvd. ✆ 407-849-5004 ⏰ M-Th 11-9, F-Sat 11-10, Sun 11-5
See Edgewater Dr location for description.

  • vegetarian • vegan friendly • organic focus • alcohol • tables • wait staff

🍎 **From I-4**, take exit 84 for State Hwy 50 W/US-92/US-17 S east on S Colonial Dr (merge onto N Hughley Ave then left from I-4W, merge onto N Garland Ave and right from I-4E) about 1 mile to Summerlin Ave. Turn right onto Summerlin almost 1 mile E Central Blvd. Turn right onto E Central to restaurant on left.

Khasyat 🍴

852 Lancaster Rd. ✆ 407-888-2147 ⏰ M, W-Sun 11:30-8:30
Indian vegetarian with a daily lunch buffet.

  • vegetarian • vegan friendly • tables • self-service • wait staff

🍎 **From I-4W**, take exit 80 on left onto S Orange Blossom Trail 3 miles to W Lancaster Rd. Turn left onto W Lancaster under ½ mile to restaurant on right after Brockbank Dr. **From I-4E,** take exit 80A onto S Orange Blossom and follow directions above. **From FL Tpke**, take exit 254 north on S Orange Blossom (merge heading north from Tpke N, right at first fork and left at second fork toward Orlando from Tpke S) 2¼-½ miles to W Lancaster. Turn right onto W Lancaster under ½ mile to restaurant.

Woodland's Pure Vegetarian 🍴 ♿

6040 S. Orange Blossom Trail ✆ 407-854-3330 ◷ Tues-Th, Sun, 11:30-9:30, F-Sat 11:30-10

South Indian vegetarian with a weekday lunch buffet.

• vegetarian • vegan friendly • tables • self-service • wait staff

🍎 **From I-4**, take US 441S/US 17S/92W exit (80 from I-4W, 80A from I-4E) onto 17S (Orange Blossom Trail) about 2½ miles to restaurant.

ORMOND BEACH

Health Foods of Ormond Beach 🛒

165 E. Granada Blvd. ✆ 386-672-2993 ◷ M-F 9:30-6, Sat 9:30-5

🍎 **From I-95**, take exit 268 toward Ormond Beach east on W Granada Blvd (left from I-95S, right from I-95N) about 5⅓ miles (over intercoastal) to store on left just before the beach.

Living Waters Health Foods 🛒

141 W. Granada Blvd. ✆ 386-672-6004 ◷ M-F 9-6:30, Sat 9-5:30

🍎 **From I-95**, take exit 268 toward Ormond Beach east on W Granada Blvd (left from I-95S, right from I-95N) about 4 miles to store on left 1½ blocks past Yonge St.

Love Whole Foods 🛒 🍴

275 Williamson Blvd. ✆ 386-677-5236 ◷ M-F 9-7, Sat 9-6

• organic produce • vegetarian friendly • fresh juice • cafe • deli • tables • self-service • take-out

🍎 **From I-95**, take exit 268 toward Ormond Beach onto SR 40E to first light at Williamson Blvd. Turn right onto Williamson about ½ mile to store (next to Regal Cinema, across from Post Office).

Peggy's Whole Foods 🛒

362A W. Granada Blvd. ✆ 386-673-1112 ◷ M-F 9:30-7, Sat 9-6

🍎 **From I-95**, take exit 268 toward Ormond Beach east on W Granada Blvd (left from I-95S, right from I-95N) about 3½ miles to store on right before railroad crossing.

OSPREY

Richard's Whole Foods 🛒

1092 S. Tamiami Trail ✆ 941-966-0596 ◷ M-Sat 9-6, Sun 11-5

🍎 **From I-75N**, take exit 195 toward Nokomis/Laurel left onto Laurel Rd about 3 miles to Tamiami Trail. Turn right onto Tamiami/US 41N about 3½ miles to store on left (41S). **From I-75S**, take exit 200 toward Venice/Osprey onto FL 681 about 3¼ miles to Tamiami Trail. Turn right onto Tamiami/US 41N about 2¾ miles to store.

OVIEDO

Chamberlin's Market & Cafe 🛒 🍴 ♿

1170 Oviedo Market Place Blvd., Ste. 1000 ✆ 407-359-7028 ◷ M-Sat 9-9, Sun 11-7

• organic produce • vegetarian friendly • fresh juice • cafe • bakery • tables • self service • take-out

🍎 **From I-4W**, take exit 101B toward Sanford/Intnl Airports onto Hwy 417S 13½ miles to Red Bug Lake Rd (exit 41). Turn right onto Red Bug about ¼ mile to Oviedo Marketplace Blvd. Turn right onto Oviedo Marketplace about ¼ mile to store on right in Oviedo Marketplace Mall. **From I 4E**, take exit 92 onto SR 436E about 4½ miles to Red Bug. Turn left onto Red Bug 5½ miles to Oviedo Marketplace Blvd. Turn left onto Oviedo Marketplace about ⅓ mile to store.

PALM BEACH GARDENS

Nutrition S'Mart 🛍️
4155B Northlake Blvd. © 61-694-0644 ⏲ M-Sat 9-9, Sun 10-6
• organic produce

🍴 **From I-95**, take exit 77 west on Northlake Blvd (right from I-95S, left from I-95N) to store on right just past hwy.

Whole Foods Market 🛍️ 🍴
11701 Lake Victoria Gardens Blvd. © 561-691-8550 ⏲ Daily 8-10
• organic produce • vegetarian friendly • cafe • self-service • take-out

🍴 **From I-95**, take exit 79 east on PGA Blvd (left from I-95S, right from I-95N) about 1 mile to Fairchild Gardens Ave. U-turn at Fairchild Gardens back onto PGA Blvd and make first right onto Lake Victoria Ave to store on left.

PALM COAST

Diane's Natural Market 🛍️
101 Palm Harbor Pkwy., Ste 105/106 © 904-808-9978 ⏲ M-Sat 9:30-7, Sun 12-5
• organic produce

🍴 **From I-95**, take exit 289 for Palm Coast east on Palm Coast Pkwy (left from I-95S, right from I-95N) over 2 miles to Palm Harbor Pkwy. Turn right onto Palm Harbor 1 mile to store on left in European Village.

PALM HARBOR

Consciousness Blossoms 🍴
3390 Tampa Rd. © 727-789-1931 © Tues-Th, Sat-Sun 8-3, F 8-3, 5-8
Run by disciples of Sri Chinmoy.
• vegetarian • vegan friendly • tables • wait staff

🍴 **From US 19**, take SR 584/Tampa Rd east (left from 19S, right from 19N) 1 mile to restaurant on right.

Palm Harbor Natural Foods, Inc. 🛍️ 🍴
30555 U.S. 19 N. © 727-786-1231 ⏲ M-Sat 8-8, Sun 9-7
• vegetarian friendly • deli • tables • self-service • take-out

🍴 On US 19 (aka 34th St N) on west side at Curlew Rd in Seabreeze Shopping Ctr.

PEMBROKE PINES

Nutrition S'Mart 🛍️
12594 Pines Blvd. © 954-437-0035 ⏲ M-Sat 9-9, Sun 10-7
• organic produce

🍴 **From I-75**, take exit 9A east on Hollywood Blvd/Pines Blvd 1¼-½ miles to store on right in Flamingo Pines Shopping Ctr.

PENSACOLA

Ever'Man Natural Foods Co-op 🛍️
315 W. Garden St. © 850-438-0402 ⏲ M-Sat 7-7, Sun 11-4
• organic produce • vegetarian friendly • deli • co-op

🍴 **From I-10**, take exit 12 right onto I-110S about 6¼ miles to exit 1C (98 Bus W/ Garden St) toward Historical District. Take Garden St about ⅔ mile to store on left.

PINECREST

Whole Foods Market 🛍️ 🍴
11701 S. Dixie Hwy. © 305-971-0900 ⏲ Daily 8-10
• organic produce • vegetarian friendly • salad bar • cafe • self-service • take-out

🍴 **From FL 826 (Palmetto Expwy)**, go south to end at US 1 (South Dixie Hwy). Merge onto 1S about 1 mile (past 2 major intersections) to 117th Ave. Turn left onto 117th and make immediate right into shopping center to store.

PLANT CITY

The Corner Store 🛍 🍴

121 E. Reynolds St. ✆ 813-754-0900 ⏰ M-Sat 10-6
Fresh hydroponic vegetables grown in the store window and freshly milled grains in baked goods.
· organic produce · vegetarian friendly · cafe · bakery · tables · self-service · take-out
🍎 **From I-4,** take exit 21 south on SR 39/N Wheeler St (right from I-4W, left fork toward Buchanan Hwy and right from I-4E) about 1⅓ miles to W Reynolds St. Turn left onto W Reynolds 3 blocks to store on right.

PLANTATION

Whole Foods Market 🛍 🍴 ♿

7720 Peters Rd. ✆ 954-236-0600 ⏰ Daily 8-10
· organic produce · vegetarian friendly · salad bar · cafe · self-service · take-out
🍎 **From I-595W,** take exit 5 (SR 817/University Dr) onto 84W almost 1 mile to S University. Turn right onto University about ½ mile to Peters Rd. Turn left onto Peters to store on left in first shopping center. **From I-595E,** take exit 4 toward Pine Island Rd onto 84E under ¼ mile to Pine Island. Turn left onto Pine Island about ½ mile to Peters. Turn right onto Peters about ⅔ mile to store on right in shopping center before University.

PORT CHARLOTTE

Richard's Whole Foods 🛍

3012 S. Tamiami Trail ✆ 941-766-0199 ⏰ M-Sat 9-7, Sun 11-5
· organic produce
🍎 **From I-75,** take exit 170 for Kings Hwy/Port Charlotte and follow signs for Port Charlotte onto Kings Hwy 3½ miles to Westchester Blvd. Turn right onto Westchester 1 mile to Gardner Dr. Turn left onto Gardner and right onto US 41/Tamiami Trail under 2 miles to store on right after Elkcam Blvd.

SunSplash Natural Gourmet Supermarket 🛍 🍴

2000 Tamiami Trail #220 ✆ 941-255-2179 ⏰ M-Sat 9-8, Sun 10-6
· organic produce · vegetarian friendly · fresh juice · salad bar · cafe · deli · bakery · tables · self-service · take-out
🍎 **From I-75,** take exit 170 for Kings Hwy/Port Charlotte and follow signs for Port Charlotte onto Kings Hwy 3½ miles to Westchester Blvd. Turn right onto Westchester 1 mile to Gardner Dr. Turn left onto Gardner and right onto US 41/Tamiami Trail 3½ miles to store on right between Cochran & Forest Nelson Blvd in Murdock Carousel Shopping Ctr.

PORT ORANGE

Debbie's Health 🛍

3850 S. Nova Rd. ✆ 386-763-7046 ⏰ M-F 9-7, Sat 9-6, Sun 12-6
· organic produce
🍎 **From I-95,** take exit 276 towards Port Orange north on SR 421 (left from I-95S, right from I-95N) 2¼ miles to Nova Rd. Turn right onto Nova about ¼ to store on right.

PORT SAINT LUCIE

Nutrition S'Mart 🛍

464 S.W. Port Saint Lucie Blvd., Ste. 106-112 ✆ 772-323-2222 ⏰ M-Sat 9-9, Sun 10-7
· organic produce
🍎 **From Florida's Tpke,** take exit 142 toward Port Saint Lucie onto SW Bayshore Blvd and turn left onto SW Port Saint Lucie Blvd to store on left just past hwy.

ROCKLEDGE

Appleseed Health Foods Cafe & Market 🛍️🍴

1007 Pathfinder Way #110 ✆ 321-631-1444 ⊕ M-F 10-6, Sat 10-3 Cafe Tues-Sat 10-3
• organic produce • vegetarian friendly • fresh juice • cafe • tables • wait-staff • take-out

🍎 **From I-95S**, take exit 195 toward Rockledge and merge north onto S Fiske Blvd almost 3 miles to Barton Blvd. Turn right onto Barton 1 mile to Murrell Rd. Turn right onto Murrell ½ mile to store on corner at Pathfinder Way in Arbor Pl. **From I-95N**, take exit 195 toward Rockledge/State Hwy 519 east on Barnes Blvd 1⅓ miles to Murrell. Turn left onto Murrell about 2¼ miles to store.

SARASOTA

Richard's Whole Foods 🛍️

3226 Clark Rd. ✆ 941-925-9726 ⊕ M-Sat 9-7, Sun 11-5

🍎 **From I-75**, take exit 205 toward Siesta Key/Sarasota onto 72W (Clark Rd) about 3¾ miles to store on opposite side (U-turn at S Lockwood Ridge Rd).

Richard's Whole Foods 🛍️

2856 Ringling Blvd. ✆ 941-316-0546 ⊕ M-Sat 9-7, Sun 11-5

🍎 **From I-75**, take exit 210 toward Sarasota/Gulf Beaches onto FL 780W/Fruitville Rd (left from I-75N, right from I-75S) about 4½ miles to Brink Ave. Turn left onto Brink 1 block to Ringling Blvd. Turn right onto Ringling to store.

Richard's Whole Foods 🛍️

8207 Cooper Creek Blvd. ✆ 941-358-8011 ⊕ M-Sat 9-7, Sun 11-5

🍎 **From I-75**, take exit 213 west on University Pkwy (merge right from I-213S, left from I-213N) ¼-½ mile to Cooper Creek Blvd. Turn right onto Cooper Creek and left onto Tourist Center Dr to store on right.

The Granary 🛍️🍴   ♿

1279 Beneva Rd. S. ✆ 941-365-3700 ⊕ M-Sat 8-8, Sun 10-6
• organic produce • vegetarian friendly • fresh juice • salad bar • deli • tables • self-service • take-out

🍎 **From I-75**, take exit 210 toward Sarasota/Gulf Beaches west on Fruitville Rd (right from I-75S, left from I-75N) about 3¼ miles to Beneva Rd. Turn left onto Beneva about 1 mile to store at Bahia Vista St.

The Granary 🛍️🍴   ♿

1930 Stickney Point Rd. ✆ 941-924-4754 ⊕ M-Sat 8-8, Sun 10-6
• organic produce • vegetarian friendly • fresh juice • salad bar • deli • tables • self-service • take-out

🍎 **From I-75**, take exit 205 toward Siesta Key/Sarasota onto 72W (Clark Rd) about 5 miles to just past US 41/Tamiami Trail where Clark becomes Stickney Rd. Store is on left.

Whole Foods Market 🛍️🍴

1451 First St. ✆ 941-955-8500 ⊕ M-Sat 8-9, Sun 9-9
• organic produce • vegetarian friendly • salad bar • cafe • self-service • take-out

🍎 **From US 41/N Tamiami Trail**, go inland on 1st St about ⅓ mile to store on left between Central & N Lemon Ave.

SOUTH DAYTONA

Peggy's Whole Foods 🛍️

1801 S. Nova Rd. ✆ 386-760-4879 ⊕ M-F 9-7, Sat 9-6

🍎 **From I-95**, take exit 260A toward Daytona onto I-4E and continue east on Bellville Rd about 3 miles to S Nova. Turn right onto S Nova ½ mile to store on left.

SPRING HILL

Green Bean Organic Market 🛍 🍴

11020 Northcliffe Blvd. ✆ 352-688-7979 ◷ M-Sat 9-7, Sun 12-5
• organic produce • vegetarian friendly • fresh juice • deli • tables • take-out

🍎 **Traveling north on US 19/Commercial Way**, turn right onto Spring Hill Dr 5½ miles to Mariner Blvd. Turn left onto Mariner 2 miles to Northcliffe Blvd. Turn left onto Northcliffe to store on left. **Traveling south on US 19/Commercial Way**, turn left onto Bayport/Cortez Blvd/SR 50 ½ mile to Deltona Blvd. Turn right onto Deltona ½ mile to Elgin Blvd. Turn left onto Elgin under 1 mile to Keysville Ave. Turn right onto Keysville about 1¼ miles to Northcliffe. Turn left onto Northcliffe about ¾ mile to store on right.

ST. AUGUSTINE

Blue Planet Co-op 🛍 🍴

846 Anastasia Blvd., Lighthouse Plaza ✆ 904-819-5888 ◷ M-F 9:30-6, Sat 9-5
• organic produce • vegetarian friendly • fresh juice • deli • counter • self-service • take-out

🍎 **From I-95**, take exit 318 toward St Augustine onto FL 16E (left from I-95S, right from I-95N) 5⅓ miles to US 1 (Ponce De Leon Blvd). Turn right onto 1S about 2 miles to King St. Turn left onto King across the Bridge of Lions onto Anastasia Blvd (A1A) 1 mile to store on left in Lighthouse Plaza.

Diane's Natural Market 🛍

240 State Rd. 312 ✆ 904-808-9978 ◷ M-Sat 9:30-7, Sun 12-5
• organic produce

🍎 **From I-95**, take exit 311 toward St Augustine Beach onto SR 207E (left from I-95S, right from I-95N) about 4 miles to SR 312. Turn right onto 312E about 1 mile to store (about ¼ mile east of US 1).

Diane's New Dawn 🛍 🍴   ♿

110 Anastasia Blvd. ✆ 904-824-1337 ◷ M-F 9:30-6, Sat 9-5
• vegetarian friendly • fresh juice • salad bar • counter • tables • self-service • take-out

🍎 **From I-95**, take exit 318 toward St Augustine onto FL 16E (left from I-95S, right from I-95N) 5⅓ miles to US 1 (Ponce De Leon Blvd). Turn right onto 1S about 2 miles to King St. Turn left onto King across the Bridge of Lions onto Anastasia Blvd (A1A) 2 blocks to store on left.

The Manatee Cafe 🍴

525 State Rd. 16 #106 ✆ 904-826-0210 ◷ M-Sat 8-4, Sun 8-3
• vegetarian friendly • vegan friendly • organic focus • tables • wait staff

🍎 **From I-95**, take exit 318 toward St Augustine onto FL 16E (left from I-95S, right from I-95N) about 4 miles to restaurant on left in Westgate Plaza.

ST. CLOUD

Mother Nature's Pantry 🛍

4042 13th St. ✆ 407-892-1962 ◷ M-Sat 9-6

🍎 **From FL Tpke S**, take exit 242 toward US 441/192/Melbourne left at fork onto Shady Ln and left onto US 441/192 about 3⅓ miles to store on left. **From FL Tpke N**, take exit 242 toward Kissimmee right onto US 441/192 almost 1½ miles to store on left.

ST. PETERSBURG

Evos Fresh & Healthy 🍴

2631 4th St. N. ✆ 727-571-3867 ◷ Daily 11-9
Healthy fast-food concept with soyburgers, veggie patties, whole wheat wraps, organic greens, vegan chili, veggie corn dogs, natural meat, "airfries™", smoothies and such.
• vegetarian friendly • tables • self-service • take-out

🍎 **From I-275**, take exit 24 east on 22nd Ave (left from I-275S, right from I-275N) about 1¼ miles to 4th St N. Turn left onto 4th about ¼ mile to restaurant at 26th Ave N.

Leafy Greens Cafe ♙

1431 Central Ave. ✆ 727-289-7087 ⏲ Tues-Th 11-7, F-Sat 11-8, Sun 11-5
Raw food and vegan emphasis with cheese added on request.
  • vegetarian • vegan friendly • organic focus • tables • wait staff
🚗 **From I-275S**, take exit 23B onto 20th St N under ½ mile to Central Ave. Turn left onto Central under ½ mile to restaurant on left after 15th St. **From I-275N**, take exit 23 onto I-375E about ¾ mile to exit 1. Merge onto 4th Ave N and turn right onto 9th St N under ½ mile to Central. Turn right onto Central ½ mile to restaurant on right. (Free parking in rear.)

Nature's Finest Foods 🛒 ♙

6651 Central Ave. ✆ 727-347-5682 ⏲ M-Sat 8-8, Sun 10-6
  • vegetarian friendly • cafe • deli • tables • self-service • take-out
🚗 **From I-275S,** take exit 23B toward Treasure Island onto 5th Ave N/US 19 AltN about 3½ miles to 58th St N. Turn left onto 58th St about ½ mile to Central Ave. Turn right onto Central about 1 mile to store on right. **From I-275N**, take exit 18 west on 26th Ave S to US 19N/34th St S. Turn right onto 19N about 2 miles Central Ave. Turn left onto Central about 3 miles to store.

Richard's Whole Foods 🛒

3455 Tyrone Blvd. ✆ 727-343-0084 ⏲ M-Sat 9-6, Sun 11-5
🚗 **From I-275S**, take exit 23B toward Treasure Island onto 5th Ave N/US 19 AltN about 3½ miles to Tyrone Blvd. Turn right onto Tyrone about 2½ miles to store.
From I-275N, take exit 18 west on 26th Ave S to US 19N/34th St S. Turn right onto 19N about 2¼ miles to 5th Ave. Turn left onto 5th about 2 miles to Tyrone Blvd N (Alt 19N). Turn right onto Tyrone about 2½ miles to store.

Rollin' Oats Market & Cafe 🛒 ♙

2842 9th St. N. ✆ 727-821-6825 ⏲ M-F 9-8, Sat 9-7, Sun 10-6
  • organic produce • vegetarian friendly • salad bar • cafe • deli • tables • self-service • take-out
🚗 **From I-275**, take exit 24 east on 22nd Ave (left from I-275S, right from I-275N) about ¾ mile to 9th St N. Turn left onto 9th under ½ mile to store.

STUART

Peggy's Natural Foods 🛒

5839 S.E. Federal Hwy. ✆ 772-286-1401 ⏲ M-F 9-6, Sat 9:30-5:30, Sun 11-4
Modest selection of produce.
🚗 **From I-95**, take exit 101 toward Stuart onto FL 76E (right from I-95N, left from I-95S) over ½ mile to Cove Rd. Turn right onto Cove 3¼ miles to US 1/Federal Hwy. Turn right onto US 1 about ¼ mile to store on left. **From FL Tpke,** take exit 133 toward Stuart onto SW Martin Downs Blvd continuing on Monterey Rd 4¾ miles to US 1/Federal Hwy. Turn right onto US 1 4 miles to store on left.

SUNRISE

Simply Natural ♙   ♿

8271 Sunset Strip ✆ 954-742-8384 ⏲ Daily 11-9
  • vegetarian friendly • organic focus • fresh juice • alcohol • tables • wait staff
🚗 **From FL Tpke**, take exit 58 (Hwy 858/Sunrise Blvd) onto 858W 3¼ miles to N University Dr. Turn right onto N University about ⅓ mile to Sunset Strip. Turn left onto Sunset to restaurant on right in University Plaza.

Udipi Cafe ♙

2100 N. University Dr. ✆ 954-748-5660 ⏲ M-F 11:30-3, 5:30-10, Sat-Sun 11:30-10
South Indian vegetarian with a lunch buffet.
  • vegetarian • vegan friendly • tables • self-service • wait staff
🚗 **From FL Tpke**, take exit 58 (Hwy 858/Sunrise Blvd) onto 858W 3¼ miles to N University Dr. Turn right onto N University about ¼ mile to restaurant on right.

TALLAHASSEE

New Leaf Market 🛒 🍴
1235 Apalachee Pkwy. ✆ 850-942-2557 ⏱ Daily 8-10
• organic produce • vegetarian friendly • deli • bakery • tables • self-service • take-out

🍎 **From I-10E**, take exit 199 onto US 27S about 3⅔ miles to Apalachee Pkwy/US 27. Turn left in front of State Capitol onto US 27S under 1 mile to store on right in Parkway Shopping Ctr. **From I-10W**, take exit 209A toward Tallahassee left onto Magnolia Dr ¾ mile to Apalachee Pkwy/US 27N. Turn right onto Apalachee to store on left.

Soul Vegetarian on Wheels 🍴
200 N. Duvall St. ✆ 850-893-8208 ⏱ M-F 11-3
Street cart selling vegan southern-style soul food.
• vegan • take-out

🍎 **From I-10,** take exit 203 south on Thomasville Rd (left from I-10W, right from I-10E) continuing onto N Monroe St 4½ miles total to E Call St. Turn right onto E Call 2 blocks to cart at N Duvall St.

Soul Vegetarian on Wheels 🍴
Railroad Ave. & W. Gaines St. ✆ 850-893-8208 ⏱ M-Sat 5:30-10
Street cart selling vegan, southern-style soul food.
• vegan • take-out

🍎 **From I-10**, take exit 203 south on Thomasville Rd (left from I-10W, right from I-10E), continuing onto N Monroe St under 5 miles total to E Jefferson St. Turn right onto E Jefferson (becomes W Pensacola St) ½ mile total to Railroad Ave. Turn left onto Railroad under ¼ mile to cart at Gaines St.

TAMPA

Evos Fresh & Healthy 🍴
157 Westshore Plaza ✆ 813-226-3867 ⏱ M-Sat 10-9, Sun 12-6
See St. Petersburg location for description.
• vegetarian friendly • tables • self-service • take-out

🍎 **From I-275S**, take exit 40A left onto NW Shore Blvd under ½ mile to W Kennedy Blvd. Turn right onto W Kennedy under ¼ mile to restaurant on right in Westshore Plaza.

Evos Fresh & Healthy 🍴
609 S. Howard Ave. ✆ 813-258-3867 ⏱ Daily 11-10
See St. Petersburg location for description.
• vegetarian friendly • tables • self-service • take-out

🍎 **From I-275**, take exit 42 toward Howard Ave/Armenia Ave south on Armenia (left from I-275S, right from I-275N) about 1 mile to Horatio St. Turn left onto Horatio 2 blocks to Howard Ave. Turn right onto Howard to restaurant.

Evos Fresh & Healthy 🍴
2774 B E. Fowler Ave. ✆ 813-969-3867 ⏱ Daily 11-10
See St. Petersburg location for description.
• vegetarian friendly • tables • self-service • take-out

🍎 **From I-275**, take exit 51 (Fowler St/SR582) east onto E Fowler (right from I-275N, merge onto N Central Ave then left from I-275S) under 2 miles to NE 30 St/Bruce Downs Blvd. U-turn back onto Fowler to restaurant on right in University Collection Shopping Ctr.

Grassroot Organic Restaurant 🍴
2702 N. Florida Ave. ✆ 813-221-7668 ⏱ Tues-Sat 11-9
• vegetarian • vegan friendly • organic focus • tables • wait staff

🍎 **From I-275S**, take exit 46A toward Floribraska Ave and merge onto N Elmo Ave to E Columbus Dr. Turn right onto E Columbus 4 blocks to N Florida Ave. Turn right onto N Florida to restaurant on left. **From I-275N**, take exit 44 and follow signs for Scott St to N Florida. Turn left onto N Florida ¾ mile to restaurant on left at E Columbus.

Nature's Harvest Market & Deli 🛒 🍴

1021 N. MacDill Ave. ✆ 813-873-7428 ⏱ M-F 10-8, Sat-Sun 10-7
• vegetarian friendly • deli • tables • self-service • take-out

🚗 **From I-275**, take exit 42 toward Howard Ave/Armenia Ave south on Armenia (left from I-275S, right from I-275N) under ⅓ mile to Cypress St. Turn right onto Cypress under ¾ mile to MacDill Ave. Turn right onto MacDill to store on right.

Nutrition S'Mart 🛒

14847 N. Dale Mabry Hwy. ✆ 813-908-9500 ⏱ M-Sat 9-9, Sun 10-7
• organic produce

🚗 **From I-275,** take exit 53 west on Bearrs Ave (right from I-275S, left from I-275N) 3 miles to SR 597 (N Dale Mabry Hwy). Turn left onto Dale Mabry to store on left.

Village Health Market 🛒 🍴

3225 S. MacDill Ave., Ste. 123 ✆ 813-831-6065 ⏱ M-Sat 8:30-9:30, Sun 10-7
• organic produce • vegetarian friendly • organic focus • fresh juice • salad bar • cafe • deli • tables • self-service • take-out

🚗 **From I-275**, take exit 41A (41C from I-275W) south on N Dale Mabry Hwy about 2½ miles to W Bay to Bay Blvd. Turn left onto W Bay under 1 mile to S MacDill Ave. Turn right onto S MacDill ⅓ mile to store on right.

Whole Foods Market 🛒 🍴

1548 N. Dale Mabry Hwy. ✆ 813-874-9435 ⏱ Daily 9-9
• organic produce • vegetarian friendly • salad bar • cafe • self-service • take-out

🚗 **From I-275,** take exit 41B north on N Dale Mabry Hwy (left from I-275N, right from I-275S) to store on left in Walters Crossing Shopping Ctr.

Udipi Cafe 🍴

14422 N. Dale Mabry Hwy. ✆ 813-962-7300 ⏱ Tues-Th 11:30-3, 5-9:30, F 11:30-3, 5-10, Sat 11:30-10, Sun 11:30-9:30
Vegetarian Indian with a weekday lunch buffet.
• vegetarian • vegan friendly • tables • self-service • wait staff

🚗 **From I-275**, take exit 53 west on Bearrs Ave (right from I-275S, left from I-275N) 3 miles to N Dale Mabry Hwy. Turn left onto Dale Mabry under ½ mile to restaurant on right.

TEMPLE TERRACE

Chuck's Natural Food Marketplace 🛒 🍴

11301 N. 56th St. ✆ 813-980-2005 ⏱ M-F 9-8, Sat 9-6, Sun 12-6 Cafe until 6 weekdays, 4 weekends
• organic produce • vegetarian friendly • organic focus • fresh juice • salad bar • cafe • tables • self-service • take-out

🚗 **From I-75**, take exit 265 west on E Fowler Ave about 2 miles to N 56th St. Turn left on N 56th to store on left inside Terrace Oaks Plaza.

VENICE

Richard's Whole Foods Market 🛒

105 E. Milan Ave. ✆ 941-484-8627 ⏱ M-Sat 9-6, Sun 11-5

🚗 **From I-75S**, take exit 200 toward Venice/Osprey onto FL 681S about 3¾ miles to Tamiami Trail (US 41). Merge onto 41S about 3¾ miles to store at Milan Ave. **From I-75N**, take exit 193 toward Venice. Turn left onto Jacaranda Blvd about 1 mile to Venice Ave. Turn right onto Venice about 3⅔ miles to Tamiami. Turn left onto Tamiami ½ mile to store at Milan.

Richard's Whole Foods Market 🛍️
593 US 41 Bypass ✆ 941-484-2354 ⏰ M-Sat 9-6, Sun 11-5
🚗 **From I-75S**, take exit 200 toward Venice/Osprey onto FL 681S about 3¾ miles to Tamiami Trail (US 41). Merge onto 41S (becomes 41 Bypass) about 3½ miles to Substation Rd. Turn left onto Substation and left onto 41 Bypass going north under ½ mile to store. **From I-75N**, take exit 193 toward Venice. Turn left onto Jacaranda Blvd about 1 mile to Venice Ave. Turn right onto Venice about 3 miles to 41 Bypass. Turn right onto 41 Bypass under 1 mile to store.

WEST PALM BEACH_____
Nutrition World 🛍️
1937 N. Military Trail, Ste. J ✆ 561-684-0777 ⏰ M-Sat 9:30-9, Sun 11-5
  • organic produce
🚗 **From I-95S**, take exit 71 west on Palm Lakes Blvd (right from I-95S, left from I-95N) 1 mile to Okeechobee Blvd. Turn right onto Okeechobee ¾ mile to N Military Trail. Turn left onto Military to store on right. **From FL Tpke**, take exit 99 east on Okeechobee (left from TpkeS, right from TpkeN) 1½ miles to N Military. Turn right onto Military to store on right.

WINTER HAVEN _____
Nature's Delight Natural Foods & Herb Shop 🛍️
3015 Cypress Gardens Rd. ✆ 863-324-1778 ⏰ M-F 9-6:30, Sat 9-5
  • organic produce
🚗 **From US 27**, go west on SR 540W/Cypress Gardens Blvd (left from 27S, right from 27N)) 4¼ miles to second Cypress Gardens Rd entrance. Turn right onto Cypress Gardens Rd 1 block to store. **From US 17**, go east on Cypress Gardens Blvd 2 miles to Cypress Gardens Rd and turn left to store.

WINTER PARK_____
Chamberlin's Market & Cafe 🛍️ 🍴   ♿
430 N. Orlando Ave. ✆ 407-647-6661 ⏰ M-Sat 8-9:30, Sun 10-7
  • organic produce • vegetarian friendly • fresh juice • cafe • bakery • tables • self-service • take-out
🚗 **From I-4E**, take exit 87 (Fairbanks Ave) right onto FL 426E 1 mile to Orlando Ave/US 12/92. Turn left onto 92N about ½ mile to Winter Park Village. Turn right into Winter Park Village to store on right. **From I-4W**, take exit 88 left onto FL 4423N/Lee Rd about 1⅓ miles to Orlando Ave/US 12/92. Turn right onto 92S about ⅓ mile to Winter Park Village. Turn left into Winter Park Village to store.

Whole Foods Market 🛍️ 🍴   ♿
1989 Aloma Ave. ✆ 407-673-8788 ⏰ Daily 8-10
  • organic produce • vegetarian friendly • salad bar • cafe • self-service • take-out
🚗 **From I-4**, take exit 87 (Fairbanks Ave) onto FL 426E (becomes Aloma Ave) almost 4 miles to store on left in shopping ctr.

YULEE _____
Michael's Market 🛍️ 🍴
463646 State Rd. 200 ✆ 904-225-4899 ⏰ M-F 9:30-8, Sat 9:30-5
  • organic produce • vegetarian friendly • organic focus • fresh juice • cafe • deli • tables • self-service • take-out
🚗 **From I-95**, take exit 373 for State Hwy 200/State Hwy A1A toward Fernandina Beach and follow fork toward Yulee onto SR 200E 8 miles to store on right in Tyler Plaza.

GEORGIA

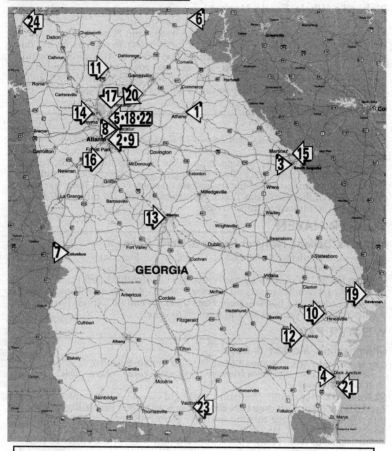

1. Athens	9. East Point	17. Roswell
2. Atlanta	10. Hinesville	18. Sandy Springs
3. Augusta	11. Jasper	19. Savannah
4. Brunswick	12. Jesup	20. Snellville
5. Chamblee	13. Macon	21. St. Simons Island
6. Clayton	14. Marietta	22. Tucker
7. Columbus	15. Martinez	23. Valdosta
8. Decatur	16. Peachtree City	24. Wildwood

ATHENS

Daily Groceries Co-op, Inc. 🛍

523 Prince Ave. © 706-548-1732 ⏰ M-F 8-10, Sat-Sun 9-10
· organic produce · vegetarian friendly · deli · take-out · co-op

🏬 **From Loop 10 around Athens,** take Chase St exit south under 1 mile to Prince St. Turn left onto Prince ½ mile to store on right. **From downtown,** go west on Broad St to Pulaski St. Turn right onto Pulaski 4 blocks to Prince. Turn left onto Prince about 2 blocks to store on left past the light at Finely/Barber St.

Earth Fare

1689 S. Lumpkin St. © 706-227-1717 ⊘ M-Sat 8-10, Sun 9-9
• organic produce • vegetarian friendly • fresh juice • salad bar • cafe • deli • bakery • tables • self-service • take-out

From Loop 10 around Athens, take Milledge Ave exit toward Whitehall Rd north about 1½ miles to 5 point intersection. Turn left onto Lumpkin St to store on left.

Phoenix Natural Food Market

296 W. Broad St. © 706-548-1780 ⊘ M-Sat 10-6

From Loop 10 around Athens, take Commerce Rd/MLK Pkwy south about 1 mile to North St. Turn left onto North (becomes Dougherty St) ¾ mile to Pulaski St. Turn left onto Pulaski ¼ mile to store at Broad St (across from UGA campus). Or, take Bus 78 (Broad St) toward Downtown to store at Pulaski.

The Grit

199 Prince Ave. © 706-543-6592 ⊘ M-Th 10-10, F 10-10:30, Sat 10-3, 5-10:30, Sun 10-3, 5-10
International vegetarian classics.
• vegetarian • alcohol • tables • wait staff

From Loop 10 around Athens, take Alt 15 (aka Prince Ave) toward Downtown about 1¾ miles to restaurant between N Newton & Pulaski St. Or, take Commerce Rd/MLK Pkwy south about 1 mile to North St. Turn left onto North (becomes Dougherty St) ¾ mile to Pulaski. Cross Pulaski onto Prince to restaurant.

ATLANTA

Broadway Cafe

2168 Briarcliff Rd. © 404-329-0888 ⊘ M-Th, Sun 11-9, F 11-3
Two entrances: One leads to a kosher dairy restaurant (which includes fish); the other to a meat-centered eatery.
• vegetarian friendly • vegan friendly • organic focus • kosher • alcohol • tables • wait staff

From I-85, take exit 89 east on N Druid Hills Rd (left from I-85S, right from I-85N) about ½ mile to Briarcliff Rd. Turn right on Briarcliff under 1 mile to restaurant on right.

Cafe Sunflower

2140 Peachtree Rd. © 404-352-8859 ⊘ Lunch M-F 11:30-2:30, Sat 12-2:30 Dinner M-Th 5-9:30, F-Sat 5-10
Multi-ethnic, very vegan friendly (including all desserts).
• vegetarian • vegan friendly • organic focus • kosher • alcohol • tables • wait staff • take-out

From I-75, take exit 252A (US 41/Northside Dr) right onto Northside to Collier Rd. Turn right onto Collier under 1 mile to Peachtree Rd. Turn left onto Peachtree under ½ mile to restaurant on left in Brookwood Square Shopping Ctr.

Cafe Sunflower

5975 Roswell Rd. © 404-256-1675 ⊘ Lunch M-F 11:30-2:30, Sat 12-2:30 Dinner M-Th 5-9:30, F-Sat 5-10
Multi-ethnic, very vegan friendly (including all desserts).
• vegetarian • vegan friendly • organic focus • kosher • alcohol • tables • wait staff • take-out

From I-285, take exit 25 toward Sandy Springs north onto Roswell Rd (right from I-285W, left from I-285E) under ½ mile to restaurant.

Cosmo's Vegan Shoppe

672 Highland Avenue N.E. © 678-921-0102 ⊘ Tues-Sat 12-8, Sun 12-5
• vegan

From I-75/85-take exit 248C onto Freedom Parkway to Boulevard NE. Turn left onto Blvd 1 block to Highland Ave SE. Turn right onto Highland under ½ mile to store on left after Sampson St.

Dynamic Dish 🍴

427 Edgewood Ave. © 404-688-4344 ① Tues-Wed 11-4, Th-F 11-4, 5-9, Sat 12-9, Sun 12-6

Modest menu based on seasonal and local ingredients in an eco-friendly space.

· vegetarian · vegan friendly · organic focus · fresh juice · tables · self-service

🍎 **From I-75S/85S**, take exit 248D for JW Hobbs Ave onto Butler St NE under ¼ mile to Edgewater Ave SE. Turn left onto Edgewater about ¾ mile to restaurant on left after Airline St. **From I-75N/85N**, take exit 248B right onto Edgewater and follow directions above. **From I-20E**, take exit 57 onto I-75N/85N and follow directions above. **From I-20W**, take exit 60 and veer right onto Moreland Ave SE to Memorial Dr SE. Turn left onto Memorial about ¾ mile to Estoria St SE. Turn right onto Estoria over ½ mile to Edgewater. Turn left onto Edgewater to restaurant on right.

Green Sprout 🍴

1529 Piedmont Ave., Ste. D © 404-874-7373 ① M-Tues, Th, Sun 11:30-9:45, F-Sat 11:30-10:15

Chinese vegetarian.

· vegetarian · vegan friendly · tables · wait staff · take-out

🍎 **From I-75/I-85 N**, take exit 250 onto Williams St and turn right onto 10th St over ½ mile to Piedmont Ave NE. Turn left onto Piedmont 1¼ miles to restaurant on right at Monroe Dr in Clear Creek Mall. **From I-85S**, take Lindberg Dr exit right onto GA 236/Lindberg Dr NE under ½ mile to GA 237/Piedmont. Turn left onto Piedmont under 2 miles to restaurant on left.

Nuts 'n Berries Natural Foods 🛍️🍴

4274 Peachtree Rd. N.E. © 404-237-6829 ① M-F 9-8, Sat 9-7, Sun 10-6 Cafe M-Sat 10-4

· vegetarian friendly · fresh juice · cafe · tables · self-service · take-out

🍎 **From I-285**, take exit 31A right onto Peachtree Industrial Rd S about 5 miles to store on right at Kendrick Rd. **From I-85**, take exit 87 onto GA 400N about 2⅓ miles to exit 2. Take GA 141E ramp toward Peachtree onto GA 141E Conn about ½ mile to Peachtree. Turn left onto Peachtree about 2 miles to store on left.

Return to Eden 🛍️

2335 Cheshire Bridge Rd. © 404-320-3336 ① Daily 9-9

A totally vegetarian market.

· organic produce · vegetarian · deli · take-out

🍎 **From I-85S**, take exit 88 left onto Lennox-Cheshire Bridge Rd about ⅓ mile to store on left in Cheshire Square Shopping Ctr. **From I-85N**, take exit 86 onto GA 16N about 2 miles to Lennox Rd. Turn right onto Lennox (becomes Cheshire Bridge) ½ mile to store.

Sevananda Natural Foods Co-op Market 🛍️   ♿

467 Moreland Ave. N.E. © 404-681-2831 ① Daily 9-10

All-vegetarian market with a vegan bakery.

· organic produce · vegetarian · salad bar · deli · bakery · take-out · co-op

🍎 **From I-75/85**, take exit 248C toward Carter Center and veer right onto Freedom Pkwy NE/GA 10E 1 mile to GA 42E exit. Follow Freedom Pkwy NE/GA 42 about ¾ mile to T-intersection at Moreland Ave. Turn right onto Moreland 1½ blocks to store on left. **From I-20**, take Moreland Ave (exit 60 from I-20W, 60A from I-20E) right 1 mile to Little Five Points shopping district to store on right.

Soul Vegetarian 🍴

652 N. Highland Ave. © 404-875-4641 ① Tues-F 11-10, Sat-Sun 10-10

Healthy, vegan, southern-style soul food. Homemade soy cheese and "ice-kream."

· vegan · tables · wait staff · take-out

🍎 **From I-75/85**, take exit 248C toward Carter Center and veer right onto Freedom Pkwy NE/GA 10E 1 mile to GA 42E exit. Follow Freedom Pkwy NE/GA 42 about ½ mile to N Highland. Turn left onto N Highland about ¼ mile to restaurant.

Soul Vegetarian 🍴
879 Ralph David Abernathy Blvd. S.W. ✆ 404-752-5194 ⏰ M-Th 11-10, F-Sat 11-11, Sun 9-1:30, 5-11
Healthy, vegan, southern-style soul food. Homemade soy cheese and "ice-kream."
 • vegan • tables • wait staff • take-out

🚗 **From I-20**, take exit 55A toward Ashby St/West End south on Joseph E. Lowrey Blvd SW (right from I-20E, left from I-20W) about ¼ mile to Ralph David Abernathy Blvd. Turn left onto Abernathy to restaurant.

Veggieland 🍴
211 Pharr Rd. N.E. ✆ 404-231-3111 ⏰ M-F 11:30-3, 5-9, Sat 11:30-8
99% vegan Thai fare.
 • vegetarian • vegan friendly • tables • wait staff

🚗 **From I-85S**, take Lindbergh Dr exit on left right onto Lindbergh Dr NE under ½ mile to Piedmont Ave NE. Turn right onto Piedmont 1 mile to Pharr Rd NE. Turn left onto Pharr ¾ mile to restaurant on left before Peachtree Rd NE. **From I-85N,** take exit 86 toward Buford Hwy onto GA 13N and take Piedmont Ave exit right onto Piedmont under 2 miles to Pharr. Turn left onto Pharr ¾ mile to restaurant.

Whole Foods Market 🛍 🍴   ♿
650 Ponce de Leon Ave. ✆ 404-853-1681 ⏰ Daily 8-10
 • organic produce • vegetarian friendly • salad bar • cafe • self-service • take-out

🚗 **From I-75/85S**, take exit 248D toward US 78/Georgia Tech left onto North Ave ½ mile to Piedmont Ave. Turn left onto Piedmont and right onto Ponce de Leon Ave about 1 mile to store on left in Midtown Place Shopping Ctr. **From I-75/85N**, take exit 248C toward Carter Center and veer right onto Freedom Pkwy about 1¾ miles where it dead ends at Ponce de Leon. Turn left onto Ponce de Leon about ½ mile to store on right.

Whole Foods Market 🛍 🍴   ♿
5930 Roswell Rd. ✆ 404-236-0810 ⏰ Daily 7:30-10
 • organic produce • vegetarian friendly • salad bar • cafe • self-service • take-out

🚗 **From I-285**, take exit 25 toward Sandy Springs north on Roswell Rd (left from 285 E, right from 285W) to store just north of exit.

Whole Foods Market 🛍 🍴   ♿
2111 Briarcliff Rd. ✆ 404-634-7800 ⏰ Daily 9-9
 • organic produce • vegetarian friendly • salad bar • cafe • self-service • take-out

🚗 **From I-85**, take exit 89 southeast on N Druid Hills Rd (left from I-85S, right from I-85N) about ⅓ mile to Briarcliff Rd. Turn right onto Briarcliff 1 mile to store at top of hill on right at LaVista Rd.

Whole Foods Market 🛍 🍴
77 W. Paces Ferry Rd., N.W. ✆ 404-324-4100 ⏰ M-Sat 7:30-10, Sun 9-9
 • organic produce • vegetarian friendly • salad bar • cafe • self-service • take-out

🚗 **From I-85S**, take Lindbergh Dr exit on left right onto Lindbergh under ½ mile to Piedmont Ave NE. Turn right onto Piedmont about 1¼ miles to E Paces Ferry Rd NE. Turn left onto E Paces Ferry under 1 mile to store on right. **From I-85N**, take exit 86 onto GA 13N and take exit for Hwy 237N right onto Piedmont Ave about 2 miles to E Paces Ferry and follow directions above.

AUGUSTA_____

New Life Natural Foods 🛍 🍴
2825 Washington Rd., Ste. C ✆ 706-737-8805 ⏰ M-Sat 9-7, Sun 12-5
 • organic produce • vegetarian friendly • fresh juice • cafe • tables • self-service • take-out

🚗 **From I-20**, take exit 199 toward Augusta east on GA 18/Washington Rd (right from I-20E, left from I-20W) about ½-¾ mile to store on left past Bertram Rd.

BRUNSWICK

Feeling Great Wellness Center 🛍️
718 Mall Blvd. ✆ 912-265-1595 🕐 M-Th 9:30-7, F-Sat 9:30-8, Sun 12:30-5:30
🚗 **From I-95**, take exit 36A toward Downtown right onto GA 25S about 5 miles to store at F St.

CHAMBLEE

Harmony Vegetarian Chinese Restaurant 🍴
4897 Buford Hwy. N.E., #109 ✆ 770-457-7288 🕐 M, W-Th, Sun 11-10:30, F-Sat 11-11
• vegan • tables • wait staff

🚗 **From I-85**, take exit 94 onto Chamblee Tucker Rd (right at fork toward Chamblee from I-85S, merge onto NE Expwy NE and left from I-85N) 1 mile to US 23/Buford Hwy. Turn left onto Buford to restaurant on left in Orient Ctr.

CLAYTON

The Rootcellar 🛍️
35 E. Savannah St. ✆ 706-782-9676 🕐 Tues, Th 9-5, W 9-2, F 9-7, Sat 9-3
🚗 GA 2, GA 76, GA 15 and US 23 intersect in Clayton. Store is east of this intersection on Rickman/E Savannah St.

COLUMBUS

Country Life Natural Food 🛍️🍴   ♿
1217 Eberhart Ave. ✆ 706-323-9194 🕐 M-Th 10-6, F 10-2, Sun 12-5 Lunch M-F 11:30-2
Run by Seventh-day Adventists.
• vegan • tables • self-service • take-out

🚗 **From I-185**, take exit 6 onto GA 22 Spur W/Macon Rd W under 1¾ miles to store at Eberhart Ave.

Peachtree Natural Foods 🛍️
2483 Airport Thruway ✆ 706-322-3282 🕐 M-F 10-7, Sat 10-5
🚗 **From I-185**, take exit 8 west on Airport Thwy (right from I-185S, left from I-185N) to store on right in Airport Thwy Plaza.

Peachtree Natural Foods 🛍️
5435 Woodruff Farm Rd. ✆ 706-565-9245 🕐 M-F 10-7, Sat 10-5
🚗 **From US 27**, take Miller Rd exit east on Miller (right from US 27N, left from US 27S), make sharp right onto Midden Rd and first left onto Woodland Farm Rd to store on right.

Peachtree Natural Foods 🛍️
6770 Veterans Pkwy., Ste. G ✆ 706-649-3071 🕐 M-F 10-7, Sat 10-5
🚗 **From I-185**, take exit 10 onto GA 80E about 1 mile (follow signs to Veterans Pkwy) and turn right onto Veterans under ½ mile to store on right.

DECATUR

Indian Delights 🍴
1707 Church St. ✆ 404-296-2965 🕐 Daily 11:30-9:30
Vegetarian Indian in a basic, no frills atmosphere.
• vegetarian • vegan friendly • tables • self-service • take-out

🚗 **From I-285**, take exit 39A toward Decatur/Atlanta onto US 78W (becomes US 29) about 2½ miles to Church St. Turn left onto Church to restaurant on left in Scott Village Shopping Ctr. **From I-20W**, merge onto I-285N and follow directions above. **From I-75S/85S**, merge onto I-285E and follow directions above.

Rainbow Natural Foods & Restaurant 🛍️🍴
2118 N. Decatur Rd. ✆ 404-633-3538 🕐 M-Sat 11-8, Sun 11-5
Cafe Monday to Saturday from 11 to 3; hot bar and salad bar during all store hours.
• organic produce • vegetarian • salad bar • cafe • deli • tables • self-service • take-out

From I-285, take exit 39A toward Decatur/Atlanta onto US 78W (becomes US 29) over 3 miles to N Decatur Rd. Turn right onto N Decatur almost 1 mile to store.

Saravana Bhavan ⑪

2179 Lawrenceville Hwy. ⓒ 404-636-4400 ⓘ M-F 11:30-2:30, 5:30-10, Sat-Sun 11:30-10
South Indian vegetarian cuisine. Part of an international chain.
· vegetarian · vegan friendly · tables · wait staff

From I-285, take exit 39A toward Decatur/Atlanta onto US 78W (becomes US 29/Lawrenceville Hwy) about ½-1 mile to exit 1 for Valley Brook Rd/N Druid Hills R. Turn right onto N Druid Hills and right onto Lawrenceville Hwy to restaurant on right. **From I-20W**, merge onto I-285N and follow directions above. **From I-75S/85S**, merge onto I-285E and follow directions above. .

Udipi Cafe ⑪   ♿

1850 Lawrenceville Hwy. ⓒ 04-325-1933 ⓘ M-Th, Sun 11:30-9:30, F-Sat11:30-10
Indian vegetarian.
· vegetarian · vegan friendly · tables · wait staff

From I-285, take exit 39A toward Decatur/Atlanta onto US 78W (becomes US 29/Lawrenceville Hwy) about 2¼ miles to restaurant on right after N Dekalb Mall. From I-20W, merge onto I-285N and follow directions above. **From I-75S/85S**, merge onto I-285E and follow directions above.

EAST POINT

Lov'n It Live ⑪

2796 East Point St. ⓒ 404-765-9220 ⓘ Tues-W 2-9, Th 2-8, F-Sat 2-10, Sun 2-8
Raw foods restaurant, art gallery, game room and meeting place.
· vegan · organic focus · fresh juice · tables · wait staff

From I-75S/85S, take exit 243 toward East Point onto Hwy 166W about 1¼ miles to Hwy 154N exit toward East Point. Turn right onto Womack Ave and right onto Main St/US 29 and stay on US 29 1¾ miles to restaurant on left after Linwood Ave. **From I-85N**, take exit 72 onto Camp Creek Pkwy 1 mile to US 29/Main St ramp. Turn left onto Main 2⅓ miles to W Cleveland Ave. Turn left onto W Cleveland and left onto E Point St 1 block to restaurant on left.

HINESVILLE

Farmer's Natural Foods 🛍

754 Elma G. Miles Pkwy. ⓒ 912-368-7803 ⓘ M-F 9-7, Sat 9-6
· organic produce · fresh juice · deli · cafe · tables · self-service · take-out

From US 84W, turn right onto General Screven Way (GA 196) ⅓ mile (across Main St) to GA 119/EG Miles Pkwy. Turn left onto Miles about 1 mile to store on left. **From 84E**, turn left onto GA 119/Slatten Dr almost 6 miles to store on left.

JASPER

Natural Market Place 🛍

69 N. Main St. ⓒ 706-253-6933 ⓘ M-F 10-6, Sat 10-5

From I-575N, continue onto Hwy 515 4 miles to Hwy 53/W Church St. From Hwy 53, go east (right from 515N, left from 515S) 1¾ miles and turn left at second light onto Main St to store on left across from court house.

JESUP

Garden of Eat'n 🛍

140 S.W. Broad St. ⓒ 912-588-9696 ⓘ M-F 10-6, Sat 10-4

US 341, US 84, US 25 and US 301 all lead to Jesup. **From US341/84 (W Cherry & S 1st St) intersection**, go 2 bocks toward Amtrak station and turn right onto SW Broad to store on right (1 block past station). **From US 34+5/301 intersection**, take E Cherry toward Amtrak station 1 mile to SW Broad (after the tracks). Turn left onto SW Broad to store.

MACON

Eden'z 🍴

617 Poplar St. ✆ 478-745-3336 ⏲ M-Th 11-7, F 11-3, Sun 11-4
• vegan • tables • wait staff

🏠 **From I-75N,** take exit 164 for Hwy 19 right onto Forsyth St under 1 mile to Plum St. Turn right onto Plum 4 blocks to 2nd St. Turn left onto 2nd 2 blocks to Popular St. Turn left onto Popular to restaurant on right. **From I-75S**, merge onto I-16E. **From I-16E**, take exit 2 for US 80, MLK Jr Blvd right onto Coliseum Dr over ½ mile to Popular. Turn right onto Popular 4½ blocks to restaurant on right between 2nd & 1st St. **From I-16W**, take exit 1B right onto 2nd St about ¾ mile to Popular. Turn right onto Popular to restaurant.

Mia's Health Food Store 🛍

3107 Vineville Ave. ✆ 78-742-0624 ⏲ M-F 10-6, Sat 10-5
• organic produce

🏠 **From I-75**, take exit 164 for Hwy 19/US 41/Hardeman Ave toward Forsyth St. Go west on 19/Vinneville Ave (right from I-75S, left from I-75N) almost 2 miles to store on right. **From I-16,** exit onto 75S and follow directions above.

MARIETTA

Harry's Farmers Market 🛍 🍴   ♿

70 Powers Ferry Rd. ✆ 770-578-4400 ⏲ M-Sat, 9-9, Sun 9-8
• organic produce • vegetarian friendly • salad bar • cafe • deli • bakery • tables • self-service • take-out

🏠 **From I-75,** take exit 263 (GA 120E) toward Roswell onto Loop 120/S Marietta Pkwy SE about ⅓ mile to Powers Ferry Rd. Turn left onto Powers Ferry about ¾ mile to store.

Life Grocery Natural Foods Co-op & Cafe 🛍 🍴   ♿

1453 Roswell Rd. ✆ 770-977-9583 ⏲ M-Sat 9-8, Sun 11-6
Cafe specializes in organic vegan and "living foods."
• organic produce • vegan • fresh juice • salad bar • cafe • counter • tables • self-service • take-out • co-op

🏠 **From I-75S,** take exit 263 for Hwy 120 Loop/S Marietta Pkwy NE right onto S Marietta Pkwy ½ mile to US 41/Cobb Pkwy N. Turn right onto Cobb about ¾ mile to Roswell Rd. Turn right onto Roswell about ½ mile to store on left. **From I-75N,** take exit 263 for Hwy 120 Loop toward Marietta/Roswell. Merge onto S Marietta Pkwy SE ⅓ mile to Powers Ferry Rd. Turn left onto Powers Ferry SE 1 mile to Roswell. Turn left onto Roswell under ¼ mile to store.

Vatica Indian Vegetarian Cuisine 🍴

1475 Terrel Mill Rd. S.E., Ste. 105 ✆ 770-955-3740 ⏲ Daily 11-3, 5-9:30
All-you-can-eat lunch and dinner Gujarati thalis and a tiffin-to-go.
• vegetarian • vegan friendly • tables • wait staff • take-out

🏠 **From I-75,** take exit 261 east on Delk Rd (left from I-75S, merge right from I-75N) ⅓-½ mile to Bentley Rd SE. Turn right onto Bentley ¾ mile to Terrill Mill Rd SE. Turn left onto Terrill Mill under ¼ mile to restaurant on right.

MARTINEZ

Earth Fare 🛍 🍴

368 Furys Ferry Rd. ✆ 706-288-3042 ⏲ M-Sat 7-10, Sun 9-9
• organic produce • vegetarian friendly • salad bar • cafe • deli • tables • self-service

🏠 **From I-20W,** take exit 200 right onto GA 104/Riverwatch Pkwy under 2 miles to Furys Ferry Rd. Turn right onto Furys Ferry under 1 mile to store on right. **From I-20E,** take exit 196B onto Bobby Jones Expwy W, continuing onto GA 232W ⅓ mile to Scott Nixon Blvd. Turn right onto Scott Nixon continuing onto Peasant Home Rd under 2 miles total to Riverwatch. Turn right onto Riverwatch about ½ mile to Furys Ferry. Turn left onto Furys Ferry to store.

PEACHTREE CITY

Peachtree Natural Foods

152 Peachtree East Shopping Center ✆ 770-487-8288 ⏰ M-F 10-7, Sat 10-5

🍎 **From GA 54,** turn onto Peachtree Ct to store on left in shopping center.

ROSWELL

Harry's Farmers Market &

1180 Upper Hembree Rd. ✆ 770-664-6300 ⏰ M-Sat 8-9, Sun 8-8
• organic produce • vegetarian friendly • salad bar • cafe • deli • bakery • tables •
self-service • take-out

🍎 **From GA 400N,** take exit 10 west on Old Milton Pkwy/GA 120W (left from 400N, right from 400S) about 3 miles to Harris Rd. Turn left onto Harris to store at light at Upper Hembree Rd.

SANDY SPRINGS

World Peace Cafe

220 Hammond Drive N.E. ✆ 404-256-2100 ⏰ Tues-W 7-6:30, Th-F 7-9, Sat-Sun 10-3
Reflects the Buddhist principles of loving kindness and respect for all living beings.
• vegetarian • vegan friendly • organic focus • tables • self-service • take-out

🍎 **From I-285,** take exit 19 toward Sandy Spring north on Roswell Rd (left from I-285E, right from I-285W) ½ mile to Hammond Dr NE. Turn left onto Hammond to restaurant on right at City Walk.

SAVANNAH

Brighter Day Natural Foods

1102 Bull St. ✆ 912-236-4703 ⏰ M-Sat 10-7, Sun 12:30-5:30
• vegetarian friendly • deli • counter • tables • self service • take-out

🍎 **From I-95,** take exit 99 toward Savannah onto I-16E about 8 miles and bear right onto W 37th St 1 mile to W Broad St/MLK Jr Blvd. Turn left onto W Broad about ½ mile to Park Ave. Turn right onto Park 5 blocks to store on right at Bull St (mural with tomatoes wearing sunglasses).

The Sentient Bean

13 E. Park Ave. ✆ 912-232-4447 ⏰ M-Th, Sun 7-10, F-Sat 7-11
Soup, quiche, paninis, salads, stuffed baked potatoes and baked goods with organic (but refined) flours. Live music and a hippy/youthful vibe.
• vegetarian • vegan friendly • organic focus • tables • self-service

🍎 **From I-95,** take exit 99 toward Savannah onto I-16E about 8 miles and bear right onto W 37th St 1 mile to W Broad St/MLK Jr Blvd. Turn left onto W Broad about ½ mile to Park Ave. Turn right onto Park 5 blocks to restaurant on right before Bull St (next to Brighter Day).

SNELLVILLE

Peachtree Natural Foods

1630 Scenic Highway S. W., Ste. V ✆ 770-982-4989 ⏰ M-F 10-7, Sat 10-5

🍎 Snellville is about 15 miles south of I-85 exit 115 on GA 20 continuing on GA 124 and 15 miles north of I-20 exit 15. Store is on east side of GA 124 (aka Scenic Hwy) north of Pharrs Rd & south of Ridgedale Dr in Presidential Commons.

Call Ahead

We suggest you call first if possible before visiting a location. Stores and restaurants have a habit of moving (and closing), and hours, services, etc. change more often than you might expect.

ST. SIMONS ISLAND

Island Natural Market 🛍 🍴

204 Retreat Village ✆ 912-634-0394 ⏰ M-Sat 9-7, Sun 12-5
  • organic produce • vegetarian friendly • fresh juice • cafe • tables • self-service •
  wait staff • take-out

🚗 **Entering St Simons Island from the Torras/St Simons Cswy,** veer right onto
Kings Hwy about ⅓ mile to first left onto New Sea Island Rd ⅓ mile to first right
onto Demere Rd. Take Demere 1 mile to Frederica Rd/Retreat Ave. Turn right onto
Frederica under ¼ mile to store in Retreat Village.

TUCKER

Mother Nature's Market 🛍

3853 Lawrenceville Hwy., Ste. E ✆ 770-491-0970 ⏰ M-F 9:30-6:30, Sat 9:30-6
🚗 **From I-285E,** take exit 36 left then right onto Northlake Pkwy 1 mile to US
29/Lawrenceville Rd. Turn left onto Lawrenceville 1 mile to store on right before
Brockett Rd. **From I-285N,** take exit 38 onto US 29/Lawrenceville Rd under 3 miles
to store on right.

VALDOSTA

Ma Perkins Natural 🛍

2110 N. Ashley St. ✆ 229-244-5440 ⏰ M-F 9:30-6, Sat 9:30-5
🚗 **From I-75,** take exit 22 toward I-75 Bus Loop/N Valdosta Rd right onto US 41S
about 6 miles to store in center of town. **From US 84,** take US 41N almost 2 miles
to store just past split off to US 221.

WILDWOOD

Wildwood Country Store 🛍

435 Lifestyle Lane ✆ 706-820-1252 ⏰ M-W 10-1, 2-6, Th 10-1, 2-7, Sun 3-6
*Vegan store run by laymen from the Seventh-day Adventist church and part of the Wildwood
Lifestyle Center and Hospital.*
  • organic produce • vegan

🚗 **From I-24,** take exit 169 toward Wildwood east on GA 299 about ¾ mile to
Lifestyle Ln. Turn left onto Lifestyle and follow as it veers right to end to store in
Wildwood Lifestyle Center.

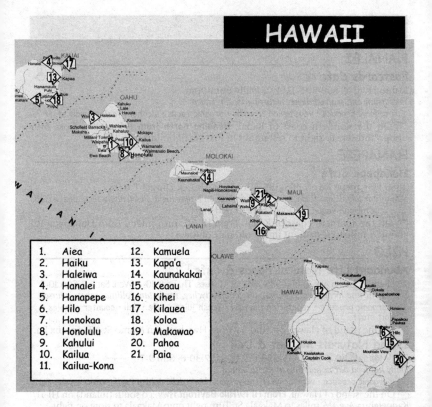

HAWAII

1. Aiea	12. Kamuela
2. Haiku	13. Kapa'a
3. Haleiwa	14. Kaunakakai
4. Hanalei	15. Keaau
5. Hanapepe	16. Kihei
6. Hilo	17. Kilauea
7. Honokaa	18. Koloa
8. Honolulu	19. Makawao
9. Kahului	20. Pahoa
10. Kailua	21. Paia
11. Kailua-Kona	

AIEA

Down to Earth Natural Foods

98-131 Kaonohi St. ☎ 808-488-1375 ⏰ Daily 8-10
· organic produce · vegetarian · deli · take-out

🏠 On the southern coast of Oahu about 9 miles north of Honolulu. **From Kamehameha Hwy (HI 99)**, turn inland onto Kaonohi St.

HAIKU

Veg-Out

810 Kokomo Rd. ☎ 808-575-5320 ⏰ M-F 10:30-7, Sat-Sun 11:30-7:30
A casual place serving sandwiches, salads, stir-fries, chili and such.
· vegetarian · vegan friendly · fresh juice · tables · self-service · take-out

🏠 On the northern side of Maui. **From Hana Hwy (HI 36)**, turn inland onto Haiku Rd (HI 366) about 1½ miles to Kokomo Rd (HI 398). Continue straight onto Kokomo to restaurant.

HALEIWA

Celestial Natural Foods & Paradise Found Cafe

66-443 Kamehameha Hwy. ☎ 808-637-4540 ⏰ Store M-Sat 9-6, Sun 9-5 Cafe M-Sat 9-5, Sun 9-4
27-item menu of sandwiches, salads, sushi, curry and other dishes with a "Thai, Japanese, Caribbean, Polynesian" influence.
· vegetarian · vegan friendly · tables · wait staff · take-out

🏠 In northern Oahu. **From the south on Hwy 99**, take the first exit onto Hwy 83 (Kamehameha Hwy) about ⅓ mile to store.

HANALEI

Postcards Cafe 🍴 ♿

Kuhio Hwy. ✆ 808-826-1191 ⏰ Daily 6pm-9pm
Vegetarian and seafood dishes featuring locally grown
  • organic produce • vegetarian friendly • organic focus • alcohol • tables • wait staff
🛑 On the northern coast of Kauai. **Heading north from Princeville,** cross over bridge and stay to right to restaurant in first small building on left.

HANAPEPE

Hanapepe Cafe 🍴

3830 Hanapepe Rd. ✆ 808-335-5011 ⏰ M-Th 7-3, Dinner F 6-9
Mainly a breakfast/lunch place with "fine dining" on Friday night. Reservations requested. BYOB.
  • vegetarian • vegan friendly • tables • wait staff
🛑 On the southern coast of Kauai. **From HI 50,** turn inland onto Hanapepe Rd about ¼ mile to restaurant in the old part of town.

HILO

Abundant Life Natural Foods & Cafe 🛍 🍴

292 Kamehameha Ave. ✆ 808-935-7411 ⏰ M, Tues, Th, Fri 8:30-7, Wed, Sat 7-7, Sun 10-5
Sells exotic and local fruits like abui, dragoneyes, lychee, rambutan, rollinia, sapote, soursop.
  • organic produce • vegetarian friendly • fresh juice • cafe • deli • counter • tables • wait staff • take-out
🛑 On the island of Hawaii on Hilo Bayfront Hwy between Mamo St & Furneaux Ln.

Island Naturals Market & Deli 🛍 🍴

303 Makaala St. ✆ 808-935-5533 ⏰ M-Sat 7:30-8, Sun 9-7
Daily hot food bar in addition to the salad bar.
  • organic produce • vegetarian friendly • salad bar • deli • tables • self-service • take-out
🛑 On the island of Hawaii. **From HI 19/Hilo Bayfront Hwy,** go south (inland) on HI 11/Kanoelehua Ave 1½ miles to Makaala St. Turn right onto Makaala to store on right.

HONOKAA

Hamakua Natural Foods 🛍 🍴

45-3321 Mamane St. ✆ 808-775-7226 ⏰ M-F 10-6, Sat 9-2
  • vegan • cafe • tables • self-service • take-out
🛑 On the NE coast of the island of Hawaii. **From HI 19/Hawaii Belt Rd heading east,** turn left onto Pakalana St ½ mile to HI 240/Mamane St. Turn right onto HI 240 and continue on Mamane about ½ mile to store on right. **From HI 19/Hawaii Belt Rd heading west,** turn right onto HI 240/Mamane St about ¾ mile to store on left.

HONOLULU

Buddhist Vegetarian Restaurant 🍴

100 N. Beretania St. ✆ 808-532-8218 ⏰ M-Tues, Th-Sun 10:30-3 Seafood side 5:30-9
Chinese Buddhist vegan lunch.
  • vegan • tables • wait staff
🛑 **From I-H1E,** exit onto HI 98 (Olomea St) ½ mile to Liliha St. Turn right onto Liliha 2 blocks to King St. Turn left onto King and bear left at fork onto Beretania St about ⅓ mile to restaurant at Maunakea St (Chinese Cultural Plaza). **From I-H1W,** exit onto HI 98 (Vineyard Blvd) ½ mile to Pali Hwy (HI 61). Turn left onto Pali ¼ mile to Beretania St. Turn left onto Beretania ¼ mile to restaurant.

Down to Earth Natural Foods 🛍

2525 S. King St. ✆ 808-947-7678 ⏰ Daily 7:30-10
  • organic produce • vegetarian • deli • take-out
🛑 **From I-H1,** take exit 24B onto University Ave heading toward the beach to S King St. Turn right onto S King to store.

Govinda Buffet 🍴

51 Coelho Way ℂ 808-595-4913 ⏰ M-F 12:15-1:15
Weekday vegetarian lunch buffet run by Hari Krishna Temple devotees.
· vegetarian · vegan friendly · tables · self-service

🚩 **From I-H1**, take exit 21A inland on Pali Hwy (HI 61) about 1¼ miles to Coelho Way. Turn left onto Coelho to restaurant and temple (across from Philippine consulate).

Huckleberry Farms 🛍

1613 Nuuanu Ave. ℂ 808-599-1876 ⏰ M-Sat 9-8, Sun 9-6
· organic produce · deli · take-out

🚩 **From I-H1**, exit onto HI 98 (Vineyard Blvd from H1W, Olomea St from H1E) ½-1 mile to Nuuanu Ave. Turn inland on Nuuanu about ¼ mile to store at School St in Nuuanu Shopping Ctr.

Kale's Natural Foods 🛍

377 Keahole St. #A-1 ℂ 808-396-6993 ⏰ M-F 9-8, Sat-Sun 9-5
· organic produce

🚩 **From HI 72 (Kalana1naole Hwy)**, turn inland onto Keaole St ½ mile to store (past Hawaii Kai Shopping Ctr).

Kokua Market 🛍

2643 S. King St. ℂ 808-941-1922 ⏰ Daily 8:30-8:30
Premade deli foods can be eaten at the tables outside.
· organic produce · deli · take-out · co-op

🚩 **From I-H11**, take exit 24B onto University Ave heading toward the beach to S King St. Turn left onto S King to store.

Marie's Organic Cafe 🛍 🍴

2155 Kalakaua Ave. ℂ 808-926-3900 ⏰ M-Sat 10-8, Sun 10-6
Cafe features local products but store is mostly supplements and body care products.
· vegetarian friendly · organic focus · cafe · tables · self-service · take-out

🚩 **From I-H1E**, take exit 23 right onto Punahou St 1 block to S Beretania St. Turn right onto S Beretania 1 block to Kalakaua Ave. Turn left onto Kalakaua about 1½ miles to restaurant on right. **From I-H1W**, take exit 25B onto Kapiolani Blvd 1½ miles to McCully St. Turn left onto McCully 2 blocks to Kalakaua. Turn right onto Kalakaua ½ mile to restaurant.

Ruffage Natural Foods 🛍 🍴

2443 Kuhio Ave. ℂ 808-922-2042 ⏰ M-Sat 9-6
· organic produce · vegetarian friendly · fresh juice · deli · cafe · tables · self-service · take-out

🚩 1 block from Waikiki beach on Kuhio Ave between Uluniu Ave & Kapuni St.

KAHULUI

Alive & Well 🛍 🍴

340 Hana Hwy. ℂ 808-877-4950 ⏰ M-F 9-7, Sat 9-6, Sun 10-4
· organic produce · vegetarian friendly · fresh juice · deli · counter · tables · self-service · take-out

🚩 On the northern coast of Maui on Hana Hwy (HI 36) about 1 mile east of Kahului Beach Rd and under ½ mile west of Dairy Rd.

Down to Earth Natural Foods 🛍

305 Dairy Rd. ℂ 808-877-2661 ⏰ M-Sat 7-9, Sun 8-8
· organic produce · vegetarian · deli · take-out

🚩 On the northern coast of Maui. **From Hana Hwy (HI 36)**, turn inland onto Dairy Rd (HI 380) ¼ mile to store.

KAILUA

Down to Earth Natural Foods 🏠
201 Hamakua Drive © 808-262-3838 ① Daily 8-10
 • organic produce • vegetarian • deli • take-out

🍎 On the northeast side of Oahu. **From south, take Pali Hwy (HI 61)** inland straight onto Kailua Rd. Follow Kailua about 1 mile to Hamakua Dr. Turn right onto Hamakua ⅓ mile to store. **From the beach in Kailua,** take Kuulei Rd inland (become Kailua Rd) ⅔ mile to Hamakua. Turn left onto Hamakua ⅓ mile to store.

The Source 🏠
32 Kainehe St. © 808-262-5604 ① M-F 9-7, Sat 9-6, Sun 10-5
A certified organic market. Produce comes in on Friday and may be gone by mid week.
 • organic produce

🍎 On the northeast side of Oahu. **From the south, take Pali Hwy (HI 61)** inland straight onto Kailua Rd. Follow Kailua about 1 mile to Hamakua Dr. Turn left onto Kainehe St to store on right. **From the beach in Kailua,** take Kuulei Rd inland (become Kailua Rd) ⅔ mile to Kainehe. Turn right onto Kainehe to store.

KAILUA-KONA

Kona Natural Foods 🏠 🍴
75-1027 Henry St. © 808-329-2296 ① Store M-Sat 8:30-9, Sun 8:30-7 Deli M-Sat 8:30-4
After deli hours food is packaged for grab & go.
 • organic produce • vegetarian friendly • fresh juice • deli • tables • self-service • take-out

🍎 On the island of Hawaii. **From HI 11 heading north,** turn inland (right) onto Henry St (before Palani Rd/HI 190) to store. **From HI 19 coming south along the coast,** turn inland (left) onto Henry (after HI 190) to store. **From HI 190 coming from the northern interior,** veer left onto Henry (nearing the coast) about ⅓ mile to store.

KAMUELA

Healthyways II 🏠 🍴
67-1185 Mamalahoa Hwy., Ste. F137 © 808-885-6775 ① M-Sat 9-7, Sun 9-5
 • organic produce • vegetarian friendly • deli • tables • self-service • take-out

🍎 On the island of Hawaii. **From HI 19,** turn inland onto Waikoloa Rd about 12 miles to Hawaii Belt Rd/HI-190. Turn right onto HI 190 4 miles to store at Parker Ranch. **From HI 11,** go north on HI 190 over 23 miles to store at Parker Ranch.

KAPA'A

Papaya's Natural Food Cafe 🏠 🍴
4-831 Kuhio Hwy. © 808-823-0190 ① M-Sat 9-8, Sun 10-5
Special Hawaiian plate on Fridays. Outdoor tables only but in Hawaii that's no problem.
 • organic produce • vegetarian friendly • salad bar • deli • tables • self-service • take-out

🍎 On the east coast of the island of Kauai. Store is on HI 56 about 1 mile south of Kapaa town center in the Kauai Village Shopping Ctr (under the clock tower, look for big Papaya truck).

The Lotus Root 🍴
4-1384 Kuhio Hwy. © 808-823-6658 ① Daily 7-6
Breakfast, light food, baked goods, vegan ice cream, huge tea menu and outdoor seating.
 • vegan • organic focus • fresh juice • bakery • tables • self-service • take-out

🍎 On the east coast of the island of Kauai. Restaurant is on HI 56 in town at Kukui St.

KAUNAKAKAI

Outpost Natural Foods 🏠
70 Makaena Place © 808-553-3377 ① M-Th 9-6, F 9-4, Sun 10-5
 • vegetarian friendly • deli • take-out

🍎 In the main town on the island of Molokai. **Coming from the west (airport),** on entering Kaunakakai turn left onto Ala Malama Ave and make first left onto Makaena Place to store. **From east,** turn right onto Ala Malama and follow directions above.

KEAAU

Keaau Natural Foods 🛍

16-586 Old Volcano Rd., © 808-966-8877 ⊙ M-F 8:30-8, Sat 8:30-7, Sun 9:30-5
• organic produce • vegetarian friendly • deli • take-out

🍎 On the east coast of Hawaii about 7 miles south of Hilo in the Keaau Town Shopping Ctr at junction of hwys 11 & 130.

KIHEI

Hawaiian Moons Natural Foods 🛍

2411 S. Kihei Rd. © 808-875-4356 ⊙ Daily 8-9
• organic produce • vegetarian friendly • salad bar • deli • take-out

🍎 On the west coast of the island of Maui. **From HI 31/Piilani Hwy**, go west (towards ocean) on Alanui Kealii Dr ½ mile to S Kihei Rd. Turn right onto S Kihei to store on right.

KILAUEA

Healthy Hut 🛍

4270 Kilauea Rd., Ste. 335 © 808-828-6626 ⊙ Daily 8:30-9
• organic produce

🍎 On the north coast of Kauai. **From HI 56/Kuhio Hwy** merge onto Kolo Rd and go north (toward ocean) on Kilauea Rd ½ mile to store on left.

KOLOA

Koloa Natural Foods 🛍

5356 Koloa Rd. Bldg. #9 © 808-742-8910 ⊙ M-F 10:30-6:30, Sun 10:30-4
🍎 On the south side of the island of Kauai. **From HI 50/Kaumauli Hwy**, go south on Koloa Rd ⅓ mile to store on left.

MAKAWAO

Down to Earth Natural Foods 🛍

1169 Makawao Ave. © 808-572-1488 ⊙ Daily 8-8
• organic produce • vegetarian

🍎 On the northern interior of Maui. Take HI 365/400 into Makawao (becomes Makawao Ave in town).

PAHOA

Island Naturals Market & Deli 🛍 🍴

15-1403 Nanawale Homestead Rd. © 808-965-8322 ⊙ M-Sat 7:30-7:30, Sun 7:30-7
The only tables are outside but in Hawaii you can use them year-round.
• organic produce • vegetarian • salad bar • deli • tables • self-service • take-out

🍎 On the island of Hawaii in the SE corner. **From HI 11**, go south on HI 130 (Pahoa Rd) about 11 miles to Nanawale Homestead Rd. Turn left onto Nanawale to big yellow store on left.

PAIA

Fresh Mint 🍴

115 Baldwin Ave. © 808-579-9144 ⊙ M-Th, Sun 5-9, F-Sat 5-9:30
Vegetarian Vietnamese cooking.
• vegan • alcohol • tables • wait staff

🍎 On the north coast of Maui. **From the Hana Hwy (HI 36)**, turn inland onto Baldwin Ave about 3 blocks to restaurant (across from post office).

Mana Foods 🛍

49 Baldwin Ave. © 808-579-8078 ⊙ Daily 8:30-8:30
• organic produce • vegetarian friendly • fresh juice • salad bar • deli • take-out

🍎 On the north coast of Maui. **From the Hana Hwy (HI 36)**, turn inland onto Baldwin Ave to store on right.

IDAHO

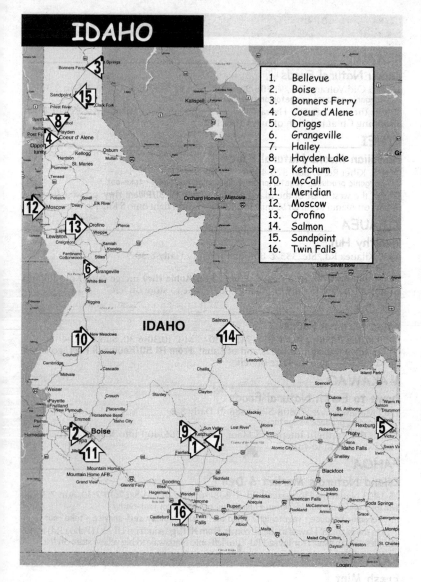

1. Bellevue
2. Boise
3. Bonners Ferry
4. Coeur d'Alene
5. Driggs
6. Grangeville
7. Hailey
8. Hayden Lake
9. Ketchum
10. McCall
11. Meridian
12. Moscow
13. Orofino
14. Salmon
15. Sandpoint
16. Twin Falls

BELLEVUE

Atkinsons' Market 🛍 🍴

757 N. Main St. © 208-788-7788 ⏰ Daily 7-9
  · organic produce · vegetarian friendly · deli · bakery · counter · tables · self-service · take-out

⛽ Take ID Hwy 75 to Bellevue where it becomes Main St. Store is on Main between Kirtley & E Spruce St.

BOISE

Boise Consumer Co-op 🛍️
888 W. Fort St. ✆ 208-342-6652 ⏰ M-Sat 9-9, Sun 9-8
• organic produce • vegetarian friendly • deli • co-op

🚗 **From I-84E**, take exit 49 onto I-184E toward City Center (184 becomes W Myrtle St) about 5 miles to S Capitol Blvd. Turn left onto Capitol ⅓ mile to W Bannock St. Turn left onto Bannock 1 block to N 8th St. Turn right onto 8th about ⅓ mile to W Fort St. Turn left onto W Fort to store. **From I-84W**, take exit 54 right onto S Broadway Ave (becomes N Ave B then E Fort St at hospital) about 3¼ miles to W Fort St. Veer right onto W Fort (State St is straight ahead) about ⅔ mile to store at 8th St.

Shangri-La Tea House 🍴   ♿
1800 W. Overland Rd. ✆ 208-424-0273 ⏰ M 10-6, Tues-10-7, W-Sat 10-8
Soups, sandwiches, salads and teas from around the world.
• vegetarian • vegan friendly • tables • wait staff

🚗 **From I-84E**, take exit 53 left onto S Vista Ave about 1½ miles to W Overland Way. Turn right onto Overland ½ mile to restaurant on left. **From I-84W**, take exit 54 right onto Broadway Ave under ¼ mile to S Federal Way. Turn left onto S Federal 1⅓ miles to W Overland. Turn left onto Overland to restaurant on right.

BONNERS FERRY

Mountain Mikes 🛍️
6769 S. Main St. ✆ 208-267-3748 ⏰ M-F 10-6, Sat 10-3
• organic produce

🚗 Store is on US 2/US 95 where Main St crosses Denver St.

COEUR D'ALENE

Pilgrim's Natural Food Market 🛍️
1316 N. 4th St. ✆ 208-676-9730 ⏰ Daily 9-8
• organic produce • vegetarian friendly • fresh juice • deli • take-out

🚗 **From I-90,** take exit 13 south on N 4th St (right from I-90E, left from I-90W) to N 3rd St. Veer right onto N 3rd St (one-way south) about ⅔ mile to Spokane Ave. Turn left onto Spokane 1 block to light at N 4th. Turn left onto N 4th to store in shopping strip on right.

DRIGGS

Barrels & Bins Community Market 🛍️ 🍴
36 S. Main St. ✆ 208-354-2307 ⏰ Daily 9-7
• organic produce • vegetarian friendly • organic focus • cafe • tables • self-service

🚗 ID 33 is the main road to Driggs. Store is on ID 33 (Main St in town) on the west side south of Little Ave.

Miso Hungry 🍴
165 N. Main St. ✆ 208-354-8015 ⏰ M-Sat 11-3
Global/ethnic foods.
• vegetarian • vegan friendly • organic focus • alcohol • tables • self-service

🚗 ID 33 is the main road to Driggs. Restaurant is on ID 33 (Main St in town) 2 blocks north of light on east side between Ashley & Wallace Ave in row of houses.

GRANGEVILLE

The Health Food Store 🛍️
221 W. Main St. ✆ 208-983-1276 ⏰ M-F 9-5:30, Sat 10-4

🚗 **From US 95**, go east on W Main St (aka ID 13) ½ mile to store on left between College & State St.

HAILEY

Atkinsons' Market 🛍 🍴

93 E. Croy St. ✆ 208-788-2294 ⏰ Daily 7-9
• organic produce • vegetarian friendly • salad bar • deli • bakery • counter • tables •
self-service • take-out

🚗 **From ID 75 traveling north**, pass the Friedman Memorial Airport, go around "S" corner into town and continue north to second light at Croy St. Turn right onto Croy 1 block to store on right in Alturas Plaza. **From ID 75 traveling south**, turn left onto Croy to store.

HAYDEN LAKE

Flour Mill Natural Foods 🛍

88 W. Commerce Drive ✆ 208-772-2911 ⏰ M-F 9-5:30, Sat 9-3
🚗 **From I-90**, take exit 12 onto US 95N (right from I-90W, left from I-90E) over 3½ miles to Honeysuckle Ave. Turn right onto Honeysuckle 1 block to Commerce Dr. Turn left onto Commerce to store on right.

KETCHUM

Akasha 🍴

160 N. Main St. ✆ 208-726-4777 ⏰ M-F Sat 9-7 (or sometimes 9), Sat-Sun 10-5
Located in the Chapter One bookstore. Mostly raw foods.
• vegan • organic focus • fresh juice • tables • self-service • take-out

🚗 Take ID Hwy 75 to Ketchum where it becomes Main St. Restaurant is on Main between 1st & 2nd St in Chapter One bookstore.

Atkinsons' Market 🛍 🍴

451 4th St. E. ✆ 208-726-5668 ⏰ Daily 7-9
• organic produce • vegetarian friendly • salad bar • deli • bakery • counter • tables •
self-service • take-out

🚗 Take ID Hwy 75 to Ketchum. Go east on 4th St to store in Giacobbi Square.

MCCALL

Huckleberry Garden 🛍

903 1st St. ✆ 208-634-8697 ⏰ M-F 10-6, Sat 11-6
• organic produce

🚗 **From ID 55N**, turn left onto Washington St and first right onto 1st St to store on right. **From 55E/E Lake St**, turn right onto 1st to store on left after Forest St.

MERIDIAN

Health Nuts Natural & Organic Market 🛍

1756 W. Cherry Lane ✆ 208-855-5756 ⏰ M-F 9-7, Sat 9-5
• organic produce

🚗 **From I-84**, take exit 44 toward Meridian north on Hwy 69/Meridian Rd (left from I-84E, merge right from I-84W) onto S Main ½ mile to E Franklin Rd. Turn left onto E Franklin 1 mile to N Linder Rd. Turn right onto N Linder 1 mile to W Cherry Ln. Turn left onto W Cherry to store on right.

MOSCOW

Moscow Food Co-op 🛍 🍴

121 E. 5th St. ✆ 208-882-8537 ⏰ Daily 7:30-9
• organic produce • vegetarian friendly • deli • bakery • counter • tables • self-service
• take-out • co-op

🚗 **From ID 95N/S Washington St**, turn left on E 5th St 1 block to store on left before Main St. **From ID 95S**, follow WC St onto Jackson St to 3rd St. Turn left onto 3rd 1 block to Main. Turn right onto Main 2 blocks to 5th. Turn left onto 5th to store on right.

OROFINO

The Health Food Store ⬡
10620 Hwy. 12 ✆ 208-476-4091 ◷ M-T, Th 9-5:30, W 9-6, F 9-12
⬡ Store is just north of Main St/Hwy 11 on Hwy St in Harper Chiropractic Clinic.

SALMON

Nature's Pantry ⬡
401 Main St. ✆ 208-756-6067 ◷ M-F 10-5:30, Sat 10-3
⬡ **From US 93/ID 28 intersection**, go northwest on US 93 (aka Main St) under ½ mile to store on south side between Andrews & Center St.

SANDPOINT

Winter Ridge Natural Foods ⬡
703 W. Lake St. ✆ 208-265-8135 ◷ M-F 8:30-7, Sat 9-5
  • organic produce • fresh juice
⬡ **From US 95N**, turn left onto Lake St under ½ mile to store on left at N Boyer Ave. **From Hwy 95S/2S (N 5th St in town)**, turn right onto Pine St under ¼ mile to Lake. Turn left onto Lake to store on right.

TWIN FALLS

Mercia's Natural Foods ⬡ 🍴
1511 Fillmore St. N. ✆ 208-734-0665 ◷ M-F 10-7, Sat 10-6
  • organic produce • vegetarian friendly • deli • tables • self-service • take-out
⬡ **From I-84**, take exit 173 toward Twin Falls onto US 93S (right from I-84E, left from I-84W) 3½-4 miles to Poleline Rd/4000N. Turn right onto Poleline ⅓ mile to first left onto Fillmore St to store on right.

The Health Food Place ⬡
1111 Blue Lakes Blvd. N. ✆ 208-733-1411 ◷ M-F 9:30-5, Sat 10-4
⬡ **From I-84**, take exit 173 toward Twin Falls onto US 93S (right from I-84E, left from I-84W) about 6 miles to store on right after Addison Ave.

ILLINOIS

1. Algonquin
2. Arlington Heights
3. Bloomington
4. Bradley
5. Carbondale
6. Champaign
7. Charleston
8. Chicago
9. Crystal Lake
10. De Kalb
11. Decatur
12. Deerfield
13. Edwardsville
14. Effingham
15. Evanston
16. Flossmoor
17. Geneva
18. Highland
19. Hinsdale
20. Lansing
21. Lombard
22. Matteson
23. Morris
24. Mount Prospect
25. New Lenox
26. Normal
27. Orland Park
28. Oswego
29. Palatine
30. Peoria
31. River Forest
32. Rockford
33. Rockton
34. Schaumburg
35. Skokie
36. Springfield
37. Streamwood
38. Urbana
39. West Dundee
40. Westmont
41. Wheaton
42. Willowbroo

ALGONQUIN

Expressly Leslie 🍴

100 S. Randall Rd. ℡ 224-567-0417 ⏱ M-Tues, Th-Sun 11-7
Middleastern offerings.

· vegetarian · vegan friendly · tables · self-service · take-out

🍴 **From I-90**, go north on Randall Rd (left from I-90E, right from I-90W) about 6¾ miles to store on northwest corner at Algonquin Rd inside Joe Caputtos market.

ARLINGTON HEIGHTS

Chowpatti Vegetarian Restaurant ♨
1035 S. Arlington Heights Rd. ✆ 847-640-9554 ⏰ Tues-Sun 11:30-3, 5-9
26-page menu with over 300 choices. Mostly Indian plus a smattering of global favorites.
   • vegetarian • vegan friendly • tables • wait staff • take-out
🍴 **From I-90**, take Arlington Heights Rd exit toward Arlington Heights north on S Arlington Heights Rd 1½ miles to restaurant.

BLOOMINGTON

Common Ground Grocery 🛍
516 N. Main St. ✆ 309-829-2621 ⏰ M-Sat 9-6
   • organic produce
🍴 **From I-74**, take exit 160A east on W Market almost 2 miles to downtown light at Main St. Turn left onto Main to store on left.

BRADLEY

Kankakee Natural Foods 🛍
1035 Mulligan Dr. ✆ 815-933-6236 ⏰ M-Th, Sat 9-5:30, F 9-7
🍴 **From I-57,** take exit 315 toward Bradley south on IL 50S 1 mile to Mulligan Dr. Turn left onto Mulligan to store.

CARBONDALE

Neighborhood Co-op 🛍 ♨
1815 W. Main St. ✆ 618-529-3533 ⏰ M-F, Sun 9-9, Sat 8-9
   • organic produce • vegetarian friendly • cafe • deli • bakery • tables • self-service •
   take-out • co-op
🍴 Rt 13 and US 51 intersect in Carbondale. Store is on Rt 13 (aka W Main St) 1¼ miles west of US 51 intersection on the south side between N Glenview & W Sycamore St.

Town Square Market 🛍
106 E. Jackson St. ✆ 618-529-2312 ⏰ M-Sat 10-7, Sun 12-6
   • organic produce • vegetarian friendly • deli • bakery • tables • wait staff • take-out
🍴 **From Rt 13/W Main St & US 51/Illinois Ave intersection**, store is 1 block north and 1 block east on north side of Jackson St after tracks.

CHAMPAIGN

Natural Gourmet 🛍
2225 S. Neil St. ✆ 217-355-6365 ⏰ M-Sat 9-6
   • organic produce • vegetarian friendly • deli • take-out
🍴 **From I-57N**, merge onto I-72E 1 mile continuing onto W University Ave ⅓ mile to Mattis Ave. Turn right onto Mattis ⅓ mile to W Springfield Ave. Turn left onto Springfield under 2 miles to S Neil St. Turn right onto Neil 1¾ miles to store on right after W Kirby/E Florida Ave. **From I-57S**, merge onto I-74E. From I-74, take exit 182 south on Neil (right from I-74E, left from I-74W) about 3¼ miles to store on right.

CHARLESTON

Natural Food & Nutrition 🛍
422 Madison Ave. ✆ 217-345-1130 ⏰ M-F 9-5:30, Sat 9-3
🍴 **From SR 16**, go north on 4th St (left from 16E, right from 16W) under 1 mile to store at Madison Ave (1 block north & 1 block west of Coles County Court).

CHICAGO

Alice & Friends Vegetarian Cafe 🍴
5812 N. Broadway © 773-275-8797 ⏱ M-F 4-10, Sat 12-9
Mix of vegetarian Asian cuisines.
• vegetarian • vegan friendly • tables • wait staff
🍎 **Take S Lake Shore Dr heading north** from downtown Chicago to where it merges onto W Hollywood Ave (just south of Sheridan Rd). Take Hollywood under ¼ mile to N Broadway St. Turn right onto N Broadway about ⅓ mile to restaurant on left after W Ardmore Ave.

Amitabul 🍴
6207 N. Milwaukee Ave. © 773-774-0276 ⏱ Tues-Sat 12-9
Vegan Korean based on Zen principles..
• vegan • tables • wait staff
🍎 **From I-90 (Kennedy Expwy)**, take exit 82A toward Nagle Ave. Turn left onto N Nagle, right onto W Huntington and left onto N Milwaukee to restaurant.

Arya Bhavan 🍴
2508 W. Devon Ave. © 773-274-5800 ⏱ M-F 12-3, 5-9:30 Sat-Sun 12-9:30 (Closed for lunch in winter)
Indian vegetarian with buffet option for lunch weekdays and dinner on the weekend.
• vegetarian • vegan • tables • self-service • wait staff
🍎 **From north of Chicago on I-94S**, take exit 39B east on Trouhy Ave to IL 50 (N Cicero). Turn onto 50 about 1 mile to W Devon Ave. Turn left onto Devon about 1 mile to restaurant. **From south of Chicago on I-94N**, take exit 47A (FullertonAve/2400N) north on Western Ave about 4¾ miles to W Devon. Turn left onto Devon to restaurant.

Chicago Diner 🍴
3411 N. Halsted St. © 773-935-6696 ⏱ M-F 11-10, Sat-Sun 10-10
Hearty vegetarian diner food and lush vegan desserts.
• vegetarian • vegan friendly • alcohol • counter • tables • wait staff • take-out
🍎 **From I-90/94**, take 45C exit east on Belmont Ave about 3 miles to Halsted St. Turn left onto Halsted 4 blocks to restaurant after Roscoe St. **From Lake Shore Dr**, go west on Belmont about ½ mile to Halsted. Turn right onto Halsted and follow directions above.

Cousin's Incredible Vitality 🍴
3038 W. Irving Park Rd. © 773-478-6868 ⏱ Daily 11-10
Menu includes raw food options.
• vegan • organic focus • fresh juice • alcohol • tables • wait staff • take-out
🍎 **From I-90/94W**, take exit 45A left onto W Addison St about ¾ mile to N Sacramento Ave. Turn left onto N Sacramento ½ mile to W Irving. Turn left onto W Irving 1 block to restaurant on right. **From I-90/94E**, take exit 47B for Fullerton Ave right onto N Western Ave about 2 miles to W Irving. Turn left onto W Irving about ¾ mile to restaurant on right at N Whipple St.

Earwax Cafe 🍴
1561 N. Milwaukee Ave. © 773-772-4019 ⏱ Daily 9-10:30
Mostly vegetarian and vegan soups, stews and sandwiches in a combination coffee house/ video store. This neighborhood place is very smoker-friendly.
• vegetarian friendly • vegan friendly • tables • wait staff
🍎 **From I-90/94**, take exit 48B west on North Ave (right from I-90E, left from I-90W) about ½ mile to N Honore St. Turn left onto Honore 2 blocks to N Milwaukee Ave. Turn right onto N Milwaukee about 1 block to restaurant (before intersection with N Damen & W North Ave).

Green Zebra 🍴

1460 W. Chicago Ave. ✆ 312-243-7100 🕐 M-Th 5:30-10, F-Sat 5-11, Sun 10:30-2, 5-9
Innovative vegetarian menu with one fish and one chicken option.
　• vegetarian friendly • vegan friendly • alcohol • tables • wait staff
🚗 **From I-90/94E**, take exit 45A onto N Racine Ave, turn right onto W Huron, right onto N Willard Ct and left onto W Chicago Ave ⅓ mile to restaurant on right at N Greenview Ave. **From I-90/94W**, take exit 49B onto W Augusta Ave to N Noble St. Turn right onto N Noble ⅓ mile to W Chicago. Turn right onto W Chicago 2 blocks to restaurant.

Handlebar Bar & Grill 🍴

2311 W. North Ave. ✆ 773-384-9546 🕐 M-Th 11am-12am, F 11am-2am, Sat 10am-2am, Sun 10am-11pm
Bar food featuring vegetarian, vegan and fish. Outdoor beer garden in warm weather.
　• vegetarian friendly • vegan friendly • alcohol • counter • tables • wait staff
🚗 **From I-90/94**, take exit 48B west on North Ave (right from I-90E, left from I-90W) 1 mile to restaurant on left after Oakley Ave.

Heartland Cafe 🍴

7000 N. Glenwood Ave. ✆ 773-465-8005 🕐 M-Th 7am-10pm, F 7am-11pm, Sat 8am-11 pm, Sun 8am-10pm Adjacent bar open until wee am
Mostly vegetarian healthy fare. Beyond the menu there's live music, poetry nights, political events, a radio show, performance space, the Red Line Tap bar and more.
　• vegetarian friendly • vegan friendly • alcohol • tables • wait staff
🚗 **From downtown Chicago,** take Rt 41 north, which becomes Sheridan Rd after Rt 14. Continue 4-5 intersections to Greenleaf Ave. Turn left onto Greenleaf (or onto Estes for parking) to Glenwood Ave. Turn left onto Glenwood to restaurant complex.

Karyn's Cooked 🍴

738 N. Wells St. ✆ 312-587-1050 🕐 M, Sun 11-9, Tues-Sat 11-10
Sandwiches, wraps and vegan comfort foods (meatloaf, lasagna, ribs) made from seitan, tofu and soy protein.
　• vegan • alcohol • tables • wait staff
🚗 **From I-90/94**, take exit 50 B onto W Ohio about 1 mile to N Franklin St. Turn left onto N Franklin about ¼ mile to W Superior St. Turn right onto W Superior and first left onto N Wells St to restaurant on left.

Karyn's Fresh Corner 🍴

1901 N. Halsted St. ✆ 773-255-1590 🕐 Cafe Daily 9-10 Restaurant 11:30-10
A "Living Foods" cafe and gourmet restaurant on the same premises.
　• vegan • organic focus • tables • self-service • take-out
🚗 **From I-90/94**, take exit 48B east on North Ave (right from I-90W, left from I-90E) almost 1 mile to Halsted St. Turn left onto Halsted to restaurant on east side.

Lake Side Cafe 🍴

1418 W. Howard St. ✆ 773-262-9503 🕐 Tues-F, Sun 5-9, Sat 12-9
Soups, salads, sandwiches, thin crust pizza and two daily entree specials.
　• vegetarian • vegan friendly • organic focus • fresh juice • tables • self-service
🚗 **From downtown Chicago**, take Rt 41/Lakeshore Dr north and turn right at end onto N Sheridan Rd over 2½ miles to W Howard St. Turn left onto W Howard to restaurant on right.

Mana Foodbar 🍴

1742 W. Division St. ✆ 773-342-1742 🕐 M-12-10, Tues-Th 4-10, F-Sat 12-11, Sun 12-9
Small place with additional seating on outdoor patio serving global vegetarian fare.
　• vegetarian • fresh juice • alcohol • counter • tables • wait staff • take-out
🚗 **From I-94E/90E**, take exit 49A right onto Division St ½ mile to restaurant on right between Hermitage & Wood St. **From I-94W/90W**, take exit 49B for Augusta Ave right onto N Milwaukee Ave under ½ mile to Division. Veer left onto Division ⅓ mile to restaurant.

New Life Health Foods 🛍 🍴
3141 W. Roosevelt Rd. ℂ 73-762-1090 ⏱ M-F 9-7, Sat 10-7
  • vegetarian • vegan friendly • cafe • tables • wait staff
🚗 **From I-290E,** take exit 27A right onto S Sacramento Blvd ½ mile to W Roosevelt Rd. Turn left onto W Roosevelt 2 blocks to store on left. **From I-290W,** take exit 2B onto W Van Buren St to S Sacramento. Turn left onto S Sacramento almost ¾ mile and follow directions above.

Newleaf Natural Grocery 🛍
1261 W. Loyola Ave. ℂ 773-743-0400 ⏱ M-F 8-7:30, Sat 9-7:30, Sun 11-6
  • organic produce
🚗 **From downtown Chicago,** take Rt 41/Lakeshore Dr north and turn right at end onto N Sheridan Rd about 1⅓ miles to W Arthur Ave. Turn left onto W Arthur to first right onto N Lakewood Ave 1 block to W Loyola Ave. Turn right onto W Loyola to store on right.

Soul Vegetarian East 🍴
205 E. 75th St. ℂ 773-224-0104 ⏱ M-Th 8-10, F-Sat 7-11, Sun 8-9
Healthy, vegan, southern-style soul food. Homemade soy cheese and "ice-kream."
  • vegan • tables • wait staff • take-out
🚗 **From I-94E,** take exit 60A toward 75th St onto S Lafayette St. Turn left onto E 75th 4 blocks to restaurant at S Indiana Ave. **From I-90/94W,** take exit 60B toward 76th St onto S State St. Turn right onto E 75th 3 blocks to restaurant.

True Nature Food 🛍 🍴
6034 N. Broadway St. ℂ 773-465-6400 ⏱ M-F, Sun 10-7, Sat 9-7
  • organic produce • vegetarian friendly • fresh juice • tables • self-service • take-out
🚗 **Take S Lake Shore Dr heading north** from downtown Chicago to where it merges onto W Hollywood Ave (just south of Sheridan Rd). Take Hollywood about ¼ mile to N Broadway St. Turn right onto N Broadway under ½ mile to restaurant on left between W Elmdale Ave & W Norwood St.

Udupi Palace Restaurant 🍴
2543 W. Devon Ave. ℂ 773-338-2152 ⏱ Daily 11:30-10
Indian vegetarian with daily lunch buffet.
  • vegetarian • vegan friendly • tables • self-service • wait staff
🚗 **From I-94E,** take exit 39B east on Trouhy Ave to IL 50 (N Cicero). Turn right onto 50S about 1 mile to W Devon Ave. Turn left onto Devon about 2¾ miles to restaurant. **From I-90W,** take exit 47A (FullertonAve/2400N) north on Western Ave about 4¾ miles to W Devon. Turn left onto Devon about 4 blocks to restaurant.

Victory's Banner 🍴
2100 W. Roscoe Ave. ℂ 773-665-0227 ⏱ M, W-Sun 8-3
Run by disciples of Sri Chinmoy. Sumptuous breakfast and lunch menu.
  • vegetarian • tables • wait staff
🚗 **From I-90/94E,** take exit 45A left onto Addison St 2 miles to N Hoyne Ave. Turn right onto N Hoyne 2 blocks to W Roscoe Ave. Turn right onto W Roscoe to restaurant on right. **From I-90/94W,** take exit 47A for Fullerton Ave right onto N Western Ave 1 mile to W Roscoe. Turn left onto W Roscoe 6 blocks to restaurant.

Whole Foods Market 🛍 🍴 ♿
30 W. Huron St. ℂ 312-932-9600 ⏱ Daily 8-10
In the downtown Chicago Loop, near the major hotels and museums.
  • organic produce • vegetarian friendly • salad bar • cafe • self-service • take-out
🚗 **From I 90-/94,** take exit 50B east on Ohio St about ½ mile to Dearborn St. Turn left onto Dearborn, pass Huron St and turn right into store garage (parking is free).

Whole Foods Market 🛍 🍴 &

3300 N. Ashland Ave. ✆ 773-244-4200 ⏰ Daily 8-10
 • organic produce • vegetarian friendly • salad bar • cafe • self-service • take-out

🚗 **From I-90/94**, take exit 45C east on Belmont Ave about 4 miles. Turn left onto Ashland Ave 1 block to store on west side. **From Lake Shore Drive**, take Belmont Ave exit west on Belmont about 2 miles. Turn right onto Ashland Ave 1 block to store.

Whole Foods Market 🛍 🍴 &

1000 W. North Ave. ✆ 312-587-0648 ⏰ Daily 8-10
 • organic produce • vegetarian friendly • salad bar • cafe • self-service • take-out

🚗 **From I 90/94**, take exit 48B east on North Ave about ½ mile to Sheffield Ave. Turn left onto Sheffield and left into store parking lot .

CRYSTAL LAKE

Crystal Lake Health Foods 🛍

25 E. Crystal Lake Ave. ✆ 815-459-7942 ⏰ M-W, F 9-6, Th 9-7, Sat 9-5
🚗 Enter Crystal Lake via Rt 176 from Rt 14 or 31. Store is in old downtown between Walkup & Main St.

DE KALB

Duck Soup Co-op 🛍

129 E. Hillcrest Drive ✆ 815-756-7044 ⏰ M-F 9-8, Sat-Sun 9-5
🚗 **From on I-88E (EW Tollway)**, take IL 23/Ann Glidden Rd/DeKalb exit onto S Annie Glidden Rd about 1⅔ miles to SR 38 (E Lincoln Hwy). Turn right onto Lincoln about 1¼ miles to IL 23. Turn left onto 23 (aka S 4th St) about 1 mile to Hillcrest Dr. Turn left onto Hillcrest to store on right. **From I-88W**, turn right onto Peace Rd about 1¾ miles to E Lincoln Hwy. Turn left onto Lincoln 1½ miles to N 4th St. Turn right onto N 4th about 1 mile to Hillcrest. Turn left onto Hillcrest to store.

DECATUR

Country Nutrition 🛍

645 W. Pershing Rd. ✆ 217-877-6502 ⏰ M-F 8:30-5:30, Sat 8:30-5
 • organic produce

🚗 **From I-72E**, take exit 138 toward Decatur/Lincoln right onto Hwy 121 (becomes W Pershing Rd) 2½ miles to store on right after Barnes Dr. **From I-72W**, take exit 141 for US 51S toward Decatur onto US 51S/Veteran's Pkwy 2¼ miles to W Pershing. Turn right onto W Pershing to store on left after MacArthur Rd.

DEERFIELD

Whole Foods Market 🛍 🍴

760 Waukegan Rd. ✆ 847-444-1900 ⏰ Daily 8-10
 • organic produce • vegetarian friendly • salad bar • cafe • self-service • take-out

🚗 **From I-94**, take Deerfield Rd east (left from I-94E, right from I-94W) about 1½ miles to Waukegan Rd. Turn right onto Waukegan to store at Deerfield Rd. **From US 41**, take Lake Cook Rd west under 2 miles to Waukegan. Turn right onto Waukegan about 1 mile to store.

EDWARDSVILLE

Green Earth Grocery 🛍 🍴 &

441 S. Buchanan ✆ 618-656-3375 ⏰ M-F 9-7, Sat 9-5, Sun 11-5 Deli M-F 11-5, Sat 11-4
 • organic produce • vegetarian friendly • fresh juice • cafe • deli • counter • tables • wait staff • take-out

🚗 **From I-55 or I-70,** merge onto I-270. **From I-270**, take exit 12 toward Edwardsville north on Hwy 159 about 3½ miles to center of town. Once road becomes S Buchanan St store is 3 blocks north in Market Basket Shopping Ctr.

EFFINGHAM

Vitalia Natural Foods 🛒

401 S. Banker St. ✆ 217-342-5483 ⏰ M-Sat 9-6
Produce sold seasonally.

🚗 **From I-57S or I-70W**, take exit 162 toward Effington left onto US 45/N 3rd St 2 miles to Fayette Ave. Turn right onto W Fayette 4 blocks to S Banker St. Turn left onto S Banker to store on right after Amtrak station. **From I-57N**, merge onto I-70E. **From I-70E**, take exit 159 right onto W Fayette about ¾ miles to S Banker. Turn right onto S Banker to store.

EVANSTON

Blind Faith Cafe 🍴

525 Dempster St. ✆ 847-328-6875 ⏰ M-Th 9-9, F 9-10, Sat 8-10, Sun 8-9
Self-serve counter for quick meals, table service for more leisurely dining.
   • vegetarian • vegan friendly • organic focus • bakery • alcohol • tables • self-service • wait staff • take-out

🚗 **From Chicago**, take Sheridan Ave north and veer left onto South Blvd under ½ mile to Chicago Ave. Turn right onto Chicago 1 mile to Dempster St. Turn right onto Dempster to restaurant on left.

JD Mills Food Company Inc. 🛒

635 Chicago Ave. ✆ 847-491-0940 ⏰ M-F 8-8, Sat 8-6:30, Sun 9-5
🚗 **From Chicago**, take Sheridan Ave north and veer left onto South Blvd under ½ mile to Chicago Ave. Turn right onto Chicago past first block to store on right.

Whole Foods Market 🛒 🍴   ♿

1640 Chicago Ave. ✆ 847-733-1600 ⏰ Daily 8-10
   • organic produce • vegetarian friendly • salad bar • cafe • self-service • take-out

🚗 **From I-94E**, take exit 37A right onto Skokie Blvd/US 41S 2 miles to Golf Rd. Turn right onto Golf 2 miles continuing onto Emerson St 1¾ miles to Sheridan Rd. Turn right onto Sheridan and veer right onto Chicago Ave 2 blocks to store at Church St. **From I-94W**, take exit 37B onto IL-58/Dempster St about 4 miles to Chicago Ave. Turn left onto Chicago 5 blocks to store.

Whole Foods Market 🛒 🍴

1111 Chicago Ave. ✆ 847-475-9492 ⏰ Daily 8-10
   • organic produce • vegetarian friendly • salad bar • cafe • self-service • take-out

🚗 **From US 41 or I-94 exit 37B**, go east on IL-58/Dempster St about 4 miles to Chicago Ave. Turn right onto Chicago about 2 blocks to store on left between Hamilton & Greenleaf St. **From Sheridan Rd**, veer right onto Chicago about 1 mile to store.

Wild Tree Cafe 🍴

1100 Davis St. ✆ 847-425-9691 ⏰ M-F 7-8:30, Sat 8-8:30, Sun 9-8:30
Emphasis is on sustainability. Outdoor seating when weather permits.
   • vegetarian friendly • vegan friendly • organic focus • tables • self-service

🚗 **From Chicago**, take Sheridan Ave north and veer left onto South Blvd under ½ mile to Chicago Ave. Turn right onto Chicago 1 mile to Dempster St. Turn left onto Dempster 4 blocks to Oak Ave. Turn right onto Oak 4 blocks to Davis St. Turn left onto Davis to restaurant on left.

FLOSSMOOR

Sunrise Health Foods 🛒 🍴

3203 Vollmer Rd. ✆ 708-365-5400 ⏰ M-F 9-8, Sat 9-7
Juice bar also makes smoothies and daily soups.
   • organic produce • vegetarian friendly • fresh juice • tables • self-service • take-out

🚗 **From I-57**, take exit 324 (342A from I-57S) right onto Vollmer Rd about 2½ miles to store on left at Kedzie Ave in Flossmoor Commons.

GENEVA
Soup To Nuts ⌂
716 W. State St. © 630-232-6646 ⏱ M-F 9-7, Sat 9-6, Sun 11-5
⌂ **From I-88,** take exit 4 toward Aurora/Batavia north on IL 31 about 7miles to IL 38 (State St). Turn left onto 38 about ½ mile to store on SW corner in Engstrom Plaza.

HIGHLAND
Highland Nutrition ⌂
320 Walnut St. © 618-654-9017 ⏱ M-F 9-7, Sat 9-5, Sun 11-5
• organic produce

⌂ **From I-70E,** take exit 24 toward Highland east on Rt 143 over 4 miles to Walnut St (where 143 & US 40 intersect). Turn right onto Walnut 1½ blocks to store. **From I-70W,** take exit 30 toward Highland west on US 40 about 4 miles to Walnut. Turn left onto Walnut 1½ blocks to store.

HINSDALE
Whole Foods Market ⌂ 🍴
500 E. Ogden Ave. © 630-986-8500 ⏱ M-F 8-10, Sat 8-9, Sun 8-8
• organic produce • vegetarian friendly • salad bar • cafe • self-service • take-out

⌂ **From I-88 (EW Tollway),** merge onto I-294. **From I-294,** take Ogden Ave exit west, make first left onto County Line Rd and turn left into store lot (sign visible from interstate).

LANSING
Sunrise Health Foods ⌂
17650 Torrence Ave. © 708-474-6166 ⏱ -F 9-9, Sat 9-7
Juice bar also makes smoothies and daily soups to go.
• organic produce • fresh juice • take-out

⌂ **From I-94 or I-80,** take exit 161 towards US 6W south on Torrence Ave (right from I-94/80E, left from I-94/80W) under ¼ mile to store on right between 176th & 177th St.

LOMBARD
Sri Ganesh Indian Cuisine 🍴
837 E. Roosevelt Rd. © 630-620-9175 ⏱ Tues-Sun 11:30-2:30, 5:30-10
Vegetarian Indian with a lunch buffet.
• vegetarian • vegan friendly, tables • self-service, wait staff

⌂ **From I-355,** take Roosevelt Rd/State Hwy 38 exit east on E Roosevelt (left from I-355E, right from I-355W) 2½-3 miles to restaurant on right past High Point Shopping Ctr between S Edgewood & Athens Ave.

MATTESON
South Suburban Food Coop ⌂
21750 Main St. © 708-747-2256 ⏱ M, Tues, F 11-8, Th 2-8, Sat 9:30-3:30
A members-only co-op but co-op members from other areas are welcome and travelers can shop one time.

⌂ **From I-57,** take exit 340 (340A from 57S) east on Lincoln Hwy/US 30E about 2 miles to Main St. Turn right onto Main under 1 mile to store on right in Stawicki Industrial Park.

MORRIS
Body & Soul ⌂
320 W. Illinois Ave. © 815-941-2611 ⏱ M-F 9:30-6, Sat 9:30-5, Sun 10-2
⌂ **From I-80,** take exit 112 onto Rt 47 south about 2¼ miles to sixth light (Main St). Turn right onto Main 2 blocks to Liberty St. Turn left onto Liberty to store on right.

MOUNT PROSPECT

Sweetgrass Vitamin & Health Market 🛍

1742 W. Golf Rd. ☏ 847-956-1939 ⏰ M-F 9:30-8, Sat 9:30-6, Sun 10-5

🚗 **From I-90 (NW Tollway)**, take N Elmhurst Rd exit north about 2 miles to W Golf Rd. Turn left onto Golf 1 mile to store on NW corner at S Busse Rd.

NEW LENOX

Natural Choices Health Food Store 🛍

1340 N. Cedar Rd. ☏ 815-485-5572 ⏰ M, W 10-5, Tues, Th-F 10-6, Sat 10-2

🚗 **From I-80,** take exit 137 right onto Rt 30E/Maple Rd 1¼-1½ miles to N Cedar Rd. Turn left onto Cedar about 1 mile to store on right.

NORMAL

Coffeehouse & Deli 🍴   ♿

114 E. Beaufort St. ☏ 309-452-6774 ⏰ M-Sat 7am-10pm, Sun 8am-9pm

Coffeehouse fare of soups, salads, sandwiches and daily specials.

• vegetarian • tables • self-service • take-out

🚗 **From I-55S,** take exit 164-165 toward Bloomington/Normal left onto Main St 2 miles to W College Ave. Turn left onto College about ¾ mile to Broadway St. Turn right onto Broadway, left onto S Linden St and left onto E Beaufort St to restaurant on right. **From I-39S or I-74E,** merge onto I-55N, take exit 165A and follow directions above. **From I-74W/I-55N,** take exit 160A right onto Market St/US 150 and follow 150 almost 2 miles to N Main. Turn left onto N Main 1¼ miles to W Beaufort. Turn right onto Beaufort about ¾ mile to restaurant on left after W North St.

ORLAND PARK

Sunrise Health Foods 🛍

15818 Harlem Ave. ☏ 708-845-5424 ⏰ M-Sat 9-7

Juice bar also makes smoothies and daily soups to go.

• organic produce • vegetarian friendly • fresh juice • take-out

🚗 **From I-80,** take exit 148B north on Harlem Ave almost 4 miles to store on left at 159th St in Home Depot Plaza.

OSWEGO

Second Opinion Health Food 🛍

4551 Rte. 71 ☏ 630-551-0222 ⏰ M-Sat 10-7

🚗 **From US 34N or Rt 31S**, cross bridge at E Washington St (right from US 34N, left from Rt 31S) under 1 mile to Rt 71. Turn right onto Rt 71 to store on right. **From US 34S,** merge onto Rt 71 at Chicago Rd under 1 mile to store on right.

PALATINE

Whole Foods Market 🛍 🍴   ♿

1331 N. Rand Rd. ☏ 847-776-8080 ⏰ Daily 8-10

• organic produce • vegetarian friendly • salad bar • cafe • self-service • take-out

🚗 **From I-90 (NW Tollway) or I-290N,** take IL 53N about 6 miles to Rand Rd. Turn left onto Rand almost 1 mile to store on right in Park Place Shopping Ctr. **From I-94 or I-294,** take Lake Cook Rd west about 5½ miles to S Arlington Rd. Turn left onto S Arlington 1 mile to W Dundee Rd. Turn right onto Dundee almost 2 miles to Rand. Make sharp left onto Rand to store on left.

PEORIA

Naturally Yours Grocery 🛍 🍴

4700 N. University St. ☏ 309-692-4448 ⏰ M-Sat 9-9

• vegetarian friendly • deli • tables • self-service • take-out

From I-74, take ext 89 onto US 150E/N War Memorial Dr 1 mile to N University St. Turn left onto N University under 1 mile to store on right in Metro Shopping Ctr.

RIVER FOREST

Whole Foods Market
7245 W. Lake St. © 708-366-1045 ⏰ Daily 8-10
• organic produce • vegetarian friendly • salad bar • cafe • self-service • take-out
From I-290, take 21B north on N Harlem Ave (left from I-290E, right from I-290W) 1 mile to Lake St. Turn left onto Lake to store on SW corner.

ROCKFORD

Choices Natural Market
6551 E. Riverside Blvd. © 815-282-1861 ⏰ M-F 9-7, Sat 9-5, Sun 11-4
• organic produce
From I-39/90, go west on E Riverside Blvd (right from I-39S/90E, left from I-39N/90W) about 1 mile to store on left.

Vitamins 'N More
1627 N. Alpine Rd. © 815-226-4605 ⏰ M-F 9-7, Sat 9-5
Specialty is gluten-free foods.
From I-39S/90E, turn right onto E Riverside Blvd 3¼ miles to N Alpine Rd. Turn left onto N Alpine about 2⅓ miles to store on left in the Shops of Edgebrook. From I-39N, take exit onto US 20W toward Rockford 2¼ miles to N Alpine. Turn right onto N Alpine almost 4½ miles to store on right. From I-90W, take US 20 Bus exit toward State St and keep right at fork onto E State 3½ miles to N Alpine. Turn right onto N Alpine 1½ miles to store.

ROCKTON

Nature's Pantry
112 W. Main St. © 815-624-8663 ⏰ M-F 10-6:45, Sat 9:30-4:45
• organic produce
From I-39/I-90, go west on E Rockton Rd (left from I-39W/I-90N, right from I-39E/I-90S) under ½ mile (becomes E Union St) to N Blackhawk Blvd. Turn left onto N Blackhawk 3 blocks to Main St. Turn right onto W Main to store on left.

SCHAUMBURG

Udupi Palace
730 Schaumburg Rd. © 847-884-9510 ⏰ M-F 11:30-3, 5-9:45 Sat-Sun 11:30-9:45
South Indian vegetarian with a daily lunch buffet.
• vegetarian • vegan friendly • fresh juice • tables • self-service • wait staff
From SR 53S, take exit 1B right onto E Higgins Rd about ¾ mile to N Meacham Rd. Turn left onto N Meacham ¾ mile to E Schaumburg Rd. Turn right onto E Schaumburg 1 mile to restaurant on right after Plum Grove Rd. From I-290W, take exit 4 left onto Biesterfield Rd under ½ mile to Rohlwing Rd. Turn right onto Rohlwing 1⅓ miles continuing onto N Martingale ⅓ mile to New Schaumburg Rd. Turn left onto New Schaumburg (becomes E Schaumburg) 2 miles to restaurant.

SKOKIE

Slice of Life
4120 W. Dempster St. © 847-674-2021 ⏰ M-Th 11:30-9, F 11:30-3, Sat ½ hour after dark-12:30am, Sun 10:30-9
This kosher restaurant has a dairy side that is vegetarian and fish and a a separate meat side.
• vegetarian friendly • vegan friendly • kosher • alcohol • tables • wait staff
From I-94, take exit 37B east on Dempster St about 1½ miles to restaurant on left between Kedvale & Karlov Ave.

SPRINGFIELD

Food Fantasies 🛍️

1512 W. Wabash Ave. ✆ 217-793-8009 ⏱ M-F 9-8, Sat 9-6, Sun 12-4

🚗 **From I-72E**, take exit 93 toward Springfield left onto IL 4N (S Veteran's Pkwy) 1⅔ miles to Wabash Ave. Turn right onto Wabash 1½ miles to store on right. **From I-55S/I-72W**, take exit 93 right onto SR 4/Veterans Pkwy 1⅓ miles to Wabash. Turn right onto Wabash and follow directions above. **From I-55N**, take exit 95A-B and continue on 55 about 1¾ miles to E Stanford Ave. Turn left onto Stanford (becomes Wabash) over 1½ miles to restaurant on left.

Holy Land Diner 🍴   ♿

107 W. Cook St. ✆ 217-544-5786 ⏱ Lunch M-Sat 11-2 Dinner F-Sat 5-9

Middleastern buffet restaurant with a big vegetarian selection and all-vegetarian Saturday night. BYOB.

• vegetarian friendly • tables • self-service

🚗 **From I-72E**, take exit 97B into I-55N about 1¼ miles to S 6th St. Continue onto S 6th 2 miles to S Grand Ave. Turn left onto S Grand 4 blocks to S 2nd St. Turn right onto S 2nd ½ mile to Cook St. Turn left onto Cook to restaurant on right. **From I-72W**, continue on SR 97W/E Clear Lake Ave 3 miles to N 2nd St. Turn left onto N 2nd over ½ mile to Cook St. Turn right onto Cook to restaurant. **From I-55S**, take exit 98B onto SR 97W and follow directions above.

STREAMWOOD

Organica Vitamin & Health Food 🛍️

289 N. Barrington Rd. ✆ 630-872-2000 ⏱ M-F 10-8, Sat 10-6

🚗 **From I-90W**, go south on N Barrington Rd 3 miles to store on left after Bode Rd. **From I-90E**, take Hwy 59 exit right onto 59/Sutton Rd 1⅓ miles to Rt 58/Evanston Elgin/Golf Rd. Turn left onto 58 2½ miles to N Barrington. Turn right onto Barrington ¾ mile to store.

URBANA

Red Herring 🍴

1209 W. Oregon S. ✆ 217-367-2340 ⏱ Tues-Th 11-8, F 11-7

Two daily soups, sandwiches, a hot entree and fresh baked items.

• vegan • organic focus • tables • self-service • co-op

🚗 **From I-74**, take exit 183 south on N Lincoln Ave (right from I-74E, left from I-74W) about 2 miles to W Oregon St. Turn left onto Oregon ¼ mile to restaurant on SE corner at Matthews Ave in basement of Channing Murray Foundation.

Strawberry Fields Natural Foods Store & Cafe 🛍️ 🍴   ♿

306 W. Springfield Ave. ✆ 217-328-1655 ⏱ M-Sat 7-8, Sun 10-6

• organic produce • vegetarian friendly • cafe • deli • bakery • tables • self-service • take-out

🚗 **From I-74**, take exit 184 onto 45S/N Cunningham Ave (right from I-74E, left from I-74W) over 1 mile to light at US 150/University Ave. Continue straight onto N Vine St ¼ mile to next light (E Main St). Turn right onto E Main ¼ mile (past 2 lights) to Race St and bear left at fork 1 block to store on right.

WEST DUNDEE

Golden Harvest Health Foods 🛍️

330 N. 8th St. (Rte. 31) ✆ 847-551-3551 ⏱ M 10-8, Tues 10:30-9, W, F 10:30-7, Sat 10:30-5

• organic produce

🚗 **From I-90**, take Rt 31N exit over 2 miles to store on left between Washington & Geneva St.

WESTMONT

Apple Valley Natural Foods 🛍️
806 E. Ogden Ave. ✆ 630-789-2270 ◷ M-W 9-6, Th 9-8, F 9-3, Sun 10-5
A vegetarian health food store.

🍴 **From I-294**, go west on Ogden Ave (right from I-294S, left from I-294N) over 1½ miles to store on right at I-83 in St James Crossing Plaza (enter about ¼ mile further from Pasquinelli Dr).

Shree 🍴   ♿
655 N. Cass Ave. ✆ 630-655-1021 ◷ Tues-F 11:30-2:30, 5:30-9:30, Sat 12:30-3, 5:30-10:30, Sun 12-3:30, 5:30-9:30
Indian vegetarian. Weekday lunch is buffet.
 • vegetarian • vegan friendly • tables • wait staff • take-out

🍴 **From I-55**, take exit 273B onto Rt 15N/Cass Ave almost 6 miles (past Rt 34/Ogden Ave) to restaurant on right in Cass & Ogden Plaza.

WHEATON

Whole Foods Market 🛍️ 🍴   ♿
151 Rice Lake Square (Butterfield Rd.) ✆ 630-588-1500 ◷ Daily 8-10
 • organic produce • vegetarian friendly • salad bar • cafe • self-service • take-out

🍴 **From I-88 (EW Tollway)**, take Naperville Rd north about 1½ miles to Butterfield Rd. Turn right onto Butterfield to second entrance to Rice Lake Shopping Ctr on left to store.

WILLOWBROOK

Whole Foods Market 🛍️ 🍴
201 W. 63rd St. ✆ 630-655-5000 ◷ Daily 8-10
 • organic produce • vegetarian friendly • salad bar • cafe • self-service • take-out

🍴 **From I-55**, take exit 274 onto Kingery Hwy/Rt 83N about 3 miles to W 63rd St. Turn left onto 63rd 1 block to store on left.

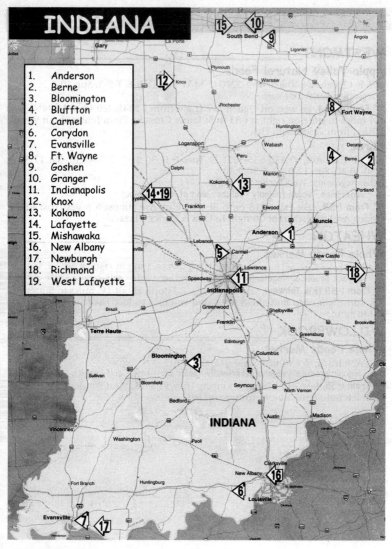

INDIANA

1. Anderson
2. Berne
3. Bloomington
4. Bluffton
5. Carmel
6. Corydon
7. Evansville
8. Ft. Wayne
9. Goshen
10. Granger
11. Indianapolis
12. Knox
13. Kokomo
14. Lafayette
15. Mishawaka
16. New Albany
17. Newburgh
18. Richmond
19. West Lafayette

ANDERSON
Frist Natural Foods
835 E. 53rd St. ☎ 765-642-8992 ⏰ M-W 9-6, Th 9-7, F 9-5, Sun 1-5
🛍 **From I-69**, take exit 26 toward Anderson (left from I-69N, right from I-69S) onto IN 9N/S Scatterfield Rd ½-¾ mile to E 53rd St. Turn left onto 53rd about ½ mile to store on left in Southdale Plaza.

BERNE
Earthen Treasures Natural Food Market 🛍 🍴   ♿
906 N. Hwy. 27 ☎ 260-589-3675 ⏰ M-F 9-6, Sat 9-3
• vegetarian friendly • cafe • deli • bakery • tables • wait staff • take-out
🛍 **From IN 218** in Berne, turn north at light onto US 27 (left from 218E, right from 218W) about ½ mile to store on west side at Pharr Rd.

BLOOMINGTON

Bloomingfoods 🛍️
419 E. Kirkwood Ave. ✆ 812-336-5300 ⏰ M-Sat 8-9, Sun 9-8
• organic produce • vegetarian friendly • deli • take-out • co-op
🚗 **From Hwy 37**, take 46 Bypass east over 1 mile to College Ave. Turn right onto College about 1⅓ miles to Kirkwood Ave. Turn left onto Kirkwood to store down alley on left.

Bloomingfoods 🛍️ 🍴
316 W. 6th St. ✆ 812-333-7312 ⏰ M-Sat 7-10, Sun 9-8
• organic produce • vegetarian friendly • salad bar • deli • tables • self-serve • take-out • co-op
🚗 **From Hwy 37**, take 46 Bypass east over 1 mile to College Ave. Turn right onto College over 1 mile to W 6th St. Turn right onto 6th 1 block to store on right.

Bloomingfoods Market & Deli 🛍️ 🍴
3220 E. Third St. ✆ 812-336-5400 ⏰ Daily 8-10
• organic produce • vegetarian friendly • salad bar • deli • tables • self-service • take-out • co-op
🚗 **From Hwy 37**, take 46 Bypass east almost 4 miles to 3rd St. Turn left onto 3rd about ¼ mile to store on right.

Laughing Planet Cafe 🍴 ♿
322 E. Kirkwood Ave. ✆ 812-323-2233 ⏰ Daily 11-9
"California Burritos & other Whole Foods in a hurry."
• vegetarian friendly • vegan friendly • organic focus • counter • self-service • take-out
🚗 **From Hwy 37**, take 46 Bypass east about 1 mile to College Ave. Turn right onto College about 1⅓ miles to Kirkwood Ave. Turn left onto Kirkwood to restaurant.

BLUFFTON

A Harvest of Health 🛍️
760 N. Main St. ✆ 260-824-1600 ⏰ M-F 9-5:30, Sat 9-3
🚗 Bluffton is about 14 miles south of I-469 on IN 1. Store is on 1 (aka Main St) on east side in Villa North Ctr strip mall.

CARMEL

Whole Foods Market 🛍️ 🍴
14598 Clay Terrace Blvd. ✆ 317-569-1517 ⏰ M-Sat 8-10, Sun 8-9
• organic produce • vegetarian friendly • salad bar • cafe • self-service • take-out
🚗 **From I-465**, take exit 31 left onto Meridian St about 5⅓ miles to Clay Terrace Blvd. Turn left onto Clay Terrace and take second exit off each traffic circle to continue on Clay Terrace to store on left at E 146th St.

CORYDON

Harmony & Health 🛍️
220 E. Chestnut St. ✆ 812-738-5433 ⏰ M-F 9-6, Sat 9-3
🚗 **From I-64**, take exit 105 toward Corydon south on Hwy 135 about ¾ mile to Old Hwy 135. Turn left then right onto Old Hwy 35 continuing onto IN 337 over 1½ miles total to Hwy 62. Turn left onto Hwy 62/E Chestnut St 2 blocks to store on left after Mulberry St.

EVANSVILLE

Adele's Naturally 🛍️
2704 Lincoln Ave. ✆ 812-471-3144 ⏰ M-F 9-6, Sat 9-4
🚗 **From IN/US 41**, go east on Lincoln Ave (left from IN 41S, right from US 41N) 1½ miles to store on left. **From Veteran's Memorial Pkwy**, merge onto US 41 and follow directions above. **From I-164S**, take exit 7B onto E Lloyd Expwy 3 miles to Vann Ave. Turn left onto Vann ½ mile to Lincoln. Turn right onto Lincoln 2 blocks to store on right.

Elbert's Natural Foods 🛍
5614 E. Virginia St. © 812-471-5071 ⏲ M-F 9-7, Sat 9-6
 • organic produce

🚗 **From I-164,** take exit 7B west on E Lloyd Expwy almost 1½ miles to Kimber Ln. Turn right onto Kimber to first left onto E Virginia 2 blocks to store on right.

Penny Lane Coffee House 🍴
600 S.E. 2nd St. © 812-421-8741 ⏲ Tues-Th 7-9, F 7-11, Sat 9-11, Sun 9-6
Coffeehouse atmosphere, art exhibitions and live music.
 • vegetarian • vegan friendly • organic focus • tables • self-service

🚗 **From I-164W,** merge onto Veteran's Pkwy 2⅓ miles to Mulberry St. Turn right then left onto Mulberry 2 blocks to restaurant on left at SE 2nd St. **From IN 41,** go west on Washington Ave (right from 41S, left from 41N) 1⅓ miles to SE 2nd. Turn right onto 2nd 3 blocks to restaurant on right at Mulberry.

River City Food Co-op 🛍🍴
116 Washington Ave. © 812-401-7301 ⏲ M-Th 10-7, F-Sat 9-5, Sun 12-5
Only meal is Monday lunch, served from 11-2:30 and usually vegetarian.
 • organic produce • vegetarian • tables • wait staff • co-op

🚗 **From I-164W,** merge onto Veteran's Pkwy 2 miles and turn right onto Shawnee Dr/Adams Ave about 4 blocks to SE 2nd St. Turn left onto SE 2nd 1 block to Washington Ave. Turn right onto Washington 2 blocks to store on left. **From IN 41,** go west on Washington (right from 41S, left from 41N) 1 mile to store on right.

FT. WAYNE

Health Food Shoppe 🛍
3515 N. Anthony Blvd. © 260-483-5211 ⏲ M-Sat 8-8
 • organic produce • salad bar • deli • take-out

🚗 **From I-69N,** take exit 111A onto US 27S about ¾ mile to Coliseum Blvd. Turn left onto Coliseum almost 2 miles to N Anthony Blvd. Turn right onto N Anthony about ½ mile to store. **From I-69S,** take exit 112A-B onto Coldwater Rd/IN 327S about 1⅔ miles to Coliseum. Turn left onto Coliseum about 1 mile to N Anthony. Turn right onto N Anthony about ½ mile to store.

Three Rivers Co-op Natural Food & Deli 🛍🍴 ♿
1612 Sherman Blvd. © 260-424-8812 ⏲ M-Sat 7-9 Sun 10-8
 • organic produce • vegetarian friendly • fresh juice • salad bar • cafe • deli • tables • self-service • co-op

🚗 **From I-69,** take exit 105A toward Ft Wayne east on Illinois Rd (right from I-69N, left from I-69S) about 2½ miles to W Main St. Veer left onto W Main ½ mile to Leesburg Rd. Turn left onto Leesburg about ¾ mile to Spring St. Turn right onto Spring about 1 mile to store at Sherman Blvd.

GOSHEN

Maple City Market 🛍
314 S. Main St. © 574-534-2355 ⏲ M-Sat 8-8
 • organic produce • deli • bakery • take-out • co-op

🚗 **From I-80/90 (Indiana EW Toll Rd),** take exit 101 left onto Rt 15 south about 11½ miles to store at Rt 33 & 15 intersection.

GRANGER

Down to Earth 🛍🍴 ♿
14678 S.R. 23 © 574-271-1497 ⏲ M-Th 9-8, F 9-7, Sat 9-5, Sun 12-5
 • organic produce • vegetarian friendly • fresh juice • counter • tables • wait staff • take-out

🚗 **From I-80/90 (Indiana EW Toll Rd),** take exit 83 north onto Capitol Ave (around to left from I-80/90E, merge straight then right from I-80/90W) to store just off hwy on SR 23.

INDIANAPOLIS

Georgetown Natural Foods Market 🛒 🍴   ♿

4375 Georgetown Rd. ✆ 317-293-9525 ⏰ M-Sat 9-8, Sun 11-5
• organic produce • vegetarian friendly • organic focus • fresh juice • salad bar • deli • counter • tables • self-service • take-out

🚗 **From I-65**, take exit 121 south on Lafayette Rd (right from I-65S, left from I-65N) ½-1 mile to Georgetown Rd. Turn left onto Georgetown to store on left. **From I-465**, take exit 17 toward Indianapolis east on 38th St about 1½ miles to Lafayette. Turn left onto Lafayette about 1 mile to Georgetown. Turn right onto Georgetown to store on right.

Good Earth Natural Food Co. 🛒

6350 N. Guilford Ave. ✆ 317-253-3709 ⏰ M-Sat 9-7, Sun 12-5
• organic produce

🚗 **From I-465E/US 421S**, take exit 31 onto US 31S/N Meridian St (right from I-465E, left from I-465/US 421S) about 3½ miles to 71st St. Turn left onto 71st about ½ mile to College Ave. Turn right onto College about ¾ mile to 64th St. Turn left onto 64th 3 blocks to Guilford Ave. Turn right onto Guilford ½ block to store on right. **From I-65S**, merge onto I-465E and follow directions above. **From I-65N**, take exit 111 and follow Market St W ramp onto E Market St to College. Turn right onto N College 7 miles to Broad Ripple Ave. Turn right onto Broad Ripple 2 blocks to Guilford. Turn left onto Guilford to store on left.

Nature's Pharm Natural Market 🛒   ♿

8215 U.S. Hwy. 31 S. ✆ 317-888-0557 ⏰ M-Sat 9-8, Sun 12-5
• organic produce

🚗 **From I-65**, take exit 101 west on County Line Rd (right from I-65S, left from I-65N) to Hwy 31. Turn right onto Hwy 31 about ¾ mile to store on right after Fed Ex/Kinkos.

Three Sisters Cafe 🍴

6360 Guilford Ave. ✆ 317-257-5556 ⏰ Daily 8-4
• vegetarian friendly • alcohol • tables • wait staff

🚗 **From I-465E/US 421S**, take exit 31 onto US 31S/N Meridian St (right from I-465E, left from I-465/US 421S) about 3½ miles to 71st St. Turn left onto 71st about ½ mile to College Ave. Turn right onto College to about ¾ mile 64th St. Turn left onto 64th 3 blocks to Guilford Ave. Turn right onto Guilford to restaurant on right. **From I-65S,** merge onto I-465E and follow directions above. **From I-65N,** take exit 111 and follow Market St W ramp onto E Market St to College. Turn right onto N College 7 miles to Broad Ripple Ave. Turn right onto Broad Ripple 2 blocks to Guilford. Turn left onto Guilford to restaurant.

Udupi Cafe 🍴

4225 Lafayette Rd. ✆ 317-299-2127 ⏰ Lunch Tues-F 11-2:30, Sat-Sun 11:30-3 Dinner Tues-Th 5:30-9:30, F-Sun 5:30-10
Vegetarian Indian with buffet option at lunch.
• vegetarian • vegan friendly • alcohol • tables • self-service • wait staff • take-out

🚗 **From I-65S**, take exit 121 right onto Lafayette Rd under 1 mile to Office Plaza Blvd. Turn left onto Office Plaza to restaurant at end of shopping center on left (at International Bazaar). **From I-65N**, take exit 119 and merge left onto W 38th St over 1½ miles to Lafayette Rd. Turn right onto Lafayette about ¾ mile to Office Plaza Blvd. Turn right onto Office Plaza to restaurant **From I-70E**, merge onto I-65N and follow directions above. **From I-465W**, take exit 17 right onto 38th St 1¾ miles to Georgetown Rd. Turn left onto Georgetown ⅓ mile to Lafayette. Turn left onto Lafayette about ¼ mile to Office Plaza. Turn right onto Office Plaza to restaurant. **From I-70W**, merge onto I-465N and follow directions above from I-465W.

Vintage Whole Foods 🛒

7391 N. Shadeland Ave. © 317-842-1032 ⏰ M-Sat 9-7
• organic produce

🚗 **From I-69S or I-465W exit 37**, take Rt 37S about ¾ mile to 75th St. Turn left onto 75th about ⅔ mile to Shadeland Ave. Turn right onto Shadeland to store in Shadeland Station Shopping Ctr. **From I-465E**, take exit 40 (56th St) toward Shadeland Ave and follow I-465N/Shadeland Ave ramp, then Shadeland Ave ramp onto Shadeland. Merge onto N Shadeland Ave about 1¾ miles to store.

Whole Foods Market 🛒 🍴 ♿

1300 E. 86th St. © 317-706-0900 ⏰ M-Sat 8-10, Sun 8-9
• organic produce • vegetarian friendly • salad bar • cafe • self-service • take-out

🚗 **From I-465E/US 421S**, take exit 31 onto US 31S/N Meridian St about 1 mile to 86th St. Turn left onto 86th about 1 mile to store on left at Evergreen Ave in Nora Plaza. **From I-465W**, take exit 33 left onto Keystone Ave N about ½ mile onto 86th St ramp toward Nora/Castleton. Turn right onto 86th about 1¼ miles to store on right. **From I-70E**, take exit 90 onto I-465N and follow directions above. **From downtown Indianapolis or I-65 exit 113**, take Meridian north to 86th. Turn right onto 86th and follow directions above.

Winding Way Farms 🛒

5888 E. 82nd St. © 317-849-3362 ⏰ M-Sat 9-8, Sun 12-5
Specialty is gluten-free foods.

🚗 **From I-465E**, take exit 35 right at fork toward Noblesville onto Allinsville Rd under ½ mile to E 82nd St. Turn left onto E 82nd about ¾ mile to store on left in Castleton Sq Mall. **From I-465N**, merge onto I-69N. **From I-69**, take exit 1 right onto E 82nd about 1 mile to store on right.

KNOX

Back to Basics 🛒 🍴

1307 S. Heaton St. (Hwy. 35) © 574-772-2345 ⏰ M-F 9:30-6, Sat 9-4
Wednesdays is "taste day" when the cafe offers free samplings.
• organic produce • vegetarian friendly • fresh juice • cafe • tables • self-service • take-out

🚗 US 30 and US 35 intersect in Knox. From US 30/35 intersection, store is south on US 35 about 7½ miles (just south of town center) on east side.

KOKOMO

Sunspot Natural Market 🛒

3717 S. Reed Rd. © 765-453-5555 ⏰ M-Sat 9-8, Sun 11-6
• organic produce

🚗 On US 31(aka Reed Rd) in Kokomo. About 35 miles due north of Indianapolis.

LAFAYETTE

Nature's Pharm Natural Market 🛒

3500 SR 38 E. © 765-446-2929 ⏰ M-Sat 9-8, Sun 11-6
• organic produce

🚗 **From I-65S**, take exit 172 toward Lafayette/Rossville right onto SR 26E 2 miles to Sagamore Pkwy. Turn left onto Sagamore over 1 mile to SR 38E. Veer left onto SR 38E ⅓ mile to store on left. **From I-65N**, take exit 168 toward Lafayette and follow right fork onto SR 38E/Walnut St about 4½ miles to store on right.

MISHAWAKA

Garden Patch Market 🛒

228 W. Edison Rd. © 574-255-3151 ⏰ M-Sat 10-7

🚗 **From I-80/90 (Indiana Toll Rd)**, take exit 83 toward Mishawaka right onto Capitol Ave ⅓ mile to Rt 23. Turn left onto 23 1½ miles to Main St (third light). Turn left onto Main about 2 miles to Edison Rd. Turn right onto Edison to store on right before Grape Rd.

Harmony Market
5616 Grape Rd. © 574-273-4026 ⊙ M-Th 9-9, F 9-6, Sun 11-6
• organic produce • vegetarian friendly • fresh juice • deli • tables • self-service • take-out

From I-80/90 (Indiana Toll Rd), take exit 83 toward Mishawaka right onto Capitol Ave ⅓ mile to SR 23. Turn left onto 23 2 miles to Grape Rd. Turn left onto Grape 1 mile to store on left after Indian River Blvd.

NEW ALBANY

Creekside Outpost Health Food Store & Intertribal Cafe
614 Hausfeldt Lane © 812-948-9118 ⊙ Tues-Sat 10-7
One menu offers Native American and "Old West" inspired vegetarian fare. A second menu features game meats (elk, wild boar, black bear, kangaroo, ostrich) as well as hormone-free meat and fowl made using separate cookware.
• organic produce • vegetarian friendly • fresh juice • cafe • tables • wait staff • take-out

From I-65, take exit 6B onto I-265W 3½ miles to exit 3. Turn right onto Grantline Rd and left at first light onto Hausfeldt Ln across tracks to restaurant in first driveway on left. **From I-64**, take exit 121 onto I-265E 3 miles to exit 3. Turn left onto Grantline to second light (Hausfeldt). Turn left and follow directions above.

Rainbow Blossom Natural Foods Market
3003 Charlestown Crossing Way © 812-941-0080 ⊙ M-Sat 9-9, Sun 11-7
• organic produce

From I-264, take exit 4 north on IN 311/Charlestown Rd (right from I-264W, left from I-264E) ⅓-½ mile to Charlestown Crossing Way. Turn left onto Charlestown Crossing to store on left.

NEWBURGH

Paradise Organics
2700 SR 261 © 812-842-0820 ⊙ M-Sat 10-6, Sun 12-4
• organic produce

From I-64, take exit 29A onto I-164S about ⅓ mile to exit 7A and merge onto IN 66E/E Lloyds Expwy 3⅓ miles to IN Hwy 261. Turn left on Hwy 261 1½ miles to store on right past Oak Grove/Casey Rd intersection at Para St.

RICHMOND

Clear Creek Food Co-op
701 National Rd. W. © 765-983-1547 ⊙ M-Th 11-8, F 11-6, Sat-Sun 12-5 May vary with school calendar so call first
On the Earlham College campus. Deli operates year-round plus hot vegetarian lunches during the academic year.
• organic produce • vegetarian • vegan friendly • deli • cafe • tables • self-service • co-op

From I-70, take exit 149A onto IN 38E almost 3 miles to National Rd W. Turn left onto National to College Ave. Turn left onto College and right onto D St to "T" intersection. Turn left then immediately right to store next to campus security office.

WEST LAFAYETTE

Sunspot Natural Foods
500 W. Sagamore Pkwy. (U.S. 52) © 765-464-1555 ⊙ M-Sat 9-8, Sun 11-6
• organic produce

From I-65, take exit 175 toward Lafayette onto IN 25/Schulyer 1⅓ miles to Sagamore Pkwy N/US 52. Turn right onto Sagamore Pkwy 2½ miles to store on right.

IOWA

AMES

John's Natural Foods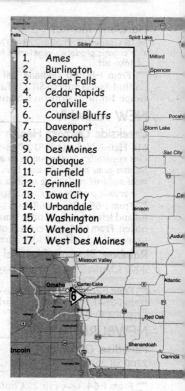

326 5th St. ✆ 515-233-1280 ⏲ M-W, F 10-7, Th 10-8, Sat 9-6

📅 **From US 30**, take exit 148 north on S Duff Ave (right from US 30W, left from US 30E) 1¼ miles to E Lincoln Way. Turn left onto E Lincoln 2 blocks to Kellog Ave. Turn right onto Kellog 2 blocks (past tracks) to 5th St. Turn left onto 5th to store on left. **From I-35N**, take exit 111B onto US 30W 1¾ miles to S Duff Ave and follow directions above. **From I-35S**, take exit 113 right onto E 13th St 2 miles to Duff. Turn left onto Duff over ½ mile to 5th St. Turn right onto 5th 2 blocks to store.

Wheatsfield Grocery Cooperative

413 Northwestern Ave. ✆ 515-232-4094 ⏲ Daily 8-9

📅 **From US 30,** take exit 148 north on S Duff Ave (right from US 30W, left from US 30E) 1½ miles to Main St (after tracks). Turn left onto Main ½ mile until it turns onto Northwestern Ave to store on left (after bridge). **From I-35N**, take exit 111B onto US 30W 1¾ miles to S Duff and follow directions above. **From I-35S**, take exit 113 right onto E 13th St 2 miles to Duff. Turn left onto Duff over ½ mile to Main. Turn right onto Main over bridge to store.

BURLINGTON

Nature's Corner

423 Jefferson St. ✆ 319-754-8653 ⏲ M-F 9:30-5:30, Sat 9:30-5

📅 **From US 34E**, take exit 263 for IA 99/Main St right onto Columbia St and left onto Main 2 blocks to Jefferson St, Turn right onto Jefferson 2 blocks to store on left. **From US 34W**, take IA 99 exit left onto Main and follow directions above.

CEDAR FALLS

Roots Market ♿

2021 Main St. ✆ 319-266-3801 ⏲ M-Sat 9-7, Sun 11-6
  • organic produce • vegetarian friendly • deli • take-out

📅 **From Hwy 58**, take 18th St exit west (left from 58N, right from 58S) 2 blocks to Main St. Turn left onto Main 3 blocks to store at 21st St. **From US 20**, take exit 225 onto 58N about 4⅓ miles to 18th St and follow directions above.

CEDAR RAPIDS

Health Hut

1512 1st Ave. N.E. ✆ 319-362-7345 ⏲ M-F 9-5:30, Sat 9-5

📅 **From I-380**, take exit 20B onto 7th St NE (left from I-380S, right from I-380N) 2 blocks to 1st Ave SE. Turn left onto 1st ¾ mile to store on left after 15th St.

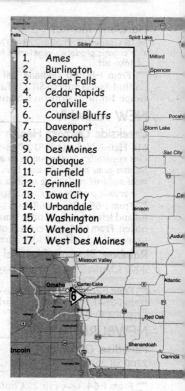

1. Ames
2. Burlington
3. Cedar Falls
4. Cedar Rapids
5. Coralville
6. Counsel Bluffs
7. Davenport
8. Decorah
9. Des Moines
10. Dubuque
11. Fairfield
12. Grinnell
13. Iowa City
14. Urbandale
15. Washington
16. Waterloo
17. West Des Moines

CORALVILLE

New Pioneer Co-op 🛍️ 🍴   ♿

1101 2nd St. ℰ 319-358-5513 ⏰ Daily 7-10 Deli 11-8 Hot entrees 11-7
 • organic produce • vegetarian friendly • fresh juice • salad bar • deli • bakery • tables
 • self-service • take-out • co-op

🚗 **From I-80E**, take exit 240 right onto Rt 965S about ¼ mile to Hwy 6. Turn left onto Hwy 6 almost 2 miles to store on left in City Center Sq. **From I-80W**, take exit 242 left onto 1st Ave about 1½ miles to Hwy 6. Turn right onto Hwy 6 ¾ mile to store on right.

COUNCIL BLUFFS

Green Acres Natural Food Market 🛍️

805 S. Main St. ℰ 712-323-5799 ⏰ M-F 10-6, Sat 9-4
 • organic produce

🚗 **From I-80W**, take exit 8 right onto US6 (E Kanesville Blvd, E then W Broadway) about 3¾ miles to S 4th St. Turn left onto S 4th ½ mile to S Worth St. Turn right onto S Worth 1 block to S Main St. Turn left onto S Main to store on left. **From I-29S**, take exit 56 on left for Hwy 192S onto N 16th St almost 1½ miles to W Broadway. Turn left onto W Broadway 1 mile to S 4th. Turn right onto S 4th and follow directions above. **From I-29N**, take exit 3 for Hwy 192N left onto S 4th about 1½ miles to S 6th Ave. Turn right onto 6th 1 block to Pearl St. Turn right onto Pearl 1 block to S Main. Turn right onto S Main 2 blocks to store on left at 8th Ave.

DAVENPORT

Greatest Grains 🛍 🍴

1600 Harrison St. ℗ 563-323-7521 ⏲ M-Sat 9-8, Sun 10-7
  • organic produce • vegetarian friendly • fresh juice • cafe • deli • bakery • tables • self-serve • take-out

🍎 **From I-80,** take exit 295A onto Hwy 61S about 4½ miles to 16th St. Turn right onto 16th to store at Harrison St.

DECORAH

Oneota Community Co-op 🛍 🍴   ♿

312 W. Water St. ℗ 563-382-4666 ⏲ M-Sat 8:30-8:30, Sun 10-7
  • organic produce • vegetarian friendly • cafe • deli • bakery • tables • self-service • take-out • co-op

🍎 **From IA 9 traveling east**, turn left onto Short St 3 blocks, bear left onto Mechanic St and at second light turn right onto Water St 1 block to store on right. **From IA 9 traveling west,** turn right at stone "Decorah" sign onto Montgomery St to end. Turn left onto Water past four lights to store on right (before 5th light).

DES MOINES

Campbell's Nutrition 🛍

4040 University Ave. ℗ 515-277-6351 ⏲ M-Th 9-7, F 9-6, Sat 9-5
  • organic produce • vegetarian friendly • fresh juice • deli • tables • self-service • take-out

🍎 **From I-235**, take 42nd St exit north on 42nd (left from I-235E, right from I-235W) under ¾ mile to University Ave. Turn right onto University to store on right between 41st & 40th St.

New City Market 🛍

4721 University Ave. ℗ 515-255-7380 ⏲ M, F 9-6:30, Tues-Th 9-8, Sat 9-6, Sun 11-5
  • organic produce

🍎 **From I-235**, take 42nd St exit north on 42nd (left from I-235E, right from I-235W) under ¾ mile to University Ave. Turn left onto University under ½ mile to store on right between 47th & 48th St.

DUBUQUE

Breitback's Market 🛍

1109 Iowa St. ℗ 563-557-1777 ⏲ M-F 10-5:30, Sat 8-5
  • organic produce

🍎 **From US 151S/US 61S**, take US 52N/IA 3W exit onto 11th St under ½ mile to Iowa St. Turn right onto Iowa to store on left. **From US 151N/61N**, exit onto IA 3/ White St over ½ mile to 11th. Turn left onto 11th 2 blocks to Iowa. Turn right onto Iowa to store. **From US 20**, go north on S Locust St (left from US 20E, right from US 20W) ½ mile to W 5th St. Turn right onto W 5th 2 blocks to Iowa. Turn left onto Iowa under ½ mile to store.

FAIRFIELD

Everybody's Market 🛍 🍴

501 N. 2nd St. ℗ 641-472-5199 ⏲ Daily 8:30-9:30
  • vegetarian friendly • cafe • tables • wait staff • take-out

🍎 **From US 34**, turn north onto Rt 1/N 2nd St (right from 34W, left from 34E) about ⅓ mile to store at E Lowe Ave.

Maharishi University of Management Cafeteria 🍴

1000 N. 4th St. ℗ 641-472-7000 ⏲ Daily 8:30-10, 11:45-1:30, 6:30-8:15
Vegetarian organic cafeteria located in the student union.
  • vegetarian • vegan friendly • organic focus • tables • self-service

🍎 **From US 34**, turn north onto Rt 1/N 2nd St (right from 34W, left from 34E) over ½ mile to W Merrill Ave. Turn left onto W Merrill 2 blocks to N 4th St. Turn right onto N 4th to Maharishi U and restaurant on left in Student Union.

Mohan Delights 🍴

101 W. Broadway Ave. ✆ 641-469-6900 ⏰ Tues-F 11:30am-1:30pm
Indian ayurvedic cuisine in an ayurvedic health center.
   • vegetarian • vegan friendly • organic focus • tables • self-service
🚗 **From US 34**, turn north onto Rt 1/N 2nd St (right from 34W, left from 34E) 1 block to W Broadway Ave. Turn right onto W Broadway about 1 block to restaurant on left before Main St.

The Raj 🍴

1734 Jasmine Ave. ✆ 641-472-9580 ⏰ M-Th 12-2, Sun seatings at 11:30 & 1
Indian ayurvedic buffet.
   • vegetarian • vegan friendly • tables • self-service
🚗 **From US 34**, turn north onto Rt 1/N 2nd St (right from 34W, left from 34E) over ½ mile to W Merrill Ave. Turn left onto W Merrill 2 blocks to N 4th St. Turn right onto N 4th/IA 1 and follow IA 1 about 3¼ miles to 170th St. Turn left onto 170th 1¼ miles to Jasmine Ave. Turn right onto Jasmine under ¼ mile to restaurant on left.

GRINNELL

Juli's Health & More Food Store 🛍

931 West St. ✆ 41-236-7376 ⏰ M-F 9-5:30 (closed for lunch 1-2), Sat 9-2
   • organic produce
🚗 **From I-80**, take exit 182 toward Grinnell onto IA 146N (left from I-80E, right from I-80W) almost 3½ miles to store on left 1 block past tracks.

IOWA CITY

Masala Indian Vegetarian Cuisine 🍴

9 S. Dubuque St. ✆ 319-338-6199 ⏰ Daily 11-2:30, 5-9:30
Indian vegetarian with lunch buffet and evening specials emphasizing local and organic produce.
   • vegetarian • alcohol • counter • tables • wait staff • take-out
🚗 **From I-80**, take exit 244 toward Iowa City south on Dubuque St (right from I-80E, left from I-80W) about 2 miles to restaurant on right after Iowa Ave.

New Pioneer Co-op 🛍

22 S. Van Buren St. ✆ 319-338-9441 ⏰ Daily 7-11
   • organic produce • vegetarian friendly • deli • bakery • take-out • co-op
🚗 **From I-80**, take exit 244 toward Iowa City south on Dubuque St (right from I-80E, left from I-80W) about 2 miles to T-junction at Washington St. Turn left onto Washington 3 blocks to store on NE corner at Van Buren St.

The Red Avocado 🍴

521 E. Washington St. ✆ 319-351-6088 ⏰ Tues-Sat 11-2:30, 5:50-9, Sun seasonal 11-2:30
BYOB (small corking charge).
   • vegetarian • vegan friendly • organic focus • fresh juice • tables • wait staff
🚗 **From I-80**, take exit 244 toward Iowa City south on Dubuque St (right from I-80E, left from I-80W) about 2 miles to T-junction at Washington St. Turn left onto Washington 3½ blocks to restaurant.

URBANDALE

Campbell's Nutrition 🛍

2749 100th St. ✆ 515 331-1390 ⏰ M-F 10-6, Sat 10-5
🚗 **From I-35N/I-80E**, take exit 125 right onto Hickman Rd 1 mile to NW 100th St. Turn right onto NW 100th under ½ mile to store on right. **From I-35S/I-80W**, take exit 125 left onto Hickman and follow directions above. **From I-235W**, take exit 2 right onto 22nd St continuing onto NW 86th St 1½ miles to Hickman Rd. Turn left onto Hickman and follow directions above.

WASHINGTON

Stone Mill Natural Foods 🛍️

105 N. Marion Ave. ✆ 319-653-5732 ◷ Tues-Th 10-7, F-Sat 9-5
• organic produce seasonally.

🚗 **From IA 1N**, turn right onto IA 92/Madison St under 1 mile to S Marion Ave. Turn right onto S Marion 3 blocks to store on left at W Main St. **From IA 1/92S**, (becomes Madison St) turn right onto S Marion and follow directions above.

WATERLOO

Green Fields Health Food Center 🛍️

2920 Falls Ave. ✆ 319-235-9990 ◷ M-F 9:30-5:30, Sat 9:30-5

🚗 **From I-380N or US 20W**, merge onto US 218N/Washington St almost 4 miles to US 63S/Sargeant Rd. Turn left onto Sargeant and right onto University Ave about 1²⁄₃ miles to Falls Ave. Make sharp right onto Falls to store on left. **From US 20E**, take exit 227 right onto 63N about 2¹⁄₃ miles to Ansborough Ave. Turn left onto Ansborough almost 1 mile to University. Turn left onto University ½ mile to Falls. Make sharp right onto Falls to store.

T&K Natural Food Store 🛍️

1023 Peoples Square ✆ 319-235-0246 ◷ M 9-7, Tues-F 9-5:30, Sat 9-4

🚗 **From I-380N**, merge onto US 20W and take exit 230 for IA-21/Hawkeye Rd toward Dysart/Waterloo right onto Hawkeye 1 block to San Marnan Dr. Turn left onto San Marnan ½ mile to Kimbell Ave. Turn left onto Kimbell 1 block to Brookeridge Dr. Turn left onto Brookeridge and left onto People's Square to store on left. **From US 20E**, turn left onto Ansborough Ave almost ½ mile to W San Marnan. Turn right onto San Marnan 1 mile to Kimbell. Turn left onto Kimbell and follow directions above.

WEST DES MOINES

Campbell's Nutrition 🛍️

5465 Mills Civic Pkwy. ✆ 515-223-0035 ◷ M-F 10-6, Sat 10-5

🚗 **From I-35** take exit toward Mills Civic Pkwy west (right from I-35S, left from I-35N) to store on right.

Fresh Cafe & Market 🍴

1721 25th St., Ste 110 ✆ 515-440-4700 ◷ M-Th 4-8, F 11-7, Sat 10-2
Organic and local ingredients in soups, salads, sandwiches and wraps.
• vegetarian friendly • vegan friendly • organic focus • fresh juice • counter • tables • self-service • take-out

🚗 **From I-35S/I-80W**, take exit 174 toward Clive left onto University Ave 2 miles to 25th St. Turn right onto 25th to restaurant on left. **From I-35N**, take exit 72C right onto University under 1 mile and follow directions above. **From I-80E/I-235**, take exit 2 toward W Des Moines/Clive north on 22nd St (left from I-80E/I235E, right from I-235W) to first left onto Westown Pkwy. Turn left onto Westown and first right onto 25th to restaurant on right.

KANSAS

1. Emporia
2. Garden City
3. Great Bend
4. Lawrence
5. Lenexa
6. Manhattan
7. Overland Park
8. Salina
9. Topeka
10. Wichita

EMPORIA

Nature's Paradise

1511 W. 6th Ave. ✆ 620-342-3166 ⊕ M-Tues, Th-Sat 9-6, W 9-7
• organic produce

🛒 **From I-35S,** take exit 133 for 6th Ave left onto US 50/E 6th Ave 3½ miles to store on left. **From I-35N,** take exit127B toward Emporia onto US 50/W 6th Ave 1¾ miles to store on right. **From I-335S,** take exit 127 onto I-35N and follow directions above.

GARDEN CITY

Harvest Pantry

605 E. Kansas Plaza ✆ 620-275-7572 ⊕ M-Sat 9-6
• organic produce

🛒 **From US 400/50/83,** exit onto E Mary St and veer right onto E Kansas Ave under ½ mile to store on right in E Kansas Plaza. **From US 83N,** take the Hwy 156 exit toward Garden City left onto E Kansas Ave and follow directions above. **From KS 83N (Main St),** turn right onto E Kansas Ave about ½ mile to store on left.

GREAT BEND

Organic Cupboard

3122 10th St. ✆ 620-792-2345 ⊕ M-F 9:30-5:30, Sat 9:30-3
🛒 US 56 and US 81 intersect in Great Bend. Store is on US 56 (aka 10th St) 1 mile west of US 81 (aka Main St) on north side after Jackson St.

LAWRENCE

Casbah Market 🗍 🍴

803 Massachusetts St. ℂ 785-842-4085 ① M-Sat 10:30-9, Sun 12-6
Jamaican-inspired healthy fast-food.
  • organic produce • cafe • vegetarian • vegan friendly • organic focus • counter • self-service • take-out

🚍 **From I-70**, take exit 204 toward Lawrence south on US 40/US 59 (right from I-70E, left from I-70W) 1⅓ miles (across river and past tracks) to W 6th St. Turn left onto W 6th 1 block to Massachusetts Ave. Turn right onto Massachusetts 2 blocks to store on right at 8th St.

Community Mercantile 🗍 🍴   ♿

901 Iowa St. ℂ 785-843-8544 ℂ Daily 7-10
  • organic produce • vegetarian friendly • salad bar • cafe • deli • bakery • take-out • co-op

🚍 **From I-70,** take exit 202 toward US 59S onto McDonald Dr about 1 mile to US 59S ramp. Merge onto 59S (aka Iowa St) about ¼ mile to store at 9th St.

Local Burger 🍴

714 Vermont St. ℂ 785-856-7827 ① M-Sat 11-9, Sun 11-8
Homemade burgers–tofu, veggie and hormone and antibiotic-free meat.
  • vegetarian friendly • vegan friendly • organic focus • alcohol • tables • self-service

🚍 **From I-70**, take exit 204 toward Lawrence south on US 40/US 59 (right from I-70E, left from I-70W) 1⅓ miles and continue onto Vermont St across river and past tracks 2 blocks to restaurant on left after W 7th St.

LENEXA

Emerald Forest Health Foods 🗍

12234 W. 95th St. ℂ 913-492-6336 ① M-F 10-8, Sat 10-7, Sun 12-4

🚍 **From I-35,** take exit 224 east on 95th St (right from I-35N, left from I-35S) to second light. Turn left into Oak Park Commons Shopping Ctr to store.

MANHATTAN

People's Grocery Co-op 🗍

523 S. 17th St. ℂ 785-539-4811 ① M-F 8-8, Sat 9-8, Sun 11-6
  • organic produce • co-op

🚍 **From I-70**, take exit 313 onto US 177N about 8½ miles (across river) to Manhattan. Merge right off ramp onto 177S to KS 18/Ft Riley Blvd. Take Ft Riley 1¼ miles to S 17th St. Turn right onto 17th 1 block to store at Yuma St.

OVERLAND PARK   ♿

Whole Foods Market 🗍 🍴

7401 W. 91st St. ℂ 913-652-9633 ① Daily 7:30-10
  • organic produce • vegetarian friendly • salad bar • cafe • self-service • take-out

🚍 **From I-435**, take exit 79 north on Metcalf Ave (US 169N) about 2¼ miles to W 91st St. Turn left onto W 91st ¼ mile to store.

Wild Oats Market 🗍 🍴   ♿

6621 W. 119th St. ℂ 913-663-2951 ① Daily 8-9
  • organic produce • vegetarian friendly • salad bar • cafe • self-service • take-out

🚍 **From I-435**, take exit 77B south on Nall Ave (right from I-435E, left from I-435W) about 1¼ miles to 119th St. Turn left onto 119th to light at Glenwood Ave. Turn left onto Glenwood to store in shopping center on SE corner.

SALINA

Prairieland Market 📷
138 S. 4th St. ✆ 785-827-5877 ⏱ Tues-Th 2-6, F 10-1, 2-6, Sat 10-1
• organic produce, co-op
🛒 **From I-135**, take exit 93 east on State St (left from I-135S, right from I-135N) under 2 miles to N 10th St. Turn right onto N 10th 1 block to W Iron Ave. Turn left onto W Iron 5 blocks to S 4th St. Turn right onto S 4th to store on right. **From I-70**, take exit 252 south on 9th St (right from I-70E, left from I-70W) 2½ miles to W Iron. Turn left onto W Iron and follow directions above.

Vita Villa 📷
2041 S. Ohio St. ✆785-827-7547 ⏱ M-F 8-6, Sat 9-5
🛒 **From I-135**, take exit 90 east on Magnolia Ave (left from I-135S, right from I-135N) about 1⅓ miles to S Ohio St. Turn right onto S Ohio ¾ mile to store on right. **From I-70**, take exit 253 south on S Ohio St (right from I-70E, left from I-70W) over 5 miles to store on left.

TOPEKA

Akin's Natural Foods Market 📷 ♿
2913 S.W. 29th St. ✆ 785-228-9131 ⏱ Daily 9-9
• organic produce
🛒 **From I-470**, take exit 4 north on Gage Blvd (right from I-470W, left from I-470E) about ½ mile to 29th St. Turn right onto 29th over ½ mile to store on right in Brookwood Shopping Ctr.

Health Food Mart 📷
1507 S.W. 21st St. ✆ 785-235-9710 ⏱ M-Th 9:30-8, F-Sat 9:30-5
• organic produce
🛒 **From I-70E**, merge onto I-470E. **From I-470E**, take exit 2 left onto SW 21st St 3 miles to store on right at SW Washburn Ave. **From I-470W**, take exit 5 right onto SW Burlingham Rd (becomes SW Washburn) about 2⅓ miles to SW 21st. Turn left onto SW 21st to store on left. **From I-70W**, take exit 363 left onto SE Branner Trfy continuing onto SE Adams Rd under 1 mile to SE 21st. Turn left onto SE 21st to store on left after SW Washburn.

Topeka Food Co-op, Inc. 📷
503 Washburn Rd. ✆ 785-235-2309 ⏱ M-F 9-7, Sat 9-5, Sun 12-5
• organic produce • co-op
🛒 **From I-70E**, take exit 358 onto SW Gage Blvd 1¼ miles to SW 6th Ave. Turn left onto SW 6th 1¾ miles to SW Washburn Ave. Turn left onto SW Washburn to store on left. **From I-70W**, take exit 362B toward 8th St and merge onto SE Madison St to SE 6th St. Turn left onto SE 6th almost 1½ miles to SW Washburn Ave. Turn right onto SW Washburn to store.

WICHITA

Food For Thought 📷
2929 E. Central Ave. ✆ 316-683-6078 ⏱ M-F 9-6:30, Sat 9-6
• organic produce • vegetarian friendly • deli • take-out
🛒 **From I-135**, take exit 7A east on Central Ave to store on right between Hillside St & Grove St.

Green Acres 📷 🍴
8141 E. 21st St. ✆ 316-634-1088 ⏱ M-Sat 8-9, Sun 10-7
• organic produce • vegetarian friendly • fresh juice • cafe • deli • bakery • tables • self-service • take-out
🛒 **From I-135**, take exit 9 east on 21st St (right from I-135N, left from I-135S) about 4½ miles to store at Rock Rd in Bradley Fair Shopping Ctr.

O'Naturals ⅋

1551 N. Rock Rd. ✆ 316-634-0222 ⏰ M-Th 7-8, F 7-7, Sat 8-5, Sun 10-4
A healthy fast-food concept featuring soups, sandwiches, salads and Asian noodle dishes.
• vegetarian friendly • organic focus • alcohol • tables • self-service • take-out
🚗 **From I-35S**, take exit 53 right at fork onto KS 96W about 1½ miles to 13th St exit. Turn left onto E 13th N 2½ miles to Rock Rd. Turn right onto Rock under ¼ mile to restaurant on right inside the Genesis Health Club. **From I-35N**, take exit 50 left at fork onto E Kellogg Dr about 1¼ miles to Rock. Turn right onto Rock 2¼ miles to restaurant after E 13th N.

Taste of Health ⅋   ♿

3100 N. Hillside Ave. ✆ 316-682-3100 ⏰ M-F 11:30-1:30
Natural foods buffet lunch. Homegrown organic produce in season. Part of the Center for the Improvement of Human Functioning.
• vegetarian friendly • organic focus • tables • self-service
🚗 **From I-135**, take exit 10 (10A from 135N) onto KS 96E 1-1½ miles to Hillside St. Turn right onto Hillside under 1 mile to Ctr for Improvement of Human Functioning on left (white stone entrance). Follow the winding road to Center and restaurant.

Whole Foods Association 🛍

6574 E. Central Ave. ✆ 316-685-4283 ⏰ M-Sat 9-8, Sun 12-5
• organic produce
🚗 **From I-35**, take exit 50 onto US 400W/Kellog Ave 1½ miles to Woodlawn St. Turn right onto Woodlawn 1 mile to store on NE corner at Central Ave in Normandy Shopping Ctr. **From I-135S**, take exit 6A onto US 400E/Kellog Ave about 3¼ miles to Woodlawn. Turn left onto Woodlawn and follow directions above.

Whole Foods Association 🛍

2172 N. Amidon Ave. ✆ 316-832-1227 ⏰ M-Sat 9-6:30, Sun 12-5
• organic produce
🚗 **From I-235**, take exit 11onto W 25th St N (left from I-235S, right from I-235N) 1 mile to Amidon St. Turn right onto Amidon 4 blocks to store on SE corner at W 21st St N in Twin Lakes Shopping Ctr.

Whole Foods Association 🛍

10555 W. 21st St. N. ✆ 316-729-4365 ⏰ M-Sat 9-8, Sun 12-5
• organic produce
🚗 **From I-235**, take exit 10 left onto Zoo Blvd almost 1 mile until Zoo becomes W 21st St N. Continue on 21st 3 miles to store after Maize Rd on south side.

Zen Vegetarian Cuisine ⅋

3101 N. Rock Rd. ✆ 316-425-7700 ⏰ Tues-Sat 11-2:30, 5-10
• vegetarian • vegan friendly • fresh juice • tables • wait staff
🚗 **From I-35**, take exit 53 onto KS 96W about 5⅓ miles to Rock Rd. Turn left onto N Rock ⅓ mile to restaurant on right past 32nd St. **From I-135**, take exit 10 onto KS 96E 3½ miles to Rock. Turn right onto N Rock ⅓ mile to restaurant.

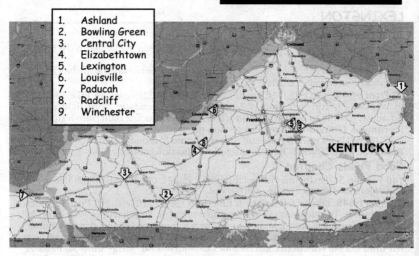

KENTUCKY

1. Ashland
2. Bowling Green
3. Central City
4. Elizabethtown
5. Lexington
6. Louisville
7. Paducah
8. Radcliff
9. Winchester

KENTUCKY

ASHLAND

Vitality Healthy Life Market

240 16th St. © 606-326-1354 ⏰ M-Sat 10-5:30
Large selection of gluten-free and organic foods. Local produce in season.

From I-64, take exit 121 toward Ashland north on US 23 (left from I-64E, right from I-6W) over 7 miles (becomes Walnut St, Center St, Winchester Ave & Greenup Ave) to 16th St. Turn left onto 16th to store on left.

BOWLING GREEN

Nutrition Center

715 U.S. 31W. Bypass © 270-846-1882 ⏰ M-W, F 9-6, Th 9-8, Sat 10-5
• organic produce

From I-65, take exit 28 toward US 31W/State Hwy 446/Bowling Green onto KY 446 about ½ mile and follow ramp onto KY 80 /Louisville Rd/US 31W under 3 miles to store on left before Nashville Rd.

CENTRAL CITY

Cornucopia of Health

1706 W. Everly Brothers Blvd. © 270-757-9342 ⏰ M-F 10-5, Sat 10-2

From Western Kentucky Pkwy, take exit 58 toward Central City onto KY-70/US-431/S 2nd St (left from Pkwy W, loop around right from Pkwy E) ½-1 mile to W Everly Bros Blvd. Turn left onto W Everly Bros 2 miles (cross back over pkwy) to store on left.

ELIZABETHTOWN

Green Apple Foods

2413 Ring Rd. © 270-982-7753 ⏰ M-Sat 9-8
• organic produce

From I-65, take exit 94 for KY-61/US-62 toward Elizabethtown onto Bardstown Rd (right from I-65S, left from I-65N) about ½ mile to Ring Rd. Turn right onto Ring 2 miles to store on left after Shepherdsville Rd.

LEXINGTON

Alfalfa Restaurant ⊮

557 S. Limestone © 859-253-0014 ⏲ Days M-F 8-2, Sat-Sun 9-2 Dinner W-Th 5:30-9, F-Sat 5:30-10

Mostly vegetarian including the signature dish, Hoppin' John. Homemade whole wheat bread.
• vegetarian friendly • alcohol • tables • wait staff

🚗 **From I-64S**, take exit 115 right at fork onto Hwy 922/Newtown Pike 3⅓ miles to W Main St. Turn left onto W Main ½ mile to Broadway. Turn right onto S Broadway ½ mile to Bolivar St. Turn left onto Bolivar to first right onto S Upper St (becomes S Limestone) ⅓ mile to restaurant on right. **From I-64W or I-75N**, take exit 113 for US 68 toward Paris and turn right onto N Broadway about 3¾ miles to Bolivar St. Turn left onto Bolivar and follow directions above.

Good Foods Chapter ⊮

140 E. Main St./Lexington Public Library © 859-422-6802 ⏲ M-F 8:30-3:30
• vegetarian friendly • tables • self-service

🚗 **From I-64S**, take exit 115 right at fork onto Hwy 922/Newtown Pike 3⅓ miles to W Main St. Turn left onto W Main 1 mile to Rose St. Turn left onto Rose 2 blocks to E Main. Turn left onto E Main 2 blocks to restaurant on left in Lexington Public Library. **From I-64W**, take exit 81 onto I-75S almost 1½ miles to exit 110 and turn left onto US 60/Winchester Rd 3⅓ miles to Midland Rd. Merge onto Midland ½ mile to E Main. Turn right onto E Main under ½ mile to restaurant in library. **From I-75N**, take exit 110 left onto Winchester Rd and follow directions above.

Good Foods Market & Cafe 🛍 ⊮

455-D Southland Drive © 859-278-1813 ⏲ Store Daily 9-10 Cafe M-F 11-2:20, 4:30-8:30 10, Sat-Sun 10-8:30
• organic produce • vegetarian friendly • fresh juice • cafe • deli • tables • self-service • take-out • co-op

🚗 **From KY 4 (New Circle Rd)** in Lexington, take exit 19 north on Nicholasville Rd about 1 mile to Southland Dr. Turn left onto Southland 1 mile to store on right.

Whole Foods Market 🛍 ⊮

161 Lexington Green Circle © 859-971-8600 ⏲ M-Sat 8-10, Sun 9-9
• organic produce • vegetarian friendly • salad bar • cafe • self-service • take-out

🚗 **From KY 4 (New Circle Rd)**, take exit 19 south on Nicholasville Rd and make first right onto Lexington Green Circle to store on right.

LOUISVILLE

Amazing Grace Whole Foods & Nutrition Center 🛍 ⊮   ♿

1133 Bardstown Rd. © 502-485-1122 ⏲ M-Sat 9-5, Sun 11-8
• organic produce • vegetarian friendly • deli • bakery • tables • self-service • take-out

🚗 **From I-64**, take exit 8 west on Grinstead Dr (left from I-64W, right from I-64E) about 1½ miles to Bardstown Rd. Turn left onto Bardstown ½ block to store on left.

Rainbow Blossom Natural Foods Market 🛍 ⊮   ♿

12401 Shelbyville Rd. © 502-244-2022 ⏲ M-Sat 9-9, Sun 11-7
• organic produce • vegetarian friendly • fresh juice • deli • bakery • tables • self-service • take-out

🚗 **From I-265**, take exit 27 west on Shelbyville (left from I-265N, right from I-265S) about 1⅓ miles to store. **From I-64**, take exit 19B onto I-265N over 1 mile to exit 27 (Shelbyville Rd) and follow directions above..

Rainbow Blossom Natural Foods Market 🛍   ♿

3608 Springhurst Blvd. © 502-339-5090 ⏲ M-Sat 9-9 Sun 11-7
• organic produce • vegetarian friendly • fresh juice • deli • take-out

🚗 **From I-265**, take exit 32 right onto Westport/KY 1447W to first right (Towne Center Dr). Turn right onto Towne Ctr about ½ mile to Springhurst Blvd. Turn left onto Springhurst to store. **From I-71**, take exit 9A onto I-265S and follow directions above. **From I-64**, take exit 19B onto I-265N and follow directions above.

Rainbow Blossom Natural Foods Market 🛍 🍴

3738 Lexington Rd. ✆ 502-896-0189 ◷ M-Sat 9-10, Sun 11-7
• organic produce • vegetarian friendly • fresh juice • salad bar • cafe • deli • bakery • counter • tables • self-service • take-out

🍎 **From I-264**, take exit 20B (US 60/Shelbyville Road) toward St Matthew's west on Shelbyville Rd 2 miles and take left fork (Lexington Rd) 2 blocks to store on left.

Sweet Surrender Dessert Cafe & Coffee Shop 🍴   ♿

1804 Frankfort Ave. ✆ 502-899-2008 ◷ Tues-Sat 10-10 Lunch Tues-Sat 11-2
Known for its decadent desserts. Lunch menu of sandwiches and salads is vegetarian.
• vegetarian friendly • tables • self-service

🍎 **From I-64W**, take exit 7 right onto Mellwood Ave and make first right onto Frankfort Ave to restaurant on right after Pope St. **From I-64E**, take exit 7 onto Story St. Take left lane and turn left onto Spring St to first left onto Mellwood and follow directions above.

Whole Foods Market 🛍 🍴

4944 Shelbyville Rd. ✆ 502-899-5545 ◷ Daily 8-10
• organic produce • vegetarian friendly • salad bar • cafe • self-service • take-out

🍎 **From I-264**, take exit 20 onto US 60W/Shelbyville Rd under ½ mile to store on left.

Zen Garden 🍴   ♿

2240 Frankfort Ave. ✆ 502-895-9114 ◷ M-Th 11-10, F-Sat 11-11
A mix of vegetarian Asian cuisines.
• vegetarian • vegan friendly • tables • wait staff

🍎 **From I-64**, take exit 8 east on Grinstead Dr (left from I-64E, right from I-64W) about ¼ mile to S Peterson Ave. Turn left onto Peterson about ⅓ mile to Frankfort Ave. Turn left onto Frankfort ⅓ mile to restaurant.

PADUCAH

Golden Carrot Natural Foods 🛍

433 Jefferson St. ✆ 270-442-0999 ◷ M-Sat 9-5:30
• organic produce

🍎 **From I-24**, take exit 4 toward Paducah east on 24/Hinkleville Rd (right from I-24W, left from I-24E) about 5 miles (becomes Park Ave, Clay St, MLK Jr Dr, then N 4th St) to Jefferson St. Turn right onto Jefferson to store on right at 5th St.

Heath Health Foods 🛍

2006 Lone Oak Rd. ✆ 270-534-4977 ◷ M-Sat 9-5:30
🍎 **From I-24**, take exit 7 toward Mayfield south on Lone Oak Rd/US 40S (right from I-24E, left from I-24W) about ½ mile to store on left.

RADCLIFF

TC Health Food 🛍

133 E. Vine St. ✆ 270-351-5022 ◷ M-F 10-6, Sat 10-4
🍎 Store is 1 block west of US 31W/S Dixie Blvd at E Vine St on north side.

WINCHESTER

Full Circle Market-Health Foods 🛍   ♿

260 Redwing Dr. ✆ 859-744-3008 ◷ M-F 10-7, Sat 10-5
• organic produce

🍎 **From I-64**, take exit 94 toward Winchester onto Bypass Rd (right from I-64E, left from I-64W) about 1 mile to Redwing Dr (at Speedway). Turn right onto Redwing to store in Colby Ridge Plaza.

LOUISIANA

1. Baton Rouge
2. Bossier City
3. Covington
4. Gonzales
5. Hammond
6. Lafayette
7. Lake Charles
8. Metairie
9. Morgan City
10. New Orleans
11. Shreveport

BATON ROUGE

Living Foods 🛍️

3033 Perkins Rd. ✆ 225-346-1886 ⏱ M-F 9-6:30, Sat 9-6, Sun 12-6
• organic produce • vegetarian friendly • deli • take-out

🏠 **From I-10E,** take exit 157A and follow ramp onto Perkins Rd to store just off hwy. **From I-10W,** take exit 157B left onto S Arcadian Thwy ¼ mile to Perkins. Turn right onto Perkins about ⅓ mile to store.

Lucy's Health Foods 🛍️

8875-A Highland Rd. ✆ 225-767-8222 ⏱ M-F 9-7, Sat 9-6, Sun 12-6

🏠 **From I-10,** take exit 162 south on Bluebonnet Dr (right from I-10E, left from I-10W) 3½ miles to Highland Rd. Turn right onto Highland about 1 mile to store in shopping center at Staring Ln.

Our Daily Bread Market & Bakery 🛍️🍴   ♿

9414 Florida Blvd. ✆ 225-924-9910 ⏱ M-F 8-6, Sat 9-6, Sun 12-6 Cafe M-Sat 11-3
• organic produce • vegetarian friendly • fresh juice • cafe • deli • bakery • tables • self-service • take-out

🏠 **From I-12,** take exit 2B onto US 61N (Airline Hwy) about 2½ miles to Florida Blvd. Turn right onto Florida about ¾ mile to store (2 blocks past Cortana Mall).

Whole Foods Market 🛍️🍴

7529 Corporate Blvd. ✆ 225-218-0452 ⏱ Daily 8-10
• organic produce • vegetarian friendly • salad bar • cafe • self-service • take-out

🏠 **From I-12W,** take exit 1B left onto Drusilla Dr and turn right onto LA 73/Jefferson Hwy about 1⅓ miles to Corporate Blvd. Turn left onto Corporate to store on right. **From I-12E,** take exit 1B left onto Essen Ln, make first left onto Jefferson Hwy and follow directions above.

BOSSIER CITY

Sunshine Health Foods 🛍️ 🍴

3011 Airline Drive, Ste. E ✆ 318-746-9788 ⏰ M-Sat 9-6
Two hot vegetarian entrees and two homemade soups daily.
- organic produce, vegetarian friendly, organic focus, fresh juice, salad bar, cafe, deli, self-service, take-out

🚗 At I-220 exit 12 on north side.

COVINGTON

Columbia Street Natural Foods 🛍️ 🍴

415 N. Columbia St. ✆ 985-893-0355 ⏰ M-F 9-6, Sat 9-5
- organic produce • vegetarian friendly • deli • tables • self-service • take-out

🚗 **From I-12**, take exit 59 toward Covington onto LA 21/Tyler Rd (left, then right from I-12E, merge right from I-12W) 3 miles to W 21st St. Turn right onto 21st under 1 mile to N Columbia St. Turn left onto Columbia to store on left.

Sunshine Garden 🛍️

124 N. Jefferson Ave. ✆ 985-893-1463 ⏰ M-F 10-6, Sat 10-5
- organic produce

🚗 **From I-12**, take exit 59 toward Covington onto LA 21/Tyler Rd (left, then right from I-12E, merge right from I-12W) 3 miles to W 21st St. Turn right onto 21st ½ mile to N Jefferson. Turn left onto N Jefferson to store on right.

GONZALES

Horn of Plenty 🛍️

623 E. Ascension St. ✆ 225-644-6080 ⏰ M-F 10-6, Sat 10-4
🚗 **From I-10E**, take exit 177 toward Gonzales left onto Hwy 30 1¾ miles to S Burnside Ave. Turn left onto S Burnside 2 miles to E Railroad St. Turn right onto E Railroad past third block and merge onto E Ascension 2 blocks to store on right. **From I-10W**, take exit 179 onto S Burnside 3 miles to E Railroad. Turn right onto E Railroad and follow directions above.

HAMMOND

The Organic Planet 🛍️ 🍴

201 W. Thomas St. ✆ 985-340-2810 ⏰ M-F 9-8, Sat 9-6
Self-service salad, soup and sandwich bars plus full service cafe.
- organic produce • vegetarian friendly • fresh juice • salad bar • cafe • deli • tables • self-service • wait staff • take-out

🚗 **From I-55S**, take exit 31 onto LA 190 (W Thomas St continuing onto W Morris St) about 2¾ miles to SW Railroad Ave. Turn left onto SW Railroad 1 block to W Thomas. Turn left onto W Thomas to store on left. **From I-55N**, take exit 28 onto US 51N/W Morrison Blvd 2 miles to W Thomas. Turn right onto W Thomas (becomes W Morris) 1⅓ miles to SW Railroad and follow directions above. **From I-12**, take exit 40 north on SW Railroad under 2 miles to W Thomas and follow directions above.

LAFAYETTE

Oil Center Health Foods 🛍️ 🍴

326 Travis St. ✆ 337-232-7774 ⏰ Store M-F 9-5, Sat 10-2 Deli M-F 11-4, Sat 10-2
- vegetarian friendly • deli • tables • self-service • take-out

🚗 **From I-10**, take exit 103A onto US 167S (becomes 90 E) about 3½ miles to 90 Bus. Turn right onto 90 Bus (becomes Pinhook Rd) 1 mile to Travis St. Turn right onto Travis 2 blocks to store on right. **From I-49S**, take exit 1 onto 167S and follow directions above.

Organically Yours 🛍 🍴

2901 Kaliste Saloom Rd. ✆ 337-989-1500 ⏱ M-F 10-6, Sat 10-5
Unfortunately not much on the cafe menu is vegetarian.
· organic produce · fresh juice · cafe · tables · self-service · take-out

🛍 **From I-10E**, take exit 100 right onto Ambassador Caffery Pkwy over 7 miles to Kaliste Saloom Rd. Turn right onto Kaliste Saloom ½ mile to store on left. **From I-10W**, take exit 103A toward Lafayette south on US 167 continuing on NW Evangeline Trwy about 3½ miles to E Pinhook Rd. Turn left onto E Pinhook over 2 miles to Kaliste Saloom. Turn right onto Kaliste Saloom about 3¾ miles to store.

Vitamins Plus 🛍

505 Bertrand Drive ✆ 337-261-0033 ⏱ M-Sat 8-9, Sun 10-6
· organic produce

🛍 **From I-10E**, take exit 100 right onto Ambassador Caffery Pkwy about 1 mile to Cameron St. Turn right onto Cameron about ½ mile to N Bertrand Dr. Turn right onto N Bertrand ¾ mile to Bertrand Dr. Turn left onto Bertrand 1 mile to store on right. **From I-10W**, take exit 101 left at fork and left onto N University Ave about 2 miles to W Congress St. Turn right onto W Congress about 1½ miles to Bertrand. Turn left onto Bertrand to store.

LAKE CHARLES

Pure Foods & Health 🛍

138 W. Prien Lake Rd. ✆ 337-905-7873 ⏱ M-F 9-6
· organic produce · vegetarian friendly · fresh juice · salad bar · deli · take-out

🛍 **From I-210E**, take exit 6A for Ryan St and make sharp right onto W College St, right onto Ernest St and right onto E Prien Lake Rd to store on left before Ryan. **From I-210W**, take exit 6A right onto Ryan, make first left onto Lucille St 1 block to June St, left onto June 2 blocks to E Prien Lake and right onto E Prien Lake to store on right.

METAIRIE

Whole Foods Market 🛍 🍴

3420 Veterans Hwy. ✆ 504-888-8225 ⏱ Daily 8-9
· organic produce · vegetarian friendly · salad bar · cafe · self-service · take-out

🛍 **From I-10E**, take exit 226 onto Clearview Pkwy about 1 mile to Veterans Blvd/ Veterans Memorial Blvd. Turn right onto Veterans about 1½ miles to store on right. **From I-10W**, take exit 228 onto N Causeway Blvd about ¼ mile to Veterans. Turn left onto Veterans to store on left.

MORGAN CITY

Out of Eden Health Market 🛍

7007 Hwy. 182 E. ✆ 985-380-3155 ⏱ M-Tues, Th-F 9:30-5:30, W 9:30-5, Sat 9:30-2
🛍 Store is on Hwy 182/E Frontage Rd between Lake Palourde Bypass Rd & Lake Palourde Rd. **From US 90**, take exit 181 south on Lake Palourde Bypass to Barrow St. Turn left onto Barrow under ½ mile to Lake Palourde Rd. Turn right onto Lake Palourde ⅓ mile to E Frontage. Turn right onto E Frontage to store.

NEW ORLEANS

Whole Foods Market 🛍 🍴   ♿

5600 Magazine St. ✆ 504-899-9119 ⏱ M-Sat 8-9, Sun 8-8
· organic produce · vegetarian friendly · salad bar · cafe · self-service · take-out

🛍 **From I-10E**, take exit 232 onto S Carrollton Ave over 2 miles to St Charles Ave. Turn left onto St Charles about 1⅓ miles to Nashville Ave. Turn right onto Nashville about ½ mile to Magazine St. Turn left on Magazine 2 blocks to store. **From I-10W**, take exit 234C toward Clairborne Ave onto 90W 2¼ miles to Jefferson Ave. Turn left onto Jefferson 1½ miles to Magazine. Turn right onto Magazine 2 blocks to store.

SHREVEPORT

Earthereal Restaurant & Bakery
3309 Line Ave. © 318-865-8947 ⊙ M-F 10-2:30 Bakery 10-3
Vegetarian except for tuna and chicken salads.
   • vegetarian friendly • bakery • tables • self-service • take-out

From I-49, take exit 205 east on Kings Hwy (left from I-49S, right from I-49N) about ½ mile to Line Ave. Turn right onto Line Ave 1 block to restaurant at Gladstone Ave. **From I-20**, take exit 17B onto I-49S and follow directions above.

Good Life Health Foods
6132 Hearne Ave. © 318-635-4753 ⊙ M-F 9-5, Sat 10-5 Deli 11-3
   • organic produce • deli • take-out

From I-20, take exit 16A onto LA 171S/Hearne Ave (left from I-20W, right from I-20E) about 2 miles to store on right (5 blocks past Hollywood Ave intersection) in small shopping complex.

Sunshine Health Foods
5751 Youree Dr. © 318-219-4080 ⊙ M-Sat 9-6
Two hot vegetarian entrees and two homemade soups daily.
   • organic produce • vegetarian friendly • fresh juice • salad bar • cafe • deli • self-service • take-out

From I-20, exit onto LA 1S/Market St (19A from I-20W, 19B from I-20E) about 4⅓ miles (becomes Youree St) to store on left after Southfield Rd.

Vitamins Plus
5819 E. Kings Hwy. © 318-861-7079 ⊙ M-Sat 9-9, Sun 10-6
   • organic produce

From I-20, exit onto LA 1S/Market St (19A from I-20W, 19B from I-20E) 4¼ miles (becomes Youree St) to Southfield Rd. Turn left onto Southfield under 1 mile to E Kings Hwy. Turn to right onto E King to store on left.

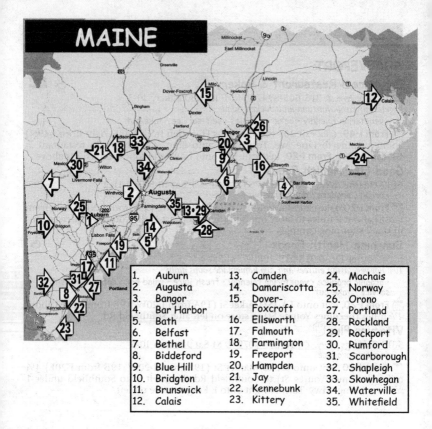

1.	Auburn	13.	Camden	24.	Machais
2.	Augusta	14.	Damariscotta	25.	Norway
3.	Bangor	15.	Dover-	26.	Orono
4.	Bar Harbor		Foxcroft	27.	Portland
5.	Bath	16.	Ellsworth	28.	Rockland
6.	Belfast	17.	Falmouth	29.	Rockport
7.	Bethel	18.	Farmington	30.	Rumford
8.	Biddeford	19.	Freeport	31.	Scarborough
9.	Blue Hill	20.	Hampden	32.	Shapleigh
10.	Bridgton	21.	Jay	33.	Skowhegan
11.	Brunswick	22.	Kennebunk	34.	Waterville
12.	Calais	23.	Kittery	35.	Whitefield

AUBURN

Axis Natural Foods 🛍

250 Center St. ✆ 207-782-3348 🕐 M-F 9-8, Sat 9-6
• organic produce

🛏 **From I-95 (ME Tpke)**, take exit 75 toward Auburn onto Rt 202E (Washington St, becomes Minot Ave, then Union St) and veer left at end onto Center St about 5½ miles total to store in small strip mall on left.

AUGUSTA

Harvest Time Natural Foods 🛍

171 Capital St. ✆ 207-623-8700 🕐 M-Tues, Sat 9-6, W-F 9-8, Sun 10-4
• organic produce

🛏 **From I-95 (ME Tpke)**, take exit 109 (109A from I-95S) right onto Western Ave/202E about ½ mile to Armory St. Turn right onto Armory to first left onto Capital St ⅓ mile to store on right after Town and Country Rd.

BANGOR

Natural Living Center 🛍 🍽

209 Longview Drive ✆ 207-990-2646 🕐 M-Th 8:30-7, F-Sat 8:30-8, Sun 11-5
• vegetarian friendly • deli • tables • self-service • take-out

🛏 **From I-95**, take exit 49 toward Bangor north on Hogan Rd (left from I-95N, ramp toward Bangor Mall Blvd from I-95S) about ½ mile to Longview Dr. Turn right onto Longview about ¼ mile to store.

BAR HARBOR

Alternative Market 👜 🍴

16 Mt. Desert St. 🕐 207-288-8225 🕐 Daily 10-6
• organic produce • vegetarian friendly • fresh juice • cafe • deli • bakery • tables • self-service • take-out

🍎 Take Rt 3 into Bar Harbor. Store is on Rt 3/Mt Desert St under ½ mile east of Eden St and 1 block west of Main St on south side.

Cafe Bluefish 🍴

122 Cottage St. 🕐 207-288-3696 🕐 Call as hours are seasonal
Cajun Tempeh and Hungarian Mushroom Strudel for vegetarians.
• vegetarian friendly • alcohol • tables • wait staff

🍎 Take Rt 3 into Bar Harbor. **From Eden St,** turn east onto Cottage St about 3 blocks to restaurant on left past Holland Ave.

Eden Vegetarian Cafe 🍴

78 West St. 🕐 207-288-4422 🕐 Call for seasonal hours
• vegetarian • vegan friendly • organic focus • alcohol • counter • tables • wait staff

🍎 Take Rt 3 into Bar Harbor. **From Eden St,** turn east onto West St (which runs along the coast) under ½ mile to restaurant on left. **From Main St,** continue to end and turn left onto West 2 blocks to restaurant on right.

BATH

Bath Natural Market 👜

36 Centre St. 🕐 207-442-8012 🕐 M-F 9-6, Sat 9-5, Sun 12-4
• organic produce

🍎 **From US 1N,** continue onto Leeman Hwy, take ramp to Vine St and turn left onto Vine 1 block to Centre St. Turn left onto Centre 1 block to store on left. **From US 1S,** corss bridge, turn right onto Vine and follow directions above.

BELFAST

Belfast Co-op 👜 🍴

123 High St. 🕐 207-338-2532 🕐 Daily 7:30-8
• organic produce • vegetarian friendly • cafe • deli • tables • self-service • take-out

🍎 **From Rt 3,** merge onto Main St to High St. Turn right onto High to store on left. **From Rt 1N,** take Northport St (becomes High) about 1 mile to store on right. **From 1S,** take ramp onto ME 137/Dowtown Belfast & Waterfront to High. Turn right onto High about ¾ mile to store on left.

BETHEL

Cafe DiCocoa's Market/Bakery 👜 🍴   ♿

119 Main St. 🕐 Store 207-824-6386S, Restaurant 207-824-5282 🕐 Market/Cafe M-Th 7-5, F-Sat 7-6, Sun 7-4 Restaurant Call for seasonal hours
A market with a café and a separate vegetarian restaurant.
• organic produce • vegetarian • fresh juice • salad bar • cafe • deli • bakery • tables • self-service • wait staff • take-out

🍎 **From Rt 26,** continue straight past "Welcome" sign (becomes Main St) to restaurant on left. Store is next door at Vernon St (aka Rt 35). **From Rt 2E,** pass "Welcome" sign and take exit for 26E right and turn right at end of road onto Main to restaurant & store.

BIDDEFORD

New Morning Natural Foods 👜 🍴

230 Main St. 🕐 207-282-1434 🕐 M-F 9-5:30, Sat 9-4 Cafe M-F 11-2
• organic produce • vegetarian friendly • cafe • tables • self-service • take-out

🍎 **From I-95/195 (ME Tpke),** take exit 4 (Biddeford) east on Rt 111 to 5 points intersection. Turn left onto Rt 1 to store at end of second block.

BLUE HILL

Blue Hill Co-op Community Market & Cafe 🛍️ 🍴 ♿
4 Ellsworth Rd. © 207-374-2165 🕐 M-F 8-7, Sat 8-6, Sun 9-5
• organic produce • vegetarian friendly • fresh juice • cafe • deli • bakery • tables • self-service • take-out • co-op

🛒 Store is at intersection of Rt 172 (Ellsworth Rd) & Main St on right as you come down hill into town.

BRIDGTON

Morning Dew Natural Foods Grocery & Deli 🛍️ 🍴 ♿
19 Sandy Creek Rd. © 207-647-4003 🕐 M-F 9-6, Sat. 9-5:30, Sun. 10-5
• organic produce • vegetarian friendly • cafe • deli • tables • self-service • take-out

🛒 From Rt 302/117 intersection, go south on Rt 117/Meadow Rd about ½ mile to store on right before High St.

BRUNSWICK

Morning Glory Natural Foods 🛍️
60 Maine St. © 207-729-0546 🕐 M-F 9-7, Sat 9-6, Sun 10-5
• organic produce

🛒 From I-95, take exit 22 toward Brunswick/Bath onto US 1N over 1 mile to Pleasant about ½ mile to Main St. Turn left onto Pleasant about ½ mile to Main St. Turn left onto Main to store.

CALAIS

Nature's Pantry 🛍️
168 C North St. © 207-454-7620 🕐 M-F 9-6, Sat 9-5
🛒 Store is on west side of Rt 1 north of Beech St and 1/8 mile south of Union St.

CAMDEN

Nature's Choice 🛍️
87 Elm St. © 207-236-8280 🕐 M-Sat 9:30-5:30
• organic produce

🛒 Store is on east side of Rt 1 just north of John St and ⅓ mile south of Park St.

DAMARISCOTTA

Rising Tide Cooperative Market 🛍️ 🍴 ♿
15 Coastal Marketplace Drive © 207-563-5556 🕐 Daily 8-7.
• organic produce • vegetarian friendly • cafe • deli • bakery • tables • self-service • take-out • co-op

🛒 From US Rt 1, take Rt 1 Bus exit to Newcastle. Cross Damariscotta River into town and continue under 1 mile to store on left in Coastal Marketplace.

DOVER-FOXCROFT

Bob's Farm Home & Garden 🛍️
15 Lincoln St. © 207-564-2581 🕐 M-F 8-5:30, Sat. 8-5
• organic produce

🛒 From Rt 7, turn left at light in town onto Main St two lights to Lincoln St. Make sharp right onto Lincoln to store.

ELLSWORTH

John Edward's Whole Foods Market 🛍️ 🍴
158 Main St. © 207-667-9377 🕐 M-Th, Sat 9-5:30, F 9-8, Sun 11-5
• vegetarian friendly • bakery • tables • self-service • take-out

🛒 From US 1/Main St & Rt 3/High St intersection, store is 1 block left on Main on left.

FALMOUTH

O'Naturals 🍴
240 U.S. Rte. 1 ℮ 207-781-8889 ⏱ Daily 10-8
A healthy fast-food concept featuring soups, sandwiches, salads and Asian noodle dishes.
 • vegetarian friendly • organic focus • alcohol • tables • self-service • take-out

📛 **From I-295N or I-95S**, take exit 10 east (toward US 1) onto Buckham Rd to Rt 1. Turn right onto Rt 1 about ⅓ mile and turn right at Staples sign to restaurant in Shops at Falmouth Village.

FARMINGTON

Better Living 🛍
181 Front St. ℮ 207-778-6018 ⏱ M-Th 7:30-6, F 7:30-3, Sun 12-5
 • organic produce

📛 **From ME 27 or ME 4**, turn onto Front St to store.

FREEPORT

Royal River Natural Foods 🛍 🍴   ♿
443 U.S. Rte. 1 ℮ 207-865-0046 ⏱ M-F 8-8, Sat 9-7, Sun 10-6
 • organic produce • vegetarian friendly • cafe • tables • self-service • take-out

📛 **From I-95S**, take exit 19 right at light onto Rt 1S about 1½ miles to store on left. **From I-95N**, take exit 17 right onto Rt 1N to store on right 1½ miles north of the Big Wooden Indian.

HAMPDEN

Hampden Natural Foods 🛍
281 Western Ave. (Rte. 9) ℮ 207-862-2500 ⏱ M-F 8-6, Sat 9-4, Sun 10-4
 • organic produce

📛 **From I-95**, take exit 180 toward Hernon/Hampden south on Coldbrook (right from I-95N, left from I-95S) about 1½ miles to US 202. Veer right onto 202 about ¾ mile to Western Ave. Turn right onto Western about ½ mile to store on right.

JAY

Organic and Otherwize 🛍
320 Main St. ℮ 207-897-1001 ⏱ M-W 9-5, Th-F 9-5:30, Sat 9-1(summer only)
 • organic produce

📛 Store is on ME 4/17 on west side 1¾ miles north of ME 133 intersection and under 1 mile south of ME 40 intersection.

KENNEBUNK

New Morning Natural Foods 🛍
3 York St. ℮ 207-985-6774 ⏱ M-Sat 9-6
 • organic produce

📛 **From I-95/195 (ME Tpke)**, take exit 3 (Kennebunk), bear right at fork and turn right at light onto Rt 1. Cross bridge to store on right.

KITTERY

Rising Tide Cooperative Market 🛍
165 State Rd. ℮ 207-439-8898 ⏱ M-Sat 9-6, Sun 11-5
 • organic produce • vegan • take-out

📛 **From I-95** take exit 2 toward Kittery onto ME 236S. At traffic circle take first right onto Rt 1S and next right to store.

MACHAIS

Whole Life Natural Market 🛍
80 Main St. © 207-255-8855 ⏰ M-F 9-6, Sat 9-4
• organic produce • vegetarian friendly • cafe • tables • self-service • take-out
🏠 Store is on Rt 1 on west side between Free & Center St.

NORWAY

Fare Share Co-op 🛍
443 Main St. © 207-743-9044 ⏰ M-W, Sat 9-6, Th-F 9-7
• deli • co-op
🏠 Rt 117 is Main St in Norway. Store is just west of intersection with Rt 26S.

ORONO

The Store & Ampersand 🛍 🍴
22 Mill St. © 207-866-4110 ⏰ M-Sat 7-7, Sun 9-4
• vegetarian friendly • cafe • bakery • tables • self-service • take-out
🏠 **From I-95**, take exit 50 toward Orono east on Kelley Rd (right off ramp from I-95N, left from I-95S) about 1 mile to end at Rt 2. Turn left onto Rt 2 about 1¼ miles to Mill St. Turn right onto Mill to store on left in center of town.

PORTLAND

Green Elephant 🍴   ♿
608 Congress St. © 207-347-3111 ⏰ Tues-Sat 11:30-2:30, 5-9:30
Pan-Asian mostly vegan menu.
• vegetarian • vegan friendly • alcohol • tables • wait staff
🏠 **From I-295**, take exit 6A onto US 1S/Forest Ave (right from I-295N, loop around from I-295S) ½-¾ mile to Congress St. Turn right onto Congress 1 block to restaurant on left.

Little Lads Bakery & Cafe 🍴
482 Congress St. © 207-871-1636 ⏰ M-Th, 10-6, F 10-2:30
Seventh-day Adventist run lunch buffet plus breakfast, sandwiches and dessert.
• vegan • tables • self-service • take-out
🏠 **From I-295**, take exit 7 onto US 1A S/Franklin Arterial ½ mile to Congress St. Turn right onto Congress under ½ mile to restaurant on left.

O'Naturals 🍴
83 Exchange St. © 207-321-2050 ⏰ M-Th, 7:30-7:30, F-Sat 7:30-8, Sun 10-3
See Falmouth location for description.
• vegetarian friendly • organic focus • alcohol • tables • self-service • take-out
🏠 **From I-295**, take exit 7 onto US 1A S/Franklin Arterial ½ mile to Congress St. Turn right onto Congress past second intersection to Exchange St. Turn left onto Exchange under 2 blocks to restaurant on left (before park).

Whole Foods Market 🛍 🍴   ♿
2 Somerset St. © 207-774-7711 ⏰ Daily 8-10
• organic produce • vegetarian friendly • salad bar • cafe • self-service • take-out
🏠 **From I-295**, take exit 7 onto US 1A S/Franklin Arterial and make second right onto Somerset St to store on left.

ROCKLAND

Good Tern Natural Food Store 🛍
750 Main St. © 207-594-8822 ⏰ M-Sat 9-6
• organic produce
🏠 Store is on west side of Rt 1 between Warren & Cedar St.

ROCKPORT

Fresh Off the Farm 🛒

495 Commercial St. ✆ 207-236-3260 🕐 M-Sat 8-7, Sun 9-5:30
  • organic produce
🛒 Store is on US 1 (aka Commercial St) on west side 4⅓ miles north of ME 17 intersection and 3 miles south of Camden, ME.

RUMFORD

Red Hill Natural Foods 🛒

228 Waldo St. ✆ 207-369-9141 🕐 M-W, F-Sat 9-6, Th 9-7
🛒 **Coming from Hanover on Rt 2**, follow Rt 2/Rumford Ave to Oxford Ave. Turn right onto Oxford 1 block to Waldo. Turn left onto Waldo to store on left. **Coming from Andover on Rt 120**, turn left onto Essex St 1 block to Waldo. Turn right onto Waldo 1 block to store on right.

SCARBOROUGH

Lois' Natural Marketplace 🛒 🍴 ♿

152 U.S. Rte. 1 ✆ 207-885-0602 🕐 M-Sat 8:30-7:30, Sun 10-6
  • organic produce • vegetarian friendly • cafe • deli • bakery • counter • tables • self-service • take-out
🛒 **From I-95N (ME Tpke)**, take exit 6A (S Portland/Portland) onto I-295 toward Rt 1/S Portland. **From I-295**, take exit 2 (US 1/Scarborough) onto Scarborough Connector (becomes 1S) about 2 miles to store on left in Scarborough Marketplace.

SHAPLEIGH

One Earth Natural Foods 🛒

191 Emery Mills Rd. ✆ 207-636-2500 🕐 M-F 10-6, Sat 10-4
  • organic produce
🛒 Store is on west side of ME109/11 (Emery Mills Rd) 1 mile south of ME11 juncture.

SKOWHEGAN

Spice of Life 🛒

338 Madison Ave. ✆ 207-474-8216 🕐 M-Th 9-6, F 9-3, Sun 10-5
  • organic produce
🛒 **From US2/201 intersection**, go north on Madison Ave 1 mile to store on right in Skowhegan Village Shopping Mall.

WATERVILLE

New Moon Rising Natural Foods 🛒

110 Pleasant St. ✆ 207-873-6244 🕐 M-F 9-6, Sat 10-2
🛒 **From I-95**, take exit 130 toward Waterville south on Main St (right from I-95N, left from I-95S) about 1 mile to Pleasant St (after tracks). Turn right onto Pleasant to store on right.

Uncle Dean's/Good News 🛒

80 Grove St. ✆ 207-873-6231 🕐 M-F 8-7, Sat 9-6
  • organic produce
🛒 **From I-95,** take exit 127 toward Waterville onto 137E/Kennedy Memorial Dr (right from I-95N, left from I-95S) over 1½ miles to Silver St. Turn right onto Silver and left onto Grove St to store on right.

WHITEFIELD

Uncas Farms Natural Food Store 🛒

98 Townhouse Rd. ✆ 207-549-5185 🕐 Tues-F 10:30-6, Sat 9-5
A 180-acre family farm and store selling their products, natural foods and Maine crafts.
  • organic produce
🛒 **From ME 126**, go south on Townhouse Rd ½ mile to store on left.

MARYLAND

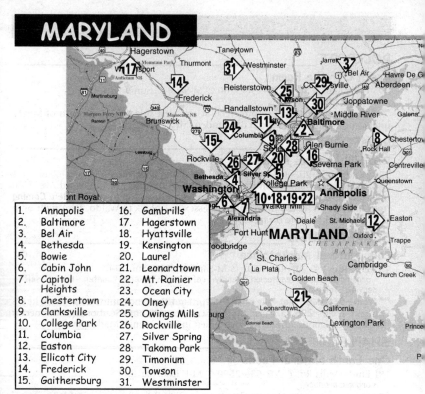

1.	Annapolis	16.	Gambrills
2.	Baltimore	17.	Hagerstown
3.	Bel Air	18.	Hyattsville
4.	Bethesda	19.	Kensington
5.	Bowie	20.	Laurel
6.	Cabin John	21.	Leonardtown
7.	Capitol Heights	22.	Mt. Rainier
8.	Chestertown	23.	Ocean City
9.	Clarksville	24.	Olney
10.	College Park	25.	Owings Mills
11.	Columbia	26.	Rockville
12.	Easton	27.	Silver Spring
13.	Ellicott City	28.	Takoma Park
14.	Frederick	29.	Timonium
15.	Gaithersburg	30.	Towson
		31.	Westminster

ANNAPOLIS

Sun & Earth Foods 🛍

1933 West St. ✆ 410-266-6862 ⏱ M-Sat 9:30-6:30, Sun 12-4
Fresh sandwiches during the week.

🚗 **From I-97**, take exit 4 onto Rt 50E. **From I-495/95**, take exit 19A onto 50E. **From 50E**, take MD exit 23 and follow 450E ramp to West St. Turn left onto West S/450E almost 1 mile to store at Lee St. **From 50W**, take exit 23A toward MD 450 onto Solomon's Island Rd (Rt 2S) to West. Turn left onto West ½ mile to store.

Whole Foods Market 🛍🍴   ♿

2504 Solomon's Island Rd. ✆ 410-573-1800 ⏱ M-Sat 8-10, Sun 8-9
• organic produce • vegetarian friendly • salad bar • cafe • self-service • take-out

🚗 **From I-97**, take exit 4 onto Rt 50E. **From I-495/95**, take exit 19A onto 50E. **From 50 E**, take exit 23 and follow 450E ramp to West St. Turn left onto West ¼ mile to Solomon's Island Rd. Turn right onto Solomon's Island about ½ mile to store on right in Harbor Ctr. **From Rt 50W**, take exit 23A toward MD 450 onto Solomon's Island Rd (Rt 2S) 1¼ miles (past 2 lights) to store.

BALTIMORE

Dogwood Deli & The Dogwood 🍴

911 W. 36th St. ✆ 410-889-0952 ⏱ Deli M-Sat 11-5 Restaurant M-Th 11-10, F-Sat 11-11
• vegetarian friendly • organic focus • fresh juice • alcohol • tables • wait staff • take-out

🚗 **From I-83S (Jones Falls Expwy)**, take exit 9A-B left onto W Cold Springs Ln under ½ mile to Falls Church Rd. Turn right onto Falls Church 1 mile to W 36th St. Turn right onto W 36th 2½ blocks to restaurant on right. **From I-83N**, take exit 8 onto Hwy 25N/Falls Rd to W 36th (after park). Turn right onto W 36th 2½ blocks to restaurant on right.

Liquid Earth 🍴

1626 Aliceanna St. ✆ 410-276-6606 🕐 Tues-Sat 9-7
· vegetarian · vegan friendly · fresh juice · counter · tables · wait staff

🍴 **From I-95N**, take exit 53 onto I-395N to Pratt St. Turn right onto Pratt about 1 mile to President St. Turn right onto President to Aliceanna St. Turn left onto Aliceanna past roundabout to restaurant. **From I-95S**, take exit 60 west on US 40/Pulaski Hwy about 4½ miles to N Broadway. Turn left onto Broadway to Aliceanna. Turn right onto Aliceanna to restaurant. **From Jones Falls Expwy (I-83S)**, follow expwy south (becomes President St) to Aliceanna. Turn left onto Aliceanna past roundabout to restaurant.

OK Natural Food Store 🛒

11 W. Preston St. ✆ 410-837-3911 🕐 M-F 9:30-8:30, Sat. 10-8:30, Sun 11-6
· organic produce

🍴 **From I-95**, take exit 53 onto I-395N to MLK Jr Blvd exit. Follow MLK Jr Blvd north about 2 miles and keep right onto W Chase St 1 block to W Biddle St. Turn right onto Biddle 2 blocks, left onto Charles St 1 block and left onto W Preston St to store. **From Jones Falls Expwy (I-83N)**, take exit 3 onto Fallsway (becomes Guilford St) to E Preston. Turn left onto Preston about ¼ mile to store. **From I-83S**, take exit 4 onto St. Paul St 1 block to Preston. Turn right onto Preston 2 blocks to store.

One World Cafe 🍴

100 W. University Pkwy. ✆ 410-235-5777 🕐 M-Sat 7:30am-2am, Sun 8-5
Mostly vegetarian/vegan with all-vegan baked goods; some fish and eggs.
· vegetarian friendly · vegan friendly · organic focus · fresh juice · alcohol · tables · wait staff · take-out

🍴 **From I-95**, take exit 53 north onto I-395N towards MLK Blvd 1¾ miles to MLK. Continue on S MLK and N MLK 1½ miles to N Howard St. Turn left onto N Howard about ¾ mile to W North Ave. Turn right onto W North 2 blocks to N Charles St. Turn left onto N Charles 1½ miles to W University Pkwy. Veer left onto W University under ¼ mile to restaurant on right after Canterbury Rd. **From I-83S**, take exit 9A/B left onto W Cold Spring Ln about ¾ mile to Roland Ave. Turn right onto Roland and merge onto University 1 mile to restaurant on left.

Red Emma's Bookstore Coffeehouse 🍴

800 St. Paul St. ✆ 410-230-0450 🕐 M-Sat 10-10, Sunday 10-6
Bagels, wraps and vegan baked goods.
· vegetarian · vegan friendly · counter · tables · self-service · take-out

🍴 **From I-83S**, take exit 4 right onto St Paul St ½ mile to restaurant on right at E Madison St. **From I-83N**, take exit 3 onto Fallsway and left onto E Chase St under ¼ mile to St Paul. Turn right onto St Paul ⅓ mile to restaurant.

Sunsplash Natural Foods for Less 🛒

7006 Reisterstown Rd. ✆ 410-486-0979 🕐 M-F 9-8, Sat 9-7, Sun 10-6
🍴 **From I-695**, take exit 20 onto Reistertown Rd/Rt 140S (left from I-695W, right from I-695E) about 2 miles to store on right.

The Yabba Pot 🍴
2433 St. Paul St. ℂ 410-662-8638 ⊙ M-Sat 11-9, Sun 11-7
Primarily carryout but there are a few tables.
• vegan • tables • self-service • take-out

🕮 **From I-95**, take exit 53 onto I-395N to MLK Jr Blvd exit. Follow MLK Jr about 1¾ miles to N Howard St. Veer left onto N Howard over 1 mile to W 25th St. Turn right onto 25th 4 blocks (about ¼ mile) to St Paul St. Turn right onto St Paul to restaurant. **From I-83 (Jones Falls Expwy)**, take exit 7 (7A from I-83N) east on W 28th St (left from I-83S, right from I-83N) about ⅓ mile to Huntingdon Ave. Turn right onto Huntingdon (becomes W 25th) about ½ mile to St Paul. Turn right onto St Paul to restaurant.

Whole Foods Market 🛍 🍴   ♿
1330 Smith Ave. ℂ 410-532-6700 ⊙ M-Sat 8-10, Sun 8-9
• organic produce • vegetarian friendly • salad bar • cafe • self-service • take-out

🕮 **From Jones Falls Expwy (I-83)**, take exit 10A onto Northern Pkwy E to first light (Falls Rd). Turn left onto Falls to third light at Smith Ave. Turn left onto Smith to store.

Whole Foods Market 🛍 🍴   ♿
1001 Fleet St. ℂ 410-528-1640 ⊙ M-Sat 8-10, Sun 8-9, Cafe from 7
• organic produce • vegetarian friendly • salad bar • cafe • self-service • take-out

🕮 In Baltimore's Inner Harbor district. **From I-95**, take I-395N about 1½ miles continuing onto S Howard St to first right onto W Pratt St. Take Pratt under 1 mile to President St. Turn right onto President about ½ mile to Fleet St. Turn left onto Fleet to store on right after Exeter St. **From I-83S (Jones Falls Expwy)**, take exit 7 onto President ½ mile to Fleet and follow directions above.

Zodiac Restaurant 🍴   ♿
1724 N. Charles St. ℂ 410-727-8815 ⊙ Tues-Th 5-10, F 5-11, Sat 3-11, Sun 3-10
• vegetarian friendly • vegan friendly • alcohol • tables • wait staff • take-out

🕮 **From I-95**, take exit 53 onto I-395N to MLK Jr Blvd exit. Follow MLK Jr north about 1¾ miles to N Howard St. Veer left onto N Howard about ½ mile to US 1N (North Ave). Turn right onto North 1 block to Maryland Ave. Turn right onto Maryland 3 blocks to W Lanvale St. Turn left onto Lanvale 1 block to E Charles St. Turn left onto Charles to restaurant on left (blue awning). **From I-83 (Jones Falls Expwy)**, take exit 5 right onto Maryland 1 block to Lanvale St. Turn right onto Lanvale and left onto Charles to restaurant.

BEL AIR

Davids Natural Market 🛍
3 Red Pump Rd. ℂ 410-803-0784 ⊙ M-F 10-8, Sat 10-5, Sun 12-5
• organic produce • fresh juice

🕮 **From I-95**, take exit 77B toward Bel Air onto MD 24N 8¼ miles. Follow MD 24N ramp onto Rock Spring Rd/MD 24 to store on left at Red Pump Rd.

BETHESDA

Whole Foods Market 🛍 🍴   ♿
5269 River Rd. ℂ 301-984-4860 ⊙ Daily 8-9
• organic produce • vegetarian friendly • salad bar • cafe • self-service • take-out

🕮 **From I-495 (Capitol Beltway)**, take exit 39 or 39B toward Washington onto River Rd (190E) about 4 miles to store on north side (190W).

BOWIE

Healthway Natural Foods 🛍   ♿
6856 Race Track Rd. ℂ 301-805-8255 ⊙ M-W, F 10-7, Th 10-8, Sat 10-6, Sun 12-5
• organic produce

🕮 **From I-495 (Capitol Beltway)**, take exit 19A onto US 50E about 7½ miles to exit 13A-B-C (US 301/MD 3). Merge onto MD 3N (toward Baltimore) about 2¾ miles to Annapolis Rd (MD 450). Turn left onto Annapolis over 1 mile to Race Track Rd. Turn right onto Race Track to store in Hilltop Plaza.

CABIN JOHN

Bethesda Co-op 🛍️

6500 Seven Locks Rd. ℂ 301-320-2530 ⏱ M-Sat 8:30-9, Sun 8:30-8
• organic produce

🚗 **From I-495S**, take exit 39 toward Hwy 90W/Potomac and veer left onto River Rd to Seven Locks Rd. Turn left onto Seven Locks 1⅓ miles to store on right at MacArthur Blvd. **From I-495N**, take exit 41 toward Echo Glen right at fork onto Clara Barton Pkwy E 1¼ miles to MacArthur Blvd exit. Take Clara Barton Access Rd and turn left onto MacArthur (signs for Cabin John) ½ mile to store on left at Seven Locks Rd.

CAPITOL HEIGHTS

Everlasting Life 🛍️ 🍴

9185 Central Ave. ℂ 301-324-6900 ⏱ M-Sat 10-9, Sun 11-7
Source of Life Juice Bar & Deli inside the store serves southern-style vegan food from the Soul Vegetarian chain.
• organic produce • vegan • fresh juice • deli • counter • self-service • take-out • co-op

🚗 **From I-495 (Capitol Beltway)**, take exit 15B west on Central Ave (214W) to store in Hampton Mall.

CHESTERTOWN

Chestertown Natural Foods 🛍️   ♿

303 Cannon St. ℂ 410-778-1677 ⏱ M-F 10-6, Sat 9-5, Sun 12-4
• organic produce

🚗 On the Delmarva Peninsula. **From MD Rt 213**, turn onto Cross St (right heading south, left heading north) about 2 blocks to Cannon St. Turn left onto Cannon to store on right.

CLARKSVILLE

Great Sage 🍴   ♿

5809 Clarksville Square Dr. ℂ 443-535-9400 ⏱ Tues-Th 11:30-9, F-Sat 11:30-10, Sun 10-9
"Global green cuisine."
• vegetarian • alcohol • organic focus • tables • wait staff • take-out

🚗 **From I-95**, take exit 38B onto MD 32W over 7 miles to exit 20. Turn right at light onto MD 108/Clarksville Pike about ¼ mile to restaurant on left in Clarksville Square Shopping Ctr. **From I-70**, take exit 87A onto Columbia Pike/US 29S about 4¼ miles to Clarksville Pike. Merge onto Clarksville (108S) about 6¼ miles to restaurant on right.

Roots Market 🛍️

5805 Clarksville Square Dr. ℂ443-535-9321 ⏱ M-Sat 9-8, Sun 10-7
• organic produce • salad bar

🚗 See Great Sage above.

COLLEGE PARK

Berwyn Cafe 🍴

5010 Berwyn Rd. ℂ 301-345-9898 ⏱ Breakfast M-F 7:30-10:30 Lunch/Dinner M-Th 11-5, F 11-8, Sat 9-5
• vegetarian • vegan friendly • organic focus • fresh juice • bakery • counter • tables • wait staff • take-out

🚗 **From I-495 (Capitol Beltway)**, take exit 25 (25B from I-495N) toward College Park/U MD onto Rt 1S about 1½ miles to Berwyn Rd. Turn left onto Berwyn 2½ blocks to restaurant on left.

MD Food Collective ♿ 🚊

B-0203 Stamp Student Union, UMD ℰ 301-314-8089 ⏰ M 7:30-6, Tues-F 7:30-8, F 7:30-7, Sat 10:30-5, Sun 12-3
Student-operated store and vegetarian eatery on the U MD campus.

• organic produce • vegetarian • cafe • deli • tables • self-service • take-out • co-op

🚘 **From I-495 (Capitol Beltway),** take exit 25 (25B from I-495N) toward College Park/U MD onto Rt 1S about 3 miles to UMD. Turn right onto Campus Drive (main entrance of UMD campus). Continue straight through circle up hill to Stamp Student Union on right. Store is in basement on north side entrance.

MOM's Organic Market ♿

9827 Rhode Island Ave. ℰ 301-220-1100 ⏰ M-Sat 9-9, Sun 10-8
• organic produce

🚘 **From I-495 (Capitol Beltway),** take exit 25 (25B from I-495N) toward College Park/U MD onto Rt 1S about ½ mile to Edgewood Rd. Turn left onto Edgewood about ⅓ mile to Rhode Island Ave. Turn right onto Rhode Island 1 block to store.

COLUMBIA

David's Natural Market

5430 Lynx Lane ℰ 410-730-2304 ⏰ M-F 8-8, Sat 9-7, Sun 10-5 Cafe M-Sat 9-4
All baked goods are vegan.

• organic produce • vegetarian friendly • fresh juice • cafe • deli • bakery • tables • self-service • take-out

🚘 **From I-95S,** take exit 41A-B toward Columbia onto 175W merging onto Little Patuxent Pkwy 5½ miles to right fork onto Governor Warfield Pkwy. Take Governor Warfield to second light and turn right onto Twin Rivers Rd ½ mile (second light) to Lynx Ln. Turn left onto Lynx to store in Wild Lake Shopping Ctr. **From I-70,** take exit 87A onto 29S 5 miles to Columbia Town Ctr ramp. Merge onto Little Patuxent Pkwy ½ mile to Governor Warfield and follow directions above. **From I-95N,** take exit 38B onto Rt 32W about 3 miles to 29N. Merge onto 29N 1½ miles to exit 18A-B and take ramp toward Columbia Town Ctr onto Broken Land Pkwy past three lights to Twin Rivers Rd. Turn left onto Twin Rivers three lights to Lynx. Turn left onto Lynx to store.

Mango Grove 🍴

6365 Dobbin Rd. ℰ 410-884-3426 ⏰ M 11:30-3, 5-9, W-F11:30-3, 5-10, Sat 12-10, Sun 12-9
Vegetarian Indian with a buffet available at lunch.

• vegetarian • vegan friendly • alcohol • tables • self-service • wait staff

🚘 **From I-95N,** take exit 41B toward Columbia onto MD 175W 2-2¾ miles to Dobbin Rd. Turn left onto Dobbin to restaurant on left in Dobbin Ctr. **From I-70,** take exit 87A onto US 29S about 5½ miles to MD 175E. Merge onto 175E almost 3 miles to Dobbin. Turn right onto Dobbin to restaurant.

MOM's Organic Market ♿

7351 Assateague Drive #190 ℰ 410-799-2175 ⏰ M-Sat 9-9, Sun 10-8
• organic produce

🚘 **From I-95,** take exit 41A-41B toward Jessup onto Hwy 175E/Little Patuxent Pkwy ½ mile to Assateague Dr (1 block past Rt 1/Washington Blvd). Turn right onto Assateague to store in Columbia East Marketplace.

EASTON

Railray Market

108 Marlboro Rd. ℰ 410-822-4852 ⏰ M-Sat 9-7, Sun 10-6
• vegetarian friendly • deli • tables • self-service • take-out

🚘 On the Delmarva Peninsula. **From Rt 50,** take MD 322/Easton Bypass to light at Marlboro Rd. Turn east (left traveling south, right traveling north) onto Marlboro to store in Marlboro Shopping Ctr (second strip mall).

ELLICOTT CITY
Sarah and Desmond's 🍴
3715 Old Columbia Pike ✆ 410-465-9700 ⏰ Tues-F 7-6, Sat 8-6, Sun 8-5
All-day breakfast, open-faced pitas and other sandwiches, salads, hot dishes.
 • vegetarian • vegan friendly • tables • self-service

🚗 **From I-695**, take exit 13 toward Catonsville west on MD 144/Frederick Rd (right from I-695S, left from I-695N) about 4¼ miles to Main St/Old Columbia Pike. Turn left onto Main to restaurant on left. **From I-70**, take exit 87A toward Columbia onto US 29S about 1½ miles to US 40E (Baltimore Ntl Pike). Merge onto 40E 1 mile to Rogers Ave. Turn right onto Rogers 1 mile to Frederick Rd. Turn left onto Frederick ¾ mile to Main. Turn left onto Main to restaurant.

FREDERICK
Common Market Co-op 🛍
5728 Buckeystown Pike ✆ 301-663-3416 ⏰ M-Sat 9-9, Sun 11-8
 • organic produce • vegetarian friendly • deli • take-out • co-op

🚗 **From I-70E**, take exit 54 toward Market St onto Rt 85/Buckeystown Pike about ½ mile to store on right in Evergreen Sq. **From I-70W**, take exit 54 toward Market right onto New Design Rd, right onto Market and right onto Buckeystown about ½ mile to store. **From I-270**, take exit 31A toward Market onto Rt 85N over ½ mile to store on left.

MOM's Organic Market 🛍   ♿
5273 Buckeystown Pike ✆ 240-566-1444 ⏰ M-Sat 9-9, Sun 10-8
 • organic produce

🚗 **From I-70**, take exit 53 onto I-270S. **From I-270**, take exit 31A onto Rt 85S/Buckeystown Pike ¼-½ mile to store on left in Westview Promenade.

GAITHERSBURG
Madras Palace 🍴
74 Bureau Dr. ✆ 301-977-1600 ⏰ Daily 11:30-3, 5:30-10
Vegetarian Indian with a daily lunch and Monday night dinner buffet.
 • vegetarian • vegan friendly • tables • self-service • wait staff

🚗 **From I-270S**, take exit 11 right onto Quince Orchard Rd across tracks and take first left onto Firstfield Rd 1 block to Bureau Dr. Turn right onto Bureau to restaurant on right. **From I-270N**, take exit 10 toward Quince Orchard right onto W Diamond Ave under ½ mile to Bureau. Turn right onto Bureau under ¼ mile to restaurant on left.

Whole Foods Market 🛍 🍴   ♿
316 Kentlands Blvd. ✆ 301-258-9500 ⏰ Daily 8-9
 • organic produce • vegetarian friendly • salad bar • cafe • self-service • take-out

🚗 **From I-270**, take exit 9 west on Sam Eig Hwy to third light. Bear right onto Great Seneca Hwy to third light (Kentlands Blvd). Turn left onto Kentlands through traffic circle to store on left.

GAMBRILLS
David's Natural Market 🛍
871 Annapolis Rd. ✆ 410-987-1533 ⏰ M-F 8-8, Sat 9-7, Sun 10-6
 • organic produce • vegetarian friendly • deli • take-out

🚗 **From I-97**, take exit 12 toward MD 3 Bus/Glen Burnie onto New Cut Rd 1¾ miles to Gambrills Rd. Veer left onto Gambrills about 2¾ miles to Annapolis Rd. Turn right onto Annapolis to store at Dairy Farm Rd.

HAGERSTOWN

Healthway Natural Foods 🛍️

13026 Pennsylvania Ave. © 301-739-1462 ⏱ M-F 10-7, Sat 10-6

🚗 **From I-81S**, take exit 3 left at fork (signs for State Line) and left onto Molly Pitcher Hwy/US 11 about 6⅓ miles (becomes Pennsylvania Ave) to store on left. **From I-81N**, take exit 9 right onto Maugans Ave over ½ mile to Pennsylvania. Turn right onto Pennsylvania about 1 mile to store.

HYATTSVILLE

Woodlands 🍽️

8046 New Hampshire Ave. © 301-434-4202 ⏱ Daily 11:30-9:30

Vegetarian Indian with buffet lunch option.

• vegetarian • vegan friendly • tables • self-service • wait staff

🚗 **From I-495 (Capitol Beltway)**, take exit 28B toward Takoma Park right onto New Hampshire Ave (MD 650S) over 2 miles to restaurant at University Blvd.

KENSINGTON

Pumpernickel's Bagelry & Catering 🍽️

3784 Howard Ave. © 301-942-5935 ⏱ M-Sat 11-7

Vegan take-out breakfast and lunch menu and vegan pizza by the slice.

• vegetarian friendly • vegan friendly • tables • self-service • take-out

🚗 **From I-495,** take exit 33 toward Kensington/Chevy Chase north on Connecticut Ave/MD 185N (right at fork from I-495W, left from I-495E) 1¾ miles to Howard Ave. Turn right onto Howard 1 block to restaurant on right after Armory Ave.

LAUREL

Laurel Health Food 🛍️

131 Bowie Rd. © 301-498-7191 ⏱ M-F 10-8, Sat. 10-6

• organic produce

🚗 **From I-95**, take exit 33 (Gorman Ave/Rt 198) east past Rt 1 to store near intersection 198 & Bowie Rd (look for Office Depot).

LEONARDTOWN

Good Earth Natural Food Company 🛍️

41675 Park Ave. © 301-475-1630 ⏱ M-F 9:30-7, Sat 9:30-5

• organic produce

🚗 **From Rt 5S**, turn right onto Hollywood Rd (becomes Washington St) to Historic Leonardtown Ctr. Turn left onto Park Ave to store on right. **From Rt 4/St Andrews Church Rd**, turn right onto Rt 5 ½ mile to Leonardtown Rd. Turn left onto Leonardtown under ½ mile to Courthouse Dr. Turn left onto Courthouse and first right onto Park to store on left after Guyther Dr.

MT. RAINIER

Glut Food Co-op 🛍️

4005 34th St. © 301-779-1978 ⏱ M, Sat-Sun 9-7, Tues-F 9-8

🚗 **From I-495 (Capitol Beltway)**, take exit 25 onto Rt 1S to Mt Rainier. Turn right onto 34th St to store on right. **From downtown Washington**, take Rhode Island Ave (1N) to Mt Rainier and turn left onto 34th to store.

Please tell these businesses
that you found them in Healthy Highways

OCEAN CITY

Ocean City Organics 🛍️
11944 Ocean Gateway ✆ 410-213-9818 ⏰ M-F 9-7, Sat 10-6, Sun 11-5
• organic produce

🚗 Store is on US 50 about 9 miles past intersection with Ocean City Expwy on right before Stephen Decatur Hwy. **From the waterfront**, go inland on US 50/ Ocean Gateway 1½ miles to store on left after Stephen Decatur Hwy.

OLNEY

Olney Ale House 🍴
2000 Olney Sandy Spring Rd. ✆ 301-774-6708 ⏰ Tues-Th, Sun 11:30-10, F-Sat 11:30-11
Vegetarian choices include veggie BLT, tofu on homemade molasses-sweetened bread and wraps.
• vegetarian friendly • alcohol • tables • wait staff

🚗 **From I-95**, take exit 33B toward Burtonville onto MD 198W (right from I-95S, loop around right from I-95N) about 6 miles to New Hampshire Ave. Turn right onto New Hampshire about 2½ miles to Olney Sandy Spring Rd. Turn left onto Olney Sandy Spring about 1¾ miles to restaurant.

Roots Market 🛍️
16800 Georgia Ave. ✆301-774-1344 ⏰M-Sat 9-8, Sun 10-7
• organic produce

🚗 Store is on MD 9 (aka Georgia Ave) north of Olney Manor Recreational Park and south of Old Baltimore Rd on west side.

OWINGS MILLS

The Flying Avocado 🍴
10210 S. Dolfield Rd. ✆ 443-471-2600 ⏰ M-F 7-6, Sat 9-5
Homemade granola, whole wheat wraps, salads, children's menu, gluten-free baked goods.
• vegetarian friendly • organic focus • tables • wait staff

🚗 **From I-795S**, take exit 4A-B left at fork toward Owings Mills Blvd and follow signs for MD 140E/Reistertown Rd onto Owings Mills 1 mile to S Dolfield Rd. Turn right onto S Dolfield under ½ mile to restaurant. **From I-795N**, take exit 4 right at fork onto Owings Mills about ½ mile to S Dolfield. Turn right onto S Dolfield under ½ mile to restaurant.

ROCKVILLE

Cafe Masala 🍴
705 1st St. ✆ 301-294-2937 ⏰ Daily 11-9
Indian vegetarian take-out.
• vegetarian • vegan friendly • take-out

🚗 **From I-270N**, take exit 4A for Montrose Rd left at fork and left onto Tower Oaks Blvd over ½ mile to Wootan Pkwy. Turn right onto Wootan continuing onto 1st St then Norbeck Rd 2 miles total when 1st turns left. Turn left onto 1st and left again to restaurant on left. **From I-270S**, take exit 6B-A left onto Hwy 28E/W Montgomery Rd continuing onto Veirs Mill Rd about 2¼ miles total to Norbeck. Turn left onto Norbeck ½ mile to 1st and follow directions above.

MOM's Organic Market 🛍️   ♿
11711 Parklawn Drive ✆301-816-4944 ⏰ M-Sat 9-9, Sun 10-8
• organic produce

🚗 **From I-495 (Capitol Beltway)**, take exit 34 north on Rockville Pike (Rt 355N) 2 miles to Nicholson Lane. Turn right onto Nicholson (becomes Parklawn Dr) ½ mile to store on right.

The Vegetable Garden 🍽

11618 Rockville Pike © 301-468-9301 ⊙ M-Th 11:30-10, F-Sat 11:30-11:30, Sun 11:30-9:30
Macrobiotic-friendly cuisine. No dairy, eggs or refined sugar.
  • vegetarian • vegan friendly • organic focus • tables • wait staff • take-out
🍎 **From I-495 (Capitol Beltway)**, take exit 34 north on Rockville Pike (Rt 355N) about 2½ miles (past White Flint Mall on right) to restaurant on left across from White Flint metro stop.

Whole Foods Market 🛍 🍽   ♿

1649 Rockville Pike © 301-984-4880 ⊙ M-Sat 8-10, Sun 8-9
  • organic produce • vegetarian friendly • salad bar • cafe • self-service • take-out
🍎 **From I-495 (Capitol Beltway)**, take exit 34 north on Rockville Pike (Rt 355N) about 3⅔ miles to store on left in Congressional Plaza.

Yuan Fu Vegetarian 🍽

798 Rockville Pike © 301-762-5937 ⊙ Daily 11-10
Vegetarian Chinese. Brown rice available.
  • vegetarian • vegan friendly • fresh juice • tables • wait staff • take-out
🍎 **From I-495 (Capitol Beltway)**, take exit 34 north on Rockville Pike (Rt 355N) about 4¾ miles to restaurant on right in small strip mall.

SILVER SPRING_____

Takoma Park Silver Springs Co-op 🛍

8309 Grubb Rd. © 240-247-2667 ⊙ Daily 9-9
  • organic produce • co-op
🍎 **From I-495E**, take exit 31B onto Georgia Ave ½ mile to 16th St. Turn right onto 16th 1 mile to East-West Hwy (410). Turn right onto 410 to light at Grubb Rd. Turn left onto Grubb a few blocks to store on left in Rock Creek Shopping Ctr. **From I-495W**, take exit 31 (MD 97/Georgia Ave) toward Silver Spring. Stay left at fork off ramp, turn left onto Georgia and follow directions above.

Whole Foods Market 🛍 🍽   ♿

833 Wayne Ave. © 301-608-9373 ⊙ Daily 8-10
  • organic produce • vegetarian friendly • salad bar • cafe • self-service • take-out
🍎 **From I-495 (Capitol Beltway)**, take exit 30B onto Colesville Rd (US 29S) about 1 mile to Spring St. Turn left onto Spring 3 blocks to Pershing Dr. Turn right onto Pershing into store lot in Downtown Silver Spring Shopping Ctr.

TAKOMA PARK_____

Takoma Park Silver Springs Co-op 🛍

201 Ethan Allen Ave. © 301-891-2667 ⊙ Daily 9-9
  • organic produce • co-op
🍎 **From I-495 (Capitol Beltway)**, take exit 28B toward Takoma Park south on New Hampshire Ave (MD 650S) about 3½ miles to East-West Hwy (MD 410). Turn right onto 410 (aka Ethan Allen Ave) about ⅔ mile to store on left.

Udupi Palace 🍽

1329 University Blvd. E. © 301-434-1531 ⊙ M 11:30-3, 5-9:30, Tues-Sun 11:30-9:30
Indian vegetarian with a lunch buffet.
  • vegetarian • vegan friendly • tables • self-service • wait staff
🍎 **From I-495 (Capitol Beltway)**, take exit 29B toward Langley Park onto 193E/University Blvd E about 2½ miles. After New Hampshire Ave turn right at first light onto University to restaurant at 14th St.

Washington Adventist Hospital

7600 Carroll Ave. © 301-891-5012 ⊕ Daily 6:30am-10am, 11:30-2, 4:30-6:30
A vegetarian cafeteria in the Seventh-day Adventist tradition.
• vegetarian • tables • self-service

🚌 **From I-495 (Capitol Beltway)**, take exit 28B toward Takoma Park south on New Hampshire Ave (MD 650S) about 1½ miles to Piney Branch Rd. Turn right onto Piney Branch ½ mile to Carroll Ave. Veer left onto Carroll about 1¼ miles to cafeteria in hospital basement (LL2).

TIMONIUM

The Natural

2149 York Rd. © 410-560-3133 ⊕ M-F 9:30-8, Sat 10-6, Sun 11-7
• organic produce • vegetarian friendly • fresh juice • cafe • deli • tables • self-service
• take-out

🚌 **From I-695 (Baltimore Beltway)**, take exit 24 onto I-83N to first exit onto Timomium Rd E. At third light turn left onto York Rd. At next light turn right into Timonium Shopping Ctr to store (across from fairgrounds).

TOWSON

Health Concern

28 W. Susquehanna Ave. © 410-828-4015 ⊕ M-F 9:30-8, Sat 9:30-6, Sun 11-5
Weekday salad bar.
• organic produce • salad bar • take-out

🚌 **From I-695 (Baltimore Beltway)**, take exit 27A onto Hwy 146S about ¾ mile to York Rd. Take third exit to continue onto York 3 blocks to Towsontown Blvd. Turn right onto Towsontown, right onto Washington Ave and right onto Susquehanna Ave to store on left.

WESTMINSTER

Harvestin' Natural Foods

66 E. Main St. © 410-857-1970 ⊕ M-Th 10-6, F 10-5, Sat 10-3

🚌 **From MD 140/Baltimore Blvd**, take Manchester Rd/MD 27 left onto Manchester ¾ mile to Main St. Turn left onto Main about 1 block to store on right.

MASSACHUSETTS

1. Allston
2. Amherst
3. Andover
4. Ashland
5. Becket
6. Bedford
7. Bellingham
8. Beverly
9. Boston
10. Brewster
11. Brighton
12. Brookfield
13. Brookline
14. Burlington
15. Cambridge
16. Centerville
17. Charlton
18. Chatham
19. Cohasset
20. Concord
21. Dennisport
22. Dorchester
23. Falmouth
24. Framingham
25. Franklin
26. Gardner
27. Gloucester
28. Great Barrington
29. Greenfield
30. Hadley
31. Hanover
32. Hingham
33. Hudson
34. Jamaica Plain
35. Lee
36. Lenox
37. Leominster
38. Leverett
39. Lowell
40. Medford
41. Melrose
42. Natick
43. Newton
44. North Andover
45. Northampton
46. Orleans
47. Osterville
48. Pittsfield
49. Plymouth
50. Provincetown
51. Quincy
52. Seekonk
53. Shelburne Falls
54. Shrewsberry
55. Springfield
56. Swampscott
57. Waltham
58. Watertown
59. Wayland
60. Wellesley
61. Westborough
62. Williamstown
63. Woburn
64. Worcester

ALLSTON

Grasshopper Vegetarian Restaurant 🍽

1 N. Beacon St. ✆ 617-254-8883 ◷ M-Th 11-10, F-Sat 11-11, Sun 12-10
Pan-Asian vegan menu.
· vegan · tables · wait staff

💾 **From Mass Pike E (I-90E)**, take exit 18 on left toward Brighton and continue toward Cambridge St. Turn right onto Cambridge 1 mile (across tpke) to N Beacon Ave. Turn right onto N Beacon to restaurant on right. **From I-90W**, take exit 20 left at fork toward Allston/Brighton to Cambridge. Turn right onto Cambridge and follow directions above.

T.J. Scallywaggle's Vegan House of Pizza & Subs 🍽

487 Cambridge St. ✆617-787-9884 ◷ M, W-Th, Sun 12-11, Tues 3-11, F-Sat 12-12
Casual coffee-house atmosphere.
· vegan · tables · self-service · take-out

💾 **From Mass Pike E (I-90E)**, take exit 18 on left toward Brighton and continue toward Cambridge St. Turn right onto Cambridge 1 mile (across tpke) to restaurant on right at N Beacon Ave. **From I-90W**, take exit 20 left at fork toward Allston/Brighton to Cambridge. Turn right onto Cambridge and follow directions above.

AMHERST

Lone Wolf 🍽

63 Main St. ✆ 413-256-4643 ◷ Daily 7am-2pm
Vegan French toast and "omelettes," tofu scrambles, multigrain pancakes and more.
· vegetarian friendly · vegan friendly · organic focus · alcohol · counter · tables · wait staff

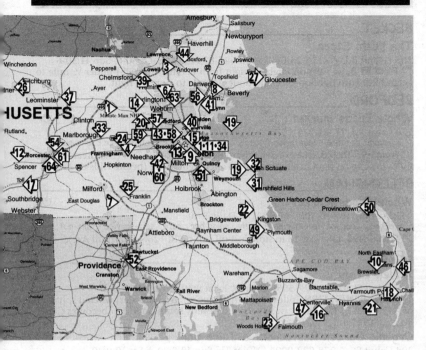

🍴 **From I-91**, take exit 19 in Northampton east on Rt 9 about 6 miles to S Pleasant St. Turn left onto S Pleasant 2 blocks to Main St. Turn right onto Main to restaurant on right.

People's Market

U Mass Student Union ✆ 413-545-2060 ⏰ M, F 8:45-4, Tues-Th 8:45-5
Student-run wholefoods store.

🍴 **From I-91**, take exit 19 in Northampton east on Rt 9 about 4½ miles to Rt 116N. Turn left onto 116 1 mile to U Mass exit to campus. The store is in the rear of the Student Union Bldg on the campus pond next to The Beach.

ANDOVER

Whole Foods Market

40 Railroad St. ✆ 978-749-6664 ⏰ M-Sat 7:30-10, Sun 8-9
• organic produce • vegetarian friendly • salad bar • cafe • self-service • take-out

🍴 **From I-93**, take exit 44 east on Rt 133 about 2 miles to 4-way light at Rt 28. Turn right onto Rt 28S three lights to store on right. **From I-495,** take exit 41 toward Andover onto 28S (N Main St) four lights to store on right.

ASHLAND

Dosa Temple

59 Pond St. ✆ 508-879-6800 ⏰ M-F 11:30-2:30, 5-9:30, Sat-Sun 11:30-10
Indian vegetarian with a lunch buffet.
• vegetarian • vegan friendly • tables • self-service • wait staff

🍴 **From I-90 (Mass Tpke)**, take exit 13 toward Framingham south on Cochituate Rd (merge right from Tpke E, left from Tpke W) about 1 mile to Concord St. Veer left onto Concord 1¾ miles to Concord/Memorial Sq. Take second exit to continue on Concord under 2 miles to restaurant on right.

BECKET

The Kushi Store 🛍

308 Leland Rd. ✆ 413-623-6679, 800-645-8744 ⏰ M-Sat 8:30-6, Sun 11:30-6

🚘 **From Rt 8,** go west on High St (right from 8N, left from 8S) under ½ mile to Leland Rd. Turn right onto Leland under ½ mile to store on right.

BEDFORD

Whole Foods Market 🛍 🍴   ♿

170 Great Rd. ✆ 781-275-1570 ⏰ Daily 8-10
  • organic produce • vegetarian friendly • salad bar • cafe • self-service • take-out

🚘 **From I-95/Rt 128,** take exit 31B toward Bedford onto Rt 4/225 (aka Great Road) 2 miles to store on right in shopping plaza after Webber Ave (before Hillside Ave).

BELLINGHAM

Whole Foods Market 🛍 🍴   ♿

255 Hartford Ave. ✆ 508-966-3331 ⏰ Daily 8-10
  • organic produce • vegetarian friendly • salad bar • cafe • self-service • take-out

🚘 **From I-495,** take exit 18 to store just off exit on Rt 126N (Hartford Ave).

BEVERLY

A New Leaf 🛍

261 Cabot St. ✆ 978-927-5955 ⏰ M-W, F-Sat 9:30-6, Th 9:30-8

🚘 **From I-95N/Rt 128N,** follow 128N right (north to Gloucester) when it splits off of I-95. **From Rt 128,** take exit 20B toward Beverly south on Rt 1A (becomes Cabot St) about 1¾ miles to store on left.

Organic Garden Restaurant & Juice Bar 🍴   ♿

294 Cabot St. ✆ 978-922-0004 ⏰ Tues-Th, Sun 10-8:30, F-Sat 10-9:30
Gourmet raw foods.

  • vegan • organic focus • fresh juice • alcohol • counter • tables • self-service • wait staff • take-out

🚘 **From I-95N/Rt 128N,** follow 128N right (north to Gloucester) when it splits off of 95. **From Rt 128N,** take exit 22E toward Beverly right onto Rt 62 about 5 miles to Cabot St. Turn right onto Cabot 2 blocks to restaurant on right (before Cabot Cinema). **From 128S,** take exit 20B toward Beverly onto Rt 1AS (becomes Cabot St) about 1¾ miles to restaurant.

BOSTON

Fresh City 🍴

201 Brookline Ave. ✆ 617-424-7907 ⏰ M-F 6:30-9, Sat 11-8
A fast-food alternative featuring wraps, stir fries, noodle dishes, soups and salads with the option to add tofu to most dishes.

  • vegetarian friendly • fresh juice • tables • self-service • take-out

🚘 **From I-93,** take exit 18 onto Mass Ave Connector (becomes Melnea Cass Blvd) over 1 mile to end at Tremont St. Turn left onto Tremont to second right (at Police Station) onto Ruggles St (runs into Louis Prang St, bears right and becomes Fenway then Park Dr) 1 mile to Brookline Ave. Turn right onto Brookline to restaurant in Landmark Ctr.

Fresh City 🍴

2 Seaport Lane ✆ 617-443-0963 ⏰ M-F 6:30-4
See Brookline Ave location for description.

  • vegetarian friendly • fresh juice • tables • self-service • take-out

🚘 **From I-93,** take exit 22 (South Station). At top of exit ramp turn left at second light onto Summer St merging onto Congress St. After merge, move left to turn left onto B St to Northern Ave. Turn right onto Northern and follow signs to Seaport Hotel. Turn right onto Seaport Ln to restaurant on left.

Fresh City

Logan International Airport, Terminal A ☉ Daily 5-8 depending on flight schedule
See Brookline Ave location for description.
· vegetarian friendly · fresh juice · tables · self-service · take-out
🏠 Terminal A, Logan International Airport.

Grezzo

69 Prince St. ✆ 857-362-7288 ☉ Tues 11-5, W-Sun 11-11
All raw, vegan, organic dining in an elegant setting.
· vegan · organic focus · alcohol · tables · wait staff

🚗 **From I-90 (Mass Pike),** take exit 24 on left onto I-93 to exit 23 toward Cross St. Keep right at fork toward North End and turn left onto Cross 2 blocks to Salem St. Turn right onto Salem several short blocks to Prince St. Turn right onto Prince to restaurant on left.

My Thai Vegetarian Cafe

3 Beach St. ✆ 617-451-2395 ☉ M-Th, Sun 11-10, F-Sat 11-11
Pan-Asian vegetarian.
· vegetarian · vegan friendly · tables · wait staff · take-out

🚗 In Chinatown. **From I-93N,** take exit 20 toward I-90/Logan Airport/South Station and follow ramp for Kneeland St toward Downtown/South Station. Turn left onto Kneeland under ¼ mile to Tyler St. Turn right onto Tyler 1 block to Beach St. Turn left onto Beach a few blocks to restaurant (on 2nd fl). **From I-93S** (becomes Fitzgerald Pkwy), take exit 22 toward South Station/Chinatown and follow Surface Rd to Kneeland. Turn right onto Kneeland and follow directions above. **From I-90E (Mass Pike),** take exit 24A toward South Station, turn left onto Kneeland and follow directions above.

Wheeler's Frozen Desserts

334B Massachusetts Ave. ✆ 617-247-0047 ☉ M-W, F-Sun 11:30-10
Vegan ice cream in exotic flavors.
· vegan · take-out

🚗 **From I-90E (Mass Pike),** take exit 22 left at fork onto Rt 9W/Huntington Ave about ⅓ mile to Mass Ave. Turn right onto Mass to restaurant on right. **From I-90W,** merge onto I-93S. **From I-93,** take exit 18 onto George Pulaski Hwy and turn right onto Mass 1 mile to restaurant at Huntington.

Whole Foods Market

15 Westland Ave. ✆ 617-375-1010 ☉ Daily 8-10
· organic produce · vegetarian friendly · salad bar · cafe · self-service · take-out

🚗 **From I-93,** take exit 18 (Mass Ave/Roxbury). Follow exit onto New Frontage Rd and Mass Ave Connector to Mass Ave. Turn right onto Mass about 1 mile to Huntington Ave (Symphony Hall on left). Take a diagonal left onto Westland to store on right on bottom floor of parking garage.

Whole Foods Market

181 Cambridge St. ✆ 617-723-0004 ☉ Daily 8-10
· organic produce · vegetarian friendly · salad bar · cafe · self-service · take-out

🚗 **From I-90E (Mass Pike),** take exit 18 toward Brighton continuing toward Cambridge St. Turn right onto Cambridge ⅓ mile to store on right. **From I-90W,** take exit 20 toward Cambridge left at fork, follow signs toward Brighton/Allston and follow directions above.

BREWSTER

Naked Earth Market

2655 Main St. ✆ 508-896-5071 ☉ M-Sat 9-6, Sun 9-5
· organic produce

🚗 **From Rt 6,** take exit 11 north on Rt 37/Brewster-Chatham Rd (toward Chatham from 6E, toward Brewster from 6W) about 2½ miles to Snow Rd. Turn right onto Snow under ½ mile and veer right onto Underpass Rd over ½ mile to Rt 6A/Main St. Turn right onto Main ½ mile to store on left in Foster Square.

BRIGHTON

Whole Foods Market 🛍 🍴   ♿

15 Washington St. ✆ 617-738-8187 ⏲ Daily 8-10
• organic produce • vegetarian friendly • salad bar • cafe • self-service • take-out

🍎 **From I-90 (Mass Pike)**, take Prudential Ctr exit onto Rt 9W about 2 miles to store at Washington Ave. **From Coolidge Corner in Brookline**, follow Beacon St outbound to Washington Square. Turn right onto Washington St 4-5 blocks to store on right at Commonwealth Ave. **From Cleveland Circle,** follow Beacon St inbound to Washington Square. Turn left onto Washington St 4-5 blocks to store.

BROOKFIELD

TipTop Country Store 🛍 🍴

8 Central St. ✆ 508-867-0460 ⏲ M-F 8-8, Sat 9-5, Sun 11-5
• organic produce • vegetarian friendly • deli • tables • self-service • co-op

🍎 **From Rt 9/148 intersection**, go 1 block east on Rt 9 to Prouty St. Turn right onto Prouty and right on Central St to store on right.

BROOKLINE

My Thai Vegetarian Cafe 🍴

404 Harvard St. ✆ 617-739-8830 ⏲ Daily 11-10
Mock meats and Thai-style tofu.
• vegetarian • vegan friendly • tables • wait staff

🍎 **From Mass Pike E (I-90E)**, take exit 18 on left toward Brighton and continue toward Cambridge St. Turn right onto Cambridge 1 mile (across tpke) to N Brighton Ave. Turn left onto Brighton ⅓ mile to Harvard Ave. Turn right onto Harvard over ½ mile to restaurant on right after Fuller St. **From I-90W**, take exit 20 left at fork toward Allston/Brighton to Cambridge. Turn right onto Cambridge and follow directions above.

BURLINGTON

Fresh City 🍴

2 Wayside Rd. ✆ 781-273-0500 ⏲ Daily 10-9
See Brookline Ave location in Boston for description.
• vegetarian friendly • fresh juice • tables • self-service • take-out

🍎 **From I-95**, take exit 33A south on Cambridge St/Rte 3A and make first right onto Wayside Rd to restaurant on right.

CAMBRIDGE

Buddhist Tea House 🍴   ♿

950 Massachusetts Ave. ✆ 617-547-6670 ⏲ Tues-Sun 11-6
In the Greater Boston Cultural Center. A Buddhist temple and cafe serving tea, vegan dim sum and a lunch special.
• vegan • tables • wait staff

🍎 **From I-90E (Mass Pike)**, take exit 18 on left onto Cambridge St across river to Memorial Dr. Turn left onto Memorial over ½ mile to Plympton St. Turn right onto Plympton 2 blocks to Mt Auburn St. Turn right onto Mt Auburn (becomes Mass Ave) under ½ mile to restaurant on right after Bay St. **From I-90W**, exit onto I-93N. **From I-93N**, take exit 26 onto Storrow Dr about 1½ miles to ramp on left for Mass Ave Bridge. Cross river continuing onto Mass about 1½ miles total to restaurant on left after Hancock St.

Harvest Co-op Market 🛍   ♿

581 Massachusetts Ave. ✆ 617-661-1580 ⏲ M-Sat 7-10, Sun 7-9
• organic produce • vegetarian friendly • salad bar • deli • self-service • take-out • co-op

🍎 **From I-90 (Mass Tpke)**, take exit 18 (from I-90E) or 20 (from I-90W) toward Cambridge/Sommerville onto Cambridge St over River St bridge onto River St. Go 12 blocks and turn right onto Bishop Allen Drive (1 block past Mass Ave) to public parking.

Veggie Planet 🍴

47 Palmer St. ✆ 617-661-1513 ◷ M-Sat 11:30-10:30, Sun 11-3, 4-10:30
Restaurant by day, restaurant/folk music Club Passim by night. Specialty is organic-crust pizza or the toppings over brown rice.
• vegetarian • vegan friendly • tables • wait staff • take-out
🚗 **From I-90 (Mass Pike)**, take exit 18 (from I-90E) or 20 (I-90W) toward Cambridge/ Sommerville onto Cambridge St to Soldiers Field Rd. Turn left onto Soldiers Field to ramp for Cambridge/Harvard Sq. Veer right onto N Harvard St over bridge onto JF Kennedy St. Take Kennedy about ¼ mile to Brattle St. Follow Brattle onto Church St onto Palmer St to restaurant on Harvard Sq inside Club Passim.

Whole Foods Market 🛍 🍴   ♿

200 Alewife Brook Pkwy. ✆ 617-491-0040 ◷ Daily 8-10
• organic produce • vegetarian friendly • salad bar • cafe • self-service • take-out
🚗 **From I-95**, take exit 29A onto MA 2E 7 miles to store on left. **From I-90 (Mass Pike)**, take exit 20 toward Cambridge onto Soldier Field Rd about 1 mile to Elliot Bridge. After crossing bridge, take Rt 2/US 3 ramp toward Arlington/Fresh Pond Pkwy onto 2W (Fresh Pond becomes Concord Ave) about 1¼ miles to roundabout and take first exit onto Alewife Brook Pkwy to store on right.

Whole Foods Market 🛍

115 Prospect St. ✆ 617-492-0070 ◷ Daily 8-10
• organic produce • vegetarian friendly • salad bar • deli • bakery • take-out
🚗 **From I-90 (Mass Pike)**, take exit 18 (from I-90E) or 20 (I-90W) toward Cambridge/ Sommerville onto Cambridge St across River St Bridge and onto River St about ⅔ mile to Western Ave. Merge onto Western then onto Prospect St ¼ mile to store.

Whole Foods Market 🛍 🍴   ♿

340 River St. ✆ 617-876-6990 ◷ Daily 8-10
• organic produce • vegetarian friendly • salad bar • cafe • self-service • take-out
🚗 **From I-90 (Mass Pike)**, take exit 18 (from I-90E) or 20 (I-90W) toward Cambridge/ Sommerville onto Cambridge St across River St Bridge and onto River St to store.

CENTERVILLE

Cape Cod Natural Foods 🛍

1600 Falmouth Rd. ✆ 508-771-8394 ◷ M-Sat 9-7, Sun 12-5:30
• organic produce
🚗 **From Rt 6 (Mid Cape Hwy)**, take exit 6 south on Rt 132 1 mile to first light and turn right onto Phinney's Lane 2 miles to next light. Turn right onto Rt 28 ¼ mile to store on right in Bell Tower Mall.

CHARLTON

Fresh City 🍴   ♿

Mass Tpke. E., Mile 81 ✆ Hdqtrs 781-453-0200 ◷ Daily 10-9
See Brookline Ave, Boston location for description.
• vegetarian friendly • self-service • take-out
🍎 On I-90E (Mass Pike) at milepost 81.

Fresh City 🍴   ♿

Mass Tpke. W., Mile 89 ✆ Hdqtrs 781-453-0200 ◷ Daily 10-9
See Brookline Ave, Boston location for description.
• vegetarian friendly • self-service • take-out
🍎 On I-90W (Mass Pike) at milepost 89.

CHATHAM

Chatham Natural Foods 🛍

1218 Main St. ✆ 508-945-4139 ◷ M-Sat 9-5:30, Sun 10-5
🚗 **From Rt 6**, take exit 11 onto Rt 137S over 2 miles to end. Turn left onto Rt 28 (Main St) about 2½ miles into Chatham to store on left.

COHASSET

All the Best Natural Foods 🛍
1 Pleasant St. ✆ 781-383-3005 ⊕ Tues-W, F-Sat 10-6, Th 10-7

🍎 **From Rt 3N**, take exit 28 onto Hwy 228N/Hingham St (becomes Main St) about 6½ miles to Rt 3A. Turn right onto 3A 2 miles to Sohier St. Turn left onto Sohier 1 mile to Ripley St. Turn right onto Ripley ⅓ mile to Pleasant St. Turn right onto Pleasant to store on right. **From Quincy,** take Rt 3A south over 8 miles to Sohier St and follow directions above.

CONCORD

Debra's Natural Gourmet 🛍 🍴
98 Commonwealth Ave. ✆ 978-371-7573 ⊕ M-W, F-Sat 8:30-6:30, Th 8:30-8:30, Sun 12-6
• organic produce • vegetarian friendly • deli • tables • self-service • take-out

🍎 **From I-495,** take exit 29A onto Rt 2E under 7 miles to Concord Rotary. Take first exit onto Commonwealth Ave ¾ mile to store on left. **From I-95S,** take exit 30B onto Rt 2AW over 7 miles to Commonwealth. Veer right onto Commonwealth to store on right (past tracks). **From I-95,** take exit 29B onto Rt 2W/Concord Pike 7 miles to Main St. Turn left onto Main ¾ mile to Commonwealth. Veer right onto Commonwealth to store.

DENNISPORT

Dennisport Natural Market 🛍
640 Main St. ✆ 508-760-3043 ⊕ -Sat 9-5:30, Sun 10-5

🍎 **From Rt 6,** take exit 9 onto Rt 134S about 2 miles to end. Turn left onto Rt 28 1⅓ miles into Dennisport to store.

DORCHESTER

Common Ground Cafe 🛍 🍴
2243-47 Dorchester Ave. ✆ 617-298-1020 ⊕ M-Th 7-10, F 7-3, Sun (store only) 10-5
Part of the Twelve Tribes Community.
• organic produce • vegetarian friendly • fresh juice • cafe • tables • wait staff • take-out

🍎 **From I-93,** take exit 11 (from I-93N) or 11B (I-90S) onto Granite Ave ½ mile to Milton St. Turn left onto Milton about ¼ mile to Adams St. Turn left onto Adams ⅓ mile to Richmond St. Turn right onto Richmond ⅓ mile to Dorchester Ave. Turn right onto Dorchester to store.

FALMOUTH

Amber Waves Natural Foods 🛍
310 Dillingham ✆ 508-540-3538 ⊕ M-Sat 9-6, Sun 12-5
• organic produce

🍎 Take Rt 28 into Falmouth (becomes Main St) to store in center of town.

FRAMINGHAM

Fresh City 🍴   ♿
Mass Tpke. W., Mile 115 ✆ Hdqtrs 781-453-0200 ⊕ Daily 10-9
See Brookline Ave, Boston location for description.
• vegetarian friendly • self-service • take-out

🍎 On I-90W (Mass Pike) at milepost 115.

Whole Foods Market 🛍 🍴
575 Worcester Rd. (Rte. 9) ✆ 508-628-9525 ⊕ Daily 8-10
• organic produce • vegetarian friendly • salad bar • cafe • self-service • take-out

🍎 **From I-90E (Mass Pike),** take exit 12 onto Rt 9E about 3½ miles to store at Prospect St on westbound side. **From I-90W,** take exit 13 onto Rt 30W toward Framingham about 2¾ miles to store on right at Prospect.

FRANKLIN

Spruce Farm Creamery ⏏

370 King St. ✆ 508-520-7900 ⏰ M-Th, Sun 11:30-9, F-Sat 11:30-9:30
Specialty is organic flatbread pizzas and calzones.
   • vegetarian friendly • organic focus • tables • wait staff
🍎 **From I-495,** take exit 16 toward Franklin onto King St (left from I-495S, right from I-495N) under ½ mile to restaurant on right.

GARDNER

Happy Trails 🛍

43 Parker St. ✆ 978-632-4076 ⏰ M-F 9:30-5:30, Sat 9:30-5
🍎 **From Rt 2,** take exit 22 toward Gardner onto Rt 68N/Donlon St (first exit off traffic circle from Rt 22W, third exit from Rt 22E) about ¾ mile to Parker St. Turn right onto Parker to store on right.

GLOUCESTER

Alchemy Cafe and Bistro ⏏

3 Duncan St. ✆ 978-281-3997 ⏰ M-Th, Sun 11:30-9, F-Sat 11:30-10
Southern cooking with a Caribbean flair plus pizza with a whole wheat option.
   • vegetarian friendly • alcohol • counter • tables • wait staff
🍎 **From Rt 128,** go south (towards water) on Washington St about ¾ mile to Prospect St. Turn left onto Prospect ⅓ mile to Pleasant St. Turn right onto Pleasant and cross Main St onto Duncan St to restaurant on right.

Common Crow 🛍

6 Elm St. ✆ 978-283-1665 ⏰ M-Sat 8-8, Sun 8-6
Two daily soups, sandwiches and raw food lunches to go.
   • organic produce • vegetarian friendly • take-out
🍎 **From Rt 128,** go south (towards water) on Washington St about ¾ mile to Prospect St. Turn left onto Prospect ⅓ mile to Pleasant St. Turn right onto Pleasant 1 block to Federal St. Turn left into Federal and right onto Elm 1 block to store on right.

GREAT BARRINGTON

Berkshire Co-op Market 🛍 ⏏   ♿

42 Bridge St. ✆ 413-528-9697 ⏰ M-Sat 8-8, Sun 10-6
   • organic produce • vegetarian friendly • organic focus • fresh juice • salad bar • cafe • deli • bakery • counter • tables • self-service • take-out • co-op

🍎 **From I-90 (Mass Pike),** take exit 2 (US 20/Lee) toward Great Barrington onto Rt 102W about 4½ miles to Rt 7. Turn left onto Rt 7 over 7 miles to light at Bridge St. Turn left onto Bridge to store on right.

Guido's Fresh Marketplace 🛍   ♿

760 S. Main St. ✆ 413-528-9255 ⏰ M-Sat 9-7, Sun 10-6
   • organic produce • bakery • take-out

🍎 **From I-90 (Mass Pike),** take exit 2 (US 20/Lee) toward Great Barrington onto Rt 102W about 4½ miles to Rt 7. Turn left onto Rt 7 about 8 miles to store on right after Big Y.

Locke Stock & Barrel 🛍

265 Stockbridge Rd. ✆ 413-528-0800 ⏰ M-Sat 9-6, Sun July, Aug, Thanksgiving-New Year 12-4
🍎 **From I-90 (Mass Pike),** take exit 2 (US 20/Lee) onto Rt 102 west about 4½ miles to Rt 7. Turn left onto Rt 7 about 5½ miles to store on right.

GREENFIELD

Greenfields Market Food Co-op 🛍 🍴 &

144 Main St. ✆ 413-773-9567 ⏰ M-F 8-8, Sat 9-6, Sun 10-5
• organic produce • vegetarian friendly • organic focus • salad bar • cafe • deli • bakery • tables • self-service • take-out • co-op

🚗 **From I-91**, take exit 26 east on Rt 2A/Mohawk Trail (first exit off traffic circle from I-91N, third exit from I-91S) 1 mile to store on left (look for green awning).

Tofu A Go-Go 🍴

265 Main St. ✆ 413-772-8638 ⏰ Tues-F 11:30-2:30, 5-8, Sat 11:30-8, Sun 11:30-2
• vegetarian • vegan friendly • tables • self-service

🚗 **From I-91**, take exit 26 east on Rt 2A/Mohawk Trail (first exit off traffic circle from I-91N, third exit from I-91S) 1 mile to restaurant on right.

HADLEY

Whole Foods Market 🛍 🍴 &

327 Russell St. (Rte. 9) ✆ 413-586-9932 ⏰ Daily 8-10
• organic produce • vegetarian friendly • salad bar • cafe • self-service • take-out

🚗 **From I-91N**, take exit 19 onto Rt 9E across bridge about 4 miles to store on right. **From I-91S**, take exit 20 left at light after ramp and left at next light onto 9E and follow directions above.

HANOVER

Good Health Natural Foods 🛍

219 Columbia Rd. (Rte. 53) ✆ 781-826-0808 ⏰ M-F 8:30-8, Sat 9-6, Sun 10-6
• organic produce

🚗 **From Rt 3,** take exit 12 west on Rt 139 (left from Rt 3S, right from Rt 3N) 2 miles and merge right onto Rt 53 ¾ mile to store on left.

HINGHAM

Whole Foods Market 🛍 🍴

94 Derby St. ✆ 781-741-8050 ⏰ Daily 8-10
• organic produce • vegetarian friendly • salad bar • cafe • self-service • take-out

🚗 **From Rt 3**, take exit 15 east on Derby St (left from Rt 3N, loop around right from Rt 3S) ⅓-½ mile to store on right.

HUDSON

Basha's Natural Market Place 🛍 🍴

196 Washington St. ✆ 978-562-2154 ⏰ M-F 9:30-7, Sat 10-6, Sun 12-6 Cafe Tues-Sat 11-3
• vegetarian friendly • cafe • tables • self-service • take-out

🚗 **From I-495,** take exit 25A onto Rt 85 (merge right from I-495N, merge onto I-290E and loop around toward Hudson from I-495S), 1⅓-¾ mile (continue on Rt 85 as it veers right onto Washington St) to store on right between Reed Rd & Overland St.

JAMAICA PLAIN

VeeVee 🍴

763 Centre St. ✆ 617-522-0145 ⏰ Tues-Sun 5:30-10
• vegetarian friendly • alcohol • tables • wait staff

🚗 **From I-90E (Mass Pike)**, take exit 22 left onto Rt 9W/Huntington Ave 2 miles and u-turn and turn right onto S Huntington 1 mile to Centre St. Veer right onto Centre ¾ mile to restaurant on right. **From I-90W,** merge onto I-93S. **From I-93S,** take exit 18 towards Mass Ave onto Genl Pulaski Skyway and turn right onto Mass Ave under ½ mile to Washington St. Turn left onto Washington about 2½ miles to Green St. Turn right onto Green about ½ mile to Centre. Turn left onto Centre under ¼ mile to restaurant on right.

Harvest Co-op Market 🛍 &

57 South St. © 617-524-1667 ⏰ Daily 8-10
• organic produce • vegetarian friendly • salad bar • deli • self-service • take-out • co-op

🚗 **From I-90E (Mass Pike)**, take exit 22 left onto Rt 9W/Huntington Ave 2 miles and u-turn and turn right onto S Huntington 1 mile to Centre St. Veer right onto Centre ¾ mile to South St. Veer left onto South 2 blocks to store on right. **From I-90W**, merge onto I-93S. **From I-93S**, take exit 18 towards Mass Ave onto Genl Pulaski Skyway and turn right onto Mass Ave under ½ mile to Washington St. Turn left onto Washington about 2½ miles to Williams St and veer left onto Carolina St ½ mile to South. Turn right onto South to store on left at Custer St.

LEE

Clover's Natural Food Market 🛍

42 Park St. © 413-243-1775 ⏰ M-Sat 10-6, Sun 12-5
• organic produce

🚗 **From I-90 (Mass Pike)**, take exit 2 (US 20/Lee) onto 20W about 1 mile to store on right.

Fresh City 🍴 &

Mass Tpke. E. © Hdqtrs 781-453-0200 ⏰ Daily 10-9
See Brookline Ave, Boston location for description.
• vegetarian friendly • self-service • take-out

🚗 On I-90E (Mass Pike) at Lee.

LENOX

Clearwater Natural Foods 🛍 &

11 Housatonic St. © 413-637-2721 ⏰ M-Sat 9:15 -6, Sun 11-3
• organic produce

🚗 **From I-90 (Mass Pike),** take exit 2 (US 20/Lee) onto 20W about 4½ miles (into Lenox) to Walker St. Turn left onto Walker 1 mile to Main St. Turn right onto Main and first right onto Housatonic St to store on left.

LEOMINSTER

Roots Natural Foods 🛍

100 Crawford St. Unit #7 © 978-534-7668 ⏰ M-W Sat 10-6, Th-F 10-7
• organic produce

🚗 **From I-190,** merge onto Rt 2W and take exit 32 toward Leominster and follow signs for Hwy 13N to Hamilton St (before tracks). Turn left onto Hamilton 2 blocks to Crawford St. Turn right onto Crawford ⅓ mile to store on left.

LEVERETT

Village Co-op 🛍 🍴

180 Rattlesnake Gutter Rd. © 413-367-9794 ⏰ Daily 7-7
• organic produce • vegetarian friendly • tables • self-service • take-out • co-op

🚗 **From I-91**, take exit 24 (Deerfield/US 5) onto 5N to Rt 116. Turn right onto 116 almost 4 miles to Bull Hill Rd. Turn left onto Bull Hill about 1⅓ miles and veer left onto Long Plain Rd (Rt 63) then right onto Depot Rd another 1½ miles to Montague St. Veer left onto Montague almost 2 miles to Rattlesnake Gutter Rd. Turn left onto Rattlesnake Gutter to store on left.

Call Ahead

We suggest you call first if possible before visiting a location. Stores and restaurants have a habit of moving (and closing), and hours, services, etc. change more often than you might expect.

LOWELL

Udupi Bhavan 🍴

717 Middlesex St. ✆ 978-654-6653 ◷Tues-F 11:30-3, 5-9:30, Sat-Sun 11:30-9:30
South Indian vegetarian specialties including dosas and uthapams.
· vegetarian · vegan friendly · tables · wait staff

🚗 **From I-495N**, take exit 33 left onto Rt 4/North Rd 1 mile to Parkhurst Rd. Turn right onto Parkhurst under 1 mile to Westford St. Turn right onto Westford continuing onto Wood St under 1 mile to Middlesex St. Turn right onto Middlesex about 3 blocks to restaurant on left. **From I-495S**, take exit 34 C-B-A left at fork and take exit 34B onto US 3N 2 miles to exit 32 for Hwy 4 toward Chelmsford. Keep right at fork onto Drum Hill Rd to Westford and follow directions above.

MEDFORD

Wild Oats Market 🛍️ 🍴   ♿

2151 Mystic Valley Pkwy. ✆ 781-395-4998 ◷ M-Sat 7-10, Sun 8-9
· organic produce, vegetarian friendly, salad bar, cafe, self-service, take-out

🚗 **From I-93N**, take exit 31 toward Arlington onto Mystic Valley Pkwy/MA 16W about 1⅔ miles to store. **From I-93S**, take exit 32 onto Rt 60W/Salem St toward Medford about ⅓ mile (across water) to Main St. Turn left onto Main and merge onto Mystic Valley Pkwy/16W 1 mile to store.

MELROSE

Green Street Natural Foods 🛍️

164 Green St. ✆ 781-662-7741 ◷ M-F 9-6, Sat. 9-5
Eveything is vegetarian and egg-free in this second-generation family-owned store.
· organic produce

🚗 **From I-95**, take exit 39 onto North Ave (left at light from I-95S, right from I-95N) to fourth light (Main St). Turn right onto Main to third light at Green St (before going down hill). Turn left onto Green to store on right (green bldg behind white house).

NATICK

Fresh City 🍴

1400 Worcester Rd. (Rt. 9 E.) ✆ 508-875-5750 ◷ Daily 11-9
See Brookline Ave, Boston location for description.
· vegetarian friendly · fresh juice · tables · self-service · take-out

🚗 **From I-90 (Mass Pike)**, take exit 13 onto Rt 30W about ½ mile to Caldor Rd. Turn left onto Caldor ⅓ mile to Rt 9/Wooster Rd. Turn right onto Rt 9 under ½ mile to restaurant on right after Shoppers World Dr.

NEWTON

Fresh City 🍴

241 Needham St. ✆ 617-244-7071 ◷ M-F 6:30am-9pm, Sat-Sun 10-9
See Brookline Ave, Boston location for description.
· vegetarian friendly · tables · self-service · take-out

🚗 **From I-95/128,** take exit 19A toward Newton Highlands onto Highland Ave (becomes Needham St) under 1 mile to restaurant on left in Marshall's Plaza. **From Rt 9W (Boston area)**, veer left onto Boylston St to Winchester St. Turn left onto Winchester to Needham and right onto Needham about ½ mile to restaurant on right.

Whole Foods Market 🛍️ 🍴   ♿

647 Washington St ✆ 617-965-2070 ◷ Daily 8-10
· organic produce · vegetarian friendly · salad bar · cafe · self-service · take-out

🚗 **From I-90 (Mass Pike)**, take exit 17 toward Newton/Watertown. **From I-90W,** go straight onto Washington St under 1 mile to store. **From I-90E,** veer right onto Center St, right onto Richardson St, right onto Church St and left onto Washington ½ mile to store.

Whole Foods Market 🛒
916 Walnut St. ✆ 617-969-1141 ⏲ Daily 8-10
 • organic produce • vegetarian friendly • salad bar • deli • self-service • take-out
🚗 **From I-95/128,** take Rt 16/Washington St exit (21 from I-95/128N, 21A from I-95/128S) right onto Beacon St about 2¼ miles to store on right after Walnut St.

NORTH ANDOVER

Fresh City 🍴
93A Tpke. St. ✆ 978-975-0410 ⏲Daily 11-9
See Brookline Ave, Boston location for description.
 • vegetarian friendly • fresh juice • tables • self-service • take-out
🚗 **From I-495,** take exit 42A onto Rt 114E/Winthrop Ave under 1 mile to restaurant on right.

NORTHAMPTON

Bela Vegetarian Restaurant 🍴
68 Masonic St. ✆ 413-586-8011 ⏲ Tues-Sat 12-8:45
Casual vegetarian dining. BYOB.
 • vegetarian • vegan friendly • tables • self-service
🚗 **From I-91N,** take exit 18 (first Northampton exit) left onto Rt 5N over 1 mile to Main St. Turn left onto Main to Masonic St. Turn right onto Masonic to restaurant on left. **From I-91S,** take exit 20 onto Rt 5S almost 1½ miles to Main. Turn right onto Main and follow directions above.

Cornucopia Foods 🛒
150 Main St. ✆ 413-586-3800 ⏲ M-W 9:30-8, Th-Sat 9:30-9, Sun 11-6
 • organic produce
🚗 **From I-91N,** take exit 18 (first Northampton exit) left onto Rt 5N almost 1½ miles to Armory St. Turn left onto Armory to parking garage. Store is in Thornes Market which is attached to garage. **From I-91S,** take exit 20 onto Rt 5S almost 1½ miles (past light on Main St) to Armory. Turn right onto Armory and follow directions above.

Haymarket Cafe 🍴
185 Main St. ✆ 413-586-9969 ⏲ M-Th 7-9:30, F-Sat 7-10
Sandwiches, salads and entrees with an Indian influence downstairs. Fresh juice, smoothies and hot drinks upstairs.
 • vegetarian • vegan friendly • fresh juice • tables • self-service
From I-91N, take exit 18 (first Northampton exit) left onto Rt 5N over 1 mile to Main St. Turn left onto Main to restaurant on right. **From I-91S,** take exit 20 onto Rt 5S almost 1½ miles to light on Main St. Turn right onto Main to restaurant.

Paul and Elizabeth's 🍴
150 Main St. ✆ 413-584-4832 ⏲ Daily11:30-9:15
Vegetarian and seafood.
 • vegetarian friendly • vegan friendly • alcohol • tables • wait staff
🚗 **From I-91N,** take exit 18 (first Northampton exit) left onto Rt 5N almost 1½ miles to Armory St. Turn left onto Armory to parking garage. Restaurant is on Main St level in Thornes Market which is attached to garage. **From I-91S,** take exit 20 onto Rt 5S almost 1½ miles (past light on Main St) to Armory. Turn right onto Armory and follow directions above.

River Valley Market 🛒🍴
330 N. King St. ✆ 413-584-2665 ⏲ Daily 9-9
 • organic produce • vegetarian friendly • salad bar • deli • bakery • tables • self-service • take-out • co-op
🚗 **From I-91,** take exit 21 onto N King St/US 5/10 (left at ramp and left from I-91N, left from I-91S) ¾ mile to store on right.

ORLEANS

Orleans Whole Food Store 📦
46 Main St. ✆ 508-255-6540 🕐 M-Sat 8:30-6, Sun 9-6 Until 9pm in summer
• organic produce • vegetarian friendly • deli • bakery • take-out
🍎 **From Rt 6W**, take Rt 6A west exit off rotary almost 1 mile to second light (Main St). Turn left onto Main to store on left. **From Rt 6E**, take exit 12 right onto Rt 6A east almost 1 mile to Main. Turn right onto Main to store.

OSTERVILLE

Earthly Delights 🍴
15 W. Bay Rd. ✆ 508-420-2206 🕐 In season M-F 7-5, Sat 8-3, Sun 8-2 Off season M-F 7-4, Sat 8-3
Just a few stools at the counter but many vegetarian choices.
• vegetarian friendly • fresh juice • counter • self-service • take-out
🍎 **From Rt 6E**, take exit 5 right at fork onto Hwy 149S 3 miles to Y at Cammett Rd. Veer left onto Cammett/The Jib about ¾ mile and veer left to merge onto Main St 2⅓ miles to W Bay Rd. Turn right onto W Bay to restaurant on left. **From Rt 6W**, take exit 7 left onto Willow St continuing onto Yarmouth Rd over 2 miles total to Iyannough Rd/Rt 28 (after airport). Turn right onto Iyannough about ¾ mile and at airport rotary take third exit onto Falmouth Rd/Rt 28 about 4⅓ miles to Five Corners Rd. Turn left onto Five Corners continuing onto Ruthelin and Old Mill Rd about 2 miles total to S Main. Turn right onto S Main about ¼ mile to W Bay. Turn left onto W Bay to restaurant.

PITTSFIELD

Guido's Fresh Marketplace 📦   ♿
1020 South St. ✆ 413-442-9912 🕐 M-Sat 9-7, Sun 10-6
• organic produce • bakery • take-out
🍎 **From I-90 (Mass Pike)**, take exit 2 (Lee/US 20) onto Rt 20W about 8½ miles until it merges with Rt 7 north. Continue on 7N about 4¾ miles to store on left.

Pittsfield Health Food Center 📦
407 North St. ✆ 413-442-5662 🕐 M-F 9:30-5:30, Sat 9:30-3:30
🍎 **From I-90 (Mass Pike)**, take exit 2 (Lee/US 20) onto Rt 20W about 8½ miles until it merges with Rt 7 north. Continue on 7N about 1 mile and after rotary bear right onto North St past two lights to store on left (across from church).

PLYMOUTH

Common Sense Wholesome Food Market 📦
53 Main St. ✆ 508-732-0427 🕐 M-Th 9-7, F 9-4, Sun 10:30-6
• organic produce
🍎 **From Rt 3**, take US 44E exit (6 from 3N, 6A from 3S) about ¾ mile to light at Court St (Rt 3A). Turn right onto Court (becomes Main St at North St) about ⅓ mile to store on left.

PROVINCETOWN

Bradford Natural Market 📦
141 Bradford St. ✆ 508-487-9784 🕐 Daily 8-6
• organic produce
🍎 Take Rt 6 into Provincetown. Turn left at traffic lights (not blinkers) onto Conwell St to Bradford St. Turn right onto Bradford 2½ blocks to store.

QUINCY

Good Health Natural Foods 📦
1627 Hancock St. ✆ 617-773-4925 🕐 M-F 9-9, Sat 9-6, Sun 10-6
• organic produce

▭ **From I-93N**, take exit 7 for Washington St onto Thomas E Burgin Pkwy 1½ miles to Paul Harold Bridge Rd. Turn right onto Paul Harold Bridge continuing on Concourse St and veer left onto Ross St to Cliveden St. Turn right onto Cliveden 1 block to Hancock St. Turn right onto Hancock 2 blocks to store on right. **From I-93S**, take exit 8 toward Quincy onto Willard St and take third exit off traffic circle onto Furnace Brook Pkwy 1 block to Copeland St. Turn right onto Copeland ½ mile and continue onto Water St 1 mile to Quincy Ave. Turn right onto Quincy under ¼ mile to store on left after Quincy becomes Hancock.

SEEKONK

The Good Seed 🛒

138 Central Ave. ✆ 508-399-7333 ⏱ M-Tues, F-Sat, 10-6, W-Th 10-7, Sun 12-4

▭ **From I-95**, take exit 2A right onto Newport Ave/Rt 1AS about ¾ mile to Benefit St. Turn left onto Benefit (becomes Central Ave) about 1 mile to store on left at Rt 152.

SHELBURNE FALLS

McCusker's Market 🛒 🍴   ♿

3 State St. ✆ 413-625-2548 ⏱ Daily 7-7

    • organic produce • vegetarian friendly • organic focus • salad bar • cafe • deli • bakery • tables • self-service • take-out • co-op

▭ **From Rt 2W**, veer left onto Maple St ⅓ mile to Bridge St. Turn left onto Bridge ½ mile and after crossing the bridge turn right onto State St to store on right. **From Rt 2E,** turn right onto State under 1 mile to store on left before the bridge.

SHREWSBERRY

Udupi 🍴

378 Maple Ave. ✆ 508-459-5099 ⏱ M, W-F 11:30-3, 5-9:30, Sat-Sun 11:30-9:30

South Indian vegetarian specialties including dosas and uthapams.

    • vegetarian • vegan friendly • tables • wait staff

▭ **From I-290E**, take exit 17 right toward Framingham onto Rt 9E/Belmont St 3 miles to Maple Ave. Veer left onto Maple to restaurant on left. **From I-290W**, take exit 22 toward Shrewsbury left onto W Main St ¾ mile to Old Mill Rd. Turn right onto Old Mill over ¾ mile to Elm St. Turn right onto Elm ⅓ mile to Edgemont Rd. Turn left onto Edgemont ⅓ mile to Maple St. Turn right onto Maple ⅓ mile to restaurant on right before Rt 9.

SPRINGFIELD

Better Life Whole Foods 🛒

1500 Allen St. ✆ 413-783-9424 ⏱ M, F 9-30-6, Tues-Th 9:30-8, Sat 9:30-5, Sun 12-5

▭ **From I-91N**, take exit 2 toward Forest Park/E Longmeadow to second light, turn right onto Rt 83E/Sumner Ave 3 miles and bear right after Wendy's to store in Bicentennial Plaza. **From I-91S**, take exit 4 (Main St). Turn left at light (do not bear left before light) and right onto Longhill St to Sumner. Turn left onto Sumner and follow directions above.

SWAMPSCOTT

Whole Foods Market 🛒 🍴

331 Paradise Rd. ✆ 781-592-2200 ⏱ M-Sat 8-10, Sun 8-9

    • organic produce • vegetarian friendly • salad bar • cafe • self-service • take-out

▭ Store is on Rt 1A (aka Paradise Rd) 1 mile north of Rt 29 intersection on west side after Parsons Dr. Traveling south on 1A store is after Longwood Dr.

WALTHAM

Masao's Kitchen 🍴
581 Moody St. ✆ 781-647-7977 ⏰ M-Sat 12-7:30
Macrobiotic focus.
• vegan • tables • wait staff

🍎 **From I-95**, take exit 26 onto Boston Post Rd/US-20/Weston St toward Waltham. Follow Weston (left from I-95S, veer right from I-95N) about 1½ miles to Prospect St. Turn right onto Prospect about ¾ mile (across water) and continue on Maple St ⅓ mile to Moody St. Turn right onto Moody to restaurant on right after Cherry St.

WATERTOWN

Deluxe Town Diner 🍴   ♿
627 Mount Auburn St. ✆ 617-926-8400 ⏰ Daily 7-10
Vegan pancakes, veggie sausage and burgers, soy milk and more.
• vegetarian friendly • alcohol • tables • wait staff • take-out

🍎 **From I-90 (Mass Pike)**, take exit 17 north on Centre St (left from I-90E, right from I-90W) continuing on Galen St (across water) and Mt Auburn St about 2 miles total to restaurant on right.

WAYLAND

Whole Foods Market 🛒 🍴
317 Boston Post Rd. ✆ 508-358-7700 ⏰ Daily 8-10
• organic produce • vegetarian friendly • salad bar • counter • self-service • take-out

🍎 **From I-95/128**, take exit 26 west on Rt 20 (aka Boston Post Rd) about 5 miles to store after Rt 27.

WELLESLEY

Whole Foods Market 🛒
278 Washington St. ✆ 781-235-7262 ⏰ Daily 8-10
• organic produce • vegetarian friendly • deli • bakery • take-out

🍎 **From I-95S**, take exit 22-21B and take ramp for Rt 16W/Wellesley to Washington St. Turn right onto Washington (Rt 16W) about 1½ miles to store after Rt 9 (across from Clocktower Park). **From I-95N**, take exit 20B onto Rt 9W about 2 miles to Rt 16 ramp. Veer left onto Washington to store.

WESTBOROUGH

Fresh City 🍴   ♿
Mass Tpke. W. ✆ Hdqtrs 781-453-0200 ⏰ Daily 10-9
See Brookline Ave, Boston location for description.
• vegetarian friendly • self-service • take-out

🍎 On I-90W (Mass Pike) at Westborough.

WILLIAMSTOWN

Wild Oats Co-op 🛒 🍴
320 Main St. ✆ 413-458-8060 ⏰ M-F 8:30-7, Sat-Sun 9-7 Hot Bar Daily 11:30-2, 4:30-7
• organic produce • vegetarian friendly • deli • bakery • tables • self-service • take-out • co-op

🍎 **From US 7/Rt 2 intersection**, go east on Rt 2 (Main St) 1⅓ miles to store on left in Colonial Shopping Ctr.

WOBURN

Fresh City 🍴
385 Washington St. ✆ 781-932-1120 🕐 M-F 6:30am-8pm, Sat 10-8
See Brookline Ave, Boston location for description.
 • vegetarian friendly • self-service • take-out

🥡 **From I-95N**, take exit 36 right onto Washington St ⅓ mile to restaurant on left. **From I-95S**, take exit 36, make 2 rights onto Washington St and follow directions above. **From I-93S,** take exit 37 onto I-95S ¼ mile to exit 36 and follow directions above. **From I-93N**, take exit 36 right at bottom of ramp onto Montvale Ave (pass under I-93) 2 blocks to Washington St. Turn right onto Washington 1 mile to restaurant on right.

Whole Foods Market 🛍 🍴
400 Cambridge Rd. ✆ 781-376-9600 ✆ Daily 8-10
 • organic produce • vegetarian friendly • salad bar • cafe • self-service • take-out

🥡 **From I-95**, take exit 33A onto Rt 3S/Cambridge St 2¾ miles to store on right.

WORCESTER

Buddha Hut 🍴
415 Chandler St. ✆ 508-459-0367 🕐 M-Th 11-9, F-Sat 11-10
Chinese vegan menu.
 • vegan • tables • wait staff • take-out

🥡 **From I-290**, take exit 13 onto Rt 122N 2 miles (becomes Madison St, then Chandler St) to restaurant on right.

Living Earth 🛍 🍴
232 Chandler St. ✆ 508-753-1896 🕐 M-F 9-9, Sat 9-7, Sun 11-6 Cafe M-F 9-8, Sat 9-6, Sun 11-5
Vegetarian , seafood, organic meat and additive-free chicken.
 • organic produce • vegetarian friendly • cafe • deli • bakery • tables • wait staff • take-out

🥡 **From I-290**, take exit 13 onto Rt 122N about 1½ miles (becomes Madison St, then Chandler St) to store on left before Rt 9 (Park Ave).

Quan Yin 🍴
56 Hamilton St. ✆ 508-831-1322 🕐 M-F 11-9, Sat 11-4, Sun 12-8
Vegan Chinese and Vietnamese. Small place, mostly take-out.
 • vegan • tables • self-service • take-out

🥡 **From I-290**, take exit 14 toward Barre/Uxbridge onto Grafton St (right from I-290N, follow Rt 122S ramp and right from I-290S) under ½ mile to Hamilton St. Turn right onto Hamilton a few blocks to restaurant.

The Artichoke Co-op 🛍
800 Main St. ✆ 508-752-3533 🕐 M-F 11-7, Sat-Sun 12-6
 • organic produce • co-op

🥡 **From I-290**, take exit 13 onto Rt 122N under ½ mile to Beacon St. Turn left onto Beacon 2 blocks to Sycamore St. Turn right onto Sycamore 1 block to Main St. Turn left onto Main ⅓ mile to store on right.

MICHIGAN

ANN ARBOR

Arbor Farms Natural Foods Market
2103 W. Stadium Rd. © 734-996-8111 ① M-Sat 8-9, Sun 10-7
• organic produce • vegetarian friendly • deli • take-out

From I-94, take exit 172 toward Ann Arbor/94Bus E onto Jackson Rd) ¼-½ mile (past Westgate Shopping Ctr) to W Stadium Blvd. Turn right onto W Stadium about ⅔ mile to store on right past Liberty St.

Earthen Jar
311 S. Fifth Ave. © 734-327-9464 ① M-Th, Sat 11-8, F 11-9
Indian vegetarian served buffet-style, charged by the pound.
• vegetarian • vegan friendly • tables • self-service • take-out

From I-94, take exit 172 onto 94Bus E (Jackson Rd) about 2¼ miles to Main St. Turn right onto Main 2 blocks to Liberty St. Turn left onto Liberty 2 blocks to 5th. Turn right onto 5th Ave to restaurant.

People's Food Co-op & Cafe Verde
216 N. Fourth Ave. © 734-994-9174 ① Store Daily 8-10 Cafe M-Sat 7-8:30, Sun 9-8:30
• organic produce • vegetarian friendly • salad bar • cafe • counter • tables • self-service • take-out • co-op

From I-94, take exit 177 north on State St about 2¼ miles to Packard St. Turn left onto Packard ½ mile to 4th Ave. Turn right onto 4th under ½ mile (2 blocks past Huron) to store at Catherine St.

Seva Restaurant
314 E. Liberty St. © 734-662-1111 ① M-Thurs 11-9, F-Sat 11-10, Sun 10-9
Multi-ethnic vegetarian cuisine.
• vegetarian • vegan friendly • alcohol • tables • wait staff • take-out

From I-94, take exit 177 north on State St about 2¼ miles to Packard St. Turn left onto Packard ⅓ mile to Division St. Turn right onto Division ⅓ mile to Liberty St. Turn left onto Liberty to restaurant on left.

Whole Foods Market
3135 Washtenaw Ave. © 734-975-4700 © Daily 8-10
• organic produce • vegetarian friendly • salad bar • cafe • self-service • take-out

From US 23, take exit 37B west on Washtenaw Ave (toward downtown Ann Arbor) about 1 mile to store in shopping plaza on right after Huron Pkwy.

1. Ann Arbor
2. Battle Creek
3. Bay City
4. Berrien Springs
5. Cadillac
6. Detroit
7. East Lansing
8. Farmington
9. Farmington Hills
10. Ferndale
11. Flint
12. Frankenmuth
13. Garden City
14. Gaylord
15. Glen Arbor
16. Grand Haven
17. Grand Rapids
18. Grosse Point
19. Hancock
20. Hillsdale
21. Holland
22. Hudsonville
23. Ionia
24. Ironwood
25. Kalamazoo
26. Kentwood
27. Kimball
28. Lake Orion
29. Lansing
30. Livonia
31. Ludington
32. Manistee
33. Marquette
34. Monroe
35. Mt. Pleasant
36. Muskegon
37. New Baltimore
38. Northville
39. Novi
40. Petoskey
41. Plymouth
42. Rochester Hills
43. Royal Oak
44. Saginaw
45. St. Joseph
46. Traverse City
47. Troy
48. West Bloomfield
49. Whitehall
50. Woodland
51. Ypsilanti

BATTLE CREEK

Apple Valley Natural Foods 🛍

5275 Beckley Rd. © 269-979-2257 ⏲ M-Th 9-8, F 9-4, Sun 11-5
All-vegetarian health food store.

🛏 **From I-94**, take exit 97 (Capital Ave) east on Beckley Rd ¼ mile to store on left.

BAY CITY

Grains & Greens 🛍

912 N. Euclid Ave. © 989-922-9454 ⏲ M-Sat 9-6, Sun 12-5
· organic produce

🛏 **From I-75**, take exit 162A toward Bay City onto Hwy 25 E about 1½ miles to S Euclid Ave. Turn left onto S Euclid 1 mile to store on right after Union St.

BERRIEN SPRINGS

Andrews University Cafeteria 🍴
U.S. 31N. © 269-471-3161 ① M-F 7-7, Sat 12:30-2, 6-7, Sun 10-7 May vary with school calendar
Vegetarian food in the Seventh-day Adventist tradition.
   · vegetarian · vegan friendly · salad bar · tables · self-service
🏠 Restaurant is on US 31 at Andrews University upstairs in the Campus Ctr.

Apple Valley Natural Foods 🛍
9067 U.S. 31 © 269-471-3131 ① M-Th 7-11, F 7-4, Sun 8-11
All-vegetarian health food store.
🏠 **From Hwy 31**, take exit 15 onto Old Hwy 31 1 mile to store on left (1 block past light).

CADILLAC

Apple Valley Natural Foods 🛍
215 N. Mitchell St. © 231-775-6211 ① M-Th 9-6, F 9-4:40
All-vegetarian health food store.
🏠 **From US 131N**, take exit 177 north onto Bus 131 2½ miles to downtown Cadillac. Store is on left next to Sears. **From US 131S**, take exit 180 (Hwy 55) toward Lake City. Turn right onto 55 1¼ miles to 131/N Mitchell St. Turn right onto Mitchell to store.

DETROIT

Detroit Evolution Laboratory 🍴
1434 Gratiot Ave. © 313-316-1411 ① Th-F 11-2
A yoga/massage center with one raw and one cooked item on the menu. Order a day ahead as quantities are limited to avoid waste.
   · vegan · organic focus · take-out
🏠 **From I-75,** take exit 51B on the left toward Gratiot Ave/State Hwy 3 onto Fisher Fwy N ⅓ mile to Gratiot Ave. Make sharp right onto Gratiot to restaurant on left. (Entrance is behind bldg not on Gratiot).

Goldengate Cafe 🍴
18700 Woodward Ave. © 313-366-2247 ① Daily 10-11
Part of the Innate Holistic Health Center. Music and other events frequently.
   · vegetarian · vegan friendly · fresh juice · counter · tables · self-service
🏠 **From I-75**, take exit 58 toward 7 Mile Rd onto Walter Chrysler Fwy and turn left onto 7 Mile under ½ mile (past tracks) to John R Rd. Turn left onto John R 3 blocks to W Robinwood St. Turn right onto W Robinwood 1 block to Charleston St. Turn left onto Charleston 1 block and right ⅓ mile to Frontage Rd/Woodward Ave. Turn left onto Frontage to restaurant on right in Innate Holistic Health Ctr.

The Traffic Jam & Snug Restaurant 🍴   ♿
511 W. Canfield St. © 313-831-9470 ① M-Th 11-10:30, F 11-12, Sat 11-12
Ample vegetarian choices, home-brewed beer and live entertainment.
   · vegetarian friendly · alcohol · tables · wait staff
🏠 **From I-94**, take exit 215A south on John Lodge Fwy (MI 10) to Forest Ave. Turn left onto Forest to 3rd St. Turn right onto 3rd to Canfield St. Turn left onto Canfield to restaurant. **From I-75**, take exit 53A west on E Warren St to Woodward Ave. Turn left onto Woodward to Hancock St. Turn right onto Hancock to Cass Ave. Turn left onto Cass to Canfield. Turn right onto Canfield to restaurant.

EAST LANSING

Better Health Market 🛍
305 N. Clippert Ave. © 517-332-6892 ① M-Sat 9-9, Sun 11-7
   · organic produce · vegetarian friendly · fresh juice · cafe · deli · tables · self-service
   · take-out
🏠 **From I-496E,** take exit 8 toward E Lansing onto Homer St under ½ mile to Vine

St. Turn right onto Vine 1 block and left onto N Clippert St to store on left. **From I-406W**, merge onto US 127N ½ mile to Kalamazoo St exit toward Michigan Ave. Merge onto Homer and follow directions above.

East Lansing Food Co-op

4960 Northwind Drive © 517-337-1266 ⏰ M-Sat 9-8, Sun 11-7

🚌 **From I-496E**, take exit 8 toward E Lansing onto Homer St under ¼ mile to Michigan Ave. Turn right onto Michigan 1⅓ miles to Grand River Ave (at Michigan State U). Veer right into Grand River 1½ miles to Northwind Dr. Turn right onto Northwind to store on left. **From I-406W**, merge onto US 127N ½ mile to Kalamazoo St exit toward Michigan Ave. Turn right onto Michigan and follow directions above.

Foods for Living

2655 E. Grand River Ave. © 517-324-9010 ⏰ M-F 9-8, Sat 9-7, Sun 11-6
 • organic produce • vegetarian friendly • deli • take-out

🚌 **From I-496E**, take exit 8 toward E Lansing onto Homer St under ¼ mile to Michigan Ave. Turn right onto Michigan 1⅓ miles to Grand River Ave (at Michigan State U). Veer right into Grand River 1¾ miles to store on right. **From I-406W**, merge onto US 127N ½ mile to Kalamazoo St exit toward Michigan Ave. Turn right onto Michigan and follow directions above.

FARMINGTON

The Tree House

22906 Mooney St. © 248-473-0624 ⏰ M 11-7, Tues-Sun 11-9
Deli offerings are vegetarian except for a salmon sandwich.
 • organic produce • vegetarian • vegan friendly • deli • tables • self-service • takeout

🚌 **From I-275**, take exit 167 east on 8 Mile Rd about 4 miles to Orchard Lake Rd. Turn left onto Orchard Lake 1 mile to Grand River Ave. Turn left onto Grand River about ¼ mile to Mooney St. Turn right onto Mooney to store.

Udipi

29210 Orchard Lake Rd. © 248-626-6021 ⏰ Lunch M-F 11:30-2:30, Sat-Sun 11:30-3:30 Dinner M-W 5:30-9, Th, Sun 5:30-9:30, F-Sat 5:30-10
Indian vegetarian with a lunch buffet.
 • vegetarian • vegan friendly • tables • self service • wait staff

🚌 **From I-696**, take exit 5 north on Orchard Lake Rd (right from I-696W, left from I-696E) 1-1¼ miles to restaurant on right before 13 Mile Rd.

FERNDALE

Angel's Cafe

214 W. 9 Mile Rd. © 248-541-0888 ⏰ Lunch Tues-Sun 11-3 Dinner Tues-Th 5-8, F-Sat 5-9
Cafe and art gallery. Over half the lunch menu is vegetarian; more fish and chicken at dinner.
 • vegetarian friendly • vegan friendly • tables • wait staff

🚌 **From I-696**, take exit 16 toward Woodward Ave/Detroit Zoo onto W 10 Mile Rd to Woodward Ave. Turn south onto Woodward (right from I-696E, left from I-696W) over 1 mile to W 9 Mile Rd. Turn right onto W 9 Mile to restaurant on right. **From I-75**, take exit 60 toward 9 Mile Rd onto N Chrysler Dr to 9 Mile Rd. Turn west onto W 9 Mile (left from I-75N, right from I-75S) 1½ miles to restaurant on right after Woodward.

Natural Food Patch

221 W. 9 Mile Rd. © 248-546-5908 ⏰ M-Th 9-7, F-Sat 9-8, Sun. 10-6
 • organic produce

🚌 **From I-696**, take exit 16 toward Woodward Ave/Detroit Zoo onto W 10 Mile Rd to Woodward Ave. Turn south onto Woodward (right from I-696E, left from I-696W) over 1 mile to W 9 Mile Rd. Turn right onto W 9 Mile to store on left. **From I-75**, take exit 60 toward 9 Mile Rd onto N Chrysler Dr to 9 Mile Rd. Turn west onto W 9 Mile (left from I-75N, right from I-75S) 1½ miles to store on left after Woodward.

Om Cafe 🍴

23136 Woodward Ave. © 248-548-1941 ⏰ M, W-Sat 11-9
A bit macrobiotic but other options as well
  • vegetarian friendly • vegan friendly • tables • wait staff
🚍 **From I-696**, take exit 16 toward Woodward Ave/Detroit Zoo onto 10 Mile Rd to Woodward Ave. Turn south onto Woodward (right from I-696E, left from I-696W) over 1 mile to restaurant on east side. **From I-75S**, take exit 61 onto I-696W 1½ miles to exit 16 and follow directions above. **From I-75**, take exit 60 toward John R St/9 Mile Rd onto N Chrysler Drive about ¼ mile to 9 Mile Rd. Turn left onto 9 Mile Rd almost 1½ miles to Woodward. Turn right onto Woodward about ¼ mile to restaurant.

FLINT

Dale's Natural Foods 🛍 🍴

4290 Miller Rd. © 810-230-8008 ⏰ M-Th 10-7, F 10-8, Sat 10-6, Sun 12-5
  • organic produce • vegetarian • fresh juice • deli • counter • tables • self-service • take-out
🚍 **From I-75**, take exit 117 (117B from I-75N) west on Miller Rd (right at fork and right from I-75S, left from I-75N) under 1½ miles to store on right in Somerset Plaza. **From I-69W**, merge onto I-75 N ½ mile and follow directions above. **From I-69E**, take exit 192 right onto Miller about 2¾ miles to store on left.

The Grainery Natural Grocery 🛍

809 Church St. © 810-235-4621 ⏰ M-F 10-7
  • organic produce • fresh juice
🚍 **From I-475**, take exit 7 toward Downtown west on Court St under ½ mile to Church St. Turn right onto Church to store. **From I-69**, take exit 136 (Saginaw St/Downtown) onto service road to Church. Turn north onto Church (left from I-69N, right from I-69S) under ½ mile to store.

FRANKENMUTH

Healthy Habitz 🛍

545 S. Main St. © 989-652-0537 ⏰ M-Th, Sun 9:30-7, F-Sat 9:30-9
🚍 **From I-75S**, take exit 144 toward Frankenmuth left onto Dixie Hwy 2 miles to Junction Rd. Turn right onto Junction 4 miles continuing onto Genesee St 1 mile to S Main. Turn right onto S Main ½ mile to store on right. **From I-75N**, take exit 136 toward Frankenmuth right onto Birch Run Rd 2 miles to S Gera Rd. Turn right onto S Gera (becomes S Main) 5½ miles to store on left.

GARDEN CITY

Krishna Catering & Restaurant 🍴

28636 Ford Rd. © 734-513-3663 ⏰ Tues-Th 10-9, F-Sat 10-10, Sun 12-8
Vegetarian Indian and Chinese fusion. Buffet lunch option weekdays.
  • vegetarian • vegan friendly • tables • self-service • wait staff • take-out
🚍 **From I-96**, take exit 176 south on Middlebelt Rd (right from I-96E, left from I-96W) 4 miles to Ford Rd. Turn left onto Ford under ½ mile to restaurant on left past Garden Ave at Hartel St. **From I-275**, take exit 25 toward Garden City east on Ford Rd (right from I-275N, left from I-275S) 6 miles to restaurant.

GAYLORD

JoJo's Natural Market 🛍

1459 S. Otsego Ave. © 989-705-8500 ⏰ M-F 9-6:30, Sat 10-6
🚍 **From I-75N**, take exit 279 for I-75 toward US 27 to S Otsego Ave (signs for Gaylord). Turn right onto Otsego almost 1½ miles to store on right. **From I-75S**, take exit 282 for I-75/MI 32 toward Gaylord left onto W Main St about ¾ mile to Otsego. Turn right onto Otsego about 1¼ mile to store on left.

GLEN ARBOR
Good Harbor Grill 🍴
6584 Western Ave. ☎ 231-334-3555 ⏱May-Oct Daily 8-9:30
• vegetarian friendly • alcohol • tables • wait staff

🛍 Glen Arbor is on Lake Michigan at the Sleeping Bear Dunes Natl Lakeshore. Restaurant is on Rt 22 just east of Ray St on the north side.

GRAND HAVEN
Health Hutt 🛍
700 Washington Ave ☎ 616-846-3026 ⏱M-Sat 9-8, Sun 12-5
• organic produce

🚗 **From US 31S/N Beacon Blvd,** turn right onto Washington St 2 blocks to store on right at 7th St. **From US 31N/S Beacon Blvd,** turn left onto Franklin Ave 1 block to S 8th St. Turn right onto S 8th 1 block to Washington. Turn left onto Washington 1 block to store.

GRAND RAPIDS
Gaia Cafe 🍴   ♿
209 Diamond Ave. S.E. ☎ 616-454-6233 ⏱ Tues-F 8-8, Sat-Sun 8-3
Healthy breakfast fare plus a selection of classics featuring beans, rice and veggies.
• vegetarian • vegan friendly • tables • wait staff • take-out

🚗 **From I-96W,** take I-196W to exit 79. Turn left onto Fuller Ave NE almost 1 mile to Hermitage St SE. Turn right onto Hermitage ¼ mile to Diamond Ave SE. Turn left onto Diamond to restaurant. **From I-96E or US 131S,** take I-196E to exit 78. Turn right onto College Ave NE about ½ mile to Fulton St E. Turn left onto Fulton to Lake Dr SE. Veer right onto Lake ½ mile to Diamond. Turn right onto Diamond to restaurant. **From US 131N,** take exit 84B (131 Bus) toward Downtown left onto Iona Ave SW to Fulton. Turn right onto Fulton under 1 mile to Lake.and follow directions above

Harvest Health Foods 🛍
1944 Eastern Ave. S.E. ☎ 616-245-6268 ⏱ M-Sat 9-7
• organic produce

🚗 **From I-96W,** take exit 43A toward Kent Co Airport west on 28th St SE about 5⅔ miles to Eastern Ave SE. Turn right onto Eastern 1 mile to store. **From I-96E,** take exit 31A onto US 131S about 6¾ miles to exit 82A. **From US 131,** take exit 82A onto Burton St SW (loop around right from 131S, right from 131N) about 1¼ miles to Eastern. Turn left onto Eastern to store.

Harvest Health Foods 🛍
6807 Cascade Rd. S.E. ☎ 616-975-7555 ⏱ M-Sat 9-8
• organic produce

🚗 **From I-96,** take exit 46B east on 28th St (loop around right from I-96E, right from I-96W) about 1¾ miles to Cascade Rd SE. Turn right onto Cascade to store.

Health Hutt 🛍
600 Monroe N.W. ☎ 616-776-9944 ⏱ M-Sat 9-8, Sun 12-5
• organic produce

🚗 **From I-196E,** exit onto Ottawa Ave NW and turn right onto Michigan St NW 1 block to Monroe Ave NW. Turn right onto Monroe across hwy to store on right. **From I-196W,** take exit 77C and veer left onto Ottawa across hwy and follow directions above.

GROSSE POINT
Better Health Market 🛍
19850 Mack Ave. ☎ 313-885-5000 ⏱ M-F 9-9, Sat 9-8, Sun 11-5
• organic produce

🚗 **From I-94,** take exit 224B toward Allard Ave south on Manchester Blvd (merge onto Harper Ave and right from I-94E, merge onto Harper, left onto Allard, left onto Harper and right from I-94W) ¾ mile to Mack Ave. Turn left onto Mack 1½ blocks to store on right after Huntington Blvd.

Sprout House 🖐️

15233 Kercheval St. ✆ 313-331-3200 ⏰ M-Sat 10-6
• organic produce • fresh juice

🍎 **From I-94**, take exit 222A onto Outer Dr E (left from I-94W, onto Edsel Ford Fwy then right from I-94E) about ¼ mile to Alter Rd. Merge straight onto Alter 1⅔ miles to Kercheval St. Turn left onto Kercheval about ¼ mile to store

HANCOCK

Keweenaw Co-op 🖐️

1035 Ethel Ave. ✆ 906-482-2030 ⏰ M-Sat 10-8, Sun 10-5
• organic produce • vegetarian friendly • deli • take-out • co-op

🍎 **From Rt 41N**, turn left onto N Lincoln Dr (before 41 veers right) and right onto Ethel Ave under ¼ mile (about 2 blocks) to store on right. **From Rt 41S**, turn left onto Summit St (before 41 turns left) 1 block to Hill St. Turn left onto Hill 1 block to Ethel. Turn right onto Ethel to store.

HILLSDALE

Hillsdale Natural Grocery 🖐️

31 N. Broad St. ✆ 517-439-1397 ⏰ M-F 9-6, Sat 9-5

🍎 Rt 34 & 99 meet in Hillsdale to become Broad St. Store is on east side.

HOLLAND

Apple Valley Health Food 🖐️

3013 West Shore Drive ✆ 616-399-8004 ⏰ M-Th 9-8, F 9-4, Sun 11-5
All-vegetarian health food store.

🍎 **From I-196E**, take US 31N about 8 miles to Felch St. Turn right onto Felch and left onto W Shore Dr ⅓ mile to store on left. **From I-196W**, take exit 52 toward 16th St right onto Adams St continuing onto 16th about 2½ miles to US 31. Turn right onto 31 2½ miles and follow directions above.

Nature's Market 🖐️ 🍴

1013 S. Washington Ave. ✆ 616-394-5250 ⏰ M-F 8-7, Sat 8-6 Cafe M-Sat 10-3
• organic produce • vegetarian friendly • organic focus • cafe • deli • tables • self-service • take-out

🍎 **From I-196E**, take US 31N under 2 miles to exit 47A. Turn right onto Blue Star Hwy/Washington Ave under ¼ mile to store before Tulip City Airport. **From I-196W**, take exit 49 right onto Lincoln Rd to E 48th St. Turn left onto E 48th 1 mile and continue onto 58th St/S Washington Ave ½ mile to store.

HUDSONVILLE

Harvest Health Foods 🖐️

4150 32nd Ave. ✆ 616-896-6630 ⏰ M-Sat 9-8
• organic produce

🍎 **From I-196**, take exit 62 toward Hudsonville onto 32nd Ave (right from I-196E, left from I-196W) to store on left just south of hwy.

IONIA

Healthy Basics 2 🖐️

576 N. State St. ✆ 616-902-3082 ⏰ M-F 10-5, Alternate Sat 10-2

🍎 **From I-96**, take exit 67 toward Battle Creek/Ionia north on Hwy 66/State Rd (left from I-96E, right from I-96W) 7¾ miles to W Lincoln Ave. Turn left onto W Lincoln 1 block to N State. Turn right onto N State 1 block to store on right.

IRONWOOD

Northwind Natural Foods Co-op

116 S. Suffolk St. © 906-932-3547 ① M-F 9-6, Sat 9-5
• organic produce • co-op

🛍 Just over the MN border. **From US 2,** turn south onto 2 Bus (Douglas St, then Suffolk St) under ¾ mile to store before Aurora St.

KALAMAZOO

Kalamazoo People's Food Co-op

436 S. Burdick St. © 269-342-5686 ① Daily 9-8
• organic produce • vegetarian • organic focus • deli • take-out • co-op

🛍 **From I-94,** take exit 76B north on Westnedge Ave (becomes S Park St) about 3½ miles total to Cedar St. Turn right onto Cedar to store at S Burdick St. **From Hwy 131/94 Bus,** take exit 36A toward Kalamazoo onto 94 Bus E (Stadium Dr, then Michigan Ave) about 4 miles to Burdick. Turn right onto Burdick about ¼ mile to store at Cedar.

Sawall Health Foods

2965 Oakland Drive © 269-343-3619 ① M-Sat 9-8, Sun 10-6
• organic produce

🛍 **From I-94,** take exit 75 north on Oakland Dr 1 mile to store on right.

KENTWOOD

Apple Valley Natural Foods

6070 Kalamazoo Ave. S.E. © 616-554-3205 ① M-Th 9-8, F 9-4, Sun 11-5
All-vegetarian health food store.

🛍 **From Hwy 131,** take exit 77 onto M 6E/Paul Henry Fwy about 2½ miles to exit 11 (Kalamazoo Ave). Turn left onto Kalamazoo ½ mile to store at 60th St.

KIMBALL

Honeycomb Natural Foods

2838 Stable Drive © 810-984-1773 ① M-W 9-7, Th-F 9-9, Sat 9-6, Sun 10-5 Deli M-F 10-6:30, Sat 10-6, Sun 12-5
• organic produce • vegetarian friendly • organic focus • fresh juice • deli • tables • self-service • take-out

🛍 **From I-69,** take exit 196 north on Wadhams Rd (left from I-69E, right from I-69W) past tracks to first right onto Horseshoe Trail. After Horseshoe turns left and becomes Stable Dr store is on right.

LAKE ORION

Lucky's Natural Foods

101 S. Broadway St. © 248-693-1209 ① M-Th 9:30-7, F 9:30-6, Sat 10-6
• organic produce

🛍 **From I-75,** take exit 81 onto M-24N (Lapeer Rd) about 6 miles. After McDonald's, veer right at historic business district onto Broadway St to store on right at Front St.

LANSING

Better Health Market

6235 W. Saginaw Hwy. © 517-323-9186 ① M-Sat 9-9, Sun 12-5
🛍 **From I-96/69,** take exit 93B for State Hwy 43 E/Saginaw Hwy/I 69 Bus onto W Saginaw under 1½ miles to store on right.

LIVONIA

Zerbo's Health Foods 🛍

34164 Plymouth Rd. ✆ 734-427-3144 ⏲ M-Sat 9:30-8, Sun 11-5
Health bar with raw vegan fare.
• organic produce

🍎 **From I-96 (Jeffers Fwy)**, take exit 174 south on Framington Rd 1 mile to Plymouth Rd. Turn right onto Plymouth under ½ mile to store.

LUDINGTON

The Evergreen Natural Foods Market 🛍

106 W. Ludington Ave. ✆ 231-843-1000 ⏲ M-Sat 10-6, Sun 12-4
• organic produce

🍎 US 10 & 31 meet in Ludington, which is on the shores of Lake Michigan. Store is 1½ miles west of 31 on 10 (Ludington Ave) on right at James St.

MANISTEE

Port City Organics 🛍

321 River St. ✆ 231-398-3060 ⏲ M-Sat 10-6:30
Local produce in season.

🍎 **From US 31**, go west on River St 1 block to store on south side.

MARQUETTE

Marquette Organic Food Co-op 🛍

109 W. Baraga Ave. ✆ 906-225-0671 ⏲ Daily 9-9
• organic produce • co-op

🍎 Take Rt 41 to Marquette. Turn onto 41 Bus/Washington St to Baraga Ave. Turn left onto Baraga to store.

MONROE

Health Matters Herbs & More 🛍

17 E. Second St. ✆ 734-240-2786 ⏲ M-F 10-6, Sat 10-2

🍎 **From I-75**, take exit 13 left onto E Front St over ⅓ mile to E 1st St. Turn right onto E 1st 2 blocks to Eastchester St. Turn left onto Eastchester 1 block to E 2nd St. Turn right onto E 2nd under 1 mile to store on right between Washington & S Monroe St.

MT. PLEASANT

Green Tree Co-op 🛍

214 N. Franklin St. ✆ 989-772-3221 ⏲ M-Sat 9-8, Sun 12-5
• organic produce • co-op

🍎 **From US 127N**, take first Mt Pleasant exit onto US 27 about 3½ miles to Mosher St. Turn left onto Mosher ⅓ mile (5 blocks) to Franklin St. Turn right onto Franklin to store on right. **From US 127S**, take first Mt Pleasant exit onto US 127/Mission St about 1½ miles to Mosher. Turn right onto Mosher and follow directions above.

MUSKEGON

Health Hutt 🛍

1519 E. River Rd. ✆ 231-744-0852 ⏲ M-Sat 9-8, Sun 12-5

🍎 **From US 31**, take M 120/Holton Rd exit east (right from US 31N, left from US 31S) ¼-½ mile to River Rd. Turn right onto River to store on right.

Health Hutt 🛍

3112 Henry St. ✆ 231-739-1568 ⏲ M-Sat 9-8, Sun 12-5
Produce sporadically.

🍎 **From US 31S,** turn right onto E Sherman Blvd 2½ miles to Temple St. Turn left onto Temple ⅓ mile (across tracks) to W Broadway Ave. Turn right onto W Broadway ⅓ mile (across hwy) to Henry St. Turn left onto Henry under ½ mile to store on left at W Lincoln Ave. **From US 31N**, take exit 110B toward US 31 right onto I-96W and continue onto 31 (Airline Rd/S Seaway Dr) under 2 miles to store.

NEW BALTIMORE

Simple of New Baltimore 🛍️
36120 Green St. ✆ 586-935-8132 ⏱ M-Sat 10-6
 • organic produce • co-op

🍎 **From I-94E**, take exit 243 toward New Baltimore right onto 23 Mile Rd/ M 29 4 miles (veer left to continue on M 29/Green St) to store on right between Clay & Base St. **From I-94W**, take exit 248 toward Marine Rd left onto 26 mile about 1½ miles to County Line Rd. Turn right onto County Line about 2½ miles to Green. Turn right onto Green under 1 mile to store on left after Base.

NORTHVILLE

Red Pepper Deli 🍴   ♿
116 W. Main St. ✆ 248-773-7671 ⏱ M-W 10:30-7:30, Th-Sat 10:30-8
Mainly raw food and vegan except for honey in some dishes.
 • vegetarian • vegan friendly • organic focus • fresh juice • tables • self-service

🍎 **From I-275S/I-96E**, take exit 167 right onto 8 Mile Rd (signs for Northville) 2½ miles to N Center St. Turn left onto N Center over ½ mile to W Main St. Turn right onto W Main to restaurant on right. **From I-275N**, take exit 167A right onto 7 Mile Rd about 2½ miles to S Main. Turn right onto S Main about 1 mile to restaurant.

NOVI

Better Health Market 🛍️
42875 Grand River Ave. ✆ 248-735-8100 ⏱ M-Sat 9-9, Sun 10-8
 • organic produce • vegetarian friendly • fresh juice • cafe • deli • tables • self-service
 • take-out

🍎 **From I-96**, take exit 162 toward Novi south on Novi Rd (right from I-96E, left from I-96W) past Novi Town Ctr to Grand River Ave. Turn left onto Grand River under ½ mile to store on right after Market St.

PETOSKEY

The Grain Train Natural Foods Co-op 🛍️🍴   ♿
220 E. Mitchell St. ✆ 231-347-2381 ⏱ M-F 8-8, Sat 9-7, Sun 11-5
 • organic produce • vegetarian friendly • cafe • bakery • tables • self-service • take-out • co-op

🍎 **From intersection US 31 & 131**, take 31N (becomes W Mitchell then E Mitchell St) to store.

PLYMOUTH

Better Health Market 🛍️
44427 Ann Arbor Rd. ✆ 734-455-1440 ⏱ M-Th 9-9, F-Sat 9-8, Sun 11-5
 • organic produce

🍎 **From I-275**, take exit 28 for Ann Arbor Rd toward Plymouth west on Ann Arbor Rd (right from I-275S, left from I-275N) about 2 miles to store on left at Sheldon Rd.

ROCHESTER HILLS

Health Foods of Rochester 🛍️
2952 S. Rochester Rd. ✆ 248-852-0336 ⏱ M-F 8-8, Sat 9-7, Sun 11-5
🍎 **From I-75**, take exit 77A toward Utica onto MI 59E (Veteran's Memorial Fwy) about 5½ miles to MI 150 exit toward Rochester/Troy. Turn left onto 150 (S Rochester Rd) about ¾ mile to store on NW corner at Auburn Rd.

Whole Foods Market 🛍 🍴

1404 Walton Blvd. ✆ 248-652-2100 ⏰ Daily 9-10
 • organic produce • vegetarian friendly • salad bar • cafe • self-service • take-out

🍎 **From I-75**, take exit 79 onto University Dr (left from I-75S, right from I-75N). Follow University at it turns left onto Squirrel Rd to E Walton Dr. Turn right onto E Walton (becomes Walton Blvd) about 2²/₃ miles to store on north side in Rochester Hills Plaza.

ROYAL OAK

Inn Season Cafe 🍴

500 E. 4th St. ✆ 248-547-7916 ⏰ Tues-Th 11:30-9, F 11:30-9:30, Sat 12-9:30, Sun 11-3
 • vegetarian • vegan friendly • organic focus • tables • wait staff

🍎 **From I-696**, take exit 16 toward Woodward Ave/Main St onto W 10 Mile Rd to Main St. Turn north onto Main (left from I-696E, right from I-696W) about 1 mile to 4th St. Turn right onto 4th 3 blocks to restaurant on right. **From I-75**, take exit 62 toward 11 Mile Rd/W 10 Mile Rd west on 11 Mile (right from I-75S, left from I-75N) about 1 mile to Phillips Pl. Turn left onto Phillips 2 blocks to 4th. Turn right onto 4th 1 block to restaurant on left.

SAGINAW

Grains & Greens 🛍

3641 Bay Rd. ✆ 989-799-8171 ⏰ M-F 9-8, Sat 9-6, Sun 12-5
🍎 **From I-75**, merge onto I-675 toward Downtown (exit 150 from I-75N, 155 from I-75S) to Tittabawasee Rd (exit 6) toward Zilwaukee. Go west on Tittabawasee 1 mile to Bay Rd. Turn left onto Bay 1¹/₃ miles to store on left.

Heritage Natural Foods 🛍

717 Gratiot Ave. ✆ 989-793-5805 ⏰ M-Sat 9:30-4:30
🍎 **From I-75**, take exit 149B onto Rt 46W/Holland Ave (becomes Sheridan, Rust & Gratiot Ave) about 2½ miles (across water). When 46 becomes Gratiot turn right 1 block to store.

ST. JOSEPH

Tim's Too Asian Grill 🍴

511 Pleasant St. ✆ 269-985-0094 ⏰ M-Th 11-9, F-Sat 11-10
Choose from the buffet of ingredients (including vegetarian "meat" and vegan sauces) that are wok-fried while you watch. Separate wok for meatless meals.
 • vegetarian friendly • vegan friendly • alcohol • tables • self-service • wait staff

🍎 **From I-94**, take exit 27 toward St Joseph west on Niles Rd (left from I-94E, right from I-94W) about 4 miles to Pleasant St. Turn left onto Pleasant 2 blocks to restaurant on right.

TRAVERSE CITY

Edson Farms Natural Foods 🛍

835 S. Garfield Ave. ✆ 231-941-5221 ⏰ M-F 9-7, Sat 9-6
 • fresh juice • deli • take-out

🍎 **Traveling north**, take M 37N to Traverse City. Turn right onto 8th St 2 miles to S Garfield St. Turn right onto S Garfield under ½ mile to store on left between Hannah Ave & Centre St. **From the waterfront on US 31, M 37 or M 72**, go south on S Garfield St under 1 mile to store.

Home Grown Organic Eatery 🍴

223 W. Grandview Pkwy. ✆ 231-932-4690 ⏰ Tues-F 11-7, Sat 9-7, Sun 9-3:30
 • vegetarian friendly • vegan friendly • organic focus • fresh juice • tables • wait staff

🍎 **Traveling north**, take M 37N to Traverse City. Turn right onto W Grandview Pkwy (M 37) ½ mile to restaurant on right. **From the waterfront on US 31, M 37 or M 72**, restaurant is on the south side of W Grandview between Hall & Union St.

Oryana Food Co-op 🛍

260 E. 10th St. ℂ 231-947-0191 ⏱ M-Sat 8-8, Sun 10-6
 • organic produce • vegetarian friendly • deli • take-out • co-op

🍎 **Traveling north**, take M 37N to Traverse City. Turn right onto 14th St about ⅔ mile to Cass Rd. Turn left onto Cass under ½ mile to E 10th St. Turn right onto E 10th to store at Lake Ave. **From the waterfront on US 31, M 37 or M 72**, turn south onto Cass about ½ mile to 10th St. Turn left onto 10th to store.

TROY _____

Good Food Company 🛍 🍴

74 W. Maple Rd. ℂ 248-362-0886 ℂ M-Sat 9-9, Sun 10-7
 • organic produce • vegetarian friendly • deli • tables • self-service • take-out

🍎 **From I-75,** take exit 65B west on 14 Mile to Main St. Turn right onto Main (becomes Livernois Rd at Maple Rd) to store on left at W Maple.

Whole Foods Market 🛍   &

2880 W. Maple Rd. ℂ 248-649-9600 ⏱Daily 8-10
 • organic produce, vegetarian friendly, fresh juice, salad bar, deli, take-out

🍎 **From I-75,** take exit 69 west on Big Beaver Rd about 2 miles to Coolidge Hwy. Turn left onto Coolidge 1 mile to store on NE corner at Maple Rd.

WEST BLOOMFIELD _____   &

Whole Foods Market 🛍 🍴   &

7350 W. Orchard Lake Rd. ℂ 248-538-4600 ⏱ Daily 8-10
 • organic produce • vegetarian friendly • salad bar • cafe • self-service • take-out

🍎 **From I-696,** take exit 5 north on Orchard Lake Rd 2 miles to 14 Mile Rd. Turn left onto 14 Mile and right to store in Gateway Shopping Plaza.

WHITEHALL_____

Healthy Pantry 🛍

3295 Colby Rd., Ste. H ℂ 231-893-3438 ⏱ M-F 9-8, Sat 9-7, Sun 11-6
Produce in season.

🍎 **From US 31**, take exit 31 toward Whitehall left (west) onto Colby Rd about ½ mile to store on left.

WOODLAND_____

Woodland Co-op 🛍

116 Martin Rd. ℂ 269-367-4188 ⏱ M, W, F 12-5

🍎 Take Rt 43 into Woodland. At blinking light turn north onto Main St to store on left (in old bank).

YPSILANTI _____

Ypsilanti Food Co-op & River Street Bakery 🛍

312 N. River St. ℂ 734-483-1520 ⏱ Daily 9-9
 • organic produce • vegetarian friendly • deli • bakery • self-service • take-out • co-op

🍎 **From I-94**, take exit 183 north on Huron St to Michigan Ave. Turn right onto Michigan ¼ mile to River St. Turn left onto River to store on right (before tracks).

MINNESOTA

AITKIN

Gramma's Pantry 🏠

223 Minnesota Ave. N. ✆ 218-927-6713 ⏱ M-F 9-5, Sat 10-4
• organic produce

🏠 MN 210 and US 169 intersect in Aitkin. Store is just north of this intersection (aka 2nd St NW & Minnesota Ave) on west side.

ALBERT LEA

Wintergreen Natural Foods 🏠   ♿

1442 W. Main St. ✆ 507-373-0386 ⏱ M-F 10-5:30, Sat 9-5
• organic produce • co-op

🏠 **From I-90W,** take exit 159A onto I-35S. **From I-35,** take exit 12 west on E Main St about 4 miles. After Broadway Ave and 2 viaducts make first right to store. **From I-90E,** take exit 154 toward Albert Lea onto MN 13S about 3¼ miles to W Main. Turn left onto Main to store.

1. Aitkin
2. Albert Lea
3. Alexandria
4. Anoka
5. Baxter
6. Bemidji
7. Blaine
8. Blue Earth
9. Brainerd
10. Burnsville
11. Cambridge
12. Chanhassen
13. Chisago
14. Columbia Heights
15. Duluth
16. Edina
17. Fergus Falls
18. Grand Marais
19. Grand Rapids
20. Hastings
21. Lake City
22. Litchfield
23. Long Prairie
24. Minneapolis
25. Minnetonka
26. Mora
27. Morris
28. Northfield
29. Orontonville
30. Owatonna
31. Pine City
32. Plymouth
33. Rochester
34. Roseville
35. Sandstone
36. Shoreview
37. St. Cloud
38. St. Paul
39. St. Peter
40. Stillwater
41. Virginia
42. Wadena
43. Willmar
44. Windom
45. Winona

ALEXANDRIA

The Grain Bin

3015 Hwy. 29 S., Ste. 4002 ✆ 320-763-6876 ⏰ M-F 10-9, Sat 10-6, Sun 11-5

🍎 **From I-94**, take exit 100 toward Alexandria north on SR 29 S (left from I-94E, right from I-94W) under 1½ miles to store on right in Viking Plaza Mall.

ANOKA

Lakewinds Natural Food Store

1917 2nd Ave. S. ✆ 763-427-4340 ⏰ M-F 8-8, Sat 9-6, Sun 11-5 Cafe M-F 11-2

• organic produce • vegetarian friendly • cafe • deli • tables • self-service • take-out • co-op

🍎 **From I-94/694**, take exit 29B onto US 169N over 8½ miles (across bridge) to Main St. Turn right onto E Main 2 blocks to S 2nd Ave. Turn right onto 2nd to store.

BAXTER

Life Preserver

14715 Edgewood Drive ✆ 218-829-7925 ⏰ M-F 9-6, Sat 9-5

• organic produce

🍎 **From Hwy 371N (past Hwy 210 intersection),** turn left onto Excelsior Rd and right onto Edgewood Dr over ½ mile to store (1 mile north of Paul Bunyan Amusement Center). **From Hwy 371S**, turn right onto Woida Rd and left onto Edgewood under ½ mile to store.

BEMIDJI

Harmony Natural Foods Co-op

117 3rd St., N.W. ✆ 218-751-2009 ⏰ M-F 9-7, Sat 9-6, Sun 12-5

• organic produce • vegetarian friendly • deli • take-out • co-op

🍎 Take US 71 or 2 to Bemidji and MN 197 to town. Turn west onto 3rd St to store.

BLAINE

Cafe Organica

4000 Pheasant Ridge Drive N.E. ✆ 763-783-4069 ⏰ M-F 7:30-2

At Aveda Headquarters. Soups, salads, sandwiches, pizza and hot entrees with a daily theme.

• vegetarian friendly • organic focus • salad bar • tables • self-service

🍎 **From I-35W,** take exit 33 (CR 17/Lexington Ave) north on Lexington about ¼ mile to Pheasant Ridge Dr. Turn left onto Pheasant Ridge to restaurant in Aveda.

BLUE EARTH

Rainbow Food Co-op

103 S. Main St. ✆ 507-526-3603 ⏰ M-F 10-5:30, Sat 10-3

🍎 **From I-90,** take exit 119 south on US 169 to 7th St. Turn right onto 7th to Main St. Turn right onto Main to store on right.

BRAINERD

Crow Wing Food Co-op 🛍️
823 Washington St. ☎ 218-828-4600 ⏰ M-F 9:30-6, Sat 10-4
• organic produce • co-op
🛒 Hwy 210 & 371 lead to Brainerd. Store is on 210 (Washington St) 3 blocks east of 371 (S 6th St) at N 9th St.

BURNSVILLE

Valley Natural Foods 🛍️🍴 ♿
13750 County Rd. 11 ☎ 952-891-1212 ⏰ M-Th 8-9, F-Sat 8-8, Sun 10-8 Drive-thru M-Sat. 6:30am-8pm, Sun. 9-8
Lots of vegetarian choices and 80% organic. Drive-thru window for early birds.
• organic produce • vegetarian friendly • organic focus • fresh juice • salad bar • deli • bakery • counter • tables • self-service • take-out • co-op
🛒 **From I-35E,** take exit 90 south on CR 11 to store just off hwy on right at McAndrews Rd.

CAMBRIDGE

City Center Market 🛍️
122 N. Buchanan St. ☎ 763-689-4640 ⏰ M-F 9-8, Sat 9-6, Sun 12-5
• organic produce • co-op
🛒 Cambridge is 12 miles west of I-35 exit 147 on MN 95. Store is just north of MN 95 (aka 1st Ave E) and west of tracks on east side of Buchanan St.

CHANHASSEN

Lakewinds Natural Foods 🛍️🍴
435 Pond Promenade ☎ 952-697-3366 ⏰ M-Sat 8-9, Sun 9-8
• organic produce • vegetarian friendly • fresh juice • salad bar • cafe • deli • bakery • tables • self-service • take-out • co-op
🛒 **From MN 312,** go right (north) on Great Plains Rd under 1 mile to Main St. Turn right onto Main 2 blocks to Pond Promenade. Turn right onto Pond Promenade to store on right.

CHISAGO

The Makers Healthy Market 🛍️
10510 South Ave. ☎ 651-257-8000 ⏰ M-F 9-7, Sat 9-4
• organic produce
🛒 Store is on the service road off Hwy 8 on the north side between West & Isabel St.

COLUMBIA HEIGHTS

Nalapak 🍴
4920 Central Ave. N.E. ☎ 763-574-1113 ⏰ M-F 11:30-3, 5:30-10, Sat-Sun 11:30-4, 5-10
Indian vegetarian with a lunch buffet.
• vegetarian • vegan friendly • alcohol • tables • self-service • wait staff
🛒 **From I-694,** take exit 38 south on Central Ave (right from I-694E, left from I-694W) under 1 mile to restaurant on right at 49th Ave NE.

DULUTH

New Scenic Cafe 🍴 ♿
5461 North Shore Drive ☎ 218-525-6274 ⏰ Mon-Th, Sun 11-9, F-Sat 11-10
Fine dining on Lake Superior. At east half the menu is vegetarian. Reservations suggested.
• vegetarian friendly • vegan friendly • alcohol • tables • wait staff
🛒 Take I-35 north to end onto Hwy 61 (North Shore Scenic Dr). Follow N Scenic Shore to restaurant (7½ miles past Lester River).

Pizza Luce 🍴

11 E. Superior St. ✆ 218-727-7400 ⏰ M-F 7am-1am, Sat-Sun 8am-1am
Whole wheat hoagies, vegan mock meats, nut-based "cheese," tofu veggieballs and pizza by the slice.
 • vegetarian friendly • vegan friendly • alcohol • tables • self-service • wait staff • take-out
🚌 **From I-35N**, take exit 256B left onto S 5th St W and right onto W Superior St under ½ mile to restaurant on left. **From I-35S**, take exit 256B right onto S Lake Ave and right onto E Superior to restaurant.

Whole Foods Co-op 🛍

610 E. 4th St. ✆ 218-728-0884 ⏰ Daily 7-9
 • organic produce • vegetarian • vegan friendly • deli • take-out • co-op
🚌 **From I-35N**, take exit 256A onto Mesabe Ave about 1¾ miles to Central Entrance. Turn right onto Central Entrance continuing onto N 6th Ave E under 1 mile to E 4th St. Turn left onto E 4th to store on right. **From I-36S,** take exit 256B right onto Lake Ave 3 blocks to E 2nd St. Turn right onto E 2nd 6 blocks to N 6th. Turn left onto N 6th 2 blocks to E 4th. Turn right onto E 4th to store.

EDINA

Good Earth Restaurant & Bakery 🍴   ♿

3460 W. 70th St. ✆ 952-925-1001 ⏰ M-Sat 7-10, Sun 7-9
A natural foods restaurant with vegetarian choices, fish and poultry.
 • vegetarian friendly • fresh juice • alcohol • bakery • tables • wait staff
🚌 **From I-494**, take exit 6B onto France Ave S/Rte 17N about 1⅓ miles to W 70th St. Turn right onto 70th to restaurant in Galleria Shopping Ctr.

FERGUS FALLS

Meadow Farm Foods 🛍

23064 County Hwy. 1 ✆ 218-739-4585 ⏰ M-W, F-Sat 9-6, Th 9-8
 • organic produce
🚌 **From I-94**, take exit 54 toward Fergus Falls west on Lincoln Ave (left from I-94E, right from I-94W) over 2 miles to light at Union Ave. Turn left onto Union 2 blocks to Summit Ave. Turn right onto Summit under ½ mile to 4-way stop and turn left onto Friberg Ave (CR 1) about 3½ miles to store on right.

GRAND MARAIS

Angry Trout Cafe 🍴

408 W. Hwy. 61 ✆ 218-387-1265 ⏰ May-Mid Oct Call for hours
Outdoor dining at the edge of Lake Superior. A Certified Green Restaurant.
 • vegetarian friendly • organic focus • tables • wait staff
🚌 Enter town on Hwy 61. Restaurant is on the harbor.

Cook County Whole Foods Co-op 🛍   ♿

20 E. 1st St. ✆ 218-387-2503 ⏰ M-Sat 9-7, Sun 10-6
 • organic produce • co-op
🚌 Take Hwy 61 into Grand Marais and turn south at only light in town onto 1st Ave E 1 block to 1st St E. Turn left onto 1st St to store.

GRAND RAPIDS

Circle Whole Foods 🛍

204 N.W. 1st Ave. ✆ 218-326-3663 ⏰ M-F 9-5:30, Sat 9-3
 • organic produce
🚌 **From US2 (4th St)/169 (Pokegamma Ave) intersection**, store is 2 blocks south and 1 block west at NW 2nd St & NW 1st Ave.

HASTINGS

Spiral Natural Foods

307 2nd St. E. © 651-437-2667 ⊕ M-F 10-6, Sat 10-5, Sun 11-5
• organic produce • vegetarian friendly • deli • tables • self-service • take-out • co-op

From Hwy 61S (from MN-St Paul area), cross the Mississippi bridge, turn right onto 3rd St, right and right again going under bridge onto 2nd St and 3 blocks to store on left (across from post office).

LAKE CITY

Oak Center General Food Store Co-op

67011 Hwy. 63 © 507-753-2080 ⊕ M-Sat 9-6

On Hwy 63 about 9 miles south of intersection Hwy 61 & 63 at top of hill on west side (look for windmill).

LITCHFIELD

Natural Foods Market

230 N. Sibley St. © 320-693-7539 ⊕ M-Sat 9-5:30
• organic produce • co-op

Store is on Hwy 12 (N Silbey St in town) on east side between 2nd & 3rd St.

LONG PRAIRIE

Everybody's Market Food Co-op

11 1st St. N. © 320-732-3900 ⊕ M-F 9-5:30, Sat 9-1

From US 71, go east on Central Ave 1 block to store on left at 1st St N. From MN 27, turn left onto 71 and follow directions above.

MINNEAPOLIS

Birchwood Cafe

3311 E. 25th St. © 612-722-4474 ⊕ M-F 7-9, Sat 8-9, Sun 9-2
• vegetarian friendly • vegan friendly • organic focus • alcohol • tables • wait staff

From I-94, take exit 235A south on Riverside Ave (right from I-94E, sharp left from I-94W) 1 block to Franklin Ave. Turn left onto Franklin 2 blocks to 31st Ave. Turn right onto 31st 4 blocks to 25th St. Turn left onto 25th 2 blocks to restaurant on right.

Cafe Agri

4300 Bryant Ave. S. © 612-822-3101 ⊕ M-F 4:30–10, Sat-Sun 8am-10pm
Focus is locally grown food using sustainable methods. Vegetarian except for trout.
• vegetarian friendly • vegan friendly • organic focus • alcohol • tables • wait staff

From I-35W, take exit 13 west on 46th St (merge onto Stevens Ave and right from I-35WS, merge onto 2nd Ave and left from I-35WN) under 1 mile to Bryant Ave. Turn right onto Bryant 3 blocks to restaurant on left at W 43rd St.

Cafe Brenda

300 1st Ave. N. © 612-342-9230 ⊕ Lunch M-F 11:30-2 Dinner M-Sat 5:30-9
"Gourmet Vegetarian and Fresh Seafood" restaurant.
• vegetarian friendly • alcohol • tables • wait staff

From I-94E, take exit 230 onto N 4th St over 1 mile to free parking on left between 2nd & 1st Ave. (Turn left onto 1st Ave to restaurant on right.) From I-94W, take exit 231A onto I-349W/US 12W 1⅓ miles to exit 9C. Turn right onto Washington Ave 2 blocks and right onto 1st 1 block to restaurant on left. From I-35W S, take exit 17C right onto Washington about 1 mile to 1st Ave N. Turn left onto 1st 1 block to restaurant. From I-35W N, take 5th Ave exit (last downtown exit) north (becomes Washington) to 3rd St. Turn left onto 3rd to restaurant.

Cafe Organica
400 Central Ave. S.E 📞 612-378-7413 🕐 Tues-Th 8-1:30, F-Sat 7:30-3
At the Aveda Institute. Small menu but always something for vegetarians.
  • vegetarian friendly • organic focus • tables • self-service

🍎 **From I-94E,** take exit 230 onto N 4th St almost 1 mile to Hennepin Ave E. Turn left onto Hennepin almost 1 mile (across river) to SE University Ave. Turn right onto University 2 blocks to Central Ave. Turn left onto Central 1 block to restaurant in Aveda Institute. **From I-94W,** take exit 235B onto Huron Blvd (becomes SE 4th St) about 1¼ miles to restaurant on right at Central. **From I-35W,** take exit 18 onto 4th (right from I-35W S, left from I-35W N) about 9 blocks to restaurant.

Eastside Food Cooperative
2551 Central Ave. N. E. 📞 612-788-0950 🕐 Daily 8-9
  • organic produce • vegetarian friendly • deli • take-out • co-op

🍎 **From I-35W N,** take exit 7B onto Johnson St NE over ½ mile to Lowry Ave NE. Turn left onto Lowry ½ mile to Central Ave. Turn right onto Central 1 block to store on right at 26th Ave. **From I-35W S,** take exit 21A right onto NE Stinson Blvd under 1 mile to Lowry. Turn left onto Lowry 1 mile to Central. Turn right onto Central 1 block to store on right.

Ecopolitan
2409 Lyndale Ave. S. 📞 612-874-7336 🕐 M-Th, Sun 9-9:30, F-Sat 9-11
Organic raw foods. A Certified Green Restaurant.
  • vegan • organic focus • fresh juice • counter • tables • wait staff

🍎 **From I-94,** take exit 231 for Hennepin/Lyndale south on Lyndale Ave 4 blocks to restaurant on left at 24th St. (For free parking turn left onto 24th and right into alleyway.)

French Meadow Bakery
2610 Lyndale Ave. S. 📞 612-870-7855 🕐 M-Th, Sun 6:30am-9pm, F-Sat 6:30-11
Organic yeast- and dairy-free breads. A Certified Green Restaurant.
  • vegetarian friendly • organic focus • alcohol • café • bakery • tables • self-service • wait staff • take-out

🍎 **From I-94,** take exit 231 for Hennepin/Lyndale south on Lyndale Ave 6 blocks to restaurant at 26th St.

Hard Times Restaurant
1821 Riverside Ave. 📞 612-341-9261 🕐 Daily 6am-4am
Collectively owned vegetarian restaurant and vegan bakery.
  • vegetarian • vegan friendly • tables • self-service

🍎 **From I-94E,** take exit 235A toward Riverside Ave onto S 9th St, turn left onto 25th Ave S and left onto Riverside over ½ mile to restaurant on left after 19th St S. **From I-94W,** take exit 234C right onto Cedar Ave under ¼ mile to Riverside. Turn right onto Riverside to restaurant on right.

Linden Hills Co-op
2813 W. 43rd St. 📞 612-922-1159 🕐 Daily 8-9
  • organic produce • vegetarian friendly • fresh juice • salad bar • deli • bakery • counter • tables • self-service • take-out • co-op

🍎 **From I-35W,** take exit 12B west on Diamond Lake Rd (aka 54th St) to Xerxes Ave. Turn right onto Xerxes to 43rd St. Turn right onto W 43rd to store on right between Vincent & Upton Ave.

For listing changes, updates and travel resources, go to HealthyHighways.com

Merlins Rest Pub ⑪

3601 E. Lake St. ✆ 612-216-2419 ⏰ M-Th 4-1am, F 3-2am, Sat 12-2am, Sun 10am-1am Kitchen daily until 10 pm
Irish/British pub with a nice vegetarian selection.
• vegetarian friendly • alcohol • counter • tables • wait staff

🚗 **From I-94W,** take exit 237 left onto N Cretin Ave over ½ mile to first right onto Marshall Ave. Turn right onto Marshall across river and onto E Lake St about 1⅓ miles total to restaurant on left at 36th Ave. **From I-94E,** take exit 235A toward 25thAve/Riverside Ave onto S 9th St and turn right onto 27th Ave about 1 mile to E Lake. Turn left onto E Lake about ½ mile to restaurant on right . **From I-35WN,** take exit 15 east onto 2nd Ave S and right onto E Lake over 2½ miles to restaurant.

Pizza Luce ⑪

119 N. 4th St. ✆ 612-333-7359 ⏰ M-Th, Sun 11am-2:30am, F-Sat 11am-3:30am
See Duluth location for description.
• vegetarian friendly • vegan friendly • alcohol • tables • self-service • wait staff • take-out

🚗 **From I-94E,** take exit 230 left onto N 4th St about 1¼ miles to restaurant on right after 2nd Ave N. **From I-94W,** take exit 231A left at fork and onto I-394W about 1⅓ miles to exit onto N 4th about ⅓ mile to restaurant.

Pizza Luce ⑪

3200 Lyndale Ave. S. ✆ 612-827-5978 ⏰ M-F, Sun11am-2:30am, F-Sat 11am-3am
See Duluth location for description.
• vegetarian friendly • vegan friendly • alcohol • tables • self-service • wait staff • take-out

🚗 From I-94, take exit 231 south on Lyndale Ave 1½-2 miles to restaurant on right at W 32nd St. **From I-35WN,** take exit 15 onto 2nd Ave S and turn left onto Lake St about ½ mile to Garfield Ave. Turn left onto Garfield 1 block, right onto W 31st St 1 block and left onto Lyndale 1 block to restaurant.

Pizza Luce ⑪

2200 E. Franklin Ave. ✆ 612-332-2535 ⏰ Daily 11am-2am
See Duluth location for description.
• vegetarian friendly • vegan friendly • alcohol • tables • self-service • wait staff • take-out

🚗 **From I-94,** take exit 235A onto Riverside Ave to 25th Ave S. Turn south onto 25th (right from I-94E, left I-from 94W) 1-2 blocks to Franklin Ave. Turn right onto Franklin 4½ blocks to restaurant on right.

Seward Community Cafe ⑪   ♿

2129 E. Franklin Ave. ✆ 612-332-1011 ⏰ M-F 7-3, Sat-Sun 8-4
Run collectively with an eye toward affordability. A good place to hang out.
• vegetarian friendly • vegan friendly • organic focus • counter • tables • self-service

🚗 **From I-94,** take exit 235A onto Riverside Ave to 25th Ave S. Turn south onto 25th (right from I-94E, left from I-94W) 1-2 blocks to Franklin Ave. Turn right onto Franklin 5 blocks to restaurant on SW corner at 22nd Ave. **From I-35W,** take exit 17A for Hiawatha Ave right onto Cedar Ave to light at Franklin. Turn left onto Franklin to restaurant

Seward Community Co-op 🛍

2111 E. Franklin Ave. ✆ 612-338-2465 ⏰ Daily 9-9
• organic produce • vegetarian friendly • fresh juice • deli • take-out • co-op

🚗 **From I-94,** take exit 235A onto Riverside Ave to 25th Ave S. Turn south onto 25th (right from I-94E, left from I-94W) 1-2 blocks to Franklin Ave. Turn right onto Franklin 4½ blocks to store on left. **From I-35W,** take exit 17A for Hiawatha Ave right onto Cedar Ave to light at Franklin. Turn left onto Franklin 2 blocks to store on right.

St. Martin's Table ⑪   ♿

2001 Riverside Ave. ✆ 612-339-3920 ⏰ M-Sat 11-2:30
Bookstore/restaurant run by the Community of St. Martin's, an ecumenical center for peace

making and justice. Simple vegetarian menu reflects solidarity with people facing hunger world wide. Tips go to hunger relief programs.
 • vegetarian • vegan friendly • organic focus • tables • wait staff • take-out

From I-94, take exit 235A northwest on Riverside Ave (slight right from I-94W, merge onto S 9th St, turn left onto 25th Ave S and left from I-94E) about ½ mile to restaurant on left at 20th Ave S.

Tao Natural Foods & Books

2200 Hennepin Ave. S. © 612-377-4630 ⏰ M-Sat 9-8, Sun 10-5
 • vegetarian friendly • vegan friendly • organic focus • fresh juice • counter • tables • wait staff

From I-94, take exit 231 for Hennepin/Lyndale south on Hennepin Ave to store 1 block south of Franklin Ave.

Wedge Community Co-op

2105 Lyndale Ave. S. © 612-874-7275 ⏰ M-F 9-10, Sat-Sun 9-9
 • organic produce • co-op

From I-94, take exit 231 for Hennepin/Lyndale south on Lyndale Ave past light at Franklin Ave to store on left.

Whole Foods Market

3060 Excelsior Blvd. © 612-927-8141 ⏰ Daily 8-10
 • organic produce • vegetarian friendly • salad bar • cafe • self-service • take-out

From I-94, take exit 231 for Hennepin/Lyndale south on Hennepin Ave about 1 mile to Lagoon Ave. Turn right onto Lagoon continuing onto Rt 3W about 1¼ miles (across water, becomes W Lake Ave, then Excelsior Blvd) to store.

MINNETONKA

Lakewinds Natural Foods

17501 Minnetonka Blvd. © 952-473-0292 ⏰ M-Sat 8-9, Sun 9-8
 • organic produce • vegetarian friendly • fresh juice • salad bar • cafe • deli • bakery • tables • self-service • take-out • co-op

From 1-494, take exit 17 west on Minnetonka Blvd 2¼ miles to store on left.

MORA

Bread 'n Honey Pantry

29 Union St. N. © 320-679-5955 ⏰ M-F 9-5:30, Sat 9-2
Take-out lunch during the week but not always something vegetarian.
 • organic produce • deli • take-out

Going north on MN 23/MN 65, turn left onto Division/Union St under 1 mile to store on left between Railroad & Maple Ave. **Going south on MN 65**, turn right onto Maple under ½ mile to Union. Turn left onto Union to store on right.

MORRIS

Pomme de Terre Food Co-op

613 Atlantic Ave. © 320-589-4332 ⏰ M-W, F 10-6, Th 10-8, Sat 10-4, Sun 12-4
 • organic produce • co-op

Rt 28, 9 & US 59 converge in Morris. Store is on Rt 9 (Atlantic Ave) at about 6th St.

NORTHFIELD

Just Food Co-op

516 Water St. S. © 507-650-0106 ⏰ M-Sat 8-9, Sun 10-7
 • organic produce • vegetarian friendly • deli • take-out • tables • self-service • take-out • co-op

From I-35, take exit 69 east on Hwy 19 (left from I-35S, right from I-35N) 7 miles (becomes 5th St W) to Water St S (after MN 3). Turn right onto Water to store on right.

ORONTONVILLE

The Granary Co-op 🛍️

47 N.W. 2nd St . ℭ 320-839-6204 ⏰ M-Sat 10-3
• organic produce

🍎 **From US 12 or US 75**, go north on MN 7/2nd St NW (veer right from US 75 or US 12 traveling west, turn left from US 12 traveling east) under ½ mile to store on right after Jackson Ave. **From MN 7 south**, store is on left after Monroe Ave.

OWATONNA

Harvest Food Co-op 🛍️

137 E. Front St. ℭ 507-451-0340 ⏰ M-F 9:30-5:30, Sat 9-1

🍎 **From I-35**, take exit 42 (14W/CR 45) onto Hoffman Dr (aka Bus 14) about 1 mile to W Rose St. Turn left onto W Rose, left onto Cedar Ave and right onto E Front St to store (across from grain elevator).

PINE CITY

Sprouts 'n More 🛍️

245 5th St. S.E. ℭ 320-629-3470 ⏰ M-F 9-5
Fresh sandwiches to go.
• organic produce

🍎 **From I-35**, take exit 169 for Co Hwy 7 toward Pine City east on Hillside Ave (left from I-35S, right from I-35N) ¾ mile to Main St. Turn left onto Main ½ mile to 3rd Ave SE. Turn right onto 3rd 1 block to 5th St SE. Turn left onto 5th to store on left.

PLYMOUTH

Fresh and Natural Natural Foods 🛍️ 🍴

4234 Lancaster Lane ℭ 763-559-0754 ⏰ M-Sat 9-9, Sun 9-7
• organic produce • vegetarian friendly • deli • tables • self-service • take-out

🍎 **From I-495**, take exit 23 east on Rockford Rd (left from I-495S, right from I-495N) under 2½ miles to Lancaster Ln. Turn right onto Lancaster to store on left in Four Seasons Mall. **From US 169,** go west on Rockford Rd under ¼ mile to Lancaster. Turn left onto Lancaster to store.

ROCHESTER

The Good Food Store 🛍️ 🍴

1001 6th St. N.W. ℭ 507-289-9061 ⏰ M-F 8-8, Sat 9-7, Sun 10-6 Deli M-F 9-3, Sat 9-5
• organic produce • vegan • organic focus • deli • tables • self-service • take-out

🍎 **From I-90,** take exit 218 north on Hwy 52 about 10 miles to Civic Center Dr NW exit. Merge east onto Civic Center about ½ mile to 11th Ave. Turn left onto 11th 1 block to 6th St NW. Turn right onto 6th to store on left.

ROSEVILLE

Good Earth Restaurant & Bakery 🍴   ♿

1901 W. Hwy. 36 ℭ 651-636-0956 ⏰ M-Sat 7-10, Sun 7-9
See Duluth location for description.
• vegetarian friendly • fresh juice • alcohol • bakery • tables • wait staff

🍎 **From I-35W**, take exit 23B onto MN 36E almost 1 mile to Fairview Ave N exit. Merge onto Fairview and back onto 36W 2 blocks to restaurant. **From I-35E**, take exit 111B onto MN 36W about 4½ miles to restaurant.

SANDSTONE

Organic Carrot 🛍
701 Hwy. 23 N. ☎ 320-245-0329 ⏰ M-W, F 9-5:30, Th 9-7
- organic produce

🚗 **From I-35**, take exit 191 toward Sandstone east on Hwy 3 (left from I-35S, right from I-35N) about ⅓ mile and veer left where it forks at Main St to stay on Hwy 23 to store.

SHOREVIEW

Fresh and Natural Natural Foods 🛍 🍴
1075 Hwy. 96 W. ☎ 651-203-3663 ⏰ M-Sat 9-9, Sun 9-7
- organic produce • vegetarian friendly • deli • tables • self-service • take-out

🚗 **From I-35E**, take exit 117 west on Hwy 96 (left from I-35ES, right from I-35EN) to first right onto Centerville Rd to store on right in Shoreview Village Mall.

ST. CLOUD

Good Earth Food Co-op 🛍 🍴
2010 8th St. N. ☎ 320-253-9290 ⏰ -Sat 8:30-9, Sun 10-6
- organic produce • vegetarian friendly • deli • tables • self-service • take-out • co-op

🚗 **From I-94**, take exit 167B for St Cloud/Kimbell onto MN 15N about 5¼ miles to 8th St N. Turn right onto 8th about 1 mile to store on right in shopping plaza.

ST. PAUL

Hampden Park Food Co-op 🛍
928 Raymond Ave. ☎ 651-646-6686 ⏰ M-F 9-9, Sat 9-7, Sun 10-7
- organic produce • vegetarian friendly • deli • bakery • take-out • co-op

🚗 **From I-94**, take exit 236 and follow signs for University Dr to merge onto Cromwell Ave. Turn right onto Franklin Ave and right onto University 1 block to Raymond Ave. Turn left onto Raymond under ¼ mile to store on right at Hampden Ave.

Mississippi Market 🛍 ♿
622 Selby Ave. ☎ 651-310-9499 ⏰ Daily 8:30-9:30
- organic produce • vegetarian friendly • fresh juice • deli • take-out • co-op

🚗 **From I-94**, take exit 240 south on Dale St about ⅓ mile to store on SW corner at Selby Ave.

Mississippi Market Natural Foods Co-op 🛍 ♿
1810 Randolph Ave. ☎ 651-690-0507 ⏰ Daily 8:30-9
- organic produce • co-op

🚗 **From I-94**, take exit 238 south on Snelling Ave (MN 51S) about 1⅔ miles to Randolph Ave. Turn right onto Randolph 4 blocks store on SE corner at Fairview Ave. **From I-35E**, take exit 104A west on Randolph over 1½ miles to store.

Pizza Luce 🍴
1183 Selby Ave. ☎ 651-288-0186 ⏰ Daily 11am-1am
See Duluth location for description.
- vegetarian friendly • vegan friendly • alcohol • tables • self-service • wait staff • take-out

🚗 **From I-94**, take exit 239B south on Lexington Pkwy N (right from I-94E, left from I-94W) under ½ mile to Selby Ave. Turn right onto Selby to restaurant on right after Dunlap St.

Whole Foods Market 🛍 🍴
30 S. Fairview Ave. ☎ 651-690-0197 ⏰ Daily 8-10
- organic produce • vegetarian friendly • salad bar • cafe • self-service • take-out

🚗 **From I-94**, exit 238 south on Snelling Ave (MN 51S) ¾ mile to Grand Ave. Turn right onto Grand ½ mile to store on at Fairview Ave.

ST. PETER

St. Peter Food Co-op 🛍 🍴

119 W. Broadway Ave. ✆ 507-934-4880 ⏱ Daily 8-8
• organic produce • vegetarian friendly • deli • tables • self-service • take-out • co-op
🍂 **From US 169**, go east on W Broadway Ave to store just off hwy.

STILLWATER

River Market Community Co-op 🛍 🍴

221 Main St. ✆ 651-439-0366
M-F 9-9, Sat 9-8, Sun 9-7
• vegetarian friendly • deli • tables • self-service • take-out • co-op
🍂 **From I-694**, take exit 52B east on MN 36 about 10 miles to Stillwater. Store is on 36/95 (aka Main St) at Commercial Ave.

VIRGINIA

Natural Harvest Whole Food Co-op 🛍 🍴

505 3rd St. N. ✆ 218-741-4663 ⏱ M-F 8-8, Sat 10-5, Sun 10-3
• vegetarian friendly • deli • tables • self-service • take-out • co-op
🍂 **From intersection Hwy 169 & 53**, take 53N (ramp on left), turn right onto 9th St N past hospital to 6th Ave. Turn right onto 6th to 2nd St N. Turn left onto 2nd and drive around onto N 3rd St to store (log cabin on lake). **From 53S,** turn left onto 9th St and follow directions above. **From 53N**, take 2nd Ave exit almost 1 mile to Chestnut St. Turn left onto Chestnut to 5th Ave. Turn right onto 5th to end. Turn left onto N 3rd St to store.

WADENA

Down Home Foods 🛍 ♿

636 N. Jefferson St. ✆ 218-631-2323 ⏱M-F 9-5:30, Sat 9-2:30
Store specializes in cheese.
🍂 **From US 10 & US 71 intersection**, store is under ½ mile north on Hwy 71N (N Jefferson St) on east side.

WILLMAR

Kandi Cupboard Food Co-op 🛍

412 Litchfield Ave. S.W. ✆ 320-235-9477 ⏱ M-F 9-6, Sat 9-3
• organic produce • co-op
🍂 **From US12 & MN 23/71 intersection**, take US12 west ⅓ mile to 5th St NW. Turn south (left) onto 5th 2 blocks and left onto Litchfield Ave to store on left.

WINDOM

Plum Creek Food Co-op 🛍 ♿

910 4th Ave. ✆ 507-831-1882 ⏱ M-F 9:30-5, Sat 10-2
🍂 **From US 71 (2nd Ave)**, go west on 9th St 2 blocks to 4th Ave. Turn right onto 4th to store on right.

WINONA

Bluff Country Co-op 🛍 🍴 ♿

121 W. 2nd St. ✆ 507-452-1815 ⏱ M-F 8-8, Sun 9-5
• organic produce • vegetarian friendly • deli • tables • self-service • take-out
🍂 **From US 61**, turn north onto Huff St toward Mississippi River (left from 61S, right from 61N) about 1⅓ miles to light at 2nd St. Turn right onto 2nd 3 blocks to store on right.

1. Biloxi
2. Clinton
3. Jackson
4. Long Beach
5. Ocean Springs
6. Picayune

BILOXI

Infinity Health Center 🛍
14501 LeMoyne Blvd. ✆ 228-392-9535 ⏱ M-F 8-6
🚗 **From I-10**, take exit 50 for Hwy 609S south on Washington Ave (right from I-10E, left from I-10W) about ¾ mile to Solomon St. Turn right onto Solomon about ¼ mile to LeMoyne Blvd. Turn right onto LeMoyne about ½ mile to store on left.

CLINTON

The Sesame Seed 🛍
505D Springridge Rd. ✆ 601-924-1012 ⏱ M-F 9:30-6, Sat 9:30-1
🚗 **From I-20**, take exit 36 south on Springridge Rd (right from I-20E, left from I-20 W) about 3 blocks past hwy to store on left.

JACKSON

Best of Health 🛍 🍴
4500 Highland Village, Ste. 235 ✆ 601-981-2838 ⏱ M-Sat. 10-6
• organic produce • vegetarian friendly • deli • tables • self-service • take-out
🚗 **From I-55**, take exit 100 east on Northside Dr (left from I-55S, right from I-55N) to first entrance on right into Highland Village Shopping Ctr. Store is on second level at south end.

Rainbow Wholefoods Cooperative Grocery 🛍 🍴　　　　　♿

2807 Old Canton Rd. ℂ 601-366-1602⊕ M-Sat 9-7, Sun 12-6 Cafe M-Sat 11:30-2
Home of High Noon cafe serving vegan food with the option to add cheese.
　• organic produce • vegetarian friendly • vegan friendly • organic focus • fresh juice •
　salad bar • cafe • deli • bakery • counter • tables • wait staff • take-out

🚘 **From I-55**, take exit 98B (98C from I-55N) west on Lakeland Dr about ½ mile
to store where it dead ends at Old Canton Rd.

LONG BEACH

Lily of the Valley Health Foods 🛍 🍴　　　　　　♿

5130 Beatline Rd. ℂ 228-865-0071 ⊕ Store M-F, Sun 9-5:30 Restaurant Tues-F, Sun
10-3
　• organic produce • vegetarian • vegan friendly • bakery • tables • wait staff

🚘 **From I-10**, take exit 28 south toward Long Beach on Beatline Rd/County Farm
Rd (right from I-10 W, left from I-10E) 3¾ miles to store on left. **From Beach Blvd**,
go north on White Harbor Rd ½ mile to W Railroad St. Turn left onto W Railroad
1 block and right onto Beatline 1¾ miles to s tore on right after Pineville Rd.

OCEAN SPRINGS

Five Seasons Whole Foods Market 🛍

601 Washington Ave. ℂ 228-875-8882 ⊕ M-Sat 9:30-5:30
🚘 **From I-10**, take exit 50 south on Washington Ave (left from I-10W, right from
I-10E) over 3 miles (past Hwy 90) to store on right.

PICAYUNE

Whole Health Connection 🛍

221 Williams Ave. ℂ 601-749-9831 ⊕ Tues-F 7-7, Sat 9-5
　• organic produce

🚘 **From I-59**, take exit 4 toward Picayune west on Memorial Blvd (right from
I-59S, left from I-59N) about 1 mile to MS 11/43. Turn right onto 11/43 about ½
mile to E Canal St. Turn left onto E Canal 1 block to N Main St. Turn right onto N
Main 1 block to Williams Ave. Turn left onto Williams 1 block to store on left.

MISSOURI

1. Ava
2. Bolivar
3. Bourbon
4. Branson
5. Cape Girardeau
6. Columbia
7. Creve Coeur
8. Fenton
9. Independence
10. Jefferson City
11. Kansas City
12. Liberty
13. Maplewood
14. Monett
15. Mountain View
16. Patton Junction
17. Springfield
18. St. Louis
19. St. Peters
20. Versailles
21. Webster Groves

AVA

Jean's Healthway 🛍️
133 S. Jefferson ✆ 417-683-3026 ⏰ M-F 9-6, Sat 9-5
• organic produce
🏠 MO 14, 5 & 76 all converge in Ava. Store is on 5 (N Jefferson St) at Washington Ave.

BOLIVAR

New Life Natural Food Store 🛍️
451 S. Springfield Ave. # B ✆ 417-326-5701 ⏰ M-Th 9-5, F 9-6, Sat 10-5
🏠 **From MO 13 & 32 intersection,** go east on MO 32 2 miles to S Springfield Ave.
Turn right onto S Springfield under ¼ mile to store on right after Walnut St.

BOURBON

CDR Naturals 🛍️
363 E. Pine St. ✆ 573-732-5900 ⏰ M 10-6, Tues-F 10-5, Sat 10-2
🏠 **From I-44,** take exit 218 toward Bourbon onto Hwy C/W Pine St (left from
I-44W, right from I-44E) under 1/2 mile to store on right.

BRANSON

Nature's Sunshine Health Foods 🛍️
1129 W. 76 Country Blvd. ✆ 417-335-4372 ⏰ M-F 9-6, Sat 9-5
🏠 **From US 65,** take State Hwy 76 exit toward Branson west on Hwy 76/W Main St
about ½ mile to store on left after W Main turns left and becomes Country Music Blvd.

CAPE GIRARDEAU

Natural Health Organic Foods 🛍

135 S. Broadview St. ✆ 573-339-0054 ⏰ M-F 10-7, Sat 10-6
• organic produce

🚗 **From I-55,** take exit 96 toward Cape Girardeau east on Williams St (left from I-55S, right from I-55N) under 1½ miles to S Broadview St. Turn left to store on left.

COLUMBIA

Clovers Natural Food 🛍

2012 E. Broadway ✆ 573-449-1650 ⏰ M-Sat 9-9, Sun 12-6
• organic produce

🚗 **From I-70,** take exit 128 toward US 63 onto Old US 63 continuing onto 63S about ¾ mile to MO WW/Broadway exit. Turn right onto Broadway about ¾ mile to store on left in Eastgate Shopping Ctr.

Main Squeeze Natural Foods Cafe & Juice Bar 🍴   ♿

28 S. Ninth St. ✆ 573-817-5616 ⏰ M-Sat 10-8, Sun 10-3
• vegetarian • vegan friendly • organic focus • fresh juice • counter • table • self-service

🚗 **From I-70**, take exit 128A toward US 63 onto Old US 63 continuing onto 63S about ¾ mile to MO WW/Broadway St exit. Turn right onto Broadway about 1 3/4 miles to 9th St. Turn left onto 9th 1 block to store on left (before Cherry St).

CREVE COEUR

The Natural Way Health Food & Vitamin Center 🛍   ♿

12345 Olive Blvd. ✆ 314-878-3001 ⏰ M-F 9:30-8, Sat 9:30-6:30, Sun 12-5
• organic produce • vegetarian • fresh juice • tables • self-service • take-out

🚗 **From I-270**, take exit 14 west on Olive Ave 2 blocks to store on right (blue awning).

FENTON

The Natural Way Health Food & Vitamin Center 🛍   ♿

468 Old Smizer Mill Rd. ✆ 636-343-4343 ⏰ M-F 9-9, Sat 9-7, Sun 10-6

🚗 **From I-44**, take exit 272 onto Rt 141S about 3½ miles to store on SW corner at Rt 30. **From I-270**, take exit 3 west on Rt 30 about 2¾ miles to store at Rt 141.

INDEPENDENCE

Nature's Pantry 🛍

19019 E. 48th St. S. ✆ 816-478-1990 ⏰ M-Sat 8-8
• organic produce • vegetarian friendly • deli • take-out

🚗 **From I-470**, take exit 16A east on US 40 (left from I-470S, right from I-470N) about ¼ mile to E 48th St. Turn right onto E 48th to store on left.

JEFFERSON CITY

JC Health Food Services 🛍

1406A Missouri Blvd. ✆ 573-636-9889 ⏰ M-F 9-6, Sat 9-3
Modest produce selection.

🚗 **From US 54/50 intersection**, store is 2 blocks south on US54 and under ½ mile west on Missouri Blvd on north side.

KANSAS CITY

Blue Bird Bistro 🍴

1700 Summit St. ✆ 816-221-7559 ⏰ -Sat 7am-10pm, Sun 10-2
• vegetarian friendly • vegan friendly • organic focus • alcohol • tables • wait staff • take-out

🚗 **From I-670**, merge onto I-35S. **From I-35S**, take exit 1D right onto 20th St 1 block to Summit St. Turn right onto Summit 2 blocks to restaurant on left at W 17th St. **From I-35N**, take exit 1 C left onto W 21st St 1 block to Summit. Turn right onto Summit 3 blocks to restaurant.

Cafe Seed 🍴

2932 Cherry St. © 816-561-7333 ① Tues-W 11-3, Th-F 11-3, 5-9, Sat 10-3, 5-9, Sun 10-3
• vegan • organic focus • fresh juice • tables • self-service

🍎 **From I-35S**, take exit 1B on left for 27th St toward Broadway right onto Penn Valley Dr continuing on Broadway ½ mile to W 31st St. Turn left onto W 31st about ¾ mile to Cherry St. Turn left onto Cherry 1 block to restaurant on left after 30th St. **From I-35N**, take exit 234 right onto S 7th St ⅓ mile to Southwest Blvd. Turn left onto Southwest ½ mile to W 31st. Turn right onto W 31st about 1½ miles to Cherry. Turn left onto Cherry 1 block to restaurant.

Eden Alley 🍴   ♿ 📧

707 W. 47th St. © 816-561-5415 ① M-Tues 11-2:30, Wed-Sat 11-9
• vegetarian • vegan friendly • organic focus • fresh juice • tables • wait staff

🍎 **From I-35S**, take exit 1A onto Southwest Tfwy (becomes Belleview Ave) about 2½ miles to 47th St. Turn left onto 47th 3 blocks to restaurant on plaza at corner of Jefferson St in Unity Temple basement. **From I-70**, take 35S and follow directions above. **From I-35N**, take exit 228B onto Shawnee Mission Pkwy/56E 6¼ miles (across MO/KS state line) to 47th St. Turn right onto 47th 2 blocks to restaurant.

Green Acres 🛍 🍴

4175 N. Mulberry Drive © 816-746-0010 ① M-Sat 8-9, Sun 10-7
• organic produce • vegetarian friendly • fresh juice • salad bar • cafe • deli • bakery • tables • self-service • take-out

🍎 **From I-29,** merge onto US 169S. **From US 169**, take the Briarcliff Pkwy exit onto NW Briarcliff (right from US 169S, left from US 169N) and right onto N Mulberry Dr to store on right in Briarcliff Village.

Wild Oats Market 🛍

4301 Main St. © 816-931-1873 ① M-F 8-9, Sat-Sun 8-8
• organic produce

🍎 **From I-35S**, take exit 1B south on Broadway about 2 miles to 43rd St. Turn left onto 43rd 1 block to store at Main St. **From I-70**, take I-35S and follow directions above.

LIBERTY

Mother Nature's Health Market 🛍

344 S. 291 Hwy. © 816-415-4638 ① M-Sat 10-8, Sun 12-4
• organic produce

🍎 **From I-35**, take exit 16 onto Hwy 152E into Liberty about ½ mile to fourth light at Hwy 291. Turn right onto 291 to store on right in Crossroads Shopping Ctr.

MAPLEWOOD

Schlafly Bottleworks 🍴

7260 Southwest Ave. © 314-241-BEER ① M-Tues, Sun 11-9, W-Th 11-10, F-Sat 11-11
Brew pub with vegetarian selections and an interesting red quinoa/black barley/kamut mix.
• vegetarian friendly • alcohol • tables • wait staff

🍎 **From I-44E**, take exit 284A left onto Jamieson Ave ⅓ mile to Arsenal St. Turn left onto Arsenal across tracks to first right onto McCausland Ave, first left onto Southwest Ave and 3 blocks to restaurant on left before Manchester Ave. **From I-44W**, take exit 285 onto Southwest 1 mile to restaurant on left. **From I-64E**, take exit 33C right onto Bellevue Ave 1 mile to Southwest (after Manchester). Turn right onto Southwest to restaurant on left. **From I-64W**, take exit 33D right onto McCausland 1¼ miles to Southwest. Turn right onto Southwest about 3 blocks to restaurant on left.

MONETT

Herb Depot 🛍

600 Bridle Lane © 417-235-5500 ① M-F 9:30-6, Sat 10-4
• organic produce

🍎 On the south side of Hwy 60 at Bridle Ln behind Wal-Mart.

MOUNTAIN VIEW

Sunshine Market Natural Foods 🛍️

208 W. 1st St. ✆ 417-934-6956 ⏱ M-F 9-5:30, Sat 9-3
• organic produce

🚗 **From US 60 & MO 17 intersection**, go south on 17 (N Elm St) ½ mile and turn right onto W 1st St to store on right.

PATTON JUNCTION

Green's Garden 🛍️

Junction Hwy. 72 & Hwy. 51 ✆ 573-866-2204 ⏱ M-Sat 8:30-6
Local produce in season. Grains gound onsite for the baked goods.
• organic produce • bakery

🛍️ Store is at intersection of MO 72 & 51.

SPRINGFIELD

Akin's Natural Foods Market 🛍️   ♿

1344 E. Battlefield Rd. ✆ 417-887-5985 ⏱ Daily 8-8
• organic produce

🚗 **From I-44**, take exit 72 east on Chestnut Expwy about 3½ miles to Rt 13/Kansas Expwy. Turn right onto Rt 13 about 3½ miles to Battlefield Rd. Turn left onto Battlefield about 2⅓ miles to store in Fremont Shopping Ctr.

Mamma Jean's 🛍️ 🍴

1727 S. Campbell Ave. ✆417-831-5229 ⏱ M-F 9-8, Sat 10-7, Sun 11-6
• organic produce • vegetarian friendly • deli • tables • self-service • take-out

🍴 **From I-44E**, take exit 77 toward Kansas City right onto N Kansas Expwy 4¾ miles to W Sunshine St. Turn left onto Sunshine 1⅓ miles to S Campbell Ave. Turn right onto S Campbell to store on left. **From I-44W,** take exit 82A onto 65S almost 5 miles to Sunshine St exit. Turn right onto Sunshine almost 4 miles to S Campbell. Turn right onto S Campbell to store.

Spring Valley Herbs & Natural Foods 🛍️

1738 S. Glenstone Ave. ✆ 417-882-1033 ⏱ M-F 10-8 Sat 10-6, Sun 12-6
🍴 **From I-44E**, take exit 80A south on N Gladstone Ave about 4½ miles to store on left at Sunshine St. From I-44W, take exit 82A onto 65S almost 5 miles to Sunshine St exit. Turn right onto Sunshine 2 miles to S Gladstone. Turn right onto Gladstone to store on right.

ST. LOUIS

Golden Grocer 🛍️ 🍴

335 N. Euclid Ave. ✆ 314-367-0405 ⏱ M-F 9-7, Sat 10-7, Sun 12-5
• organic produce • vegetarian • deli • tables • self-service • take-out

🚗 **From I-70**, take exit 244 south on N Kingshwy Blvd almost 3 miles to Maryland Ave. Turn left onto Maryland 1 block to Euclid Ave. Turn left onto Euclid to store on left (set back from road). **From I-44,** take exit 287A north on S Kingshwy over 1½ miles to Maryland. Turn right onto Maryland and left onto Euclid to store. **From I-64 (US 40)**, take exit 36B north on S Kingshwy to Maryland and follow directions above.

Govinda's Vegetarian Restaurant 🍴

3926 Lindell Blvd. ✆ 314-535-8085 ⏱ M-F 11:30-2:30, 5-8:30, Sun around 7pm
Lunch buffet in the Hare Krishna temple. Free Sunday dinner after the 5 pm program.
• vegetarian • vegan friendly • tables • self-service

🍴 **From I-64E (US 40)**, take exit 36D left onto Vandeventer Ave about ¾ mile to Lindell Blvd. Turn right onto Lindell to restaurant in Hare Krishna temple (next to St Louis U). **From I-64W**, take exit 38A onto Forest Park Blvd ¼ mile to S Grand Blvd. Turn right onto Grand about ¼ mile to Lindell. Turn left onto Lindell about ½ mile to restaurant.

Kaldi's Coffee House & Market Bakery ⅋🍴

700 De Mun Ave. ✆ 314-727-9955 ⏲ M-Sat 7am-11pm, Sun 7-9
• vegetarian • bakery • tables • self-service • take-out

🚌 **From I-64E (US 40E),** take exit 33D north on Skinker Blvd about ¼ mile to light at Rosebury Ave. Turn left onto Rosebury to end at De Mun Ave. Turn right onto De Mun to restaurant at end. **From I-64W (US 40W),** take exit 34B right onto Skinker and follow directions above.

Sappington International Farmers Market 🛍

8400 Watson Rd. ✆ 314-843-7848 ⏲ M-Sat 7-10, Sun 7-8
• organic produce

🚌 **From I-44,** take exit 280 south on S Elm St (right from I-44E, left from I-44W) 1 mile to Watson Rd. Turn left onto Watson about ⅓ mile to store on right in General Grant Plaza.

Schlafly Taproom 🍴

2100 Locust St. ✆ 314-241-BEER ⏲ M-Tues, Sun 11-9, W-Th 11-10, F-Sat 11-12
Brew pub with vegetarian options.
• vegetarian friendly • alcohol • tables • wait staff

🚌 **From I-64E,** take exit 38C left onto S Jefferson Ave ½ mile to Locust St. Turn right onto Locust 3 blocks to restaurant on right at 21st St. **From I-64W,** take exit 39A left onto Market St 1 block to N 23rd St. Turn right onto N 23rd about 3 blocks to Locust. Turn right onto Locust 2 blocks to restaurant.

Whole Foods Market 🛍🍴   &

1601 S. Brentwood Blvd. ✆ 314-968-7744 ⏲ Daily 8-11
• organic produce • vegetarian friendly • salad bar • cafe • self-service • take-out

🚌 **From I-64/US 40,** take exit 31 (31A from I-64W) right onto Brentwood Blvd to store on right in Brentwood Square.

Whole Foods Market 🛍🍴   &

8823 Ladue Rd. ✆ 314-721-8004 ⏲ Daily 8-10
• organic produce • vegetarian friendly • salad bar • cafe • self-service • take-out

🚌 **From I-170,** take exit 1F east on Ladue Rd past 2 lights to store on right.

ST. PETERS

Nutrition Stop Inc. 🛍

4101 Mexico Rd. ✆ 636-928-7550 ⏲ M-F 9-8, Sat 9-7
• organic produce

🚌 **From I-70,** take exit 225 south (left from I-70W, right from I-70E) onto Cave Springs Rd about ¼ mile to Mexico Rd. Turn right onto Mexico about ⅓ mile (first light) to store on left corner.

VERSAILLES

Nature's Friend 🛍

300 S. Monroe St. ✆ 573-378-2501 ⏲ M-F 9-5
Part of the Healing Arts Center with a spa and health services.

🚌 **From MO 52/MO 5 intersection,** go east on W Newton St ½ mile to W Monroe St. Turn right onto W Monroe almost 4 blocks to store on right in the Healing Arts Ctr.

WEBSTER GROVES

The Natural Way Health Food & Vitamin Center 🛍   &

8110 Big Bend Blvd. ✆ 314-961-3541 ⏲ -F 9-9, Sat 9-7, Sun 10-6
• organic produce

🚌 **From I-44E,** take exit 282 right onto Laclede Station Rd 1 block to Murdock Ave. Turn right onto Murdock to first big intersection (Big Bend Blvd). Turn left onto Big Bend 1 block to store on left (large tomato sign). **From I-44W,** take exit 283 left off ramp onto Shrewsbury Ave 1 block to Big Bend. Turn left onto Big Bend 4 blocks to store.

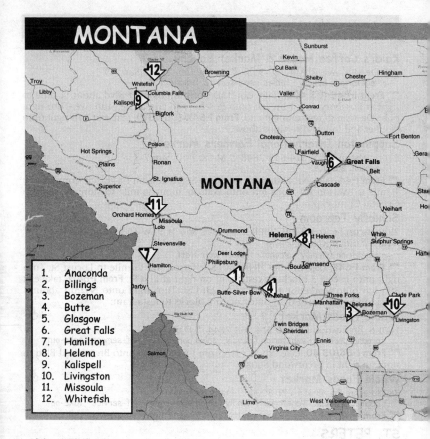

MONTANA

1. Anaconda
2. Billings
3. Bozeman
4. Butte
5. Glasgow
6. Great Falls
7. Hamilton
8. Helena
9. Kalispell
10. Livingston
11. Missoula
12. Whitefish

ANACONDA _____

Heart Rock Market 🍎

321 W. Park Ave. ☏ 406-563-5077 ⏲ Daily 8-8
• organic produce

🍎 Store is on MT 1 (aka W Park Ave) on south side between Locust & Maple Ave.

BILLINGS _____

Bonanza Health Foods 🍎

923 Grand Ave. ☏ 406-252-4923 ⏲ M-F 9-6, Sat 9-5

🚗 **From I-90E,** take exit 446 left at fork onto 90 Access/Laurel Rd almost 1½ miles to Moore Ln. Turn left onto Moore ½ mile to Central Ave. Turn right onto Central 1 block to 10th St W. Turn left onto 10th 1 mile to Grand Ave. Turn right onto Grand 1 block to store on left. **From I-90W,** take exit 450 right onto S 27th St 1⅓ miles to 1st Ave N. Turn left onto 1st 4 blocks to N 31st St. Turn right onto N 31st 4 blocks to 6th Ave N. Turn left onto 6th and veer right onto Grand about 1¼ miles to store on right after 9th St W.

Good Earth Market 🍎 🍴

3024 2nd Ave. N. ☏ 406-259-2622 ⏲ M-Sat 8-8, Sun 10-6
• organic produce • vegetarian friendly • deli • tables • self-service • take-out • co-op

🚗 **From I-90/94,** take exit 450 (MT 3) towards City Center onto 27th St (right from I-90W, left from I-90E) about 2 miles to 10th Ave N. Turn left onto 10th 4½ blocks to store between 31st & 32nd St.

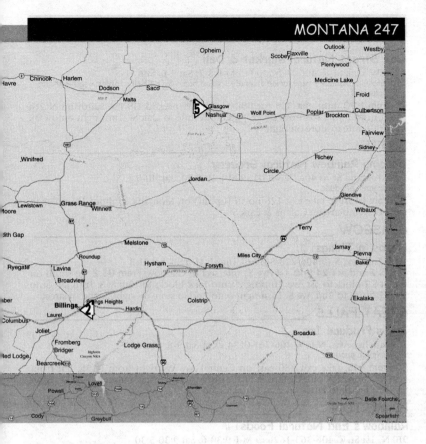

Mary's Health Foods 🛍️

2564 King Ave. W., Ste. J ✆ 406-651-0557 ⏰ M-F 9-8, Sat 9-6
• organic produce

🚗 **From I-90**, take exit 446 west on King Ave (right fork and left from I-90E, right from I-90W) about 1¼ miles to store on left between S 24th St & S 29th St W.

BOZEMAN

Community Food Co-op 🛍️ 🍴   ♿

908 W. Main St. ✆ 406-587-4039 ⏰ Daily 7-10 Deli 8-8
• organic produce • vegetarian friendly • juice bar • salad bar • cafe • deli • bakery •
counter • tables • self-service • take-out • co-op

🚗 **From I-90**, take exit 306 south on N 7th Ave (right from I-90E, right then immediately left from I-90W) about 1⅓ miles to Main St. Turn right onto Main 2 blocks to store at 9th Ave (big, funky barn).

Montana Harvest Natural Foods 🛍️

31 S. Willson Ave. ✆ 406-585-3777 ⏰ M-F 9-8, Sat 9-7, Sun 10-6

🚗 **From I-90**, take exit 309 for Main St/US-191 towards Bozeman right onto E Main 1½ miles to Willson Ave. Turn left onto Willson to store on right.

Oak Street Natural Market & Deli 🛍️ 🍴

1735 W. Oak St. ✆ 406-582-5400 ⏰ M-F 8-7, Sat 9-6, Sun 11-5
  • organic produce • vegetarian friendly • salad bar • cafe • deli • tables • self-service
  • take-out

🍎 **From I-90**, take exit 306 for I-90/N 7th Ave toward US-191 south on N 7th (right from I-90E, left from I-90W) about ¼ mile to Oak St. Turn right onto Oak about ½ mile to store on right.

BUTTE

Dancing Rainbow Natural Grocery 🛍️   ♿

9 S. Montana St. ✆ 406-723-8811 ⏰ M-F 10-5:30, Sat. 10-5
  • organic produce

🍎 **From I-15/90**, take exit 126 north (uphill) on Montana St about 1½ miles to store on left between Galena & Park St.

GLASGOW

Herbs 'n Things 🛍️

1102 2nd Ave. S. ✆ 406-228-8617 ⏰ Tues-F 11-5:30, Sat 11-3

🍎 US 2 and MT 24 (aka 1st Ave S) intersect in Glasgow. **From US 2**, go south on 6th St S 1 block to 1st Ave. Turn right onto 1st 4 blocks to 10th St S. Turn left onto 10th 1 block to 2nd Ave S. Turn right onto 2nd to store on right at end of street.

GREAT FALLS

2-J's Produce Inc. 🛍️

105 Smelter Ave., N.E. ✆ 406-761-0134 ⏰ M-Sat 9-8, Sun 10-7
  • organic produce

🍎 **From I-15**, take exit 280 east on Central Ave W (right from I-15E, left from I-15W) about 1¼ miles to 3rd St NW. Turn left onto 3rd about 1 mile to Division St. Turn left onto Division ⅓ mile to store at Smelter Ave.

HAMILTON

Rainbow's End Natural Foods 🛍️

910 N. 1st St. ✆ 406-363-1626 ⏰ M-F 9:30-6, Sat 9:30-5:30
  • organic produce

🍎 US 93 runs through Hamilton. Store is on 93 (aka 1st St) on west side at Adirondac Ave.

HELENA

No Sweat Cafe 🍴

427 N. Last Chance Gulch ✆ 406-442-6954 ⏰ Tues-F 7-2, Sat-Sun 8-2
Wholesome breakfasts, organic grains, locally-grown produce and naturally-raised meat.
  • vegetarian friendly • organic focus • counter • tables • wait staff • take-out

🍎 **From I-15**, take exit 192 west on Prospect Ave about 1½ miles to Montana Ave. Turn left onto Montana to 11th Ave. Turn right onto 11th almost 1 mile to downtown. When 11th ends, turn left onto Last Chance Gulch 2 blocks to restaurant on left.

Real Food Market & Deli 🛍️ 🍴   ♿

1096 Helena Ave. ✆ 406-443-5150 ⏰ M-Sat 8-8, Sun 9-7
  • organic produce • vegetarian friendly • salad bar • deli • tables • self-service • take-out

🍎 **From I-15**, take exit 192 (192B from I-15N) towards Capitol Area onto Hwy 12W almost 2 miles to Boulder Ave. Turn left onto Boulder 1 block to stop sign at Helena Ave. Turn left onto Helena to store on right in Hustad Ctr. **From Hwy 12E**, turn right onto National Ave (about 1 mile past Main St) to store.

KALISPELL

Mountain Valley Foods 🛍
25 Commons Way ✆ 406-756-1422 ⏱ M-Sat 7-7, Sun 10-4
• organic produce

🛒 **From US 93/US 2 intersection**, go north on US 93 1½ miles to Commons Loop. Turn right onto Commons Loop and left onto Commons Way to store on right.

Withey's Health Foods 🛍
1231 S. Main St. ✆ 406-755-5260 ⏱ M-Sat 9-6

🛒 **From US 93/US 2 intersection,** go south on US 93 (aka Main St) 1 mile to store on left between 11th & 12th St.

LIVINGSTON

Food Works Natural Market 🛍
412 E. Park St. ✆ 406-222-8223 ⏱ M-F 9-7, Sat 9-6, Sun 12-5
• organic produce

🛒 **From I-90**, take exit 333 for US 89 S right onto W Park St over 1½ miles to store on right at N D St.

MISSOULA

Good Food Store 🛍 🍴
1600 S. 3rd St. W. ✆ 406-541-3663 ⏱ Daily 7-10
• organic produce • vegetarian friendly • deli • tables • self-service • take-out

🛒 **From I-90**, take exit 104 south on Orange St 2 miles to S 3rd St W. Turn right onto S 3rd under 1 mile to store on right between S Russell & S Caitlin St.

WHITEFISH

Third Street Market 🛍
244 Spokane Ave. ✆ 406-862-5054 ⏱ M-Sat 8:30-7
• organic produce

🛒 Take Hwy 93 to Whitefish. Store is on corner of 93 & 3rd St.

NEBRASKA

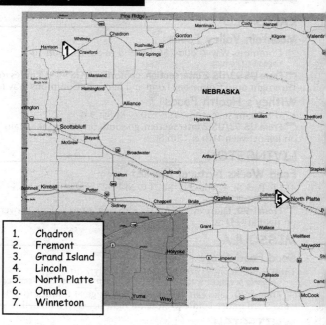

1. Chadron
2. Fremont
3. Grand Island
4. Lincoln
5. North Platte
6. Omaha
7. Winnetoon

CHADRON

Chadron Natural Food Co-op
248 Main St. ✆ 308-432-6595 ⏰ M-F 9:30-5:30, Sat 9:30-3:30
· organic produce · co-op
🏪 **From US 20 (aka 3rd St)**, go north on Main St (left from US 20E, right from US 20W) 1 block to store on east side.

FREMONT

Harvest Health and Coffee
419 N. Main St. ✆ 402-721-7031 ⏰ M-F 8-5:30, Sat 9-3
🏪 **From US 77 (Broad St)**, go east on W 6th St (right from US 77N, left from US 77S) 2 blocks to N Main St. Turn right onto N Main 2 blocks to store on right before 4th St.

GRAND ISLAND

Natural Food Products
707 W. State St. ✆ 308-382-0869 ⏰ M-W, F 9-5:30, Th 9-7, Sat 10-4
🏪 **From I-80**, take exit 312 toward Grand Island onto US 281N over 8 miles to State St. Turn right onto State 1⅓ miles to store on right after Broadwell Ave.

LINCOLN

Akin's Natural Foods Market   ♿
6900 "O" St., Ste. 100 ✆ 402-466-5713 ⏰ Daily 9-9
· organic produce
🏪 **From I-80**, take exit 409 west on Cornhusker Hwy/Hwy 6W about 2½ miles to N 84th St. Turn left onto 84th about 4¼ miles to O St. Turn right onto O 1 mile to store on right in Meridian Park Shopping Ctr.

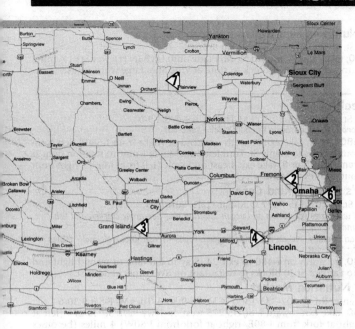

Maggie's ⚐

311 N. 8th St. ✆ 402-477-3959 ⏱ M-F 8-3, Sat 10-3

Vegetarian soups, wraps, daily specials and organic vegan baked goods.

• vegetarian • vegan friendly • fresh juice • tables • self-service • take-out

🍎 **From I-80W**, take exit 401 toward Downtown/9th St and follow ramps onto US 34E about 3½ miles continuing onto 9th St to Q St. Turn right onto Q 1 block to 8th St. Turn right onto 8th to restaurant. **From I-80E**, take exit 397 onto US 77S (Salt Valley Rd) 1⅓ miles to Capitol Pkwy. Turn left onto Capitol (becomes K St) 2 miles to 10th St. Turn left onto 10th ½ mile to Q. Turn left onto Q 2 bocks to 8th. Turn right onto 8th to restaurant.

Open Harvest Natural Foods ⚐ ⚐

1618 South St. ✆ 402-475-9069 ⏱ Daily 8-9

• organic produce • vegetarian friendly • deli • bakery • tables • self-service • take-out • co-op

🍎 **From I-80W**, take exit 401 toward Downtown/9th St and follow ramps onto US 34E about 3½ miles continuing onto 9th St about 1½ miles (through downtown) to South St (next major intersection after A St). Turn left onto South 8 blocks to 17th St. Turn left onto 17th and left to store in South St Mall. **From I-80E**, take exit 397 onto US 77S (Salt Valley Rd) 2½ miles to NE 2E (Van Dorn Rd). Take 2E to 10th St. Turn left onto 10th St about 5 blocks to South. Turn right onto South 6 blocks to store.

NORTH PLATTE _____

Happy Heart Specialty Foods ⚐

301 S. Jeffers St. ✆ 308-532-1505 ⏱ M-F 10-5:30, Sat 10-5

• organic produce

🍎 **From I-80**, take exit 177 toward North Platte onto US 83N (Dewey St) 1¼ miles to C St. Turn left onto C 1 block to store at Jeffers St.

Natural Nutrition House 🛍️
203 W. 6th St. ☎ 308-532-9433 ⏰ M-Sat 9-5:30
🚗 **From I-80**, take exit 177 toward North Platte onto US 83N (Dewey St) 1¾ miles to 6th St. Turn left onto 6th 1 block to store at Vine St in large white house.

OMAHA

Jane's Health Food 🛍️
6103 Maple St. ☎ 402-558-8911 ⏰ M-Th 9-7, F 9-6, Sat 9-5
• organic produce • vegetarian friendly • deli • take-out
🚗 **From I-680E or W**, take exit 9 south on 72nd St (right from I-680E, left from I-680W) about 4 miles to Maple St. Turn left onto Maple 1 mile to store on right at N 61st St. **From I-680N or S**, take exit 4 east on Maple (left from I-680S, right from I-680N) about 4 miles to store.

McFoster's Natural Kind Cafe 🍴   ♿
302 S. 38th St. ☎ 402-345-7477 ⏰ M-Sat 11-11, Sun 10-3
Natural foods with huge vegetarian and vegan selection plus free-range chicken and fish. Vegetarian Sunday brunch.
• vegetarian friendly • vegan friendly • organic focus • fresh juice • alcohol • tables • wait staff • take-out
🚗 **From I-80**, go north on I-480 to exit 2A. Stay in left lane to second light and turn left onto Farnam St 10 blocks to restaurant on SW corner at 38th St.

No Name Nutrition Market 🛍️
14469 W. Center Rd. ☎ 402-333-1300 ⏰ M, Th 9:30-8, Tues-W, F-Sat 9:30-6
🚗 **From I-80**, take exit toward L St/US 275 west on Hwy 92/L St/US 275 (left at fork then right at fork from I-80E, right at fork from I-80W) 4 miles (becomes Industrial Rd) to W Center Rd. Turn right onto W Center about ¾ miles to store before S 14th St.

No Name Nutrition Market 🛍️
2032 N. 72nd St. ☎ 402-393-5813 ⏰ M 9:30-8, Tues-Sat 9:30-6
• organic produce
🚗 **From I-80**, take exit 449 north on 72nd St (left from I-80E, right from I-80 W) about 4 miles to store on left after Blondo St.

Whole Foods Market 🛍️ 🍴
10020 Regency Circle ☎ 402-393-1200 ⏰ Daily 8-9
• organic produce • vegetarian friendly • salad bar • cafe • self-service • take-out
🚗 **From I-680**, take exit 3 onto US 6E/W Dodge Rd and take Regency Pkwy exit left onto Regency and right onto Regency Cir to store on right.

WINNETOON

Town & Country Natural Foods Store 🛍️
312 Main St. ☎ 402-847-3368 ⏰ M-F 8-4, Sat 8-10
In the Winnetoon Mall, a "Boardwalk Back in Time."
🚗 Winnetoon is 3 miles west of Hwy 13 or 4 miles east of Hwy 14 on SR 59. Store is on SR 59 (Main St in town).

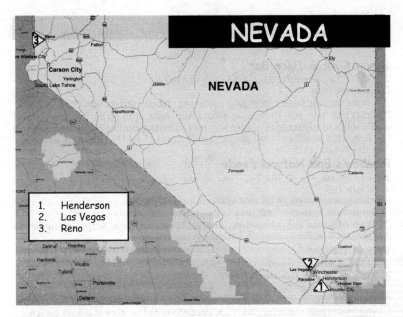

1. Henderson
2. Las Vegas
3. Reno

HENDERSON

Evos Fresh & Healthy 🍴

10895 S. Eastern Ave. © 702-269-1389 ⏰ Daily 11-10
Healthy fast-food concept with soyburgers, veggie patties, whole wheat wraps, organic greens, vegan chili, veggie corn dogs, natural meat, "airfriesTM", smoothies and such.
· vegetarian friendly · tables · self-serve · take-out

🏠 **From I-15N**, take exit 27 toward Henderson onto W Lake Mead Dr/Henderson Cuttoff Rd about 4½ miles to S Eastern Ave. Turn right onto S Eastern over 1 mile to restaurant. **From I-5S**, onto I-215E. **From I-215E**, take exit 7 and follow signs for Eastern Ave S. Merge onto S Eastern about 2½ miles to restaurant. **From I-215W**, take exit 5 and follow signs onto Green Valley Pkwy S 1⅓ miles to W Horizon Ridge Pkwy. Turn right onto W Horizon Ridge almost 1½ miles to S Eastern Ave. Turn left onto S Eastern about ½ mile to restaurant.

Whole Foods Market 🛒 🍴

100 S. Green Valley Pkwy. ©702-361-8183 ⏰ Daily 7-10
· organic produce · vegetarian friendly · salad bar · cafe · self-service · take-out

🏠 **From I-215**, take exit 5 onto Green Valley Pkwy S to store on left just off hwy.

Wilds Oats Market 🛒 🍴   ♿

517 N. Stephanie St. © 702-458-9427 ⏰ Daily 8-9
· organic produce · vegetarian friendly · salad bar · cafe · self-service · take-out

🏠 **From I-515**, take exit 70 toward Henderson/Phoenix south on Boulder Hwy (left from I-515S, right from I-515N) 2 miles to E Flamingo Rd. Turn left onto E Flamingo under 1 mile to Jimmy Durante Blvd. Turn right onto Jimmy Durante ¾ mile to Stephanie St. Turn left onto Stephanie to store.

LAS VEGAS

Goraw Café & Juice Bar 🛒 🍴   ♿

2381 E. Windmill Lane #18 © 702-450-9007 ⏰ M-Sat 8-8, Sun 8-5
Primarily raw foods.
· vegan · organic focus · fresh juice · salad bar · tables · self-service

🏠 **From I-215E**, take exit 8 onto Windmill Ln East ramp. Turn left onto E Windmill under 1 mile to restaurant. **From I-215W**, take exit 7 right onto S Eastern Ave almost 1¼ miles to E Windmill. Turn left onto E Windmill to restaurant.

Goraw Café & Juice Bar 🛍 🍴
2910 Lake East Drive © 702-254-5382 ⏰ M-Sat 9-9
Primarily raw foods.
- • vegan • organic focus • fresh juice • salad bar • tables • self-service

🚗 **From I-15**, take exit 40 west on Sahara Ave (right from I-15S, left from I-15N) over 6 miles to S Durango Dr. Turn left onto S Durango under ½ mile to Starboard Dr. Turn right onto Starboard about ¼ mile to Lake East Dr. Turn right onto Lake East to store in Lakes Ctr.

Rainbow's End Natural Foods 🛍 🍴
1100 E. Sahara Ave. © 702-737-7282 ⏰ M-F 9-8, Sat 10-8, Sun 11-5 Cafe M-Sat 10-5, Sun 11-5
Cafe is vegetarian except for the tuna sandwich.
- • vegetarian friendly • fresh juice • cafe • tables • self-service • take-out

🚗 **From I-15,** take exit 40 toward Convention Ctr/Las Vegas Strip east on Sahara Ave about 1¾ miles to store on left.

Veggie Delight 🍴
3504 Wynn Rd. © 702-310-6565 ⏰ Daily 11-9
Asian vegetarian with Taiwanese, Cantonese and Vietnamese dishes.
- • vegetarian • vegan friendly • tables • wait staff

🚗 **From I-15**, take exit 39 west on Spring Mtn Rd (right from I-15S, right fork from I-15N) ¾-1⅓ miles to Wynn Rd. Turn left onto Wynn to store at corner on left.

Whole Foods Market 🛍 🍴
7250 W. Lake Mead Blvd. © 702-942-1500 ⏰ Daily 8-9
- • organic produce • vegetarian friendly • salad bar • cafe • self-service • take-out

🚗 **From US 95S**, take exit 82 toward Lake Mead Blvd onto Rock Springs Dr to W Lake Mead Blvd. Turn right onto W Lake Mead to store on right. **From 95N**, take exit 82B (Rainbow North) and follow ramp right onto W Lake Mead ½ mile to store. **From I-515 or I-15**, merge onto US 95N and follow directions above.

Whole Foods Market 🛍 🍴
8855 W. Charleston Blvd. © 02-254-8655 ⏰ Daily 7-10
- • organic produce • vegetarian friendly • salad bar • cafe • self-service • take-out

🚗 **From US 95S**, take exit 81 onto Summerlin Pkwy W 2½ miles to Rampart Blvd. Turn left onto N Rampart 1½ miles to W Charleston Blvd. Turn left onto W Charleston 1 block to store on right. **From US 95N** continue onto Summerlin and follow directions above. **From I-15 or I-215**, merge onto US 95N and follow directions above.

RENO

Pneumatics 🍴
501 W. 1st St. © 775-786-8888x106 ⏰ M 12-11, Tues-F 11-11, Sat 9-11, Sun 8-11
- • vegetarian • vegan friendly • alcohol • tables • wait staff

🚗 **From I-80,** take exit 12 south on Keystone Ave (left from I-80W, right from I-80E) about ½ mile to 2nd St. Turn left onto 2nd ⅓ mile to Ralston St. Turn right onto Ralston 1 block to 1st Stß. Restaurant is upstairs in Truckee River Apts.

Whole Foods Market 🛍 🍴
5695 S. Virginia St. © 775-829-8666 ⏰ Daily 8-9
- • organic produce • vegetarian friendly • salad bar • cafe • self-service • take-out

🚗 **From I-80**, take exit 15 onto US 395S about 4⅓ miles to exit 63. Take S Virginia St ramp and turn left onto S Virginia/395 Bus under ½ mile to store.

NEW HAMPSHIRE

1. Amherst
2. Concord
3. Dover
4. Exeter
5. Hampton
6. Hooksett
7. Keene
8. Littleton
9. Manchester
10. Marlborough
11. Meredith
12. Nashua
13. New London
14. Newington
15. North Conway
16. Northwood
17. Peterborough
18. Plaistow
19. Plymouth
20. Portsmouth
21. Salem
22. Wolfeboro

AMHERST

Earthward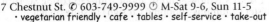

42 Rte. 101A ✆ 603-673-4322 ⏲ M-Sat 9-6, Sun 9-5
• organic produce

Store is in town on north side of 101A (aka Amherst St).

CONCORD

Concord Food Co-op

24½ S. Main St. ✆ 603-225-6840 ⏲ M-Sat 8-8, Sun 10-6
• organic produce • vegetarian friendly • cafe • deli • bakery • tables • self-service • take-out • co-op

From I-93, take exit 13 toward Downtown Concord onto Rt 3N under 1 mile to store on left at Pleasant St.

Granite State Natural Foods

164 N. State St. ✆ 603-224-9341 ⏲ M-F 9-6:30, Sat 9-5, Sun 10-5

From I-93, take exit 15W onto US 202W toward US 3/N Main St about ⅔ mile to Rt 3. Turn right onto 3 (Bouton St, becomes N State) about ½ mile to store across from City Park at Penacook St.

DOVER

Dover Natural Foods & Cafe

7 Chestnut St. ✆ 603-749-9999 ⏲ M-Sat 9-6, Sun 11-5
• vegetarian friendly • cafe • tables • self-service • take-out

From Rt 16 (Spaulding Tpke), take exit 8E onto Rt 9/Silver St to second light (Locust St). Turn left onto Locust past Police Station to fork in road. Bear left onto Chestnut St to store on right (past light and over bridge).

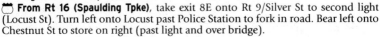

EXETER

The Blue Moon Market • Cafe • Yoga
8 Clifford St. ✆ Store 603-778-6850 Cafe 603-778-2670 ⏰ M-F 8:30-7, Sat 8:30-6
• organic produce • vegetarian friendly • cafe • deli • cafe • tables • self-service • take-out
🍎 **From I-95**, take exit 2 west on Rt 101 about 4 miles to exit 11 toward Exeter. Take Rt 108S about 1½ miles to Pleasant St. Turn right onto Pleasant, left onto String Bridge, left onto Water St (108E) and right onto Clifford St to store on left.

HAMPTON

Hampton Natural Foods   ♿
580 Lafayette Rd. ✆ 603-926-5950 ⏰ M-F 9-6, Sat 9-5, Sun 10-5
Take out soup and salad bar.
• organic produce • salad bar • take-out
🍎 **From I-95**, take exit 2 toward Exeter/Hampton Beach onto Rt 101E about 2½ miles to Rt 1N/Lafayette Rd (exit on left). Take 1N about 1 mile to store on left (under ¼ mile past Exeter Rd/High St intersection).

HOOKSETT

Natural Choice Market
270 Londonderry Tpke. ✆ 603-669-6977 ⏰ M-Sat 9-7:30, Sun 10-5:30
• organic produce
🍎 **From US 93**, take exit 9N onto US3N/Hwy 28N/Hooksett Rd 1½-2 miles to Whitehill Rd. Turn right onto Whitehill ⅓ mile to Londonderry Tpke. Turn right onto Londonderry ⅓ mile to store on right.

KEENE

Blueberry Fields   ♿
49 Emerald St. ✆ 603-358-5207 ⏰ M-F 9-7, Sat 9-5
• organic produce
🍎 **From Rt 101**, turn north onto Main St (left from 101E, right from 101W) about ⅔ mile to Emerald St (second left). Turn left onto Emerald 1 block to store on left.

Country Life Inspired Vegetarian Cuisine
15 Roxbury St. ✆ 603-357-3975 ⏰ Store M-F 9-5 Restaurant M-F 11:30-3, Sun 10-3
Vegan lunch buffet. Part of New England Wellness & Education Center.
• vegan • salad bar • deli • bakery • tables • self-service • take-out
🍎 **From Rt 101**, turn north onto Main St (left from 101E, right from 101W) under 1 mile to light at traffic circle. Turn right onto Roxbury St to store on right.

LITTLETON

Healthy Rhino
106 Main St. ✆ 603-444-2177 ⏰ M-Sat 9-6, Sun 11-4
• organic produce
🍎 **From I-93,** take exit 41 toward Littleton north on Cottage St (right from I-93N, left from I-93S) about ⅔ mile (past hospital) to light at Main St. Turn left onto Main 2 blocks to store on right in Parker's Mktplace.

MANCHESTER

A Market Natural Foods
125 Loring St. ✆ 603-668-8445 ⏰ Daily 9-8
• organic produce
🍎 **From I-293**, take exit 1 onto S Willow St north about 1 mile to Loring St. Turn left onto Loring (Manchester Commons Shopping Ctr sign) to store on left.

Bonne Sante Natural Foods 🛒

425 Mast Rd. ✆ 603-623-1613 ⏰ M-W, F 9:30-5:30, Th 9:30-6, Sat 9:30-4:30

🚗 **From I-293S,** take exit 4 for Hwy 114A toward Manchester left onto Harvells St 2 blocks to S Main St. Turn right onto S Main over ½ mile to Varney St/114A. Turn left onto 114A (becomes Mast Rd) about 1 mile to store on right. **From I-239N,** take exit 4 right onto 2nd St under ¼ mile to Hancock St. Turn left onto Hancock under ¼ mile to Log St. Turn right onto Log and continue on 114A about 1 mile to store.

MARLBOROUGH

Jitter Beans Cafe 🍽

174 Main St. ✆ 603-876-3441 ⏰ M-Th, 7-7, F 7-8, Sat 8-8, Sun 8-7
Soups, sandwiches, wraps, salads and all-day breakfast.
  · vegetarian · vegan friendly · tables · self-service
🍴 Restaurant is on Rt 101 (aka Main St) on north side.

MEREDITH

Good Foods Conspiracy 🛒

11 Main St. ✆ 603-279-3341 ⏰ M-Th 9:30-5:30, F 9:30-6, Sat 9:30-5
🛒 Store is on the north side of Main St 1 block west of US 3 & Rt 25 intersection.

Lakes Region Nutrition Center 🛒

52 NH Rte. 25 ✆ 603-279-4165 ⏰ M-Sat 9:30-5:30
  · organic produce
🚗 **From Rt 104/US 3 intersection,** take US 3 1 mile to Rt 25. Turn right onto Rt 25 3 miles to store on right.

NASHUA

Earth Energies Natural Foods 🛒

295 Daniel Webster Hwy. ✆ 603-888-2900 ⏰ M-F 10-8, Sat 10-6, Sun 12-6
🚗 **From NH on Rt 3S,** take exit 2 onto S Daniel Webster Hwy ramp toward S Nashua right onto DW Hwy 1¼ mile to store on right across from Pheasant Lane Mall. **From MA on Rt 3N,** take exit 36 toward S Nashua left onto Middlesex Rd (becomes DW Hwy) ¼ mile to store on left.

NEW LONDON

14 Carrots Natural Foods Co-op 🛒

52 Newport Rd. ✆ 603-526-2323 ⏰ M-Th 9-5:30, F 9-6, Sat 9-5, Sun 11-3
  · organic produce · vegetarian friendly · fresh juice · deli · salad bar · take-out · co-op
🚗 **From I-89,** take exit 12 toward New London/Sunapee east on Newport Rd (right from I-89N, left from I-89S) about 1 mile (into town) to store on right in New London Plaza.

NEWINGTON

Fresh City 🍽

45 Gosling Rd. ✆ 603-334-6006 ⏰ Daily 11-9
A fast-food alternative featuring wraps, stir fries, noodle dishes, soups and salads with the option to add tofu to most dishes.
  · vegetarian friendly · fresh juice · tables · self-service · take-out
🚗 **From I-95,** take exit 7 northwest on Market St (left from I-95N, right from I-95S) continuing onto Woodbury Rd under 1½ miles total to Gosling Rd. Turn left onto Gosling to restaurant on right in The Crossing at Fox Run.

NORTH CONWAY

Katrina's Organic Market 🛒 🍽

2988 White Mountain Hwy. ✆ 603-356-6068 ⏰ M-Sat 9-7, Sun 10-6
  · organic produce · vegetarian friendly · deli · tables · self-service · take-out
🛒 Store is on Rt 2/US 302 (aka White Mtn Hwy) between Worcester Hill Rd & Memorial Hospital on the west side.

NORTHWOOD

Susty's Cafe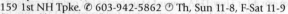

159 1st NH Tpke. © 603-942-5862 ⊘ Th, Sun 11-8, F-Sat 11-9

"Sustainable Sustenance" (ergo Susty's).
• vegan • organic focus • table • wait staff

⌂ On Rt 4 (aka 1st NH Tpke) on north side before lights at juncture of Rt 43, 9 & 202.

PETERBOROUGH

Maggie's Marketplace

14 Main St. © 603-924-7671 ⊘ M-F 9-6, Sat. 9-5
• organic produce

⌂ **From Rt 101,** turn north onto Grove St (left from 101E, right from 101W) ½ mile to Main St. Turn right onto Main 1½ blocks to store.

PLAISTOW

Bread & Honey

18 Plaistow Rd., Plaza 125 © 603-382-6432 ⊘ M-F 9-5:30, Sat 9-4

⌂ **From I-495,** take exit 51B onto Rt 125N about 1½ miles (veer right on 125 when it becomes Plaistow Rd) across MA/NH border to store on left.

PLYMOUTH

Peppercorn Natural Foods

43 Main St. © 603-536-3395 ⊘ M-F 9-6, Sat 9-5
• organic produce

⌂ **From I-93,** take exit 25 toward Plymouth right onto Bridge St about ½ mile (over bridge) to stop sign at Main St. Turn left onto Main, go around the common and follow 3S/Main south about 2 blocks to store on left (next to movie theater).

PORTSMOUTH

Portsmouth Health Foods

151 Congress St. © 603-436-1722 ⊘ M-F 9-7, Sat 9-6, Sun 10-6
• organic produce

⌂ **From I-95,** take exit 7 toward Portsmouth east on Market St (right from I-95N, left from I-95S) about 1 mile to US 1S. Turn left onto 1S (becomes Congress St) under ¼ mile to store at Maplewood Ave.

SALEM

Natural Marketplace

419 S. Broadway © 603-893-2893 ⊘ M-W 10-6, Th-F 10-8, Sat 10-5:30

⌂ **From I-93,** take exit 1 toward Rt 28 onto Rockingham Park Blvd about ⅓ mile to S Broadway/28S. Turn right onto Broadway about 1⅔ miles to store on left.

WOLFEBORO

Evergrain Natural Foods

45 N. Main St. © 603-569-4002 ⊘ M-Sat 9:30-5:30
• organic produce

⌂ **From Rt 28/109 intersection,** go south on 28/109 into town to blinking light at top of hill at 109S/Main St. Turn right onto Main 5 blocks to store on right (set back from road and below ground—look for Evergrain sign).

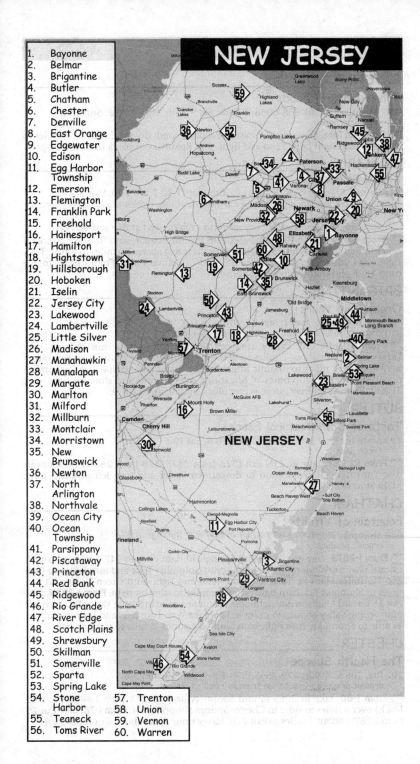

1. Bayonne
2. Belmar
3. Brigantine
4. Butler
5. Chatham
6. Chester
7. Denville
8. East Orange
9. Edgewater
10. Edison
11. Egg Harbor Township
12. Emerson
13. Flemington
14. Franklin Park
15. Freehold
16. Hainesport
17. Hamilton
18. Hightstown
19. Hillsborough
20. Hoboken
21. Iselin
22. Jersey City
23. Lakewood
24. Lambertville
25. Little Silver
26. Madison
27. Manahawkin
28. Manalapan
29. Margate
30. Marlton
31. Milford
32. Millburn
33. Montclair
34. Morristown
35. New Brunswick
36. Newton
37. North Arlington
38. Northvale
39. Ocean City
40. Ocean Township
41. Parsippany
42. Piscataway
43. Princeton
44. Red Bank
45. Ridgewood
46. Rio Grande
47. River Edge
48. Scotch Plains
49. Shrewsbury
50. Skillman
51. Somerville
52. Sparta
53. Spring Lake
54. Stone Harbor
55. Teaneck
56. Toms River
57. Trenton
58. Union
59. Vernon
60. Warren

NEW JERSEY

NEW JERSEY

BAYONNE
John's Natural Foods 🛍
486 Broadway ✆ 201-858-0088 ⏰ M-W, Sat 9:30-6, Th-F 9:30-8, Sun 10-6
• organic produce

🚗 **From NJ Tpke,** take exit 14A toward Bayonne south on Ave E about 1¾ miles to 22nd St. Turn right onto 22nd and right onto Broadway ½ block to store on right.

BELMAR
Kaya's Kitchen 🍴
817 Belmar Plaza ✆ 732-280-1141 ⏰ Tues-Sat 11:30-2:30, 5-10, Sun 5-9
Vegan menu features tofu and seitan in international dishes. Option to add cheese (prepard with separate utensils).
• vegetarian • vegan friendly • organic focus • tables • wait staff • self-service

🚗 **From Garden State Pkwy,** take exit 98 toward Belmar onto Rt 138E almost 4 miles to Rt 35. Merge onto 35N (becomes River Rd) about 1⅓ miles to 8th St. Turn right onto 8th over tracks to store on right in Belmar Plaza. **From I-195E,** merge onto 138E and follow directions above.

BRIGANTINE
Organically Yours 🛍
1018 W. Brigantine Ave. ✆ 609-266-0100 ⏰ M-F 10-6, Sat 10-5, Sun 12-5
• organic produce • fresh juice • counter • take-out

🚗 **From Atlantic City Expwy,** take exit 1 toward Brigantine onto Atlantic City Expwy Connector about 2 miles to Rt 87/Brigantine Blvd. Continue on Brigantine Blvd about 2¼ miles to Atlantic Brigantine Blvd and take second exit to continue on Brigantine Blvd (becomes W Brigantine Ave) 1¼ miles to store on right after 11th St. **From beachfront,** store is one block inland after 11th St.

BUTLER
Taste of Dawn Natural Foods 🛍
192 Main St. ✆ 973-838-0287 ⏰ M-F 10-8, Sat 10-6
• fresh juice

🚗 **From Rt 287,** take Rt 23N exit (52A from 287S, 52B from 287N) to Boonton Ave. Turn right onto Boonton to downtown Butler and turn left at tracks onto Main St to store.

CHATHAM
Fountain of Vitality 🛍
650 Shunpike Rd. ✆ 973-377-8663 ⏰ M-F 9-8, Sat 9:30-6, Sun 11-4
• organic produce

🚗 **From I-287S,** take exit 37 toward Springfield right onto Rt 24E 1 mile to exit 2A toward Hwy 510W/Morristown. Merge onto Columbia Tpke and turn left onto Park Ave 2½ miles Main St. Turn left onto Main and right onto Green Village Rd 1⅓ miles to Shunpike Rd. Turn right onto Shunpike to store on right. **From I-287N,** take exit 35 toward Madison Ave right onto South St 1 mile to Spring Valley Rd. Turn left onto Spring Valley about 1½ miles to Loantaka Way. Turn left onto Loantaka about ¾ mile to Shunpike. Turn right onto Shunpike about ¾ mile to store on left.

CHESTER
The Health Shoppe 🛍
207 Rte. 206 S. ✆ 908-879-7555 ⏰ M-F 9-9, Sat 9-7, Sun 9-6
• organic produce • vegetarian friendly • deli • take-out

🚗 **From I-80,** take Rt 206S toward Sommerville (exit 27A from I-80W, 27 from I-80E) over 8 miles to store in Chester Springs Shopping Ctr. **From I-78,** take exit 29 onto I-287N about 2 miles to exit 22B. Merge onto 206N about 8 miles to store.

DENVILLE

Grass Roots Natural Market 🛍 🍴 &

20 First Ave. © 973-627-5440 ⏰ M-F 9-8, Sat 9-7, Sun 10-5
• organic produce • vegetarian friendly • fresh juice • salad bar • cafe • deli • bakery • counter • self-service • take-out

🍎 **From I-80E**, take exit 38 onto Rt 46E toward Rt 53/Denville about 1 mile. Take Rt 53 ramp and bear right onto E Main St to Broadway. Turn right onto Broadway to first left onto First Ave to store on right. **From I-80W**, take exit 39 onto 46E and follow directions above. **From 46W**, bear right at fork onto Bloomfield Ave about ¼ mile, veer right onto Broadway and make second right onto First to store.

EAST ORANGE

Olive May Natural Foods 🛍

516 Main St. © 973-673-7306 ⏰ M-F 9:30-7, Sat 9:30-6
• fresh juice

🍎 **From Garden State Pkwy**, take exit 145 toward West Orange/Newark and follow I-280W exit on left toward The Oranges. Take the Clinton St/E Orange ramp on right to S Burnett St. Turn right onto Burnett and left onto Main St to store on left.

EDGEWATER

Su 🍴

725 River Rd. © 201-840-7988 ⏰ Tues-Sun 11:30-3, 5-10
Asian/Mediterranean/Italian influenced. BYOB.
• vegetarian • vegan friendly • tables • wait staff

🍎 **From George Washington Bridge or I-95**, exit onto CR 505/Hudson Terrace and go south on Main St (becomes River Rd) 2 miles to restaurant on left in Marketplace at Edgewater Shopping Ctr. **From the Lincoln Tunnel or Rt 495**, take Blvd E north continuing on Kennedy Blvd E about 1½ miles to CR 505/Hillside RD. Turn right onto Hillside over ½ mile to River Rd. Veer left onto River about 2¾ miles to restaurant on right.

Whole Foods Market 🛍 🍴

905 River Rd. © 201-941-4000 ⏰ Daily 8-10
• organic produce • vegetarian friendly • salad bar • cafe • self-service • take-out

🍎 **From west or south**, take I-95 or Rt 4 toward George Washington Bridge to Palisades Pkwy/Fort Lee exit. Follow exit onto service road to T intersection. Turn right to stop sign at River Rd. Turn left onto River Rd into Edgewater and store at Hilliard St. **From north or east**, take George Washington Bridge/Upper Level to NJ. Follow Fort Lee signs and take Hudson Terrace exit. Turn right at light off ramp to stop sign. Turn left onto River Rd and follow directions above.

EDISON

Jhupdi Vegetarian Restaurant 🍴

1679 Oak Tree Rd. © 732-906-2121 ⏰ Tues-Sun 11:30-10
Indian vegetarian in an area that caters to an Indian population.
• vegetarian • vegan friendly • tables • wait staff

🍎 **From Garden State Pkwy**, take exit 131 toward Metuchan/Edison right onto Rt 2 7⅓ mile to Wood Ave. Turn right onto Wood ½ mile to Oak Tree Rd. Turn left onto Oak Tree under ½ mile to restaurant on left.

Saravana Bhavan 🍴

149 Wood Ave. © 732-767-0033 ⏰ M-F, Sun 11:30-3, 5:30-10, F-Sat 11:30-3, 5:30-10:30
South Indian vegetarian. Part of an international chain.
• vegetarian • vegan friendly • tables • wait staff

🍎 **From Garden State Pkwy,** take exit 131 toward Metuchan/Edison right onto Rt 27⅓ mile to Wood Ave. Turn right onto Wood under ½ mile to restaurant on left in Oak Tree Plaza.

EGG HARBOR TOWNSHIP

Bonterra Market 🛍️

3112 Fire Rd. © 609-484-1550 ⏰ M-F 9-7:30, Sat 9-5, Sun 11-4
• organic produce • vegetarian friendly • deli • take-out

🚗 **From Garden State Pkwy,** take exit 36 onto Rt 563E (Tilton Rd) and make first right onto Fire Rd to store.

EMERSON

Old Hook Farm 🛍️

650 Old Hook Rd. © 201-265-4835 ⏰ Tues-Sat 9-5, Sun 9-4
• organic produce

🚗 **From Garden State Pkwy N,** take exit 168 toward Westwood right onto Washington Ave (becomes Old Hook Rd) about 4¼ miles to store on left.

FLEMINGTON

Basil Bandwagon 🛍️ 🍴

276 Hwy. 202/31 © 908-788-5737 ⏰ M-Sat 9-9, Sun 9-8
• organic produce • vegetarian friendly • vegan friendly • organic focus • fresh juice •
deli • counter • self-service • take-out

🍎 Store is on west side of US 202 in shopping complex just south of Main St intersection.

FRANKLIN PARK

Udipi Cafe 🍴

3029 Rte. 27S. © 732-422-8301 ⏰ Daily 11-11
Indian vegetarian.
• vegetarian • vegan friendly • tables • wait staff

🍎 Restaurant is on Rt 27 between Bennington Pkwy & Claremont Rd.

FREEHOLD

Pauline's Health Foods 🛍️

3585 Rte. 9 N. © 732-303-0854 ⏰ M-Th 9:30-8, F 9:30-7, Sat 9:30-6, Sun 11-5

🚗 **From NJ Tpke,** take exit 8 onto Rt 33E about 12½ miles to Rt 9S. Turn right onto 9S about ¼ mile to Schanck Rd ramp. Turn left onto Schanck and left onto Rt 9N about ½ mile to store on right. **From I-195,** take exit 28B onto Rt 9N about 6¼ miles to store.

HAINESPORT

Hainesport Health Haven 🛍️ 🍴

1443 Rte 38 © 609-267-7744 ⏰ M-F 10-6, Sat 10-4
• vegetarian • vegan friendly • deli • counter • tables • self-service • take-out

🚗 **From I-295,** take exit 47A toward Mt Holly onto Rt 541S/Burlington Mt Holly Rd (right from I-295N, loop around right from I-295S) about 5¼ miles to Rt 38. Turn right onto Rt 38W to store on right at Lumberton Rd.

HAMILTON

Vasanta Bhavan 🍴

3800 Quakerbridge Rd. © 609-586 7899 ⏰ Tues-Th 12-2:30, 5:30-9:30, F-Sun 12-3, 5:30-10
Indian vegetarian.
• vegetarian • vegan friendly • tables • wait staff • take-out

🚗 **From I-295,** take exit 65A onto Sloan Ave under 1 mile to second light (Quakerbridge Rd). Turn left onto Quakerbridge 1⅓ miles to second light (Youngs Rd). Turn left onto Youngs to restaurant on right in Quakerbridge Shoppes.

HIGHTSTOWN
Black Forest Acres 🛍
553 Rte. 130 ✆ 609-448-4885 ⏰ M-F 9:30-7, Sat 9:30-6, Sun 12-4
Ready-made sandwiches and salads.
  • organic produce

🚗 **From NJ Tpke,** take exit 8 toward Freehold/Hightstown right at first fork in ramp and left at next fork in ramp onto Rt 33 (Franklin St) ½ mile to Stockton St. Turn right onto Stockton over ½ mile to Dutch Neck Rd. Turn left onto Dutch Neck about ½ mile to Rt 130N. Turn right onto 130N to store on right.

HILLSBOROUGH
Fountain of Vitality 🛍
601 Rte. 206 ✆ 908-874-3866 ⏰ M-F 9-8, Sat 9:30-6, Sun 11-4
  • organic produce

🚗 **From I-287S,** take exit 17 onto 202S/206S 1 mile to ramp to Somerville Cir. Take ramp left at fork onto Somerville Cir to third exit (US 206). Take US 206 6 miles to store on left. **From I-287N,** take exit 14B on left toward Clinton onto US 22W 2¼ miles to ramp for US 202/US206. Take ramp left at fork onto Somerville Cir and follow directions above.

HOBOKEN
Basic Food 🛍
204 Washington St. ✆ 201-610-1100 ⏰ M-Sat 8-10, Sun 9-9
  • organic produce • fresh juice

🚗 **From Holland Tunnel, I-78E, Pulaski Hwy or Rt 1 & 9,** go north on Luis Munoz Marin Blvd (right from NY, left from I-78E), almost ½ mile to Newark St/Observer Hwy intersection. Jog around to right onto Vezzetti Way almost ½ mile to Washington St. Turn left onto Washington about ¼ mile to store on left after 2nd St.

Hoboken Farm Boy 🛍 🍴
127 Washington St. ✆ 201-656-0581 ⏰ Daily 8-10
  • vegetarian friendly • deli • counter • self-service • take-out

🚗 **From Holland Tunnel, I-78E, Pulaski Hwy or Rt 1 & 9,** go north on Luis Munoz Marin Blvd (right from NY, left from I-78E), almost ½ mile to Newark St/Observer Hwy intersection. Jog around to right onto Vezzetti Way almost ½ mile to Washington St. Turn left onto Washington about ¼ mile to store on right between 1st & 2nd St.

ISELIN
Sukhadia's 🍴
1507 Oak Tree Rd. ✆ 732-548-1888 ⏰ Daily 10-10
Indian vegetarian with lunch and dinner buffet options.
  • vegetarian • vegan friendly • tables • self-service • wait staff

🚗 **From Garden State Pkwy,** take exit 131 toward Metuchan/Edison right onto Rt 27 1 block to Magnolia Rd. Turn right onto Magnolia under ½ mile to Oak Tree Rd. Turn right onto Oak Tree to restaurant on right.

JERSEY CITY
Dosa Hut 🍴
777 Newark Ave. ✆ 201-420-6660 ⏰ Daily 10-10
South Indian dosas.
  • vegetarian • vegan friendly • tables • self-service • take-out

🚗 **From US 1N,** take Tonnele Ave exit right onto Tonnele about ¼ mile to Newark Ave. Turn left onto Newark past Liberty Ave to restaurant on right. **From I-78W,** take Rt 139 onto Hoboken Ave and turn left then right to continue on Hoboken about ½ mile total to Newark. Turn left on Newark ⅓ mile to restaurant on left. **From I-78E,** take exit for Jersey City/Columbus Dr left onto Montgomery St 1 mile to Hudson Blvd/JFK Blvd. Turn right onto Hudson 1 mile to Newark. Turn left onto Newark to restaurant.

Krishna Cuisine 🍴

795 Newark Ave. © 201-659-8700 ⊙ Tues-Sun 10-10
Indian vegetarian.
   • vegetarian • vegan friendly • tables • wait staff

🍎 **From US 1N**, take Tonnele Ave exit right onto Tonnele about ¼ mile to Newark Ave. Turn left onto Newark to 1 block to restaurant on right. **From I-78W**, take Rt 139 onto Hoboken Ave and turn left then right to continue on Hoboken about ½ mile total to Newark. Turn left on Newark ⅓ mile to restaurant on left. **From I-78E**, take exit for Jersey City/Columbus Dr left onto Montgomery St 1 mile to Hudson Blvd/JFK Blvd. Turn right onto Hudson 1 mile to Newark. Turn left onto Newark 1 block to restaurant.

Satkar 🍴

806 Newark Ave. © 201-963 6309 ⊙ Tues-Sun 10:30-10
Indian vegetarian.
   • vegetarian • vegan friendly • tables • wait staff

🍎 **From US 1N**, take Tonnele Ave exit right onto Tonnele about ¼ mile to Newark Ave. Turn left onto Newark to 1 block to restaurant on left. **From I-78W**, take Rt 139 onto Hoboken Ave and turn left then right to continue on Hoboken about ½ mile total to Newark. Turn left on Newark ⅓ mile to restaurant on right. **From I-78E**, take exit for Jersey City/Columbus Dr left onto Montgomery St 1 mile to Hudson Blvd/JFK Blvd. Turn right onto Hudson 1 mile to Newark. Turn left onto Newark about 1 block to restaurant.

Sri Ganesh's Dosa House 🍴

809 Newark Ave. © 201-222-3883 ⊙ Daily 10:30-10
South Indian dosas.
   • vegetarian • vegan friendly • tables • self-service • take-out

🍎 **From US 1N**, take Tonnele Ave exit right onto Tonnele about ¼ mile to Newark Ave. Turn left onto Newark to 1 block to restaurant on right. **From I-78W**, take Rt 139 onto Hoboken Ave and turn left then right to continue on Hoboken about ½ mile total to Newark. Turn left on Newark ⅓ mile to restaurant on left. **From I-78E**, take exit for Jersey City/Columbus Dr left onto Montgomery St 1 mile to Hudson Blvd/JFK Blvd. Turn right onto Hudson 1 mile to Newark. Turn left onto Newark about 1 block to restaurant.

LAKEWOOD

Supreme Health Food Center 🛍

415 Cedar Bridge Ave. © 732-367-1055 ⊙ M-Tues 10-6, W 10-8, F 10-2, Sun 11-6
   • organic produce

🍎 **From Rt 9**, go east on Cedarbridge Ave ½ mile to store. **From Garden State Pkwy S**, take exit 89 toward Lakewood onto Airport Rd and turn left onto Cedarbridge 2⅓ miles to store. **From GSP N**, take exit 90 toward Lakewood onto Chambersbridge Rd and veer right then left back onto Chambersbridge (toward pkwy) ½ mile to Ocean Ave. Turn left onto Ocean 1 mile to New Hampshire Ave. Turn left onto New Hampshire under 1 mile to Cedarbridge. Turn right onto Cedarbridge 1¼ miles to store.

LAMBERTVILLE

Big Bear Natural Food 🛍

239 N. Union St. © 609-397-4499 ⊙ M-F 9-8 Sat 10-5, Sun 11-5
   • organic produce • vegetarian friendly • fresh juice • deli • take-out

🍎 **From US 202**, go south on Main St about ¼ mile to Cherry St. Turn right onto Cherry 1 block to N Union St. Turn left onto Union to store.

LITTLE SILVER

Healthfair 🛍

625 Branch Ave. © 732-747-3140 ⊙ M-F 9-8, Sat-Sun 9-6
Big take-out selection and only "meat" is tuna.

• organic produce • vegetarian friendly • fresh juice • deli • salad bar • take-out

🍎 **From Garden State Pkwy,** take exit 109 east on Newman Springs Rd about 2 miles to end at Rt 35. Turn right onto 35 and left onto White Rd almost 1 mile to end at Branch Ave. Turn right onto Branch over ½ mile to store.

MADISON

Whole Foods Market

222 Main St. © 973-822-8444 ⏰ Daily 8-10
• organic produce • vegetarian friendly • salad bar • cafe • self-service • take-out

🍎 **From I-24 (easily accessed from I-287 or I-78),** take Rt 124W (exit 7B-A from I-24W, 7 from I-24E) toward Chatham onto Main St about 2 miles to store . **From I-287N,** take exit 35 onto South St and turn left onto Woodland Ave about 1⅓ miles to Kitchell Ave. Turn left onto Kitchell ⅔ mile to Madison Ave/Rt 124. Turn right onto Madison (becomes Main) about 2½ miles to store.

MANAHAWKIN

Pangaea Natural

511 Rte. 72 E. © 609-597-0017 ⏰ M-Sat 10-7
• organic produce

🍎 **From Garden State Pkwy,** take exit 63 toward Long Beach Island onto Rt 72E 2½-3 miles to store on right in Driftwood Plaza. **From Rt 9,** take Rt 72E 1 mile to store.

MANALAPAN

Pauline's Health Foods

299 Rte. 9 S. © 732-308-0449 ⏰ M-Th 9:30-8, F 9:30-7, Sat 9:30-6, Sun 11-5
🍎 **From Garden State Pkwy,** take exit 123 toward Sayreville/Old Bridge onto Rt 9S about 11 miles to store.

MARGATE

Pamela's Health and Harmony

8508 Ventnor Ave. © 609-822-8828 ⏰ M-F 10-6, Sat 10-5, Sun 11-4
• organic produce

🍎 **Coming from the mainland on Margate Blvd,** merge onto Jerome Ave to Ventnor Ave (Rt 152). Turn right onto Ventnor 2 blocks to store on left. **Coming from the beach,** go inland 2 blocks to store between S Kenyon & S Lancaster Ave.

MARLTON

Whole Foods Market

940 Rte. 73 N. © 856-797-1115 ⏰ M-Sat 8-10, Sun 8-9
• organic produce • vegetarian friendly • salad bar • cafe • self-service • take-out

🍎 **From NJ Tpke,** take exit 4 onto Rt 73S towards Marlton/Berlin about 3 miles to Greentree Rd. Take jughandle across 73 onto Greentree to store on corner in Greentree Shopping Ctr.

MILFORD

The Healthy Habit

57 Bridge St. © 908-995-7653 ⏰ M-F 9:30-6, Sat 9:30-5, Sun 10-2
• organic produce • fresh juice

🍎 **From I-78W,** take exit 7 and loop around right onto Rt 173W to Church St. Turn right onto Church 1 block to Willow St. Turn right onto Willow ½ mile to Milford Rd. Turn left onto Milford and merge left at end onto Statts Rd. Continue on Statts (becomes Myler Rd) about 1⅓ miles total to Hawks Schoolhouse Rd. Turn right onto Hawks Schoolhouse 1⅔ miles to Rt 519 (Milford Warren Glen Rd). Turn left onto 519 4 miles to Bridge St. Turn right onto Bridge to store. **From I-78E,** take exit 6 right onto Bloomsbury Rd, merge onto 173W and follow directions above.

MILLBURN

Whole Foods Market ☆ ⚏ ♿
187 Millburn Ave. Ⓒ 973-376-4668 Ⓢ Daily 7:30-10
• organic produce • vegetarian friendly • salad bar • cafe • self-service • take-out

🚗 **From I-78W**, take exit 50B toward Millburn right onto Vauxhall Rd about ¾ mile to Millburn Ave. Turn left onto Millburn 2½ blocks to store on right. **From I-78E**, take exit 49B toward Maplewood onto Rt 124/Springfield Ave continuing onto Valley Rd about ¾ mile total to Vauxhall. Turn left onto Vauxhall 2 blocks to Millburn. Turn left onto Millburn to store.

MONTCLAIR

The Energy Bar Vegetarian Cafe ⚏
307C Orange Rd. Ⓒ 973-746-7003 Ⓢ M- F 10-6 Sat 12-8
Raw foods, light vegan fare and order-ahead boxed lunches geared to school children.
• vegan • fresh juice • counter • tables • self service • take-out

🚗 **From Garden State Pkwy**, take exit 148 for Bloomfield Ave. **From PkwyS**, turn right onto Montgomery St and continue onto Municipal Plaza to Bloomfield Ave. Turn right onto Bloomfield about ¾ mile to Ridgewood Ave. Turn left onto Ridgewood ½ mile to Washington St. Turn right onto Washington ½ mile to Orange Rd. Turn right onto Orange to restaurant on right. **From PkwyN**, stay straight onto JFK Drive N, turn left into JFK S, right onto Bloomfield and follow directions above.

The Health Shoppe ▣
539 Bloomfield Ave. Ⓒ 973-746-3555 Ⓢ M-F 9-7, Sat 9-6, Sun 11-5

🚗 **From Garden State Pkwy**, take exit 148 for Bloomfield Ave. **From PkwyS**, turn right onto Montgomery St and continue onto Municipal Plaza to Bloomfield Ave. Turn right Bloomfield about 2 miles to store on right after Park St. **From PkwyN**, stay straight onto JFK Drive N, turn left onto JFK S, right onto Bloomfield and follow directions above.

Udupi Village ⚏
511 Bloomfield Ave. Ⓒ 973-233-1905 Ⓢ M-Th 11:30-3:15, 5:30-9:30, F-Sun 11:30-9:30
Indian vegetarian with daily lunch buffet.
• vegetarian • vegan friendly • tables • self service • wait staff

🚗 **From Garden State Pkwy,** take exit 148 for Bloomfield Ave. **From PkwyS**, turn right onto Montgomery St and continue onto Municipal Plaza to Bloomfield Ave. Turn right Bloomfield about 2 miles to restaurant on right before Park St. **From PkwyN**, stay straight onto JFK Drive N, turn left onto JFK S, right onto Bloomfield and follow directions above.

Veggie Heaven ⚏
631 Valley Rd. Ⓒ 973-783-1088 Ⓢ M-Th 11:30-10, F-Sat 11:30-11, Sun 11:30-9:30
Extensive Vegetarian Chinese kosher menu
• vegetarian • vegan friendly • kosher • tables • wait staff

🚗 **From Garden State Pkwy**, take exit 151 toward Montclair onto Watchung Ave (left from GSP N, merge right from GSP S) about 1¾ miles to Valley Rd. Turn right onto Valley under 1 mile to restaurant on right at Lorraine Ave.

Whole Foods Market ▣
701 Bloomfield Ave. Ⓒ 973-746-5110 Ⓢ Daily 8-10
• organic produce, vegetarian friendly, deli, bakery, take-out

🚗 **From Garden State Pkwy**, take exit 148 for Bloomfield Ave. **From PkwyS,** turn right onto Montgomery St and continue onto Municipal Plaza to Bloomfield Ave. Turn right Bloomfield about 2½ miles to store on right across from the Montclair Art Museum. **From PkwyN**, stay straight onto JFK Drive N, turn left onto JFK S, right onto Bloomfield and follow directions above.

MORRISTOWN

The Health Shoppe
66 Morris St. ✆ 973-538-9131 ⏰ M-F 9-9, Sat 9-7, Sun 9-6
• organic produce • vegetarian friendly • deli • salad bar • take-out

🍎 **From I-287S**, take exit 36 toward Morris Ave straight onto Lafayette Ave to second light (Morris St). Turn right onto Morris to store on right. **From I-287N**, take exit 36B right onto Lafayette and follow directions above.

NEW BRUNSWICK

George Street Co-op
89 Morris St. ✆ 732-247-8280 ⏰ M-F 10-8, Sat 10-6, Sun 11-6
• organic produce • co-op

🍴 **From NJ Tpke or Rt 1**, take Rt 18N (exit 9 on Tpke). Stay right after Commercial Ave and exit onto New St to third light (Livingston Ave). Turn left onto Livingston and next left onto Morris St to store in on left.

NEWTON

Sussex County Food Co-op
30 Moran St. ✆ 973-579-1882 ⏰ M-Th, Sat 9:30-5:30, F 9-9, Sun 1:15-5
Premade sandwiches and salads.
• organic produce • co-op

🍴 Take Rt 206 into downtown Newton. Store is 1 block east of 206 between Trinity & E Clinton St.

NORTH ARLINGTON

Surrey International Natural Foods
33 Ridge Rd. ✆ 201-991-1905 ⏰ M-F 10-7:30, Sat 10-5 (no food service)
• vegetarian • fresh juice • salad bar • tables • self-service • take-out

🍴 **From Rt 3E**, take Ridge Rd exit onto Rutherford Ave and turn right onto Ridge Rd 2½ miles to store on right before Belleville Ave. **From Rt 3W**, turn left onto Ridge Rd (signs for Lyndhurst) and follow directions above. **From Rt 17S**, merge onto Rt 3W and follow directions above.

NORTHVALE

Organica Natural Foods
246 Livingston St. ✆ 201-767-8182 ⏰ M-F 9-7, Sat 9-6, Sun 10-5
• organic produce, vegetarian friendly, fresh juice, deli, bakery, take-out

🍴 **From Palisades Pkwy S,** take exit 5S toward Tappan onto Rt 303S about 1¾ miles (merges into Livingston St) to store on left.

OCEAN CITY

Luna Sea Health Food Market
301 E. 10th St. ✆ 609-398-5750 ⏰ M-Sat 9-6, Sun 10-3
• organic produce

🍴 **From Garden State Pkwy S**, take exit 30 onto Laurel Dr continuing onto MacArthur Pkwy 1¼ miles to Somers Point Cir. Take second exit onto Rt 52/US 9S about 2½ miles (across bay) to West Ave. Turn right onto West 1 block to E 10th St. Turn left onto E 10th to store on left. **From GSP N**, take exit 29 toward Ocean City onto New Rd continuing onto Atkinson Dr to Mays Landing Rd. Turn right onto Mays Landing about ¾ mile to Somers Point Cir and follow directions above. **From the beachfront**, go inland 5 blocks to store at corner E 10th & West.

OCEAN TOWNSHIP

Dean's Natural Food Market 🛍️

1119 Hwy. 35N © 732-517-1515 ⏰ M-F 9-8, Sat 9-6, Sun 10-6
• organic produce • fresh juice • salad bar • take-out

🚗 **From Garden State Pkwy N,** take exit 100A onto Rt 66E about 3⅓ miles. Continue straight onto Asbury Ave/NJ 35 and left onto 35 after Seaview Square Mall to store on right between Sunset & Allaire Ave. **From GSP S,** take exit 102 onto Asbury Ave about 3 miles (where NJ 35 turns left) and follow directions above.

PARSIPPANY

Chand Palace 🍴

257 Littleton Rd. © 973-334-5444 ⏰ Lunch M-F 11:30-2:15, Sat-Sun 12-2:45 Dinner M-Th, Sun 5:30-9:30, F-Sat 5-10
Indian vegetarian with a lunch and dinner buffet option.
• vegetarian • vegan friendly • tables • self-service • wait staff

🚗 **From I-80W,** take exit 43B toward Rt 46. Turn right onto Smith Rd to stop sign at Littleton Rd. Turn left onto Littleton ½ mile to restaurant on left in shopping mall before light. **From I-287N,** take exit 41A, turn left onto Smith and follow directions above. **From I-80E (west of I-287),** take exit 42A-C (Rt 202N) left at first fork in ramp and right at second fork onto Littleton about ¾ mile (past first light) to restaurant on right. **From I-287S,** take exit 42 (Rt 202S) left onto Parsipanny Blvd about ¾ mile to Littleton. Turn left onto Littleton to restaurant on left.

The Health Shoppe 🛍️

1123 Rte. 46 E. © 973-263-8348 ⏰ M-F 9-9, Sat 9-6, Sun 11-6

🚗 **From I-80E (west of I-287),** take exit 42A-C (Rt 202N) left at first fork in ramp and right at second fork onto Littleton Rd. Take Littleton about 1¼ miles to Rt 46E. Veer left and curve right onto 46E about 1½ miles to store on right in Whippany Shopping Ctr. **From I-80W,** take exit 47 onto 46W about 1½ miles to Baldwin Rd. Turn around at Baldwin back onto 46E over ½ mile to store.

Veggie Heaven 🍴

1119 Rte. 46 E. #8A © 973-335-9876 ⏰ M-Th, Sun 11:30-9:30, F-Sat 11:30-10
Chinese vegetarian.
• vegetarian • vegan friendly • tables • wait staff

🚗 **From I-80E (west I-of 287),** take exit 42A-C (Rt 202N) left at first fork in ramp and right at second fork onto Littleton Rd. Take Littleton about 1¼ miles to Rt 46E. Veer left and curve right onto 46E about 1½ miles to restaurant on right. **From I-80W,** take exit 47 onto 46W about 1½ miles to Baldwin Rd. Turn around at Baldwin back onto 46E over ½ mile to restaurant.

PISCATAWAY

Chand Palace 🍴   ♿

1296 Centennial Ave. © 732-465-1474 ⏰ Lunch M-F 11:30-3, Sat-Sun 12-3 Dinner M-Th, Sun 5:30-9:45, F-Sat 5-10
Indian vegetarian with a daily lunch and dinner buffet option.
• vegetarian • vegan friendly • tables • self-service • wait staff

🚗 **From I-287** take exit 6 toward Piscataway south on S Washington Ave (loop around right from I-287N, left and then right to stay on S Washington from I-287N) to first intersection at Centennial Ave. Turn left onto Centennial under ¼ mile to restaurant on right in Centennial Plaza.

Malabar House 🍴

1665 Stelton Rd. © 732-819-0400 ⏰ M-F 12-3, 5:30-9:30, Sat 12-10:30, Sun 12-9:30
Vegetarian Indian.
• vegetarian • vegan friendly • tables • wait staff

🚗 **From I-287,** take exit 5 south on Stelton Rd (right from I-287S, left from I-287N) 1¾-2 miles to restaurant.

Sukh Sagar ⑪

1347 Stelton Rd. ✆ 732-777-9595 ⏰ M-F, Sun 11:30-3:30, 5-9:30, F-Sat 11:30-10
Vegetarian Indian with a lunch buffet.
· vegetarian · vegan friendly · tables · wait staff

🚗 **From I-287**, take exit 5 south on Stelton Rd (right from I-287S, left from I-287N)
1¼-1½ miles to restaurant.

PRINCETON

Olive May Natural Food 🛍 ⑪   ♿

225 Nassau St. ✆ 609-924-4993 ⏰ Daily 7:30-9:30
· organic produce · vegetarian friendly · fresh juice · salad bar · cafe · deli · bakery ·
counter · tables · self-service · take-out

🍎 **From Rt 206**, turn onto Nassau St (Rt 27) about ½ mile to store on right between
Washington Rd & Harrison St. **From Rt 1**, turn northwest onto Washington St (right
from US 1S, take jughandle left then right across 1 from 1N) over 1½ miles to
Nassau. Turn right onto Nassau about ¼ mile to store.

Whole Earth Center 🛍 ⑪   ♿

360 Nassau St. ✆ 609-924-7429 ⏰ M-F 8:30-8, Sat 9-7, Sun 10-5
· organic produce · vegetarian friendly · fresh juice · cafe · deli · bakery · tables ·
self-service · take-out

🍎 **From Rt 206**, turn onto Nassau St (Rt 27) 1 mile to store on left after Harrison St.
From Rt 1, take Lower Harrison St exit north (becomes Harrison) about 1½ miles to
third light (Nassau). Turn right onto Nassau and make first left into driveway to store.

Whole Foods Market 🛍 ⑪

3495 Rte. 1 S. ✆ 609-799-2919 ⏰ Daily 8-10
· organic produce · vegetarian friendly · salad bar · cafe · self-service · take-out

🏠 Store is on Rt 1 between Quakerbridge & Meadow Rd in Wintergreen Shopping Ctr.

Zen Palate ⑪

301 N. Harrison St. ✆ 609-279-9888 ⏰ M-Th, Sun 11:30-9, F-Sat 11:30-9:30
Zen menu featuring soy and gluten faux meat.
· vegan · tables · wait staff

🍎 **From Rt 206N,** turn onto Nassau St (Rt 27) 1 mile to Harrison St. Turn left onto
Harrison about ¾ mile to restaurant on right in Princeton Shopping Ctr. **From Rt
206S**, turn right onto Ewing St under ½ mile to Harrison. Veer left onto Harrison
about ½ mile to restaurant on left. **From Rt 1**, take Lower Harrison St exit north
(becomes Harrison) 2¼ miles to restaurant on right.

RED BANK

Eurasian Eatery ⑪   ♿

110 Monmouth St. ✆ 732-741-7071 ⏰ Tues-Th 11:30-8:30, F-Sat 11:30-9:30, Sun 4-8:30
Many creative vegetarian and vegan choices. BYOB.
· vegetarian friendly · vegan friendly · organic focus · tables · wait staff

🚗 **From Garden State Pkwy S**, take exit 109 toward Red Bank north on Half Mile
Rd (left from GSP N, veer left onto Newman Springs Rd then right across hwy and
right from GSP S) over ½ mile to W Front St. Turn right onto W Front 1⅓ miles to
West St. Turn right onto West 2 blocks to Monmouth St. Turn left onto Monmouth
past Pearl St to restaurant on left across from Count Basie Theater.

Whole Foods Market 🛍 ⑪

471 Rte. 35 N. ✆ 732-758-1688 ⏰ Daily 8-10
· organic produce · vegetarian friendly · salad bar · cafe · self-service · take-out

🚗 **From Garden State Pkwy S**, take exit 114 left onto Red Hill Rd (signs for
Middletown) 1 mile to Bamm Hollow Rd. Turn right onto Bamm Hollow continuing
onto Oak Hill Rd 2½ miles total to Rt 35/Minnesink Rd. Turn left onto Rt 35 to store
on right. **From GSP N**, take exit 109 left onto Half Mile Rd about ½ mile to W Front
St. Turn right onto W Front 1 mile to Rector Pl. Turn left onto Rector continuing
onto Rt 35 across water about 1¾ miles to store on right after Chapel Hill.

RIDGEWOOD

Whole Foods Market 🛍 🍴 &

44 Godwin Ave. © 201-670-0383 ⏱ Daily 8-10
• organic produce • vegetarian friendly • salad bar • cafe • self-service • take-out

🍴 **From Rt 17**, take Linwood Ave exit toward Ridgewood (west) about 1½ miles to Maple Ave. Turn left onto Maple about ¼ mile to Franklin Ave. Turn right onto Franklin (becomes Garber Sq, then Wisley Sq, then Godwin Ave) about ⅔ mile to store in Ridgewood Plaza.

RIO GRANDE

Back to Nature Health Food Store 🛍

4 S. Railroad Ave. © 609-886-4027 ⏱ M-F 9-6, Sat 9-1

🍴 **From Garden State Pkwy**, take exit 4 (4A from GSP S) onto Rt 47N about 1 mile to S Railroad Ave. Turn left onto S Railroad to store on left.

Green Street Market 🛍

3167 Rte. 9 S. © 609-463-0606 ⏱ M-F 10-6, Sat-Sun 10-5
• organic produce

🍴 **From Garden State Pkwy,** take exit 4 (4A from GSP S) onto Rt 47N about ½ mile to Rt 9S. Turn right onto Rt 9/Shore Rd under ½ mile to store on left.

RIVER EDGE

Happy Carrot 🛍

636 Kinderkamack Rd. © 201-986-0818 ⏱ M-F 9:30-7, Sat 9:30-6, Sun 11-4
• organic produce • fresh juice

🍴 **From Rt 4W**, turn right onto Grand Ave and make second left onto Kinderkamack Rd about 1¼ miles to store. **From Rt 4E**, turn right onto Johnson Ave, left onto Jefferson Ave and left onto Kinderkamack (across hwy) about 1½ miles to store. **From Rt 17N**, merge onto Rt 4E and follow directions above.

SCOTCH PLAINS

Autumn Harvest Natural Foods 🛍

1625 E. 2nd St. © 908-322-2130 ⏱ M, F 9:30-7, Tues-Th 10-8, Sat 10-5:30, Sun 12-4
• organic produce

🍴 **From I-78**, take exit 41 toward Scotch Plains right onto Drift Rd and right onto Plainfield Ave. Follow Plainfield (becomes Bonnie Burn Rd) about 2 miles to Park Ave. Turn right onto Park about ⅔ mile to 2nd St. Turn right onto 2nd about ⅓ mile to store on right.

SHREWSBURY

Dean's Natural Market 🛍

490 Broad St. © 732-842-8686 ⏱ M-F 9-8, Sat 9-6, Sun 10-6
• organic produce • fresh juice • salad bar • take-out

🍴 **From Garden State Pkwy**, take exit 109 toward Red Bank east on Newman Springs Rd (left from GSP S, right from GSP N) about 2 miles to Broad St. Turn right onto Broad 2½ blocks to store on right.

SKILLMAN

Princeton Health Food 🛍

1273 Rte. 206 © 609-279-1636 ⏱ M-F 10-6:30, Sat 10-5, Sun
• organic produce • fresh juice

🍴 Store is at intersection Rt 206 & Rt 518.

SOMERVILLE

Fig Tree 🛒 🍴

194 W. Main St. ✆ 908-725-7716 ☺ M-W, F 10-6, Th 10-7, Sat 10-5
  • vegetarian friendly • fresh juice • counter • self-service • take-out

🍎 **From US 206**, go east on Somerset St (left from 206S, right from 206N) about ⅓ mile to W Main St. Turn right onto Main to store.

SPARTA

Harmony Health Foods 🛒

155 Woodport Rd. ✆ 973-726-9199 ☺ M-F 9:30-7, Sat 9-5
Emphasis on gluten-free foods.
  • organic produce

🍎 **From Rt 15**, take Lake Mohawk/Sparta exit onto Rt 181/Woodport Rd over 1 mile to store on right.

SPRING LAKE

Nature's Corner 🛒 🍴

2407 Hwy. 71 ✆ 732-449-4950 ☺ M-Th 9-8, F 9-7, Sat-Sun 10-6
  • organic produce • vegetarian friendly • vegan friendly • organic focus • fresh juice • salad bar • deli • counter • tables • self-service • take-out

🍎 **From I-195E**, continue onto Rt 138E and merge onto Hwy 35N toward Belmar/Asbury Park about ⅓ mile to 16th Ave. Turn right onto 16th about ½ mile to H St (Hwy 71). Turn right onto 71 under 1 mile to store. **From Garden State Pkwy**, take exit 98 onto 138E and follow directions above.

STONE HARBOR

Green Cuisine 🍴

302 96th St. ✆ 609-368-1616 ☺ Mother's Day-Mid Sept Daily 11-8:30 (call to verify)
  • vegetarian friendly • fresh juice • alcohol • tables • wait staff

🍎 **From Garden State Pkwy**, turn east onto Stone Harbor Blvd (left from GSP S, right from GSP N) across water (becomes 96th St) about 3⅔ miles to restaurant at 3rd Ave.

TEANECK

Aquarius 🛒

408 Cedar Lane ✆ 201-836-0601 ☺ M-F 10-7, Sat 10-6, Sun 10-2
  • organic produce

🍎 **From Rt 4W,** take Teaneck Rd ramp toward Ridgefield Park right onto Teaneck Rd (across hwy) ½ mile to Cedar Ln. Turn right onto Cedar about ¾ mile to store. **From Rt 4E**, turn right onto Belle Ave ¼ mile to Claremont Ave. Turn left onto Claremont 1 block to Garrison Ave. Turn left onto Garrison 3 blocks to Cedar. Turn left onto Cedar past first block to store.

Veggie Heaven 🍴

473 Cedar Lane ✆ 201-836-0887 ☺ M-Th, Sun 11-10, F-Sat 11-11
Extensive Vegetarian Chinese kosher menu.
  • vegetarian • vegan friendly • kosher • tables • wait staff

🍎 **From Rt 4W**, take Teaneck Rd ramp toward Ridgefield Park right onto Teaneck Rd (across hwy) ½ mile to Cedar Ln. Turn right onto Cedar about 1 mile (past Garrison Ave) to restaurant. **From Rt 4E**, turn right onto Belle Ave ¼ mile to Claremont Ave. Turn left onto Claremont 1 block to Garrison. Turn left onto Garrison 3 blocks to Cedar. Turn right onto Cedar to restaurant.

TOMS RIVER

Natural Foods 🛍 🍴

675 Batchelor St. ✆ 732-240-0024 ⏱ M-Tues, Th-F 10-6, W 10-8, Sat 10-5, Sun 12-5 Cafe M-F 10-2
• organic produce • vegetarian friendly • fresh juice • cafe • tables • self-service • take-out
🚗 **From Garden State Pkwy,** take exit 82 onto Rt 37E 2 miles to Peter Ave. Turn right onto Peter and right onto Batchelor St to store.

TRENTON

Black Forest Acres 🛍 🍴

1100 Rte. 33 ✆ 609-586-6187 ⏱ M-F 9:30-7:30 Deli 10-6, Sat 9:30-6 Deli 10-4, Sun 11-4 (Deli & Juice bar closed)
• organic produce • vegetarian friendly • fresh juice • deli • tables • self-service • take-out
🚗 **From I-195,** take exit 3B toward Hamilton Sq north on Hamilton Yardville Rd (right from I-195W, loop around right from I-195E) about 1¾ miles to Rt 33. Turn left onto Rt 33 ⅓ mile to store at Paxson Ave.

UNION

Health Best 🛍

1350 Galloping Hill Rd. ✆ 908-687-4575 ⏱ M-F 10-8, Sat 10-6, Sun 10-5
🚗 **From Garden State Pkwy,** take exit 138 onto Galloping Hill Rd (follow ramp toward Union right from GSP N, follow ramp tow ard Roselle Park/Elizabeth from GSP S) ½ mile to store (before Union Hospital).

VERNON

Healthy Thymes 🛍

287 Rte. 94 ✆ 973-209-855 ⏱ M-F 10-7, Sat 10-5, Sun 11-5
Hot soup to go in winter, smoothies in summer.
• organic produce • fresh juice
🚗 **From Rt 515/94 intersection,** store is under ¼ mile south on Rt 94 on north side.

WARREN

Fountain of Vitality 🛍

100 Mountain Blvd. Ext. ✆ 732-469-0088 ⏱ M-F 9-8, Sat 9:30-6, Sun 11-4
• organic produce
🚗 **From I-78,** take exit 36 toward Warrenville south on King George Rd (left from I-78S, right from I-78N) 1 mile continuing onto Mt Bethel Rd 2 miles to Washington Valley Rd. Turn right onto Washington Valley ⅓ mile to store on right. **From I-287,** merge onto Rt 22E 2¼ miles to N Mountain Ave. Exit onto N Mountain continuing onto Morning Glory Rd 2½ miles total to Washington Valley. Turn right onto Washington Valley almost ⅔ mile to store.

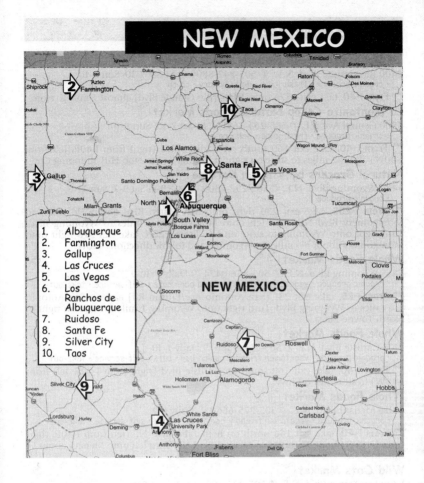

NEW MEXICO

1. Albuquerque
2. Farmington
3. Gallup
4. Las Cruces
5. Las Vegas
6. Los Ranchos de Albuquerque
7. Ruidoso
8. Santa Fe
9. Silver City
10. Taos

ALBUQUERQUE

Annapurna World Vegetarian Cafe 🍴 &

2201 Silver Ave. S.E. ✆ 505-262-2424 ⏰ M-Sat 7-9, Sun 10-8
Organic vegetarian Ayurvedic food. Gluten-free..

· vegetarian · vegan friendly · organic focus · tables · self-service

🍴 **From I-25N**, take exit 223 right onto Ave Cesar Chavez 1 mile (past UNM athletic facilities) to Yale Blvd. Turn left onto Yale about ⅔ mile to restaurant at Silver Ave (a few blocks south of UNM campus). **From I-25S**, take exit 224A onto Locust St to Central Ave. Turn left onto Central under 1 mile to Yale. Turn right onto Yale 2 blocks to restaurant.

Fei Health Cafe 🍴

2114 S.E. Central Ave. ✆ 505-243-3390 ⏰ M-Sat 10-7, Sun 12-5
Chinese vegetarian.

· vegetarian · vegan friendly · tables · wait staff

🍴 **From I-25E,** take exit 224A onto Oak St and turn right onto Central Ave SE under 1 mile to restaurant on right between Buena Vista Dr & Yale Blvd. **From I-25S,** take exit 224B onto Locust St SE, turn left onto Central and follow directions above. **From I-40**, take I-25S and follow directions above.

La Montanita Co-op Natural Foods Market 🛍

2400 Rio Grande Blvd. N.W. ✆ 505-242-8800 ⏰ M-Sat 7-10, Sun 8-10
• organic produce • fresh juice • deli • bakery • co-op

🍎 **From I-40,** take exit 157A onto 194N (Rio Grande Blvd) almost 1 mile to store.

La Montanita Co-op Natural Foods Market 🛍

3500 Central Ave. S.E. ✆ 505-265-4631 ⏰ M-Sat 7-10, Sun 8-10
• organic produce • fresh juice • deli • co-op

🍎 **From I-40,** take exit 160 south on Carlisle Blvd (right from I-40E, left from I-40W) about 2 miles to store on right at Central Ave in Nob Hill Shopping Ctr.

Natural Grocers by Vitamin Cottage 🛍

4420 Wyoming Blvd. N.E. ✆ 505-292-7300 ⏰ M-F 9-8, Sat 9-7, Sun 11-6
• organic produce

🍎 **From I-25S,** take exit 230 right onto San Mateo Blvd about 1½ miles to Montgomery Blvd NE. Turn left onto Montgomery 2 miles to Wyoming Blvd. Turn right onto Wyoming to store on left. **From I-25N,** take exit 228 right onto Montgomery about 3⅓ miles to Wyoming and follow directions above.

Whole Foods Market 🛍 🍴   ♿

5815 Wyoming Blvd. N.E. ✆ 505-856-0474 ⏰ Daily 7:30-9
• organic produce • vegetarian friendly • salad bar • cafe • self-service • take-out

🍎 **From I-25,** take exit 231 (San Antonio Ave/Ellison Rd) east on San Antonio 1½ miles to Wyoming Blvd. Turn right onto Wyoming 1 mile to store on right in North Towne Plaza.

Whole Foods Market 🛍 🍴   ♿

2103 Carlisle Blvd. N.E. ✆ 505-260-1366 ⏰ Daily 7-10
• organic produce • vegetarian friendly • salad bar • cafe • self-service • take-out

🍎 **From I-40,** take exit 160 south on Carlisle Blvd (right from I-40E, left from I-40W) to store just off hwy.

Whole Foods Market 🛍 🍴   ♿

11015 Menaul Blvd. N.E. ✆ 505-275-6660 ⏰ Daily 8-9
• organic produce • vegetarian friendly • salad bar • cafe • self-service • take-out

🍎 **From I-40,** take exit 166 north on Juan Tabo Blvd NE (left from I-40E, right from I-40W) about 2¼ miles to Menaul Blvd NE. Turn left onto Menaul about ¼ mile to store.

Wild Oats Market 🛍 🍴   ♿

6300 San Mateo Blvd. N.E. ✆ 505-823-1933 ⏰ Daily 8-9
• organic produce • vegetarian friendly • salad bar • cafe • self-service • take-out

🍎 **From I-25,** take exit 230 south on San Mateo Blvd to store just off exit in Far North Shopping Ctr

FARMINGTON

Wildly Natural Foods 🛍

2501 E. 20th St. ✆ 505-326-6243 ⏰ M-Sat 9-6:30, Sun 11-4
• organic produce • fresh juice

🍎 **From Rt 64,** go north on Scott Ave (left from 64W, right from 64E) ½ mile to E Main St. Turn right onto E Main 1 mile to Hutton Ave. Turn left onto Hutton ½ mile to 20th St. Turn left onto 20th to store on left.

GALLUP

La Montanita Co-op Natural Foods Market 105 E. Coal Ave. ✆ 505-

863-5383 ⏰ M-Sat 10-7, Sun 11-6
• organic produce • fresh juice • deli • co-op

🍎 **From I-40,** take exit 22 toward Myamora Dr south on Ford Dr (right from I-40E, left from I-40W) over tracks to Hwy 66. Turn right onto Hwy 66 under 1 mile to S Puerco Dr. Turn left onto S Puerco 1 block to E Coal Ave. Turn left onto Coal 1 block to store on right.

LAS CRUCES

Mountain View Market &

1300 El Paseo St. © 505-523-0436 ⏰ -Sat 8-8, Sun 10-7
• organic produce • vegetarian friendly • fresh juice • tables • self-service • take-out • co-op

🍎 **From I-10**, take exit 140 east on NM 28N (becomes Idaho Ave) about 1¼ miles to El Paseo St. Turn right onto El Paseo to store on right. **From I-25**, take exit 6 toward Las Cruces onto 70W (becomes Main St) 2½ miles. Merge onto N Water St (478S) almost 1 mile to El Paseo. Turn left onto El Paseo ½ mile to store after Idaho.

LAS VEGAS

Semilla Natural Foods &

510 University Ave. © 505-425-8139 ⏰ M-F 10-6, Sat. 10-5
• organic produce

🍎 **From I-25**, take exit 345 (NM 65W) onto University Ave towards town (left from I-25N, right from I-25S) 1½ blocks to store on right.

LOS RANCHOS DE ALBUQUERQUE

Moses Kountry Health Foods

7115 4th St. N.W. © 505-898-9763 ⏰ M-Sat 9-6

🍎 **From I-25S**, take exit 232 onto service road and right onto Paseo de Norte NE about 2 miles to Hwy 47 exit (on left). Turn left onto 2nd St NW 1 mile to Roehl Rd NW. Turn right onto Roehl under ½ mile to 4th St NW. Turn left onto 4th to store on right. **From I-25N**, take exit 233 onto Pan Am Fwy (signs for Las Crucas/I-25S), turn left onto Alameda Blvd, left onto Pan Am, take ramp on left toward Belen onto I-25S and follow directions above.

RUIDOSO

The Wild Herb Market

1715 Sudderth Drive © 505-257-0138 ⏰ M-F 9-6, Sat 9-5, Juice bar 9-4, Deli 9-3
• organic produce • vegetarian friendly • fresh juice • deli • tables • self-serve • take-out

🍎 **From NM 70**, go west on NM 37/NM 48 (Sudderth Rd) over 2 miles to store on left.

SANTA FE

Annapurna World Vegetarian Cafe &

905 W. Alameda St. © 505-988-9688 ⏰ M-Sat 10-9
Organic vegetarian Ayurvedic food. Gluten-free.
• vegetarian • vegan friendly • organic focus • tables • self-service

🍎 **From I-25**, take exit 282B onto US 84N/St Francis Dr (left from I-25N, right from I-25S) about 3½ miles to light at W Alameda Ave. Turn left onto W Alameda 1½ blocks to restaurant on right in Solana Ctr.

Body Cafe

333 Cordova Rd. © 505-986-0362 ⏰ Daily 7:30-9
Mostly vegetarian and raw with some fish and poultry. Located in Body, a holistic health center.
• vegetarian friendly • vegan friendly • organic focus • fresh juice • alcohol • tables • wait staff

From I-25, take exit 282B onto US 84N/St Francis Dr (left from I-25N, right from I-25S) about 2½ miles to W Cordova Rd. Turn right onto W Cordova under ½ mile to restaurant on left at Don Diego Ave.

Cloud Cliff Bakery & Cafe

1805 2nd St. © 505-983-6254 ⏰ Tues-Sun 7:30-4 (cafe menu until 2:30)
Southwestern vegetarian, free-range meat and poultry. Homemade organic baked goods.
• vegetarian friendly • organic focus • bakery • tables • wait staff

🍎 **From I-25**, take exit 282B onto US 84N/St Francis Dr (left from I-25N, right from I-25S) 1 mile to St Michael's Dr ramp. Turn left onto St Michael's ½ mile to Calle Lorca. Turn right onto Lorca 1 block to W San Mateo Rd. Turn left onto San Mateo (becomes 2nd St) to restaurant.

La Montanita Co-op Natural Foods Market 🛍️🍴
913 W. Alameda St. ✆ 505-984-8863 ⏱ M-Sat 7-10, Sun 8-10
• organic produce • vegetarian friendly • fresh juice • salad bar • cafe • deli • tables •
self-service • take-out • co-op

📷 **From I-25**, take exit 282B onto US 84N/St Francis Dr (left from I-25N, right from I-25S) about 3½ miles to Alameda Ave. Turn left onto Alameda 1½ blocks to store on right in Solana Ctr.

Whole Foods Market 🛍️🍴
753 Cerrillos Rd. ✆ 505-992-1700 ⏱ Daily 7:30-10
• organic produce • vegetarian friendly • salad bar • cafe • self-service • take-out

📷 **From I-25**, take exit 282B onto US 84N/St Francis Dr (left from I-25N, right from I-25S) about 2⅔ miles to Cerrillos Rd. Turn right onto Cerrillos about ¼ mile to store on right.

Wild Oats Market 🛍️🍴
1090 St. Francis Drive ✆ 505-983-5333 ⏱ Daily 7:30-10
• organic produce • vegetarian friendly • salad bar • cafe • self-service • take-out

📷 **From I-25**, take exit 282B onto US 84N/St Francis Dr (left from I-25N, right from I-25S) about 2½ miles to store on left.

Natural Grocers by Vitamin Cottage 🛍️
3328 Cerrillos Rd. ✆ 505-474-0111 ⏱ M-F 9-8, Sat 9-7, Sun 11-6
• organic produce

📷 **From I-25**, take exit 278 (278B from I-25S) onto Cerrillos Rd about 3½ miles to store on right.

SILVER CITY _____

Peace Meal Co-op 🍴
601 N. Bullard St. ✆ 505-388-0106 ⏱ M-Sat 11-3
Worker-owned restaurant/deli. Sandwiches, salads and daily hot specials at affordable prices.
• vegetarian • vegan friendly • organic focus • tables • self-service

📷 **From US 180/NM 90 intersection**, go south on NM 90 (N Hudson St) ½ mile to E College Ave. Turn right onto E College 1 block to N Bullard St. Turn left onto N Bullard 2 blocks to restaurant on right at 7th St.

Silver City Food Co-op 🛍️
520 N. Bullard St. ✆ 505-388-2343 ⏱ M-Sat 9-7
• organic produce • co-op

📷 **From US 180/NM 90 intersection**, go south on NM 90 (N Hudson St) ½ mile to E College Ave. Turn right onto E College 1 block to N Bullard St. Turn left onto N Bullard 2½ blocks to store on right between 7th & 6th St.

TAOS _____

Cid's Food Market 🛍️
623 Paseo del Pueblo Norte ✆ 505-758-1148 ⏱ M-Sat. 7:30-7
• organic produce • vegetarian friendly • deli • bakery • take-out

📷 Store is on Hwy 64/68 (aka Paseo de Pueblo Norte) about 1 mile north of Taos Plaza (2 blocks past second light) on right.

The Appletree Restaurant 🍴
123 Bent St. ✆ 505-758-1900 ⏱ Lunch Daily 11:30-3 Dinner W-Sun 5-9
• vegetarian friendly • alcohol • tables • wait staff

📷 **From Hwy 64/68 (aka Paseo de Pueblo Norte)**, turn west onto Bent St (opposite Taos Plaza) to restaurant.

SIX HEALTHY HIGHWAYS'
"RULES FOR THE ROAD"

1. Choose different ethnic foods when possible. *Gained*: New foods, greater variety, new experiences.

2. Order vegetarian. Even if you aren't a vegetarian, seize every opportunity to eat like one. This will automatically improve your diet because meatless dining depends on beans, grains, vegetables, fruit, nuts, and seeds. *Gained*: More variety, more fiber, less saturated fat.

3. Go for salad and vegetables (but go light on dressing and sauce). There is no such thing as too many vegetables. *Gained*: Numerous vitamins, minerals, fiber, health-protecting phytochemicals.

4. Avoid unnecessary fats. Chefs are accustomed to using butter, oil and other fats when they cook, so don't add to this yourself. Be sparing with dressings, sauces, butter on bread (even the trendy olive oil.) Order foods poached or broiled instead of fried. *Gained*: Less fat, fewer calories.

5. Always ask if there is whole grain bread or brown rice. Even if there isn't, with enough requests they may start to stock it. *Gained*: More fiber, greater restaurant awareness.

6. Just desserts. Many of us find dessert hard to pass up. Even in health-oriented eateries, desserts are often calorie-laden. Look for lower fat options (sorbet, biscotti), something fruit-based (apple crisp, strawberry shortcake), or a treat with some nutritious ingredients (baked custard, rice pudding). If you can't resist something really indulgent, suggest sharing. *Lost*: Empty calories, fat and sugar.

1.	Albany	44.	Jamaica
2.	Amagansett	45.	Jamaica Hills
3.	Amherst	46.	Jeffersonville
4.	Babylon Village	47.	Jericho
5.	Ballston Spa	48.	Johnson City
6.	Beacon	49.	Katonah
7.	Bedford Village	50.	Kingston
8.	Binghamton	51.	Larchmont
9.	Boiceville	52.	Liberty
10.	Bronx	53.	Little Falls
11.	Brooklyn	54.	Mahopac
12.	Buffalo	55.	Manhasset
13.	Cambridge	56.	Massapequa
14.	Canton	57.	Montauk
15.	Catskill	58.	Mt. Kisco
16.	Chestnut Ridge	59.	Nanuet
17.	Clifton Park	60.	New City
18.	Commack	61.	New Hartford
19.	Cross River	62.	New Paltz
20.	Delhi	63.	New York
21.	East Hampton	64.	Northport
22.	East Meredith	65.	Nyack
23.	East Setauket	66.	Oceanside
24.	East Syracuse	67.	Oliverea
25.	Ellenville	68.	Oneonta
26.	Endicott	69.	Phoenicia
27.	Flushing	70.	Pine Bush
28.	Forest Hills	71.	Plainview
29.	Fresh Meadows	72.	Plattsburgh
30.	Garden City	73.	Port Jefferson
31.	Ghent	74.	Port Washington
32.	Glen Cove	75.	Potsdam
33.	Glens Falls	76.	Poughkeepsie
34.	Great Neck	77.	Rhinebeck
35.	Hamburg	78.	Riverhead
36.	Hamilton	79.	Rochester
37.	Hampton Bays	80.	Rockville Centre
38.	Hicksville	81.	Rocky Point
39.	High Falls	82.	Rosendale
40.	Hudson	83.	Sag Harbor
41.	Hunter	84.	Saranac Lake
42.	Huntington	85.	Saratoga Springs
43.	Ithaca	86.	Saugerties

87.	Sayville
88.	Scarsdale
89.	Spring Valley
90.	Staten Island
91.	Suffern
92.	Syracuse
93.	Tivoli
94.	Troy
95.	Watertown
96.	West Seneca
97.	Westhampton Beach
98.	White Plains
99.	Williamsville
100.	Woodstock

ALBANY

A Taste of Greece 🍴

193 Lark St. ℰ 518-426-9000 ⏲ M-F 11-2, 5-10, Sat 4-10

Vegetarian dishes you rarely see unless you are invited home for dinner by a Greek friend.

• vegetarian friendly • alcohol • tables • wait staff • take-out

🍎 **From I-90**, take exit 6 onto US 9S almost 1 mile to US 9/Clinton Ave. Turn left onto Clinton and right onto Lark St about ⅓ mile to restaurant on right at Spring St. **From I-87S (Northway)**, merge onto I-90E via exit 1 and follow directions above. **From I-87N**, take exit 23 onto I-787 N (toward Downtown Albany) 1¾ miles to exit 3 (US 9S/20E). Take Empire Plaza ramp straight onto S Mall Arterial ½ mile to S Swan St. Turn right onto S Swan ¼ mile to Washington Ave. Turn left onto Washington ¼ mile to Lark. Turn left onto Lark 1 block to restaurant.

Honest Weight Food Co-op

484 Central Ave. © 518-482-2667 ◷ M-Sat 7-8, Sun 9-7
· organic produce · vegetarian · vegan friendly · fresh juice · cafe · deli · bakery ·
tables · self service · take-out · co-op

From I-90, take exit 5 south on Everett Rd (right from I-90E, left from I-90W) about ½ mile to end at Central Ave/NY 5. Turn left onto Central ¾ mile to store on right (behind Family Dollar store). **From I-87S,** merge onto I-90E via exit 1E and follow directions above. **From I-87N,** take exit 23 onto I-787N 1¾ miles to exit 3 (US 9S/20E) toward Empire Plaza. Take Empire Plaza ramp onto S Mall Arterial to S Swan St. Turn right onto S Swan ¼ mile to Washington Ave. Turn left onto Washington to Central. Turn right onto Central about 1 mile to store on left.

Little Anthony's ⑪

450 Madison Ave. ✆ 518-463-1881 ⊕ M-Th, Sun 11-8, F-Sat 11-10:30
Vegan pizza, calzone, subs and "meatballs" along with more typical fare.
   • vegan friendly • tables • self-service • take-out

🚗 **From I-90,** take exit 6 south onto US 9 over ½ mile to Clinton Ave. Turn left onto Clinton 1 block and right onto Lark St ¾ mile to Madison Ave. Turn right onto Madison to restaurant on left. **From I-87,** take exit 23 toward Albany right at fork toward US 9W and left at fork toward Albany to Southern Blvd/US 9W. Turn left onto Southern about 1 mile to end at Delaware Ave. Turn right onto Delaware 1⅓ miles to Madison. Turn left onto Madison to restaurant.

Little Anthony's ⑪

1095 Central Ave. ✆ 518-459-5959 ⊕ M-Th 10-10, F-Sat 10-11, Sun 10-9
See Madison Ave location for description.
   • vegan friendly • tables • self-service • take-out

🚗 **From I-90,** take exit 5 south on Everett Rd (right from I-90E, left from I-90W) about ½ mile to end at Central Ave/NY 5. Turn right onto Central 1 mile to restaurant on left. **From I-87S,** take exit 2E toward Albany south on Central 2 miles to restaurant. **From I-87N,** take exit 24 onto I-87N/I-90E. Take exit 1N toward Montreal onto I-87N to exit 2E and follow directions above.

AMAGANSETT

Hampton Chutney Co. ⑪

Main St, Amagansett Square ✆ 631-267-3131 ⊕ Daily 10-5 (later in season)
Indian dosas, sandwiches and a daily vegetarian thali. Seating at picnic tables on the lawn.
   • vegetarian friendly • take-out

🚗 Take Rt 27 (Montauk Hwy) into Amagansett. Turn onto Hedges Ln (right from the Hamptons, left from Montauk) 1 block and turn left into parking lot for Amagansett Square. Store is on right entering from lot.

AMHERST

Feel-Rite Fresh Market ⬆⑪

3912 Maple Rd. ✆ 716-834-3385 ⊕ M-Sat 9-9, Sun 10-7
   • organic produce • vegetarian friendly • fresh juice • deli • tables • self-service • take-out
🚗 **From I-290,** take exit 3 south on Niagara Falls Blvd to Maple Rd. Turn left onto Maple to store on left.

BABYLON VILLAGE

Sherry's The Healthy Gourmet ⬆   ♿

89 Deer Park Ave. ✆ 631-661-5552 ⊕ M-F 9-7, Sat-Sun 9-5
   • organic produce
🚗 Take Montauk Hwy (27A) to Deer Park Ave in the heart of Babylon. Turn north onto Deer Park ½ block to store on right.

BALLSTON SPA

Wild Thyme Whole Food & Tea Co. ⬆

108 Milton Ave. ✆ 518-885-7275 ⊕ M-F 9-7, Sat 9-6, Sun 12-5
A few tables but primarily grab-and-go soups and sandwiches.
   • organic produce • vegetarian friendly • tables • self-service • take-out

🚗 **From I-87S,** take exit 13N toward Saratoga Springs onto Rt 9 to Old Post Rd. Turn left onto Old Post 2 miles to Malta Ave/CR 63. Veer right onto CR 63 1½ miles to Milton Ave/Rt 50. Turn right onto Milton to store on right. **From I-87N,** take exit 12 for State Hwy 67 W toward Ballston Spa. At traffic circle take third exit onto Rt 67/Dunning St. At next two traffic circles take first exit to continue on Rt 67 about 4⅓ miles (becomes Church Ave then Milton) to store on right.

BEACON

Beacon Natural Market 🛍 🍴
348 Main St. ✆ 845-838-1288 ⊕ M-Sat 9-7, Sun 10-5
 • organic produce • deli • tables • self-service • take-out
🍎 **From I-84**, take exit 11 toward Beacon south on 9D about ¾ mile to Main St.
Turn left onto Main over ½ mile to store on left after Eliza St.

BEDFORD VILLAGE

Near and Natural 🛍 🍴
1 Court Rd. ✆ 914-205-3545 ⊕ M-F 7-6, Sat 8-3, Sun 8-2
 • organic produce • vegetarian friendly • deli • salad bar • tables • self-service • take-out
🍎 **From I-684**, take exit 4 east on S Bedford Rd (left from I-684S, right from
I-684N) over 1½ miles to Old Post Rd. Turn left onto Old Post/Rt 22 over 1 mile
to Court Rd. Turn right onto Court to store on right.

BINGHAMTON

SUNY Binghamton Co-op 🛍 🍴
Student Union, SUNY ✆ 607-777-4258 ⊕ M-F 11-4, Kitchen 12-3
 • vegan • organic focus • cafe • tables • self-service • take-out • co-op
🍎 **From I-81**, take exit 6 toward Rt 12/Chenango Bridge onto Rt 11S ⅓ mile to
Front St (Rt 12). Turn left onto Front almost 1⅓ miles (follow signs to SUNY
Binghamton). Store is in student union. **From I-88**, take exit 2 toward Chenango
Bridge onto Rt 12A (Chenango Bridge Rd) 1 mile to Front. Turn left onto Front to
SUNY Binghamton and store in student union.

Whole in the Wall Restaurant 🍴   ♿
43 S. Washington St. ✆ 607-722-5138 ⊕ Tues-Sat 11:30-9
Natural foods restaurant. BYOB. Live music weekends.
 • vegetarian friendly • vegan friendly • tables • wait staff • take-out
🍎 **From Rt 17 & I-81**, take exit 4S (Rt 7S) onto Rt 363W about 1¾ miles to Rt 434W
toward Vestal. Merge onto 434W, cross bridge and stay left. Make first left onto S
Washington St to restaurant on left.

BOICEVILLE

Bread Alone 🍴
Rte. 28 ✆ 845-657-3328 ⊕ Daily 7-5
Organic bread baked in wood-fired ovens, soups, salads and sandwiches.
 • vegetarian friendly • bakery • tables • self-service • take-out
🍎 **From I-87 (NY Thwy)**, take exit 19 (Kingston). Take first exit off rotary onto Rt
28W toward Pine Hill about 16 miles to bakery on right (set back on access road).

BRONX

Green Garden Health Foods 🛍 🍴
3584 White Plains Rd. ✆ 718-652-9535 ⊕ M-Sat 11-9
Caribbean veggie patties.
 • vegetarian • vegan friendly • fresh juice • counter • take-out
🍎 **From Bronx River Pkwy N**, take exit 9 right onto E Gun Hill Rd under ¼ mile to
White Plains Rd. Turn left onto White Plains about 3 blocks to restaurant on right.
From Bronx River Pkwy S, take exit 10 onto Webster Ave about 1⅓ miles to E Gun Hill.
Turn left onto E Gun Hill about ⅓ mile to White Plains and follow directions above.

*Please tell these businesses
that you found them in Healthy Highways*

Katashe's Vegetarian Food 🍴

1312 E. Gun Hill Rd. ✆ 718-231-9885 ⏱ M-F, Sun 10-9
Caribbean vegan and fish. Take out only.
  • vegetarian friendly • vegan friendly • take-out

🍎 E Gun Hill Rd is east of Bronx River Pkwy, west of NE Thwy & Hutchinson River Pkwy, and north of Pelham Pkwy. Restaurant is on E Gun Hill between Young & Burke Ave on south side.

Vegan's Delight 🍴

3565C Boston Rd. ✆ 718-653-4140 ⏱ M-Sat 7:30-7
  • vegan • organic focus • fresh juice • self-service • take-out

🍎 **From I-95S (New England Thwy)** take exit 13 toward Baychester Ave onto Hollers Ave and turn right onto Delavalle Ave and left onto US1/Boston Rd about 1 mile to restaurant on right after E 222nd St. **From I-95N**, take exit 12 on left onto Baychester Ave about ¾ mile to US 1/Boston Rd. Turn left onto Boston under ½ mile to restaurant.

BROOKLYN

Back to the Land Natural Foods 🛍

142 Seventh Ave. ✆ 718-768-5654 ⏱ Daily 9-9
  • organic produce • deli • take-out

🍎 In Park Slope. **From Manhattan Bridge**, take Flatbush Ave Ext (continuing onto Flatbush Ave) under 1 mile to 7th Ave. Turn right onto 7th under ½ mile to store on right between Carroll St & Garfield Pl (a few blocks west of Prospect Park). **From Belt Pkwy or Gowanus Expwy**, take exit 23 onto 38th St and turn left onto 4th Ave 2 miles to Carroll. Turn right onto Carroll 3 blocks to 7th Ave. Turn right onto 7th to store.

Bliss Cafe 🍴

191 Bedford Ave. ✆ 718-599-2547 ⏱ M-F 9-11, Sat-Sun 10-11
  • vegetarian • vegan friendly • tables • wait staff

🍎 **From Williamsburg Bridge**, turn right onto Broadway 2 blocks to Bedford Ave. Turn right onto Bedford over ½ mile to restaurant on right between N 6th & N 7th St. **From Brooklyn Queens Expwy (BQE)** east, take exit 32 toward Manhattan onto Rodney St to Metropolitan Ave. Turn left onto Metropolitan 2 blocks, veer right onto N 4th St 3 blocks and turn right onto Bedford 2½ blocks to restaurant. **From BQE west**, take exit 32B onto Meeker Ave to N 6th. Turn left onto N 6th 4 blocks to Bedford. Turn right onto Bedford to restaurant.

Cafe Paris Vegetarian 🍴

4424 16th Ave. ✆ 718-853-2353 ⏱ M-Th 9-5
Vegetarian and fish. No flour or sugar in anything.
  • vegetarian friendly • vegan friendly • kosher • tables • wait staff

🍎 **From I-278W (Gowanus Expwy)**, take exit 24 on left onto Prospect Expwy continuing onto Ocean Pkwy 2½ miles total to 18th Ave. Turn right onto 18th under ½ mile to 45th St. Turn right onto 45th and make second right onto 16th Ave 1 block to restaurant on left. **From I-278E**, take exit 23 onto 38th St 2 blocks to 5th Ave. Turn right onto 5th and left onto 39th St over ½ mile to New Utrecht Ave. Veer right onto New Utrecht about ⅓ mile to Fort Hamilton Pkwy. Make sharp left onto Fort Hamilton and right onto 44th St under ½ mile to 16th. Turn right onto 16th to restaurant on right.

D'Ital Shak 🍴

989 Nostrand Ave. ✆ 718-756-6557 ⏱ M 9am-Sun 9 pm (Closed only Sun pm-M am)
Jamaican Ital food.
  • vegan • counter • tables • self-service • take-out

🍎 **From Eastern Pkwy**, go south on Nostrand Ave (right from Pkwy E, left from Pkwy W) under ½ mile to restaurant on east side between Sullivan Pl & Empire Blvd. **From Prospect Expwy,** take exit 5 toward Ft Hamilton Pkwy onto E 5th St and turn left onto Caton Ave 1 mile to Flatbush Ave. Turn left onto Flatbush ½ mile continuing onto Washington Ave about ½ mile to Montgomery St. Turn right onto Montgomery ½ mile to Nostrand Ave. Turn right onto Nostrand to restaurant.

Earth Tonez 🍴

349 5th Ave. ✆ 718-395-1516 🕐 Daily 12-10
Soup, panini, wraps, burgers. Bio-degradable tableware and take-out packaging.
   • vegetarian • vegan friendly • fresh juice • counter • tables • self-service • take-out

🥡 In Park Slope. **From Manhattan Bridge** take Flatbush Ave Ext (continuing onto Flatbush Ave) 1 mile to 4th Ave. Turn right onto 4th about 1 mile to 3rd St. Turn left onto 3rd 1 block to 5th Ave. Turn right onto 5th to restaurant on left between 4th & 5th St. **From Belt Pkwy or Gowanus Expwy,** take exit 23 onto 38th St and turn left onto 4th Ave 1¾ miles to 5th St. Turn right onto 5th 1 block to 5th Ave. Turn left onto 5th to restaurant on right.

Everything Natural 🛍

1661 Ralph Ave. ✆ 718-531-9192 🕐 M, Th 10:15-7, Tues, W, F 10:15-6, Sat 10:15-3
   • organic produce

🚗 **From Belt Pkwy,** take exit 13 onto Rockaway Pkwy about 1¼ miles to Flatlands Ave. Turn left onto Flatlands 1¼ miles to Ralph Ave. Turn right onto Ralph 2 blocks to store on right between Glenwood & Farragut Rd.

Flatbush Food Co-op 🛍

1318 Cortelyou Rd. ✆ 718-284-9717 🕐 Daily 7-11
   • organic produce • co-op

🚗 **From Brooklyn Queens Expwy (I-278),** take Prospect Expwy (first exit past Brooklyn Battery Tunnel on left), which becomes Ocean Pkwy once lights begin. At second light turn left onto Beverly Rd about ⅓ mile to Westminster Rd. Turn right onto Westminster and make first left onto Cortelyou to store on right after E 13th St.

Foodswings 🍴

295 Grand St. ✆ 718-388-1919 🕐 Tues-Th 5pm-12am, F 5-2am, Sat 2-2, Sun 2-11
Vegan fast food.
   • vegan • tables • self-service • take-out

🥡 In Williamsburg. **From Williamsburg Bridge,** turn left onto Havemeyer 5 blocks to Grand St. Turn right onto Grand to restaurant on right. **From Brooklyn Queens Expwy (BQE) east**, take exit 32 onto Rodney St to Metropolitan Ave. Turn left onto Metropolitan 1 block to Marcy Ave. Turn left onto Marcy 2 blocks to Grand. Turn right onto Grand 1½ blocks to restaurant between Havemeyer & Roebling St. **From BQE west,** take exit 32B onto Meeker Ave 1 block to Marcy. Turn left onto Marcy and follow directions above.

Imhotep 🍴

734 Nostrand Ave. ✆ 718-493-2395 🕐 Daily 9-9
Vegan Caribbean fare.
   • vegan • organic focus • tables • wait staff • take-out

🚗 **From Eastern Pkwy,** go north on NY Ave (left from Pkwy E, right from Pkwy W) 5 blocks to Prospect Pl. Turn left onto Prospect and left onto Nostrand 1 block to restaurant on left. **From Atlantic Ave going east**, turn right onto Nostrand 6 blocks to restaurant on right. **From Atlantic Ave going west**, turn right onto Perry Pl, right onto Herkimer Pl, right onto Nostrand and follow directions above.

Natural Frontier Market 🛍

1104 Cortelyou Rd. ✆ 718-284-3593 🕐 Daily 8-11
   • organic produce

🚗 **From Prospect Expwy,** continue onto Ocean Pkwy 3 blocks to Cortelyou Rd. Turn left onto Courtelyou 4 blocks to Coney Island Ave. Turn left onto Coney Island and right onto Coretelyou 1 block to store on right after 11th St.

Red Bamboo 🍴

271 Adelphi St. ✆ 718-643-4352 🕐 M-W 12-11, Th-Sun 11-12
Caribbean soul cuisine.
   • vegetarian • vegan friendly • fresh juice • alcohol • tables • wait staff

🚗 **From the Brooklyn Queens Expwy (I-278),** go south on Adelphi St (right from I-278E, left from I-278W) 3 blocks to restaurant on left at DeKalb Ave.

Scoops 🍴

624 Flatbush Ave. ✆ 718-282-5904 🕐 Tues-Sat 10-10
Food and vegan ice cream.

• vegetarian • vegan friendly, tables, self-service

🚗 **From Manhattan Bridge**, take Flatbush Ave Ext continuing onto Flatbush Ave 3 miles to restaurant on right between Rutland Rd & Fenimore St. **From Prospect Expwy**, take exit 5 toward Ft Hamilton Pkwy onto E 5th St and turn left onto Caton Ave 1 mile to Flatbush. Turn left onto Flatbush 5 blocks to restaurant on left after Fenimore.

Second Helpings 🍴

448 9th St. ✆ 718-965-1925 🕐 M-F 8-8:30, Sat-Sun 10:30-8

• vegetarian friendly • vegan friendly • organic focus • fresh juice • tables • self-service • take-out

🚗 In Park Slope. **From Manhattan Bridge** take Flatbush Ave Ext (continuing onto Flatbush Ave) 1 mile to 4th Ave. Turn right onto 4th about 1¼ miles to 9th St. Turn left onto 9th 3 blocks to restaurant right at 7th Ave. **From Belt Pkwy or Gowanus Expwy**, take exit 23 onto 38th St and turn left onto 4th Ave 1½ miles to 9th St. Turn right onto 9th 3 blocks to restaurant.

Siggy's Good Food 🍴

76 Henry St. ✆ 718-237-3199 🕐 M, W-Th 11-10:30, F-Sun 9-10:30
vegetarian, organic meat, fish and chicken. Organic beer and wine.

• vegetarian friendly • vegan friendly • organic focus • fresh juice • alcohol • tables • wait staff

🚗 **From Brooklyn Queens Expwy (I-278)**, take exit 28 (28A from BQE E) onto Old Fulton St/Cadman Plaza (left from BQE W, right from BQE E) and turn right onto Henry St to restaurant on right between Pineapple & Orange St.

'sNice 🍴

315 5th Ave. ✆ 718-788-2121 🕐 M-Sat 7:30am-10pm, Sun 8am-10pm
Breakfast, sandwiches and salads.

• vegetarian • vegan friendly • tables • self-service • take-out

🚗 In Park Slope. **From Manhattan Bridge** take Flatbush Ave Ext (continuing onto Flatbush Ave) 1 mile to 4th Ave. Turn right onto 4th about 1 mile to 3rd St. Turn left onto 3rd 1 block to 5th Ave. Turn left onto 5th to restaurant on right. **From Belt Pkwy or Gowanus Expwy**, take exit 23 onto 38th St and turn left onto 4th Ave 1¾ miles to 3rd St. Turn right onto 3rd 1 block to 5th Ave. Turn left onto 5th to restaurant.

Strictly Vegetarian 🍴

2268 Church Ave. ✆ 718-284-2543 🕐 M-Th 11:30-9:30, F-Sat 11:30-10:30, Sun 12:30-7
Ital Caribbean food. A few seats but mostly take-out.

• vegan • self-service • take-out

🚗 **From Prospect Expwy**, take exit 5 toward Ft Hamilton Pkwy onto E 5th St and turn left onto Caton Ave 1 mile to Flatbush. Turn right onto Flatbush 3 blocks to Church Ave. Turn left onto Church to restaurant on right.

The V-Spot 🍴

156 5th Ave. ✆ 718-622-2275 🕐 Tues-Th 11-10, F-Sat 11-10:30, Sun 11-9
Extensive menu with all the "meat" dishes wheat or soy protein.

• vegan • alcohol • tables • wait staff

🚗 In Park Slope. **From Manhattan Bridge** take Flatbush Ave Ext (continuing onto Flatbush Ave) 1 mile to 5th Ave. Turn right onto 5th about 7 blocks to restaurant on right between Douglass & Degraw St. **From Belt Pkwy or Gowanus Expwy**, take exit 23 onto 38th St and turn left onto 4th Ave 2¼ miles to Douglass St. Turn right onto Douglass 1 block to 5th Ave. Turn right onto 5th to restaurant.

Vegetarian Palate 🍴

258 Flatbush Ave. ✆ 718-623-8808 🕐 M-Th, Sun 11:30-10:30, F-Sat 11:30-11:30
Chinese vegetarian. Only eight tables.

· vegetarian · vegan friendly · tables · wait staff · take-out

From Manhattan Bridge, take Flatbush Ave Ext continuing onto Flatbush Ave almost 1½ miles to restaurant on right between St Marks Ave & Prospect Pl. **From Brooklyn Queens Expwy (BQE) west**, take exit 29 toward Manhattan Bridge onto Tillary St, turn left onto Flatbush Ave Ext and follow directions above. **From BQE east,** take exit 27 onto Atlantic Ave 1⅓ miles to Flatbush Ave. Turn right onto Flatbush under ½ mile to restaurant.

Wendy's Plate 🍴

434 Ave. U ✆ 718-376-3125 ⏰ M-Th 11-10, F 11-2:30, Sat 1 hour after sundown-12am
A kosher dairy restaurant which means fish but no meat.

· vegetarian friendly · kosher · tables · wait staff

From Prospect Expwy, continue onto Ocean Pkwy 3⅓ miles to Ave U. Turn right onto U to restaurant on left after 4th St. **From Belt Pkwy,** take exit 7 (7B from Pkwy W) north (away from water) onto Ocean Pkwy 1 mile to Ave U. Turn left onto U to restaurant.

Wild Ginger Brooklyn 🍴

212 Bedford Ave. ✆ 718-218-8828 ⏰ M-Th, Sun 12-10:30, F-Sat 12-11
98% vegan Chinese, Japanese, Thai and Vietnamese. Brown rice with all entrees.

· vegetarian · vegan friendly · alcohol · tables · wait staff · take-out

In Williamsburg. **From Williamsburg Bridge** turn right onto Broadway 2 blocks to Bedford Ave. Turn right onto Bedford ½ mile to restaurant on left between N 5th & N 6th St. **From Brooklyn Queens Expwy (BQE) east,** take exit 32 toward Manhattan onto Rodney St to Metropolitan Ave. Turn left onto Metropolitan 2 blocks, veer right onto N 4th St 3 blocks and turn right onto Bedford to restaurant after N 5th. **From BQE west,** take exit 32B onto Meeker Ave to Metropolitan. Veer right onto Metropolitan and follow directions above.

BUFFALO

Feel-Rite Natural Food Shop 🛍

2141 Delaware Ave. ✆ 716-837-7661 ⏰ M-Sat 9-9, Sun 10-7

From I-190, take exit 11 onto Squajaquada Expwy E/RT 198 2 miles to Delaware Ave. Merge onto Delaware over ½ mile to store on right.

Lexington Real Foods Community Co-op 🛍

807 Elmwood Ave. ✆ 716-884-8828 ⏰ Daily 8-10
· organic produce · co-op

From I-190N, take exit 9 right onto Busti Ave continuing onto Niagara St over ½ mile to W Ferry St. Turn right onto W Ferry 1 mile to Elmwood Ave. Turn right onto Elmwood about 3 blocks to store on right after Auburn Ave. **From I-190S,** take exit 11 onto Squajaquada Expwy E/RT 198 1½ miles to exit for Elmwood Ave (after Buffalo State College). Turn right onto Iroquois Dr and left onto Elmwood 1 mile to store on left after Lafayette Ave.

CAMBRIDGE

Village Store Co-op 🛍

25 E. Main St. ✆ 518-677-5731 ⏰ M, W-Sat 10-5, Th 10-8
· organic produce · co-op

From Rt 22, go west on E Main St (left from 22N, right from 22S) to store right in town.

CANTON

Nature's Storehouse 🛍

21 Main St. ✆ 315-386-3740 ⏰ M-F 9-6, Sat 10-5, sun 12-4
· organic produce

From US 11N, turn right at first light in town onto Main St to store on left. **From US 11S,** store is 1¼ miles past Rt 68/310 intersection on right.

CATSKILL
Kaaterskill Farm Natural Storehouse 🛍
280 Grandview Plaza ✆ 518-943-1919 ⏰ M-Th, Sat 9:30-6, F 9:30-7, Sun 12-5
 • organic produce

🍎 **From I-87 (NY Thwy)**, take exit 21 (Catskill) onto 23E about 1 mile to Rt 9W. Turn right onto 9W about 1 mile to Grandview Ave. Store is on right in Grandview Plaza.

CHESTNUT RIDGE
Hungry Hollow Co-op 🛍
841 Chestnut Ridge Rd. ✆ 845-356-3319 ⏰ M-F 8-7, Sat 9-7, Sun 11-5
 • organic produce • deli • take-out • co-op

🍎 **From Garden State Pkwy N**, take exit 172 and turn left at light onto Grand Ave. Turn right at first light onto Chestnut Ridge (becomes Rt 45) 2½ miles (across NY border and past three lights) to store on left at Hungry Hollow Rd. **From NY Thwy**, take exit 14A (Garden State Pkwy). Take first exit (Red Schoolhouse Rd). Turn right at stop sign and left at first light onto Chestnut Ridge (Rt 45) to store.

CLIFTON PARK
Antipasto's 🍴
1028 Rte. 146 ✆ 518-383-1209 ⏰ M, Sun 4:30-8:30, Tues 4:30-9, W-Sat 4:30-10
Mostly vegetarian Italian/Mediterranean menu (with vegan meatballs). .
 • vegetarian friendly • vegan friendly • alcohol • tables • wait staff • take-out

🍎 **From I-87**, take exit 9 (9W from I-87S) west on Rt 146/Clifton Park Blvd (left from I-87N, merge right from I-87S) about 2¼ miles to restaurant on left before Vischer Ferry Rd.

The Green Grocer 🛍
1505 Rte. 9 ✆ 518-383-1613 ⏰ M-F 10-8, Sat. 10-6, Sun. 12-5
 • organic produce

🍎 **From I-87**, take exit 8A east on Grooms Rd (right from I-87N, left from I-87S) 1½ miles to Rt 9. Turn left onto Rt 9 to first right into Half Moon Plaza to store.

COMMACK
The Mung Bean 🛍
6522 Jericho Tpke. ✆ 631-499-2362 ⏰ M-F 9-7, Sat 9-6, Sun 10-5
 • organic produce • fresh juice

🍎 **From LIE (I-495)**, take exit 52 north on CR 4N/Commack Rd about 2¾ miles to Jericho Tpke. Turn right onto Jericho to store in Commack Corners Shopping Ctr. **From Northern Pkwy**, take exit 43 onto CR 4N/Commack Rd almost 2 miles to Jericho and follow directions above.

CROSS RIVER
Nature's Temptations 🛍 🍴
890 Rte. 35 ✆ 914-763-5643 ⏰ M-F 9:30-7, Sat 9-5, Sun 10-3
 • organic produce • vegetarian friendly • fresh juice • salad bar • deli • bakery • tables
 • self-service • take-out

🍎 **From I-684**, take exit 6 east on Rt 35 (Cross River Rd) about 3¾ miles to store at Rt 121 in Cross River Plaza.

DELHI
Good Cheap Food 🛍
53 Main St. ✆ 607-746-6562 ⏰ M-Sat 10-6
 • organic produce

🍎 Store is on south side of Main St just east of Rt 28W/Kingston St intersection.

EAST HAMPTON

Babette's 🍴 ♿

66 Newton Lane ☎ 631-329-5377 🕒 Labor Day-Memorial Day Daily 8am-10pm, Memorial Day-Dec M, Th-Sun 9-10 Jan-Labor Day F-Sat 9-10, Sun 9-5

• vegetarian friendly • organic focus • alcohol • counter • tables • wait staff • take-out

🚗 **From Rt 27E**, turn left onto Main St about 1 mile to Newton Ln. Turn left onto Newton 1½ blocks to restaurant on ri ght. **From tip of LI on Rt 27W (Montauk Hwy)**, turn right onto Newton and follow directions above.

EAST MEREDITH

Fable/ Stone & Thistle Farm 🍴

1211 Kelso Rd. ☎ 607-278-5800 🕒 Dinner May-Dec Sat 7pm Farm Daily 11-6

A "farm to table," prix-fixe, one seating 4-hour Saturday dinner and farm tour featuring home-grown or locally raised vegetables and animal products. Reservations required; vegetarian must be requested ahead.

• vegetarian friendly • organic focus • alcohol • tables • wait staff

🚗 **From Rt 23**, take Meridale Davenport Ctr Rd/Rt 10 continuing onto Elk Creek Rd 3 miles to fork at Kelso Rd. Continue onto Kelso 1 mile to farm on left. **From Rt 28 in Meredith**, take Turnpike Rd 4 miles to Elk Creek. Veer left onto Elk Creek 1 mile and keep left to stay on Elk Creek 1½ miles to Kelso. Turn sharp right onto Kelso 1 mile to farm.

EAST SETAUKET

Wild By Nature 🛍 🍴

198 Main St. ☎ 631-246-5500 🕒 M-Sat 8-9, Sun 8-8

Fresh wok cookery at the cafe-in-the-round at the center of the store.

• organic produce • vegetarian friendly • salad bar • cafe • deli • counter • self-service • wait staff • take-out

🚗 **From LIE (I-495)**, take exit 62 onto 97N almost 10 miles to Rt 25A. Turn right onto 25A about 1½ miles to store on right at Gnarled Hollow Rd.

EAST SYRACUSE

Natur-Tyme 🛍

5898 Bridge St. ☎ 315-488-6300 🕒 M-F 9-8, Sat 9-6, Sun 12-5

🚗 **From I-481**, merge onto I-690W. **From I-690W,** take exit 17 toward E Syracuse and merge onto Bridge St to store on left (u-turn at Widewaters Pkwy to access). **From I-690E**, take exit 16S-N toward E Syracuse and turn left onto Bridge to store on right.

ELLENVILLE

Aroma Thyme Bistro 🍴

165 Canal St. ☎ 845-647-3000 🕒 M, Th 5-11, F 11-12am, Sat 12-12, Sun 4-11

Wholefoods focus with vegan, antibiotic- and hormone-free meat and sustainable fish options.

• vegetarian friendly • vegan friendly • organic focus • alcohol • tables • wait staff

🚗 **From Rt 209/52 intersection**, restaurant is 1 block north and 2 blocks east on south side of Canal St between Maple Ct & Maiden Ln.

ENDICOTT

Down to Earth Whole Foods, Inc. 🛍

305 Grant Ave. ☎ 607-785-2338 🕒 M-F 8-9, Sat 9-6, Sun 12-6

• organic produce • vegetarian friendly • fresh juice • deli • take-out

🚗 **From Rt 17**, take exit 67N toward Endicott and follow Rt 26N ramp onto Rt 26/E Main St which loops around to Grant Ave. Turn right onto Grant to store.

FLUSHING

Buddha Bodai 🍴

4296 Main St. ℰ 718-939-1188 ⏱ M-F 11-10:30, Sat-Sun 10:30-10:30
Chinese vegetarian.
    • vegan • kosher • tables • wait staff

🚗 **From LIE (I-475),** take exit 23 toward Main St onto Horace Harding Expwy north on Main St (right from LIE W, left from LIE E) about ¾ mile to restaurant on left 2 blocks past park (near Queens Botanical Gardens). **From Van Wyck Expwy,** take exit 12A onto 57th Rd and turn left onto College Point Blvd under ½ mile to Blossom Ave. Turn right onto Blossom, right onto Crommelin Ave, left onto Cherry St and right onto Main to restaurant.

Dosa Hutt 🍴

45-63 Bowne St. ℰ 718-961-5897 ⏱ Daily 9-9
Indian vegetarian in a simple storefront on styrofoam plates.
    • vegetarian • vegan friendly • tables • self-service

🚗 **From LIE (I-475),** take exit 24 onto Horace Harding Expwy north on Kissena Blvd (right from LIE W, left from LIE E) ½ mile to Rose Ave. Turn right onto Rose 2 blocks to Bowne St. Turn left onto Bowne ½ mile to restaurant on right between Holly & 45th Ave. **From Van Wyck Expwy,** take exit 12A onto 57th Rd and turn left onto College Point Blvd ½ mile to Maple Ave. Turn right onto Maple under ½ mile to Kissena. Turn right onto Kissena 4 blocks to 43rd/Cherry Ave. Turn left onto Cherry 3 blocks to Bowne. Turn right onto Bowne 1½ blocks to restaurant on left.

Happy Buddha Vegetarian Restaurant 🍴

135-37 37th Ave. ℰ 718-358-0079 ⏱ Daily 11-10
Huge Asian vegetarian menu with faux meats and brown rice available.
    • vegetarian • vegan friendly • tables • wait staff

🚗 **From the Van Wyck Expwy, Grand Central Pkwy or BQE,** exit onto Rt 25A (Northern Blvd) and go east to Main St. Turn right onto Main 1 block to 37th Ave. Turn right onto 37th 2 blocks to restaurant. **From Eastern LI or Clearview Expwy,** go west on Northern Blvd to Main. Turn left onto Main and right onto 37th 2 blocks to restaurant.

The Oneness-Fountain-Heart 🍴   ♿

157-19 72nd Ave. ℰ 718-591-3663 ⏱ M-F 11:30-9, Sat 12:30-9, Sun 10:30-9
Run by disciples of Sri Chinmoy.
    • vegetarian • vegan friendly • tables • wait staff

🚗 **From LIE (I-475),** take exit 24 onto Horace Harding Expwy south on Parsons Blvd (left from LIE W, right from LIE E) about ¾ mile to 72nd Ave. Turn right onto 72nd to restaurant on right. **From Grand Central Pkwy W,** take exit 17 right onto Parsons about ¾ mile to 72nd. Turn left onto 72nd to restaurant. **From Grand Central Pkwy E,** take exit 16 left onto Parsons 1 mile to 72nd and follow directions above.

FOREST HILLS

Tierra Sana 🍴

100-17 Queens Blvd. ℰ 718-830-0544 ⏱ M-Th 11:30-10, F-Sat 10-11, Sun 10-10
Choices includ sushi made with quinoa or brown rice.
    • vegan friendly • organic focus • fresh juice • kosher • tables • wait staff

🚗 **From Grand Central Pkwy W,** take exit 11 E-W onto 69th Rd about ½ mile to Queens Blvd. Turn right onto Queens under ½ mile to restaurant on right between 67th Rd & 67th Ave. **From GSP E,** take exit 11 toward Jewel Ave/69th Rd right onto 68th Ave about ½ mile to Queens Blvd. Turn right onto Queens 3 blocks to restaurant.

FRESH MEADOWS

Quantum Leap 🛍 🍴

65-60 Fresh Meadows Lane ℰ 718-762-3572 ⏱ M-Th, Sun 10-10, F-Sat 10-11
Store and full-service natural foods restaurant. Vegetarian, vegan and fish.

• organic produce • vegetarian friendly • vegan friendly • cafe • tables • wait staff

From LIE (I-495), take exit 25 onto Utopia Pkwy ⅓ mile to 67th Ave. Turn right onto 67th 2 blocks to Fresh Meadows Ln. Turn right onto Fresh Meadows to store.

Queens Health Emporium
15901 Horace Harding Expwy. © 718-358-6500 ① M-Sat 9:30-8, Sun 10-6
• vegetarian friendly • deli • tables • self-service • take-out

From LIE (I-495) west, take exit 24 toward Kissena Blvd onto Horace Harding Expwy N to store on at 159th St. **From LIE east,** take exit 24 toward Kissena Blvd onto Horace Harding Expwy S to 164th St. Turn left onto 164th and left onto Horace Harding Expwy N to store.

GARDEN CITY
Food For Thought
154 7th St. © 516-747-5811 ① M-F 9-6:30, Sat 9:30-5:45, Sun 10:30-3:30
• vegetarian friendly • fresh juice • deli • tables • self-service • take-out

From Northern State Pkwy, take exit 31 and follow Glen Cove Rd ramp toward Hempstead onto Glen Cove Rd (becomes Clinton St) about 1¾ miles to Stewart Ave. Turn right onto Stewart about ¾ mile to Franklin Ave. Turn left onto Franklin 1 block to 7th St. Turn left onto 7th to store. **From Meadowbrook Pkwy,** take exit M3W onto Merchants Concourse to Stewart Ave. Turn right onto Stewart 2¼ miles to Franklin Ave. Turn left onto Franklin and left onto 7th to store.

GHENT
Hawthorne Valley Farm Store
327 Rte. 21C © 518-672-7500 ① M-Sat 7:30-7, Sun 9-5
Biodynamic farm, dairy and bakery where grains are freshly milled.
• organic produce • deli • bakery • take-out

From Taconic State Pkwy, take Rt 217/Philmont/Harlemville exit right at end of ramp onto Rt 21C and go east 1½ miles to store on left.

GLEN COVE
Rising Tide Natural Market
42 Forest Ave. © 516-676-7895 ① M-F 9-8, Sat 9-7, Sun 10-6
• organic produce • vegetarian friendly • fresh juice • deli • tables • self-service • take-out

From LIE (I-495), take exit 39 north on Glen Cove Rd over 6 miles to end. Turn right onto Brewster St (becomes Forest Ave) about ¾ mile (past 5 lights) to store on right.

GLENS FALLS
Pure & Simple Natural Foods
4 E. Washington St. © 518-798-4047 ① M-W 9:30-6, Th 9:30-7, F 9:30-4
From I-87, take exit 18 east on Main St (right from I-87N, left from I-87S) continuing onto Broad St almost 2 miles to South St. Veer left onto South continuing onto Bay St under ½ mile to E Washington St. Turn right onto E Washington to store on left.

GREAT NECK
The Health Nuts   ♿
45 Northern Blvd. © 516-829-8414 ① M, Sat, 9:30-7, Tues-F 9:30-8, Sun 10-5
• organic produce • vegetarian • juice bar • deli • tables • self-service • take-out

From LIE (I-495), take exit 32 onto Horace Harding Expwy north on Little Neck Pkwy (left from I-495E, right from I-495W) ¾ mile to Northern Blvd. Turn right onto Northern ¼ mile to store on left.

HAMBURG

Feel-Rite Fresh Market 🛒

6000 S. Park Ave. ✆ 716-649-6694 ⏰ M-Sat 9-9, Sun 10-7
• organic produce

🚗 **From I-90 (NY Thwy),** take exit onto Rt 75S over 1 mile to Legion Dr. Turn left onto Legion over ½ mile to Rt 62. Turn left onto 62 (aka S Park Ave) almost ½ mile to store.

HAMILTON

Hamilton Whole Foods 🛒 🍴

28 Broad St. ✆ 315-824-2930 ⏰ M-Sat 10-6
• vegetarian friendly • deli • tables • self-service • take-out

🚗 **From US 20,** take Rt 46 south about 4 miles (becomes 12B, then Broad St in town). Turn right onto Broad to store across from village green.

HAMPTON BAYS

Wild By Nature 🛒 🍴

260 W. Montauk Hwy. ✆ 631-723-3071 ⏰ M-Sat 8-9, Sun 8-8
• organic produce • vegetarian friendly • fresh juice • salad bar • cafe • deli • tables • self-service • take-out

🚗 **From Sunrise Hwy,** take exit 65S onto Rt 24S/Riverhead-Hampton Bays Rd to first left onto CR 80/Montauk Hwy 1 mile to store on right after Cedar Ln.

HICKSVILLE

Dosa Diner 🍴

128 Broadway ✆ 516-681-5151 ⏰ M-Th, Sun 11:30-10, F-Sat 11:30-11
South Indian vegetarian with a lunch buffet option.
• vegetarian • vegan friendly • tables • self-service • wait staff

🚗 **From Northern State Pkwy,** take exit 35S toward Hicksville onto N Broadway Ave about 1¼ miles to restaurant on left. **From LIE W (I-495),** merge onto Northern State and follow directions above. **From LIE E,** take exit 41S onto N Broadway and follow directions above.

House of Dosas 🍴

416 S. Broadway ✆ 516-938-7517 ⏰ Daily 11:30-10
South Indian vegetarian cuisine.
• vegetarian • vegan friendly • tables • wait staff

🚗 **From LIE (I-495),** take exit 41S toward Hicksville onto N Broadway/NY 106S/107S. Take Broadway/107S (keep left after about 1 mile) about 2 miles to restaurant on right (across from Motor Vehicle Dept). **From Northern State Pkwy,** take exit 35S onto Broadway and follow directions above.

HIGH FALLS

High Falls Food Co-op 🛒

1398 Route 213 ✆ 845-687-7262 ⏰ M-Sat 9-7, Sun 9-6
• organic produce • co-op

🚗 **From Kingston,** take Rt 209S to Rt 213. Turn left onto 213 about 1¾ miles to store on right. **From New Paltz,** take Main St west to Springtown Rd. Turn right onto Springtown ½ mile to Mohonk Mt Rd. Veer left onto Mohonk Mt about 8 miles (twists , turns, climbs and descends) to Rt 213. Turn right onto 213 to store.

Call Ahead

We suggest you call first if possible before visiting a location. Stores and restaurants have a habit of moving (and closing), and hours, services, etc. change more often than you might expect.

HUDSON

Earth Foods 🍴

523 Warren St. ✆ 518-822-1396 ⏰ M, W-Th 9-3, F-Sun 9-4
Menu runs from tofu to beef with plenty of selections in every category.
• vegetarian friendly • fresh juice • alcohol • counter • tables • wait staff

🍎 **From Rt 23**, take Rt 23B/9G (left from 23E, right from 23W) almost 3 miles to Warren St. Turn right onto Warren ⅓ mile to store on left between 5th & 6th St.

Kaaterskill Farm Natural Storehouse 🛍

173 Healy Blvd. ✆ 518-822-0790 ⏰ M-F 9:30-7, Sat. 9-6, Sun. 12-5
• organic produce

🍎 **From Rt 23**, take Rt 23B/9G (left from 23E, right from 23W) almost 3 miles into Hudson. Continue right on 23B (Columbia St) through town about 1 mile to Rt 66 (Union Tpke). Turn left onto 66¾ mile to store at Healy Blvd in Corner Plaza.

HUNTER

Catskill Mountain Foundation Farm Market & Cafe 🛍 🍴

7970 Main St. ✆ 518-263-2040 ⏰ M-Th, Sun 10-6, F-Sat 10-7
Part of a complex with local crafts, a bookstore, art gallery and movie theater.
• organic produce • vegetarian friendly • tables • self-service • take-out

🍎 **From Rt 214/23A intersection**, store is 2½ miles west on Rt 23A (aka Main St) on north side.

HUNTINGTON

Wild By Nature 🛍 🍴

369 W. Main St. ✆ 631-424-6480 ⏰ M-Sat 8-9, Sun 8-8
• organic produce • vegetarian friendly • fresh juice • salad bar • cafe • deli • tables • self-service • take-out

🍎 **From LIE (I-495),** take exit 49N onto Rt 110N (becomes NY Ave) about 7 miles to W Main St (RT 25A). Turn left onto W Main about ¼ mile to store on right.

ITHACA

Greenstar Cooperative Market 🛍

701 W. Buffalo St. ✆ 607-273-9392 ⏰ Daily 7-11
• organic produce • vegetarian friendly • deli • bakery • take-out • co-op

🍎 **From Rt 13**, go west on Seneca St (right from 13S, left from 13N). Turn right into store parking lot. **From Rt 96**, 96 becomes Buffalo St in town. Follow to parking lot on right before Fulton St.

Greenstar Cooperative Market 🛍 🍴

215 N. Cayuga St. ✆ 607-273-8213 ⏰ M-Sat 8-8, Sun 10-6
• organic produce • vegetarian friendly • deli • bakery • tables • self-service • take-out

🍎 **From Rt 13**, go east on Buffalo St to Cayuga St. Store is on right in DeWitt Mall.

Ludgate Farms 🛍

1552 Hanshaw Rd. ✆ 607-257-1765 ⏰ Daily 9-9
• organic produce

🍎 **From Ithaca**, take Rt 13 north to Warren Rd. Turn right onto Warren about ½ mile to 4-way stop sign. Turn left onto Hanshaw Rd to store about ½ mile uphill on left after Sapsucker Woods Rd on left & Freese Rd on right.

Moosewood Restaurant 🍴

215 N. Cayuga St. ✆ 607-273-9610 ⏰ M-Sat 11:30-3 Dinner (Summer) M-Th, Sun 5:30-9, F-Sat 6-9:30 (Winter) M-Th, Sun 5:30-8:30, F-Sat 5:30-9 Bar/Cafe M-Th, Sun 11:30-8:30, F-Sat 11:30-9
This natural foods restaurant has a vegetarian outlook but also serves seafood.
• vegetarian friendly • organic focus • alcohol • tables • wait staff • co-op

🍎 **From Rt 13**, go east on Buffalo St to Cayuga St. Restaurant on is right in DeWitt Mall.

Temple of Zeus 🍴

Goldwin Smith Hall © 607-255-3499 ⏰ M-F 8-6
Famous for its soups which generally run out by noon.
· vegetarian friendly · vegan friendly · take-out

🍎 **From RT 79/State St in downtown Ithaca,** go north (uphill) on Stewart Ave about ½ mile to Campus Rd. Turn right onto Campus to enter Cornell U. Goldwin Smith Hall is on the west side of the "Quad" north of the Student Union and Tower Rd. **From Dryden Rd,** turn right onto E State and right onto Stewart and follow directions above.

JAMAICA

Guru's Health Food 🛍️

86-18 Parsons Blvd. © 718-291-7406 ⏰ M-Tues, Th-Sat 10-8, W 10-7, Sun 10-6

🍎 **From Grand Central Pkwy E,** take exit 16 (Parsons Blvd) onto E Service Rd to Parsons. Turn right onto Parsons about ½ mile to store between 86th & 87th Ave. **From Grand Central W,** take exit 17 (168th St) onto Service Rd almost 1 mile to Parsons. Turn left onto Parsons about ½ mile to store.

Smile of the Beyond 🍴

86-14 Parsons Blvd. © 718-739-7453 ⏰ M-F 7–4, Sat 7–3
· vegetarian · vegan friendly · tables · wait staff

🍎 **From Grand Central Pkwy W,** take exit 17 toward 168th St onto Service Rd and left onto Parsons Blvd ½ mile to restaurant on right. **From Grand Central Pkwy E,** take exit 16 toward 164th St onto Service Rd, turn right onto Parsons and follow directions above.

JAMAICA HILLS

Annam Brahma 🍴 ♿

84-43 164th St. © 718-523-2600 ⏰ M-Tues, Th-Sat 11-10, W 11-4, Sun 12-10
Indian slant plus salads, burgers, tofu and brown rice. International Smorgasbord Sunday until 8. Run by disciples of Sri Chinmoy.
· vegetarian · vegan friendly · tables · self-service · wait staff

🍎 **From Grand Central Pkwy W,** take exit 17 toward 168th St onto Service Rd and turn left onto 164th St about ¼ mile to restaurant on left. **From Grand Central Pkwy E,** take exit 16 toward 164th/Parsons Blvd onto Service Rd, turn right onto 164th and follow directions above.

JEFFERSONVILLE

The Good Earth 🛍️

4874 Main St. © 845-482-3131 ⏰ M-F 10-5:30, Sat 10-5, Sun 10-2
· organic produce

🍎 **From Rt 17,** take exit 100 (Liberty) onto Rt 52W about 12 miles to Jeffersonville. Store is in center of town on north side in blue Victorian bldg.

JERICHO

Green Melody 🍴 ♿

519 N. Broadway © 516-681-5715 ⏰ M-Th 11-10, F 11-11, Sat 11:30-11, Sun 12-10
Chinese vegetarian. Brown rice available.
· vegetarian · vegan friendly · fresh juice · tables · wait staff

🍎 **From LIE (I-495),** take exit 41N toward Oyster Bay onto N Broadway Ave ⅓ mile to restaurant on right. **From Northern State Pkwy,** take exit 35N onto N Broadway and follow directions above.

Whole Foods Market 🛍️ 🍴

429 N. Broadway © 516-932-1733 ⏰ Daily 8-10
· organic produce · vegetarian friendly · salad bar · cafe · self-service · take-out

🍎 **From I-495 (Long Island Expwy),** take exit 41N onto N Broadway Ave to store on right. **From Northern State Pkwy,** take exit 35N onto N Broadway under ½ mile (past LIE) to store.

JOHNSON CITY

Health Beat Natural Foods 🛍 🍴 &

214 Main St. ✆ 607-797-1001 ⏰ M-F 9-8, Sat 10-6, Sun 12-5
  • organic produce • vegetarian friendly • vegan friendly • organic focus • deli • tables •
  self-service • take-out

🚘 **From I-81**, merge onto Rt 17W about 2 miles to exit 71S toward Johnson City.
Follow exit onto Rt 301S to CFK Blvd. Turn right onto CFK and left onto Lester Ave
about ¼ mile to Main St (17C). Turn left onto Main to store after Ave B. **From Rt
17**, take exit 71S and follow directions above.

KATONAH

Mrs. Green's Natural Market 🛍

202 Katonah Ave. ✆ 914-232-7574 ⏰ M-W, F 8:30-6:30, Th 8:30-7, Sat 8:30-6, Sun 10-5
  • organic produce • fresh juice

🚘 **From I-684**, take exit 6 toward Rt 35/Katonah. Follow Saw Mill Pkwy ramp
toward I-684S to Jay St. Turn right onto Jay and left onto Katonah Ave to store.

KINGSTON

Mother Earth's Storehouse 🛍 🍴 &

440 Kings Mall Court ✆ 845-336-5541 ⏰ M-F 9-9, Sat 9-7, Sun 12-5
  • organic produce • vegetarian • vegan friendly • salad bar • deli • tables • self-service • take-out

🚘 **From I-87 (NY Thwy)**, take exit 19 (Kingston). Take first exit off rotary onto
Rt 28. Take first exit on right onto Rt 209N 3½ miles to US 9WS. Exit onto 9WS
(Ulster Ave) ¾ miles to store on left in Kings Mall.

Nature's Pavillion 🛍

618 Ulster Ave. ✆ 845-340-4561 ⏰ M-F 9:30-7:30, Sat 9:30-6, Sun 11-5

🚘 **From I-87 (NY Thwy)**, take exit 19 (Kingston). Take third exit off rotary onto
Chandler Dr 1⅓ miles to Albany Ave. Turn left onto Albany continuing onto Ulster
Ave 1⅓ miles total to store on right.

LARCHMONT

Mrs. Green's Natural Market 🛍 🍴

2460 Boston Post Rd. ✆ 914-834-6667 ⏰ M,W, F 9-8, Tues, Th 9-9, Sat 9-7, Sun 10-6
  • organic produce • vegetarian friendly • deli • tables • self-service • take-out

🚘 **From I-95 (NE Thwy)**, take exit 16 toward Cedar St onto Cross Westchester Ave
(becomes Cedar) to Ramada Plaza. Turn left onto Ramada Plaza and right onto
River St (becomes Echo Ave) under ¼ mile to Main St/Rt 1N. Turn left onto 1
(becomes Boston Post Rd) under 1 mile to store.

LIBERTY

The Sunflower Health Food Store 🛍

71 N. Main St. ✆ 845-292-3535 ⏰ M-Sat 10-6

🚘 **From Rt 17W**, take exit 100 left at light off ramp onto Sullivan Ave and left at
next light onto Rt 52W. Follow 52 onto Main St past 3 lights (1⅓ miles) to store
on right after School St. **From Rt 17E**, take exit 99 toward Liberty and follow exit to
N Main. Turn left onto Main almost 1 mile to store on left.

LITTLE FALLS

Community Co-op 🛍 &

589 Albany St. ✆ 315-823-0686 ⏰ Tues, W, F 9:30-5, Th 9:30-8, Sat 9:30-1
  • organic produce • co-op

🚘 **From Rt 5**, turn north at light at Ann St (left from 5E, right from 5W) 1 block to
Albany St. Turn right onto Albany 2 blocks to store on right. **From I-90 (NY Thwy)**,
take exit 29A or 30 to Rt 5E or W and follow directions above.

MAHOPAC

Mrs. Green's Natural Market 🛒

Lake Plaza Shopping Center, Rte. 6 ✆ 845-628-0533 ⏱ M-Sat 9-7, Sun 10-5
• organic produce • fresh juice

🍴 **From I-84**, take exit 19 toward Carmel right at first light onto Rt 312 1⅓ miles to Rt 6. Turn left onto Rt 6 about 5 miles to store on left in Lake Plaza Shopping Ctr.

MANHASSET

Whole Foods Market 🛒 ♿

2101 Northern Blvd. ✆ 516-869-8900 ⏱ Daily 8-10
• organic produce • vegetarian friendly • salad bar • deli • bakery • take-out

🍴 **From LIE (I-495)**, take exit 36 north on Searingtown Rd (right from I-495W, left from I-495E) 1¼ miles to Northern Blvd. Store is on NW corner across from Americana Shopping Ctr.

MASSAPEQUA

Eden's Way Natural Foods 🛒

37 Broadway ✆ 516-798-5670 ⏱ M-Th 10-6:30, F 9-7:30, Sat 9-5
• organic produce • fresh juice

🍴 **From Southern State Pkwy**, exit onto Seaford Oyster Bay Expwy about 2 miles to exit 2E (Sunrise Hwy). Merge onto Sunrise Hwy (NY 27E) about 1⅓ miles to Broadway. Turn left onto Broadway 2 blocks to store.

MONTAUK

Joni's 🍴

9 S. Edison Plaza ✆ 631-668-3663 ⏱ M-Tues, Th 9-3, F-Sun 9-4 (Closed mid Dec-Feb, open F-Sun March-May)
Vegetarian, fish and free-range poultry. Hours flexible depending on business.
• vegetarian friendly • tables • self-service

🍴 Take Montauk Hwy (27E) all the way to the tip of LI. **From Montauk Hwy,** take The Plaza toward the sound (left from 27E, right from 27W) onto Edgemere St 2 blocks and continue right onto Edison Ext to restaurant.

Naturally Good Foods & Cafe 🛒 🍴 ♿

38 S. Etna Ave. ✆ 631-668-9030 ⏱ M-Sat 7-5 (kitchen to 4), Sun 7-4:30 (kitchen to 3)
• organic produce • vegetarian friendly • fresh juice • cafe • deli • bakery • tables • self-service • take-out

🍴 Take Montauk Hwy (27E) all the way to the tip of LI. **From Montauk Hwy**, turn toward the ocean on S Essex St (right from 27E, left from 27W) 1 block to store at S Etna Ave.

MT. KISCO

Mrs. Green's Natural Market 🛒 🍴

666 Lexington Ave. ✆ 914-242-9292 ⏱ M-F 9-7, Sat-Sun 10-7
• organic produce • vegetarian friendly • deli • tables • self-service • take-out

🍴 **From I-684**, take exit 4 west on NY 172/S Bedford Rd 2 miles to Main St. Turn left onto Main about ⅔ mile to Lexington Ave. Turn left onto Lexington to store in shopping plaza.

NANUET

Gourmet Garden 🍴

102 Rte. 59 E. ✆ 845-624-8972 ⏱ M-F 11-6, Sat-Sun 11-5
• vegetarian friendly • tables • self-service • take out

🍴 **From Palisades Pkwy**, take exit 8W toward Spring Valley onto Rt 59W about 1 mile to restaurant on right in center of Toys R Us Plaza. **From I-287/87 (NY Thwy)**, take exit 13S onto Palisades Pkwy and follow directions above.

NEW CITY

Back to the Earth Natural Foods 🛍️

306A S. Main St. ✆ 845-634-3511 🕐 M-F 9-7:30, Sat 9-6, Sun 10-6
 • deli • vegetarian friendly • take-out

🍎 **From Palisades Pkwy**, take exit 10 toward New City east on Germonds Rd (right from Pkwy N, left from Pkwy S) about ¾ mile to S Main (Rt 304). Turn left onto S Main about 1½ miles to store on right after Collyer Ave.

NEW HARTFORD

Peter's Cornucopia 🛍️ 🍴

38 New Hartford Shopping Center ✆ 315-724-4998 🕐 M-F 9-8, Sat 9-6, Sun 11-4
 • organic produce • vegetarian friendly • fresh juice • cafe • tables • self-service • take-out

🍎 Rt 8, 12 and 5 converge in New Hartford. **From the N-S Arterial Hwy traveling east**, take 8S exit and make first right into New Hartford Shopping Ctr to store. **From N-S Arterial Hwy traveling west**, take Campion Rd exit toward New Hartford and follow Campion right then left to store on left.

NEW PALTZ

Earthgoods 🛍️

71 Main St. ✆ 845-255-5858 🕐 M-F, Sun 10-9, Sat 9-9
 • organic produce

🍎 **From I-87 (NY Thwy)**, take exit 18 (New Paltz) left onto Rt 299 (becomes Main St) about 1½ miles into town to store on right.

Health and Nutrition Center 🛍️

15 New Paltz Plaza ✆ 845-256-0256 🕐 M-F 9-8, Sat 9-7, Sun 10-6
 • organic produce, fresh juice

🍎 **From I-87 (NY Thwy)**, take exit 18 (New Paltz) left onto Rt 299 under ½ mile to store on right in New Paltz Plaza.

Karma Road 🍴

11 Main St. ✆ 845-255-1099 🕐 Daily 8-8
Sandwiches, salads, wheat- and dairy-free desserts.
 • vegetarian • vegan friendly • organic focus • fresh juice • counter • tables • self-service • take-out

🍎 **From I-87 (NY Thwy)**, take exit 18 (New Paltz) left onto Rt 299 (becomes Main St) about 1½ miles into town to restaurant on right.

NEW YORK

4th Street Food Co-op 🛍️

58 E. 4th St. ✆ 212-674-3623 🕐 M-Tues, F-Sun 11-9, W 1-9, Th 9-9
 • organic produce • co-op

🍎 Manhattan's Lower East Side on E 4th St between Bowery & 2nd Ave on south side.

Angelica Kitchen 🍴

300 E. 12th St. ✆ 212-228-2909 🕐 Daily 11:30-10:30
 • vegan • organic focus • tables • wait staff

🍎 Manhattan's Lower East Side on E 12th St between 1st & 2nd Ave on south side.

Aruveyda Cafe 🍴

706 Amsterdam Ave. ✆ 212-932-2400 🕐 Daily 11-10:30
A price-fixed vegetarian/mostly vegan meal that changes daily.
 • vegetarian • vegan friendly • tables • wait staff

🍎 Manhattan's Upper West Side on west side of Amsterdam Ave between W 94th & W 95th St.

B & H Vegetarian Restaurant 🍴
127 2nd Ave. ✆ 212-5-5-8065 ⏰ Daily 7-10
Vegetarian with a few fish dishes in the kosher dairy tradition.
  • vegetarian friendly • kosher • counter • tables • self-service • take-out
🚪 Manhattan's Lower East Side on 2nd Ave between 7th & 8th St on west side.

Babycakes NYC 🛍
248 Broome St. ✆ 212-677-5047 ⏰ M, Sun 10-8, Tues-Th 10-10, F-Sat 10-11
  • vegan • organic focus • bakery • take-out
🚪 Manhattan's Lower East Side on Broome St between Orchard & Ludlow St on north side.

Bell Bates Natural Foods 🛍
97 Reade St. ✆ 212-267-4300 ⏰ M-F 9-7, Sat. 10-6
  • organic produce • vegetarian friendly • fresh juice • deli • take-out
🚪 Lower Manhattan Tri-beca area on Reade St between Church St & W Bwy on south side.

Blossom Vegan Restaurant 🍴
187 9th Ave. ✆ 212-627-1144 ⏰ M-Th 5-10, F-Sun 12-2:45, 5-10
Gourmet vegan dining
  • vegan • organic focus • alcohol • kosher • tables • wait staff
🚪 In Chelsea on 9th Ave between W 21st & W 22nd St on west side.

Bonobo's 🍴
18 E. 23rd St. ✆ 212-505-1200 ⏰ Daily 11-8
Live (gently heated) and raw foods.
  • vegan • organic focus • tables • self-service
🚪 On E 23rd St between Broadway & Park Ave S on south side.

Broadway East 🍴
171 E. Broadway ✆ 212-228-3100 ⏰ Daily 12-4, 5:30-11
Food from the Northeast and NY State in particular. Vegetarian with some fish and chicken.
  • vegetarian friendly • vegan friendly • organic focus • alcohol • counter • tables • wait staff
🚪 Manhattan's Lower East Side on the east side of Broadway between Jefferson & Rutgers St.

Buddha Bodai 🍴
5 Mott St. ✆ 212-566-8388 ⏰ Daily 10-10
Chinese vegetarian with many mock meat offerings.
  • vegan • kosher • tables • wait staff
🚪 In Chinatown on Mott St at Worth St.

Cafe Blossom 🍴
466 Columbus Ave. ✆ 212-875-2600 ⏰ M-F 11-10, Sat 11-10:30, Sun 11-9:30
  • vegan • organic focus • alcohol • tables • wait staff
🚪 Manhattan's Upper West Side on west side of Columbus Ave between W 82nd & W 83rd St.

Cafe Viva 🍴
2578 Broadway ✆ 212-663-8482 ⏰ Daily 11:30-11:30
Pasta and antipasto-type salads. Largely take-out.
  • vegetarian • tables • self-service • take-out
🚪 Manhattan's Upper West Side on east side of Broadway between W 97th & W 98th St.

Cafe Viva 🍴
179 2nd Ave. ✆ 212-420-8801 ⏰ M-Th, Sun 11-11:30, F-Sat 11-1:30am
Vegetarian pasta, pizza and antipasto-type salads. Largely take-out.
  • vegetarian • tables • self-service • take-out
🚪 Manhattan's East Side on west side of 2nd Ave between E 11th & E 12th St.

Candle 79 ⑪

154 E. 79th St. ℂ 212-537-7179 ⓣ M-Sat 12-3:30, 5:30-10:30, Sun 12-4, 5-10
Elegant health-conscious, vegan, organic dining.
  • vegan • organic focus • alcohol • tables • wait staff
☐ Manhattan's Upper East Side on E 79th St east of Lexington Ave on south side.

Candle Cafe ⑪

1307 3rd Ave. ℂ 212-472-0970 ⓣ M-Sat 11:30-10:30, Sun 11:30-9:30
Certified Green Restaurant and networking center for animal rights people and environmentalists.
  • vegan • organic focus • alcohol • tables • wait staff
☐ Manhattan's Upper East Side on 3rd Ave at E 75th St on east side.

Caravan of Dreams ⑪

405 E. 6th St. ℂ 212-254-1613 ⓣ Daily 11-11
Mediterranean vegan menu with an emphasis on raw foods.
  • vegan • organic focus • fresh juice • alcohol • kosher • counter • tables • wait staff
☐ In the East Village on E 6th St between 1st Ave & Ave A on north side.

Chennai Garden ⑪

129 E. 27th St. ℂ 212-689-1999 ⓣ Tues-F 11:30-3, 5-10, Sat-Sun 12-10
Indian vegetarian with a lunch buffet.
  • vegetarian • vegan friendly • alcohol • tables • self-service • wait staff
☐ Manhattan's Midtown East Side on E 27th St between Park & Lexington Ave on north side.

Commodities Natural Market ⑪

165 1st Ave. ℂ 212-260-2600 ⓣ Daily 9-9
  • organic produce
☐ Manhattan's Lower East Side on 1st Ave between E 10th & E 11th St on west side.

Counter ⑪

105 1st Ave. ℂ 212-982-5870 ⓣ M-Th 5pm-12am F 5pm-1am, Sat 11-4, 5-12am, Sun 11-4, 5-12am
Vegetarian restaurant and wine bar.
  • vegetarian • vegan friendly • organic focus • alcohol • counter • tables • wait staff
☐ Manhattan's Lower East Side on 1st Ave between E 6th & E 7th St on west side.

Curly's Vegetarian Lunch ⑪

328 E. 14th St. ℂ 212-598-9998 ⓣ M-F 11-10, Sat-Sun 10-11
Vegetarian diner-style comfort food.
  • vegetarian • vegan friendly • alcohol • tables • wait staff • take-out
☐ On E 14th St between 1st & 2nd Ave on north side.

Dang Lai Palace ⑪

180 Third Ave. ℂ 212-505-2000 ⓣ Daily 11-11
Pan Asian menu. Brown and red rice available.
  • vegetarian • vegan friendly • fresh juice • kosher • tables • wait staff • take-out
☐ On 3rd Ave between E 16th & E 17th St on west side.

Dirt Candy ⑪

430 E. 9th St. ℂ 212-228-7732 ⓣ Tues-Sat 5:30-11
  • vegetarian • vegan friendly • alcohol • tables • wait staff
☐ In the East Village on E 9th St between 1st & Ave A on south side.

Earth Matters ⑪

177 Ludlow St. ℂ 212-475-4180 ⓣ Daily 8-11
  • organic produce • vegetarian friendly • vegan friendly • organic focus • fresh juice • salad bar • cafe • tables • self-service • take-out
☐ Manhattan's Lower East Side on Ludlow St between Houston & Stanton St on west side.

Franchia Tea House ⏐⏐

12 Park Ave. ✆ 212-213-1001 ⏰ Daily 11:30-10
A Korean teahouse. Lunch until 3 followed by afternoon tea and dinner at 5.
  • vegan • alcohol • tables • wait staff • take-out
🛍 On Park Ave between E 34th & E 35th St on west side.

GoBo ⏐⏐

401 6th Ave. ✆ 212-255-3902 ⏰ Daily 11:30-10:30
  • vegan • organic focus • fresh juice • alcohol • tables • wait staff • take-out
🛍 In the West Village on west side of Broadway between W 8th St & Waverly Pl.

GoBo ⏐⏐

1426 Third Ave. ✆ 212-288-4686 ⏰ Daily 12-10:45
  • vegan • organic focus • fresh juice • alcohol • tables • wait staff • take-out
🛍 Manhattan's Upper East side on west side of 3rd Ave at E 81st St.

Good Health ⏐⏐

1435 1st Ave. ✆ 212-517-9898 ⏰ M-F 11:30-10, Sat-Sun 10-10
Mostly vegetarian with a few fish and organic chicken options:
  • vegetarian friendly • vegan friendly • tables • wait staff • take-out
🛍 Manhattan's Upper East Side on west side of 1st Ave between E 74th & E 75th St.

Hangawi ⏐⏐

12 E. 32nd St. ✆ 212-213-0077 ⏰ M-F 12-3, 5-10:15, Sat-Sun 12-10:30
An elegant vegan Korean meal in a serene, zen-like atmosphere.
  • vegan • alcohol • tables • wait staff
🛍 On south side of E 32nd St between 5th & Madison Ave.

Health For You 🛍

432 Park Ave. S. ✆ 212-532-2644 ⏰ M-F 8-8, Sat 10-7
Salad bar on weekdays only.
  • salad bar • take-out
🛍 On west side of Park Ave between E 29th & E 30th St.

High Vibe Health & Healing 🛍

138 E. 3rd St. ✆ 212-77-6645 ⏰ M-F 10-8, Sat-Sun 12-7
Store is entirely devoted to "healing with living foods."
🛍 In the East Village on south side of E 3rd St at Ave A.

House of Vegetarian ⏐⏐

68 Mott St. ✆ 212-226-6572 ⏰ Daily 11-10:30
Chinese vegetarian.
  • vegan • tables • waitstaff
🛍 In Chinatown on Mott St between Canal & Bayard St on east side.

Integral Yoga Natural Foods 🛍

229 W. 13th St. ✆ 212-243-2642 ⏰ M-F 8-9:30, Sat-Sun 8-8:30
Hot and cold food bar. Yoga center next door holds open classes.
  • organic produce • vegetarian • vegan friendly • salad bar • deli • take-out
🛍 In the West Village on W 13th St between 7th & 8th Ave on north side.

Josie's Restaurant & Juice Bar ⏐⏐

300 Amsterdam Ave. ✆ 212-769-1212 ⏰ M-W 12-11, Th-F 12-11:30, Sat 11-11:30, Sun 10:30-10:30
Emphasis is organic including vegetarian, vegan, meat, poultry and fish.
  • vegetarian friendly • vegan friendly • organic focus • fresh juice • alcohol • counter • tables • wait staff
🛍 Manhattan's Upper West Side on Amsterdam Ave at W 74th St on north side.

Josie's Restaurat & Juice Bar 🍴

565 3rd Ave. © 12-490-1558 ⊙ M-Th 12-10:30, F 12-11, Sat 11:30-11, Sun 11-10
See Amsterdam Ave location for description.
· vegetarian friendly · vegan friendly · organic focus · fresh juice · alcohol · counter · tables · wait staff

On Manhattan's East Side on 3rd Ave at E 37th St on east side.

Kate's Joint 🍴

58 Ave. B © 212-777-7059 ⊙ M-Th, Sun 10-11, F-Sat 10-1am
· vegetarian · vegan friendly · tables · wait staff

Manhattan's Lower East Side corner Ave B & E 4th St.

Life Thyme Natural 🛍🍴

410 6th Ave. © 212-420-9099 ⊙ M-F 8-10, Sat-Sun 9-10
· organic produce · vegetarian friendly · fresh juice · salad bar · bakery · tables · self-service · take-out

In the West Village on east side of 6th Ave between W 8th & W 9th St.

Liquiteria 🍴

170 2nd Ave. © 212 358-0300 ⊙ M-F 7-10, Sat-Sun 8-10
Mostly juice and smoothies with some breakfast items, sandwiches and soup.
· vegetarian · vegan friendly · fresh juice · counter · self-service

In the East Village on east side of 2nd Ave at E 11th St.

Little Lads Bakery 🍴

120 Broadway, Lower Arcade © 212-227-5744 ⊙ M-Th 7:30am-10:30am, 11:30am-4:30pm, F 7:30-10:30, 11:30-3:30
Run by Seventh-day Adventists. Hot food until 2:30, sandwiches until closing.
· vegan · tables · self-service · take-out

In the Financial District on east side of Broadway between Cedar & Pine St (1 block north of Wall St).

Madras Mahal 🍴

104 Lexington Ave. © 212-684-4010 ⊙ M-Th 11:30-3, 5-10, F 11:30-3, 5-10:30, Sat 12-10:30, Sun 12-10
Kosher Indian vegetarian with a weekday lunch buffet.
· vegetarian · vegan friendly · kosher · tables · self-service · wait staff

On Lexington Ave between E 27th & E 28th St on west side.

Mana Restaurant 🍴 ♿

646 Amsterdam Ave. © 212-787-1110 ⊙ M-Sat 11:30-10:30, Sun 11:30-10
Macrobiotic fare.
· vegan · tables · wait staff · take-out

Manhattan's Upper West Side on Amsterdam Ave beween W 91st & W 92nd St on west side.

Maoz Vegetarian 🍴

38 Union Square © 212-260-1988 ⊙ M-Th 11-12, F-Sat 11am-2am, Sun 11-10
Falafel, salads and fries.
· vegetarian · vegan friendly · fresh juice · tables · self-service · take-out

In lower Manhattan at Union Square between 16 & 17th St

Maoz Vegetarian 🍴

59 E. 8th St. © 212-420-5999 © M-Th, Sun 7-10:30, 11-11, F-Sat 7-10:30, 11-12
Falafel, salads and fries.
· vegetarian · vegan friendly · fresh juice · tables · self-service · take-out

In the West Village on north side of E 8th St between Broadway and University Ave.

Natural Frontier Market 🛍

1424 3rd Ave. © 212-794-0922 ⊙ M-F 8:30-9:30, Sat-Sun 9-9:30
· organic produce

Manhattan's Upper East Side on west side of 3rd Ave at E 84th St.

Natural Frontier Market 🛍️

325 3rd Ave. ☎ 212-228-9133 ⏰ M-F 8-10, Sat-Sun 9-10
• organic produce • vegetarian friendly • fresh juice • salad bar • deli • take-out
🏠 East Side of Manhattan on east side of 3rd Ave between E 24th & 25th St.

Organic Market 🛍️

275 7th Ave. ☎ 212-243-9927 ⏰ M-F 8-8, Sat-Sun 10-7
• organic produce
🏠 In Chelsea on 7th Ave just past W 26th St on east side.

Ozu 🍴

566 Amsterdam Ave ☎ 212-787-8316 ⏰ M-Sat 11:30-10:30, Sun 11:30-10
Japanese/macrobiotic with whole grains, vegan and fish dishes.
• vegetarian friendly • vegan friendly • kosher • alcohol • tables • wait staff • take-out
🏠 Manhattan's Upper West Side on Amsterdam Ave between W 87th & W 88th St on west side.

Pongal 🍴

110 Lexington Ave. ☎ 212-696-9458 ⏰ M-F 12-3, 5-10:30, Sat-Sun 12-10:30
Indian kosher vegetarian.
• vegetarian • vegan friendly • kosher • alcohol • tables • wait staff
🏠 On Lexington Ave between E 27th & E 28th St on west side.

Pukk 🍴

71 1st Ave. ☎ 212-253-2742 ⏰ M-Th, Sun 11:30-10:30, F-Sat 11:30-11:30
Vegetarian Thai.
• vegetarian • vegan friendly • alcohol • tables • wait staff
🏠 In the East Village on 1st Ave between E 4th & E 5th St on west side.

Pure Food & Wine 🍴

54 Irving Place ☎ 212-477-1010 ⏰ Daily 5:30-11
Raw foods in an upscale wine bar/restaurant.
• vegan • fresh juice • organic focus • alcohol • tables • wait staff
🏠 On the north side of Irving Pl at E 17th St (3 blocks west of E 14th St and 1 block north of Union Square).

Quantum Leap 🍴

226 Thompson St. ☎ 212-677-8050 ⏰ M-F 11:30-11, Sat 11-11, Sun 11-10
An eclectic mix of tofu, seitan, veggie burgers, Mexican dishes and more.
• vegetarian • vegan friendly • tables • wait staff
🏠 In the West Village on east side of Thompson St between W 3rd & Bleecker St.

Quantum Leap 🍴

203 1st Ave. ☎ 212-673-9848 ⏰M-F 11:30-11, Sat-Sun 11-10:30
See Thompson St location for description.
• vegetarian • vegan friendly • tables • waitstaff
🏠 Manhattan's East Side on 1st Ave between E 12th & E 13th St on west side.

Quartino Bottega Organica 🍴

11 Bleecker St. ☎ 212-529-5133 ⏰ M-W 12-11, Th-F 12-11:30, Sat 11-11:30, Sun 11-10
Vegetarian Italian with one fish dish. Homemade, organic, whole grain pasta, pizza and foccacia.
• vegetarian friendly • organic focus • alcohol • tables • wait staff
🏠 In Lower Manhattan on Bleecker St 1 block north of E Houston St and 1 block west of the Bowery on north side.

Quintessence 🍴   ♿

263 E. 10th St. ☎ 646-654-1823 ⏰ M-Th, Sun 11:30-10, F-Sat 11:30-11
Gourmet raw foods.
• vegan • organic focus • tables • wait staff • take-out
🏠 Manhattan's Lower East Side on E 10th St between Ave A & 1st Ave on north side.

Raw Soul 🍴
348 W. 145th St. ✆ 212-491-5859 ⏱ Tues-Sat 11-9, Sun 12-5
Raw foods.
  • vegan • organic focus • fresh juice • tables • self-service • take-out
🍎 In Harlem on south side of W 145th St between St Nicolas & Edgecombe Ave.

Red Bamboo 🍴
140 W. 4th St. ✆ 212-260-1212 ⏱ Daily 12:30-11:15
Caribbean soul cuisine. Non-vegan items clearly noted.
  • vegetarian • vegan friendly • alcohol • tables • wait staff
🍎 In the West Village on W 4th St between 6th Ave & Macdougal St on south side.

Sacred Chow 🍴
227 Sullivan St. ✆ 212-337-0863 ⏱ M-Th, Sun 11-10, F-Sat 11-11
  • vegan • organic focus • fresh juice • alcohol • kosher • tables • wait staff
🍎 In the West Village on east side of Sullivan St between W 3rd & Bleecker St.

Saravanaas 🍴
81 Lexington Ave. ✆ 212-679-0204 ⏱ M-F 8:30-3, 5:30-10, Sat-Sun 8:30-4, 6-10
South Indian vegetarian. Part of an international chain.
  • vegetarian • vegan friendly • alcohol • tables • wait staff
🍎 On east side of Lexington Ave at E 26th St.

'sNice 🍴
45 8th Ave. ✆ 212-645-0310 ⏱ M-F 7:30am-10pm, Sat-Sun 8am-10pm
Breakfast, sandwiches and salads.
  • vegetarian • vegan friendly • counter • tables • self-service • take-out
🍎 In the West Village on west side of 8th Ave at W 4th St.

Souen 🍴
28 E. 13th St. ✆ 212-627-7150 ⏱ M-Sat 10:15-11, Sun 10:15-10
Organic macrobiotic vegan and fish dishes.
  • vegan friendly • organic focus • alcohol • tables • wait staff
🍎 In the West Village on south side of E 13th St between University Pl & 5th Ave.

Souen 🍴
210 6th Ave. ✆ 212-807-7421 ⏱ M-F 12-10:30, Sat 11-10:30, Sun 11-10
Organic macrobiotic vegan and fish dishes.
  • vegan friendly • organic focus • alcohol • tables • wait staff
🍎 In SoHo on east side of 6th Ave at Prince St.

Soy & Sake Cafe 🍴
47 7th Ave. S. ✆ 212-255-2848 ⏱ M-Th 12-11:30, F-Sat 12-12:30, Sun 12-11
Vegetarian Japanese/Pan Asian menu.
  • vegetarian • vegan friendly • alcohol • tables • wait staff
🍎 In the West Village on the east side of 7th Ave between Morton & Bleecker St.

Spring Street Natural Restaurant 🍴 ♿
62 Spring St. ✆ 212-966-0290 ⏱ M-Th 9am-11:30pm, F 9am-12:30am, Sat 10:30am-12:30am, Sun 10:30am-11:30pm
Gourmet-style healthy food. Vegetarian, vegan, oganic chicken and fish.
  • vegetarian friendly • vegan friendly • organic focus • alcohol • tables • wait staff
🍎 In SoHo on SW corner Spring & Lafayette St.

Strictly Roots 🍴
2058 Adam Clayton Powell Blvd. ✆ 212-864-8699 ⏱ Daily 8-10
Afro-Caribe menu: barbecued gluten, tofu, curries, brown rice & peas and more.
  • vegan • fresh juice • tables • self-service
🍎 In Harlem on Adam Clayton Powell Blvd & W 123rd St on west side.

Teany Cafe 🍴
90 Rivington St. ✆ 212-475-9190 ⏰ M-Th, Sun 10-11, F-Sat 10am-1am
• vegetarian • vegan friendly • alcohol • tables • wait staff
🍎 Manhattan's Lower East Side on the north side of Rivington St between Ludow & Orchard St.

The Health Nuts 🛍
2141 Broadway ✆ 212-724-1972 ⏰ M-Sat 9-9, Sun 11-7
🍎 Manhattan's Upper West Side on Broadway between W 75th & W 76th St on west side.

The Health Nuts 🛍 🍴
2611 Broadway ✆ 212-678-0054 ⏰ M-Sat 9-9, Sun 11-8
• deli • vegetarian friendly • tables • self-service • take-out
🍎 Manhattan's Upper West Side on Broadway between W 98th & W 99th St on west side.

The Health Nuts 🛍 🍴
1208 2nd Ave. ✆ 212-593-0116 ⏰ M-F 9-9, Sat.-Sun. 10-8
• deli • vegetarian friendly • tables • self-service • take-out
🍎 Manhattan's Upper East Side on 2nd Ave between E 63rd & E 64th St on east side.

The Health Nuts 🛍
835 2nd Ave. ✆ 212-490-2979 ⏰ M-F 8:30-8:30, Sat 10-8, Sun 11-7
• deli • vegetarian friendly • take-out
🍎 Manhattan's Midtown East Side on 2nd Ave between E 45th & E 46th St on west side.

The Natural Gourmet Cookery School 🍴
48 W. 21st St. ✆ 212-645-5170 ⏰ Friday 6:30
Friday night 4-course, prix fixe wholefoods dinner prepared by instructors and students in the Chef's Training Program. BYOB. Reservations required.
• vegetarian • vegan friendly • organic focus • tables • wait staff
🍎 On W 21st St between 5th & 6th Ave on north side (on 2nd floor).

The Organic Grill 🍴
123 1st Ave. ✆ 212-477-7177 ⏰ M-F 11-10, Sun10-10
Menu favors sustainable agriculture and artisanal food producers.
• vegetarian • vegan friendly • fresh juice • alcohol • tables • wait staff
🍎 In the East Village on west side of 1st Ave between E 7th St & St Marks Place.

The Pump Energy Food Restaurant 🍴
40 W. 55th St. ✆ 212-246-6844 ⏰ M-F 8-9:30, Sat 10-8, Sun 11-9
Low fat, high protein menu. Tofu, legumes and veggie burgers for vegetarians. Whole grains, no added fat or salt.
• vegetarian friendly • fresh juice • tables • self-service
🍎 Midtown Manhattan on south side of W 55th St between 5th & 6th Ave.

The Pump Energy Food Restaurant 🍴
113 E. 31st St. ✆ 212-213-5733 ⏰ M-F 8-10:30, Sat 10-8, Sun 11-9
See W55th St location for description.
• vegetarian friendly • fresh juice • tables • self-service
🍎 Midtown Manhattan on north side of E 31st St between Park & Lexington Ave.

Uncle Mike's Organic Cafe 🍴
235 E. 53rd St. ✆ 212-421-6444 ⏰ M-F 11-9:30, Sat 12-7:30, Sun 12-8:30
Mostly take out and vegan with limited fish, chicken and seating.
• vegetarian friendly • vegan friendly • organic focus • fresh juice • tables • self-service • take-out
🍎 Midtown Manhattan on north side of E 53rd St between 2nd & 3rd Ave.

Uptown Juice Bar ⏍
54 W. 125th St. ✆ 212-987-2660 ⏱ Daily 8-9
Caribbean-style vegan eatery.
• vegan • organic focus • fresh juice • counter • self-service
🍎 In Harlem on W 125th St between Lenox & 5th Ave on south side.

Uptown Whole Foods 🛍
2421 Broadway ✆ 212-874-4000 ⏱ Daily 8-11
• organic produce • vegetarian friendly • fresh juice • salad bar • deli • bakery • take-out
🍎 Manhattan's Upper West Side on west side of Broadway at W 89th St.

Vatan ⏍
409 3rd Ave. ✆ 212-689-5666 ⏱ Tues-Th, Sun 5:30-9, F-Sat 5:30-10
Price-fixed Indian Gujarat menu unlimited refills.
• vegetarian • vegan friendly • fresh juice • alcohol • tables • wait staff
🍎 On southeast corner 3rd Ave & E 29th St.

Vegetarian Dim Sum House ⏍
24 Pell St. ✆ 212-577-7176 ⏱ Daily 10:30-10:30
Chinese vegetarian.
• vegetarian • vegan friendly • tables • wait staff • take-out
🍎 In Manhattan's Chinatown on north side of Pell St between the Bowery and Mott St.

Vegetarian's Paradise 2 ⏍
144 W. 4th St. ✆ 212-260-7130 ⏱ M-Th., Sun 12-11, F-Sat 12-12
Chinese vegetarian with lots of mock meat.
• vegetarian • vegan friendly • tables • wait staff • take-out
🍎 In the West Village on W 4th St between 6th Ave & McDougal St on south side (1 block west of Washington Square Park).

Village Natural ⏍
46 Greenwich Ave. ✆ 212-727-0968 ⏱ Daily 11-11
• vegetarian • organic focus • alcohol • counter • tables • wait staff • take-out
🍎 In the West Village on north side of Greenwich Ave between 6th & 7th Ave (entrance down a short flight of stairs).

Westerly Health Foods 🛍
911- 913 8th Ave. ✆ 212-586-5262 ⏱ M-F 7am-12am, Sat 8-12am, Sun 9-12am
• organic produce
🍎 On east side of 8th Ave between W 54th & W 55th St.

Whole Earth Bakery & Kitchen ⏍
30 St. Marks Place ✆ 212-677-7597 ⏱ Daily 9-10:30
Whole grain, sugar-free baked goods plus pizzas, soups and salads.
• vegan • organic focus • counter • self-service
🍎 In the East Village on St Marks Place between Ave A & 1st Ave on south side.

Whole Foods Market 🛍
250 7th Ave. ✆ 212-924-5969 ⏱ Daily 8-11
• organic produce • vegetarian friendly • salad bar • deli • bakery • take-out
🍎 In Chelsea on 7th Ave between W 25th & W 24th St on west side.

Whole Foods Market 🛍 ⏍
4 Union Square S. ✆ 212-673-5388 ⏱ Daily 8-11
• organic produce • vegetarian friendly • salad bar • cafe • self-service • take-out
🍎 On E 14th St side of Union Sq at Broadway.

Whole Foods Market 🛍 ⏍
10 Columbus Circle ✆ 212-823-9600 ⏱ Daily 8-11
• organic produce • vegetarian friendly • salad bar • cafe • self-service • take-out
🍎 W 59th St where 8th Ave & Broadway meet. Concourse level of Time Warner Ctr.

Whole Foods Market 🛍 🍴
95 E. Houston St. ✆ 212-420-1320 ⏰ Daily 8-11
  • organic produce • vegetarian friendly • salad bar • cafe • self-service • take-out
🏢 Manhattan's Lower East Side on south side of Houston St between Bowery & Chrystie St.

Wild Ginger 🍴
380 Broome St. ✆ 212-966-1883 ⏰ M-Th 11:30-10:30, F-Sat 11:30-11, Sun 12:30-10:30
98% vegan Chinese, Japanese, Thai and Vietnamese. Brown rice with all entrees.
  • vegetarian • vegan friendly • alcohol • tables • wait staff • take-out
🏢 In SoHo on the north side of Broome St between Mulberry & Mott St.

World of Vegetarian 🍴
24 Pell St. ✆ 212-577-7176 ⏰ Daily 10:30-10:30
Chinese vegetarian.
  • vegetarian • vegan friendly • tables • wait staff
🏢 In Chinatown on Pell St between Bowery & Mott St on north side.

Zen Palate 🍴
663 9th Ave. ✆ 212-582-1669 ⏰ Daily 11:30-10:30
Vegan Zen menu featuring soy and gluten faux meats.
  • vegan • tables • wait staff
🏢 On west side of 9th Ave at W 46th St.

Zen Palate 🍴
104 John St. ✆ 212-962-4208 ⏰ M-F 11:30-10:30, Sat-Sun 12-10
Vegan Zen menu featuring soy and gluten faux meat.
  • vegan • tables • wait staff
🏢 In Manhattan's Financial District on south side of John St between Gold & Pearl St just east of Cliff St.

Zenith 🍴
311 W. 48th St. ✆ 212-262-8080 ⏰ M-F 11-10:30, Sat-Sun 12-10:30
Vegetarian Asian menu.
  • vegetarian • vegan friendly • alcohol • tables • wait staff
🏢 On north side of 48th St between 8th & 9th Ave.

NORTHPORT

Organically Yours 🛍
114 Main St. ✆ 631-754-2150 ⏰ M-Sat 10-6
  • organic produce • vegetarian friendly • fresh juice • deli • take-out
🏢 **From Northern State Pkwy**, take exit 42N toward Northport onto Deer Park Rd (CR 66N, becomes E Jericho Tpke) about 1 mile to Elwood Rd. Turn left onto Ellwood (becomes Reservoir Ave) about 4¼ miles to Scudder Ave. Turn left onto Scudder about ½ mile to Union Pl. Turn right onto Union 1 block to Main St. Turn left onto Main to store.

NYACK

Back to Earth 🛍
1 S. Broadway ✆ 845-353-3311 ⏰ M-F 9-7, Sat 9-6, Sun 10-6
  • vegetarian friendly • deli • take-out
🏢 **From I-287E/87S (NY Thwy)**, take exit 11 toward Nyack onto Rt 59 (becomes Main St) about 1 mile into town to Broadway. Turn right onto Broadway to store on left corner. **From I-287W/87N,** take exit 11 onto High Ave ½ mile, turn right onto Franklin St, left onto Main and follow directions above.

OCEANSIDE

Jandi's 🛍 🍴   ♿
3000 Long Beach Rd. ✆ 516-536-5535 ⏰ Daily 8-8
Eat-in/take-out deli is wheat-, yeast- and refined sugar-free.

• organic produce • vegetarian • vegan friendly • organic focus • fresh juice • deli • counter • tables • self-service • take-out

🔔 **From Merrick Rd,** go south on Long Beach Rd about 1 mile to store on right after Atlantic Ave. **From Southern State Pkwy**, take exit 17 (Ocean Ave) south 1 block, stay left of fork over tracks about 7 miles then over more tracks to next light at Atlantic. Turn right onto Atlantic to store.

OLIVEREA

Shangri-La 🍴

212 McKinley Hollow Rd. ✆ 845-254-6000 ⏰ Daily 8-10, 11-1:30pm, 4:30-9
Lodge serving Indian vegetarian food. Restaurant, spa services and free hiking trails open to all.
• vegetarian • vegan friendly • kosher • alcohol • tables • wait staff

🍴 **From Rt 28,** turn onto Rt 47 (left from 28W, right from 28E) 3 miles to McKinley Hollow Rd. Turn right onto McKinley Hollow 1 mile to resort.

ONEONTA

Annie's Bread & Butter 🛍 🍴

18 Clinton Plaza Drive ✆ 607-436-8801 ⏰ M-Sat 7-7
• organic produce • vegetarian friendly • deli • tables • self-service • take-out

🍴 **From I-88E,** take exit 14 toward Oneonta left onto Main St ½ mile to Chestnut St. Turn left onto Chestnut under ½ mile to Clinton St. Turn right onto Clinton to store on left in Clinton Plaza. **From I-88W,** take exit 15 toward Oneonta Colleges onto NY 23W about ½ mile to light at Main. Turn left onto Main over ¾ mile to Clinton. Turn right onto Clinton to store on left.

Autumn Cafe 🍴

244 Main St. ✆ 607-432-6845 ⏰ Tues-Sat 11-9, Sun 10:30-2:30
Tofu and tempeh along with chicken, tuna and pastrami. Homemade whole wheat bread.
• vegetarian friendly • alcohol • tables • wait staff • take-out

🍴 **From I-88E,** take exit 14 toward Oneonta left onto Main St about ⅔ mile to restaurant. **From I-88W,** take exit 15 toward Oneonta Colleges onto NY 23W about ½ mile to light at Main. Turn left onto Main to restaurant.

Green Earth Natural Foods 🛍   ♿

4 Market St. ✆ 607-432-6600 ⏰ M-F 8-8, Sat 8-6, Sun 11-4
• organic produce • vegetarian friendly • organic focus • cafe • bakery • counter • tables • self-service • take-out

🍴 **From I-88E,** take exit 14 toward Oneonta left onto Main St to Market St (first right after tracks). Turn right onto Market to store on right at top of hill. **From I-88W,** take exit 15 toward Oneonta Colleges onto NY 23W about ½ mile to light at Main. Turn left onto Main 3-4 blocks to Market. Turn left onto Market to store on left.

PHOENICIA

Sweet Sue's 🍴

49 Main St. ✆ 845-688-7852 ⏰ M-Th, Sun 8-3, F-Sat 8-3, 5-9
Hearty pancakes plus homemade soups, salads and sandwiches on homemade bread.
• vegetarian friendly • counter • tables • wait staff

🍴 **From I-87 (NY Thwy),** take exit 19 (Kingston). Take first exit off rotary onto Rt 28W toward Pine Hill about 22 miles to Rt 214. Turn right onto 214 (Main St in town) to restaurant in first block of stores on left

PINE BUSH

Pure City 🍴

100 Main St. ✆ 845-744-8888 ⏰ Tues-Th 11-10, F-Sat 11-11
Chinese vegetarian, brown barley, chocolate tofu silk pie.
• vegetarian • vegan friendly • tables • wait staff

🍴 Pine Bush is about 15 miles northwest of NY Thwy exit 17 (Newburgh). Restaurant is on Rt 52 (aka Main St) at north end of town on east side at Rt 302.

PLAINVIEW

Dr. B. Well Naturally 🛍️🍴   ♿

8 Washington Ave. ✆ 516-932-9355 ⏰ M-F 8-8, Sat 9-7, Sun 11-6
  • organic produce • vegetarian friendly • fresh juice • deli • tables • self-service • take-out

🚘 **From LIE (I-495) eastbound**, take exit 45 onto Manetto Hill Rd south to Washington Ave. Turn left onto Washington to store on left. **From LIE westbound**, take exit 48 left onto Round Swamp Rd and merge right onto Old Country Rd about 1½ miles to Manetto Hill. Turn right onto Manetto Hill and right onto Washington to store on right.

PLATTSBURGH

North Country Co-op 🛍️

25 Bridge St. ✆ 518-561-5904 ⏰ M-F 9-7, Sat 9-5, Sun 12-5

🚘 **From I-87**, take exit 38A toward Plattsburgh onto Rt 22S about 1¼ miles to Rt 3. Turn left onto Rt 3 about ¼ mile to Rt 9 (historic district). Turn right onto 9 (Margaret St) and follow left (becomes Bridge St) to store across from city parking lot.

PORT JEFFERSON

Tiger Lily Cafe 🍴

156 E. Main St. ✆ 631-476-7080 ⏰ M-Th, Sun 11-7, F-Sat 11-10 (spring and summer, otherwise call for closing time)
A "funky" cafe with local art work and live performances.

  • vegetarian friendly • organic focus • fresh juice • counter • tables • self-service • take-out

🚘 From Northern State Pkwy, continue until it becomes NY 347E (between Commack & Hauppauge). Follow 347E 14 miles to NY 112/Port Jefferson Rd. Turn left onto 112 (becomes Main St) about 1¾ miles to E Main. Turn right onto E Main and follow around to left to restaurant.

PORT WASHINGTON

Twin Pines Co-op 🛍️   ♿

382 Main St. ✆ 516-883-9777 ⏰ Tues, W, F 10-5, Th 10-6, Sat 10-4:30
  • organic produce • co-op

🚘 **From LIE (I-495)**, take exit 36 north on Searingtown Rd about 4½ miles into Port Washington. Turn left onto Main St (post office on far right corner) about 1½ miles to store at at Prospect St in Mertz Community Ctr (across from town dock).

POTSDAM

Potsdam Food Co-op 🛍️

24 Elm St. ✆ 315-265-4630 ⏰ M-F 7:40-7, Sat 8-6, Sun 12-4
  • organic produce • co-op

🍎 Take Rt 11 into Potsdam. Turn left onto Union St and right onto Elm St to store on left.

POUGHKEEPSIE

Health Connection 🛍️

704 Freedom Plains Rd. ✆ 845-473-1275 ⏰ M-F 9:30-7, Sat 9:30-4
🚘 **From the Taconic Pkwy**, take Rt 55W exit onto Freedom Plains Rd about 2¾ miles to store on left.

Mother Earth's Storehouse 🛍️   ♿

1955 South Rd. ✆ 845-296-1069 ⏰ M-F 9-9, Sat 10-8, Sun 12-6
  • organic produce

🍎 On Rt 9 on west side by the Galleria Mall entrance.

RHINEBECK

Bread Alone 🍴

45 E. Market St. ✆ 845-876-3108 ⏰ Daily 7-5

Organic bread baked in wood-fired ovens, soups, salads and sandwiches.
• vegetarian friendly • bakery • tables • self-service • take-out

From Rt 9 in Rhinebeck, turn east onto Market St (main light in town) ½ block to store on left.

Garden Street Cafe
24 Garden St. © 845-876-2005 ① M-Sat 9:30-4
Vegetarian/vegan except for tuna salad.
• vegetarian friendly • organic focus • fresh juice • cafe • tables • self-service • take-out

 Inside Rhinebeck Health Food (see below).

Rhinebeck Health Foods
24 Garden St. © 845-876-2555 ① M-Sat 9:30-6, Sun 10-3
• organic produce

From Rt 9 in Rhinebeck, turn west onto Market St (main light in town). Make first right onto Garden St to end. Turn left into parking lot to store on right.

RIVERHEAD

Green Earth Natural Foods Market
50 E. Main St. © 631-369-2233 ① M-F 9:30-6, Sat 10-6, Sun 11-5
• organic produce • vegetarian friendly • fresh juice • salad bar • cafe • deli • bakery • tables • self-service • take-out

From LIE (I-495), take exit 72 onto Rt 25E (becomes W Main, then E Main St) about 5 miles into Riverhead to store on north side (left), 1 block past light in downtown business district.

ROCHESTER

Abundance Cooperative Market
62 Marshall St. © 585-454-2667 ① M-F 8-8, Sat 9-7, Sun 10-7
• organic produce • vegetarian friendly • deli • tables • self-service • take-out • coop

From I-490E, take exit 15 (Inner Loop/South Ave) toward Rt 15. Take Inner Loop ramp and follow toward Monroe Ave onto Howell St to Broadway. Turn right onto Broadway to Marshall St (store parking lot is just before Marshall). Turn left onto Marshall to store on left. **From I-490W**, take exit 17 (Goodman St) straight onto Broadway ½ mile to fork. Take right fork onto Union St to Monroe. Turn left onto Monroe and left onto Marshall to store on right before Broadway.

Lori's Natural Foods Center
900 Jefferson Rd. © 585-424-2323 ① M-Sat 8-9, Sun 10-6
• organic produce • vegetarian • vegan friendly • deli • take-out

From I-390N, take exit 14 left onto Rt 15A N ½ mile to Rt 252. Turn left onto Rt 252 ½ mile to store on right in Genessee Valley Regional Mkt Complex. **From I-390S**, take exit 14 right onto Rt 252 1 mile to store.

Natural Oasis Cafe
288 Monroe Ave. © 585-325-1831 ① M-Sat 11-8, Sun 11-3
Vegan and Ethiopian buffet.
• vegan • cafe • tables • self-service • take-out

From I-490E, take exit 15 (Inner Loop/South Ave) toward Rt 31/Monroe Ave onto Howell Ave. Veer right onto Monroe about 2 blocks to restaurant on left. **From I-490W**, take exit 18 on left for Monroe and veer right onto Monroe under 1 mile to restaurant on right after Alexander St.

Natural Vibes
348-350 Thurston Rd. © 585-235-0770 ① M-Sat 8:30-8
Jamaican Rasta vegetarian and fish.
• vegetarian friendly • vegan friendly • tables • wait staff

From I-390, take exit 18A east on Brooks Ave (merge from I-390S, right from I-390N) ½-¾ mile to Thurston St. Turn left onto Thurston ½ mile to restaurant on right before Ravenwood Ave.

New Health Cafe 🍴

133 Gregory St. ℂ 585-301-4095 🕑 Tues-F 5-9, Sat 9-9, Sun 10-4
   • vegetarian • vegan friendly • tables • wait staff • take-out

🏠 **From I-490E,** take exit 15 onto South Ave and turn right onto Mt Hope Ave about ½ mile to Gregory St. Turn left onto Gregory 2 blocks to restaurant on right at Ashland St. **From I-490W,** take exit 17 for Goodman St (signs for Inner Loop) and veer right onto Broadway to Meigs St. Turn left onto Meigs across hwy and right onto S Clinton Ave 1 block to Gregory. Turn left onto Gregory ½ mile to restaurant on left.

ROCKVILLE CENTRE

It's Only Natural 🛍

4 S. Village Ave. ℂ 516-766-4449 🕑 M-F 9-6:30, Sat 9-6, Sun 10-5
Fresh juice but otherwise more supplements than food.
   • organic produce • fresh juice

🏠 **From Merrick Rd,** go south on Village Ave ½ block to store on west side. **From Southern State Pkwy eastbound,** take exit 18 (Eagle Ave). Turn right off exit to end. Turn right onto Penninsula Blvd to light at Lakeview Ave. Turn left onto Lakeview to Village Ave. Turn right onto Village to store ½ block past Merrick Rd on right.

ROCKY POINT

Back To Basics Natural Food 🛍

632 Rte. 25A ℂ 631-821-0444 🕑 M-Th, Sat 10-6:30, F 10-7:30, Sun 11-5
   • organic produce

🏠 **From Northern State Pkwy heading east,** continue on NY 347E about 15 miles where it becomes NY 25A E. Continue almost 6 miles to store.

ROSENDALE

Rosendale Cafe 🍴 ♿

435 Main St. ℂ 845-658-9048 🕑 M 5-10, Tues-Th 11-10, F-Sat 11-11:30, Sun 10-10
Healthy food and weekend entertainment.
   • vegetarian • vegan friendly • alcohol • tables • wait staff • take-out

🏠 **From I-87N (NY Thruway),** take exit 18 (New Paltz). Turn left at light onto Rt 299 through town to Rt 32N. Turn right onto Rt 32N almost 7½ miles to Rt 213 (immediately after Roundout Bridge) Turn left onto Rt 213 under ½ mile (almost to end of town) to restaurant on right. **From I-87S,** take exit 19 (Kingston). Take second right off traffic circle onto Washington Ave to end. Turn right onto Rt32S about 6½ miles to Rt 213 (before Roundout Bridge). Turn right onto Rt 213 and follow directions above.

The Alternative Baker 🍴 ♿

407 Main St. ℂ 845-658-3355 🕑 M, W, Sun 7-5, Th-Sat 7-7 closed W in winter
Specializes in vegan and gluten-free baking. Small, mostly veg sandwich and soup menu.
   • vegetarian friendly • vegan friendly • tables • self service • take-out

🏠 **From Rt 32,** turn onto Main St/Rt 213 (left from Rt 32N, right from Rt 32S) under ½ mile to restaurant on left across from Rosendale theater.

SAG HARBOR

Provisions 🛍 🍴

Bay & Division Sts. ℂ 631-725-3636 🕑 Daily 8:30-6, until 7 June-Sept Cafe 8:30-4
   • organic produce • vegetarian friendly • fresh juice • cafe • tables • self-service • take-out

🏠 **From Rt 27 (Montauk Hwy),** go north on Rt 79/Sag Harbor Tpke (left from 27E, right from 27W) about 4½ miles to Bay St. Turn right onto Bay to store at Division St.

SARANAC LAKE

Nori's Whole Foods 🛍 🍴

68 Main St. ℂ 518-891-6079 🕑 M-F 9-7, Sat 9-5, Sun 10-4
   • organic produce • vegetarian • deli • tables • self-service • take-out

🏠 Store is on Rt 86 (Main St in Saranac Lake) on west side (behind Sears).

SARATOGA SPRINGS

Four Seasons Natural Foods Store & Cafe 🛍️ 🍴

33 Phila St. ✆ 518-584-4670 ⏱ Daily 9-8 Cafe 11:30-8
• organic produce • vegetarian • vegan friendly • fresh juice • salad bar • cafe • deli •
bakery • counter • tables • self-service • take-out

🍎 **From I-87**, take exit 13N onto Rt 9N toward Saratoga Springs about 4½ miles to
Phila St. Turn right onto Phila 1 block to store on left at Putnam St.

SAUGERTIES

Mother Earth's Storehouse 🛍️

249 Main St. ✆ 845-246-9614 ⏱ M-Th 9-7, F 9-8, Sat 9-6, Sun 12-6
• organic produce

🍴 **From I-87N (NY Thwy)**, take exit 20 right onto Ulster Ave almost 1 mile to end
at Market St. Turn right onto Market to first left (Main St). Turn left onto Main to
store on left. **From I-87S**, take exit 20 left onto Rt 32 to "T" at Rt 212. Turn left onto
Ulster Ave and follow directions above.

New World Home Cooking 🍴

1411 Rte. 212 ✆ 845-246-0900 ⏱ M-Th 5-10, F 5-11, Sat 11:30-2:30, 5-11 Sun
11:30-2:30, 4-10
Local and organic ingredients in many dishes. Menu is eclectic but specialty is "spicy."
• vegetarian friendly • vegan friendly • alcohol • tables • wait staff

🍴 **From I-87N (NY Thwy)** take exit 20 left onto Rt 32 to "T" at Rt 212. Turn right onto 212
toward Woodstock about 1½ miles to restaurant.

SAYVILLE

Cornucopia Natural Foods 🛍️

39 N. Main St. ✆ 631-589-9579 ⏱ M-F 9-7, Sat 9-6, Sun 11-5
• organic produce • vegetarian friendly • fresh juice • deli • tables • self-service • take-out

🍴 **From Sunrise Hwy**, go south on Lakeland Ave (right from Sunrise Hwy E, left
from Sunrise Hwy W) continuing onto Railroad Ave under 2 miles total to end
at Montauk Hwy (Main St in Sayville). Turn left into shopping ctr to store. **From
Montauk Hwy**, store is in town.

SCARSDALE

Mrs. Green's Natural Market 🛍️ 🍴

365 Central Park Ave. ✆ 914-472-9675 ⏱ M, W, F-Sat 9-7, Tues, Th 9-8, Sun 11-6
• organic produce • vegetarian friendly • deli • counter • self-service • take-out

🍴 **From I-287,** take exit 4 south on Rt 100A (toward Hartsdale) about 2¼ miles to
Central Park Ave (Rt 100). Turn right onto Central Park under 1 mile to store.

Mrs. Green's Natural Market 🛍️ 🍴

780 White Plains Rd. ✆ 914-472 0111 ⏱ M,W, F 8:30-8, Tues,Th 8:30-9, Sat-Sun 9-7
• organic produce • vegetarian friendly • deli • tables • self-service • take-out

🍴 **From Bronx River Pkwy**, take exit 10. Go east on Strathmore Rd (becomes
Harney Rd, then Brook St) about ¾ mile to White Plains Rd (aka Rt 22). Turn
right onto White Plains 1½ blocks to store on left.

SPRING VALLEY

Caribreeze Vegetarian Cafe 🍴

42 N. Main St. ✆ 845-426-2600 ⏱ M-Th 11:30-7, F-Sat 11:30-8
No frills vegan Jamaican food. A few seats but mainly take-out.
• vegan • tables • self service • take-out

🍴 **From I-87 (NY Thwy)**, take exit 14 west on Rt 59W about 1¼ miles to Main St.
Turn right onto Main ⅓ mile to restaurant on right after W Church St.

STATEN ISLAND

Tastebuds Natural Food 🛍 🍴
1807 Hylan Blvd. ✆ 718-351-8693 🕑 M-Sat 9-8, Sun 10-6:30
  • vegetarian friendly • deli • counter • self-service • take-out
🏠 **From I-278**, take exit 13 (Clove Rd/Richmond Blvd/Hylan Blvd) straight off exit to Richmond Rd. Turn south onto Richmond (right from I-278W, left from I-278E) almost 1 mile to Old Town Rd. Turn left onto Old Town under ½ mile to Hylan Blvd. Turn right onto Hylan under 1 mile to store on right.

Tuttoriso Ristorante Cafe 🍴   ♿
36 Richmond Terrace ✆ 718-273-7644 🕑 M 9-9:30, Tues-Th 9-10, F 9am-2am, Sat 11-11:30, Sun 11-9
Many vegetarian, vegan, gluten-free as well as omnivore choices.
  • vegetarian friendly • vegan friendly • alcohol • tables • wait staff • take-out
🏠 **From ferry terminal**, go north 1 block to restaurant on left. **From I-278E**, take exit 9 onto Rt 440N to exit 12 for Forest Ave N. Merge onto Willow Rd E and turn right onto Forest under 1 mile to Jewett Ave. Turn left onto Jewett under 1 mile to Richmond Terrace. Turn right onto Richmond 3¼ miles to restaurant on right. **From I-278W**, take exit 13 onto Narrows Rd and turn right onto Targee St about 1⅓ miles to Van Duzer St. Turn right onto Van Duzer 1 mile continuing onto Montgomery St ⅓ mile to first right onto Ft Place, first left onto St Marks Pl and first right onto Wall St 3 blocks to Richmond. Turn right onto Richmond to restaurant.

SUFFERN

Mrs. Green's Natural Market 🛍
26 Indian Rock Shopping Center 🕑 845-369-6699 🕑 M-W, F-Sat., 9-7, Th 9-8, Sun 10-6
  • organic produce
🏠 **From I-287W**, take exit 14B south on Airmont Rd ⅓ mile to Rt 59. Turn right onto Rt 59 under 1 mile to store in Indian Rock Shopping Ctr.

SYRACUSE

Strong Hearts Cafe 🍴
719 E. Genesee St. ✆ 315-478-0000 🕑M 8-6, Tues-Th 8am-12am, F 8am-2am, Sat 10am-2am, Sun 10am-12am
Casual dining and social center for the health-oriented, progressive community.
  • vegan • organic focus • tables • self-service • take-out
🏠 **From I-81S**, take exit 18 toward Adams St, merge onto Almond St and turn left onto Adams 3 blocks to Irving St. Turn left onto Irving 3 blocks to E Genesee St. Turn left onto E Genesee 1 block to restaurant on right after Forman Ave. **From I-81N**, take exit 18 for Adams toward Harrison St and merge onto Almond to Cedar St. Turn right onto Cedar 1 block to Irving. Turn left onto Irving 1 block to E Genesee. Turn left onto E Genesee to restaurant.

Syracuse Real Food Cooperative 🛍
618 Kensington Rd. ✆ 315-472-1385 🕑 M-Sat 8-9, Sun 8-6
  • organic produce • fresh juice • co-op
🏠 **From I-81S**, take exit 18 onto Harrison St, turn right onto S Townsend St and right onto E Genesee St almost 1½ miles to Westcott St. Turn right onto Westcott 1 mile to Kensington Rd. Turn left onto Kensington 1 block to store on right after Roosevelt Ave. **From I-81N**, take exit 18 toward Harrison, merge onto Almond St, turn left onto E Genesee, left onto Almond, left onto E Genesse and follow directions above. **From I-690**, take exit 14 south on Teall Ave (left from I-690W, right from I-690E) about ½ mile (becomes Columbus Ave) to Genessee. Turn left onto Genesee 1 block to Westcott. Turn right onto Westcott 1 mile to Kensington. Turn left onto Kensington to store.

TIVOLI

Luna 61 🍴 &

55 Broadway © 845-758-0061 ⏱ Tues-Th 5-9, F-Sat 5-10, Sun 10-3, 5-9
   • vegetarian • vegan friendly • organic focus • alcohol • counter • tables • wait staff
🏠 **From Rt 9G,** go west on CR 78/Broadway 1 mile to restaurant on right.

TROY

Uncle Sam's Good Natural Products 🛍

77 4th St. © 518-271-7299 ⏱ M-F 9-6:30, Sat 9-5
   • organic produce

🍎 **From I-87N (NY Thwy),** take exit 23 onto I-787N to exit 8 (23rd St toward Watervliet/Green Island). Turn left onto 23rd and left onto Broadway about ¼ mile to Rt 2E. Turn left onto 2E ½ mile to 4th St. Turn left onto 4th to store on right. **From I-87S,** take exit 7 onto Rt 7E toward Troy. Take Downtown Troy exit onto 6th St and head south over ½ mile to Congress St (Rt 2E). Turn right onto Congress 2 blocks to 4th St. Turn right onto 4th to store on left.

WATERTOWN

The Mustard Seed 🛍 &

969 Arsenal St. © 315-788-2463 ⏱ M-Sat 8:30-8, Sun 10-6
Hot lunch specials weekdays from 11 to 3.
   • organic produce • vegetarian friendly • organic focus • cafe • deli • tables • self-service • take-out

🍎 **From I-81N,** take exit 45 toward Sackets Harbor west on Arsenal St/Rt 3 (left from I-81S, right from I-81N) about 1 mile to store on right after Palmer St.

WEST SENECA

Feel-Rite Natural Food Shop 🛍

3521 Seneca St. © 716-675-6620 ⏱ M-Sat 9-9, Sun 10-7
   • organic produce

🍎 **From I-90 (NY Thwy),** take exit 55 onto Ridge Rd E ramp toward W Seneca. Follow Ridge almost 2 miles (turns right, then becomes Seneca St) to store in Seneca Ridge Plaza.

WESTHAMPTON BEACH

Westhampton Natural Foods 🛍

132-3 Main St. © 631-288-8947 ⏱ M-Sat 10-6, Sun 11-4 (some seasonal changes)
   • organic produce • vegetarian friendly • fresh juice • deli • take-out

🍎 **From Sunrise Hwy (NY 27),** take exit 63S toward Westhampton Beach onto CR 31S (Old Riverhead Rd, becomes Oak St) 3½ miles to traffic circle. Take second exit onto Potunk Ln under ½ mile to Main St. Turn left onto Main to store on right (behind bank).

WHITE PLAINS

Manna Foods, Inc. 🛍 🍴

171 Mamaroneck Ave. © 914-946-2233 ⏱ M-F 9-6, Sat 9-5
Vegetarian lunch weekdays from 11:30-2:30.
   • vegetarian • fresh juice • tables • self-service • take-out

🏠 **From Hutchinson River Pkwy,** take exit 23 north on Mamaroneck Ave about 3½ miles to store on right.

Whole Foods Market 🛍️ 🍴
110 Bloomingdale Rd. © 914-288-1300 ⏱ Daily 8-10
• organic produce • vegetarian friendly • salad bar • cafe • self-service • take-out
🚘 **From I-287W (Cross Westchester Expy)**, take exit 8 onto Westchester Ave under 1 mile to Bloomingdale Rd. Turn left onto Bloomingdale under ½ mile to store on right. **From I-287E**, take exit 8W onto Westchester Mall Pl and turn left onto Bloomingdale ⅓ mile to store.

WILLIAMSVILLE
Feel-Rite Fresh Market 🛍️ 🍴
5425 Transit Rd. © 716-636-1000 ⏱ M-Sat 10-10, Sun 10-7
• organic produce • vegetarian friendly • fresh juice • deli • tables • self-service
🚘 **From I-90 (NY Thwy)**, take exit 49 toward Depew/Lockport onto Rt 78N (aka Transit Rd) ¾ mile to store.

WOODSTOCK
Bread Alone 🍴
22 Mill Hill Rd. © 845-679-2108 ⏱ M-F, Sun 7-5, Sat 7-6
Organic bread baked in wood-fired ovens, soups, salads and sandwiches.
• vegetarian friendly • bakery • counter • tables • self-service • takeout
🚘 **From I-87S**, take exit 20 (Saugerties) left onto Rt 32 to "T" at Rt 212. Turn right onto 212 about 10 miles into Woodstock. Restaurant is at top of hill on left corner Mill Hill Rd & Maple Lane. **From I-87N**, take exit 19 (Kingston). Take first exit off rotary onto Rt 28W toward Pine Hill about 8 miles to light at Rt 375. Turn right onto 375 to end. Turn left onto Tinker St (aka Mill Hill Rd) 1 mile to restaurant.

Garden Cafe 🍴
6 Old Forge Rd. © 845-679-3600 ⏱ M, W-Sun 11:30-9
High quality vegan cuisine.
• vegan • organic focus • alcohol • tables • wait staff • take-out
🚘 **From I-87S**, take exit 20 (Saugerties) left onto Rt 32 to "T" at Rt 212. Turn right onto 212 about 10 miles into Woodstock. Restaurant is at top of hill on right after Rock City Rd. **From I-87N**, take exit 19 (Kingston). Take first exit off rotary onto Rt 28W toward Pine Hill about 8 miles to light at Rt 375. Turn right onto 375 to end. Turn left onto Tinker St (aka Mill Hill Rd) 1 mile to restaurant.

Joshua's 🍴 ♿
51 Tinker St. © 845-679-5533 ⏱ Winter M-Tues, Th 11-9, F 11-10, Sat 10-10, Sun 10-9 Summer 1 hour later M, Tues, Th, Sat
Middleastern plus nontraditional vegetarian and vegan options. Whole wheat pita on request.
• vegetarian friendly • alcohol • tables • wait staff
🚘 **From I-87S**, take exit 20 (Saugerties) left onto Rt 32 to "T" at Rt 212. Turn right onto 212 about 10 miles to center of Woodstock to restaurant on left corner Tinker St & Tannery Brook Rd. **From I-87N**, take exit 19 (Kingston). Take first exit off rotary onto Rt 28W toward Pine Hill about 8 miles to light at Rt 375. Turn right onto 375 to end. Turn left onto Tinker St about 1 mile to restaurant.

Sunflower Natural Foods 🛍️ ♿
75 Mill Hill Rd. © 845-679-5361 ⏱ M-Sat 9-9, Sun 10-7
• organic produce
🚘 **From I-87S**, take exit 20 (Saugerties) left onto Rt 32 to "T" at Rt 212. Turn right onto 212 about 9½ miles. As you enter Woodstock store is in shopping plaza on right. **From I-87N**, take exit 19 (Kingston). Take first exit off rotary onto Rt 28W toward Pine Hill about 8 miles to light at Rt 375. Turn right onto 375 to end. Turn left onto Tinker St (aka Mill Hill Rd) about ¼ mile to store.

Sunfrost Farms 🛍️ 🍴

217 Tinker St. © 845-679-6690 ⏲ Daily 9-6
Produce market/juice bar with light meals and homemade take-out.
 • organic produce • vegetarian friendly • fresh juice • deli • counter • tables • self-service • take-out

🚗 **From I-87S**, take exit 20 (Saugerties) left onto Rt 32 to "T" at Rt 212. Turn right onto 212 almost 11 miles (through Woodstock) to store on left. **From I-87N,** take exit 19 (Kingston). Take first exit off rotary onto Rt 28W toward Pine Hill about 8 miles to light at Rt 375. Turn right onto 375 to end. Turn left onto Tinker St (aka Rt 212) 1½ miles to store.

Taco Juan's 🍴

31 Tinker St. © 845-679-9673 ⏲ Daily 11:30-7
Vegan beans, tofu chili and Mexican (brown) rice. The fast-food choice for locals and tourists.
 • vegetarian friendly • tables • self-service • take-out

🚗 **From I-87S**, take exit 20 (Saugerties) left onto Rt 32 to "T" at Rt 212. Turn right onto 212 about 10 miles to center of Woodstock to restaurant on left. **From I-87N,** take exit 19 (Kingston). Take first exit off rotary onto Rt 28W toward Pine Hill about 8 miles to light at Rt 375. Turn right onto 375 to end. Turn left onto Tinker St about 1 mile to restaurant.

NORTH CAROLINA

ASHEVILLE

Early Girl Eatery 🍴

8 Wall St. ℂ 828-259-9292 ⏰ M 7:30-3, Tues-F 7:30-3, 5-9, Sat 9-3, 5-9, Sun 9-3
Southern cooking with vegetarian, vegan, hormone-free beef, free-range chicken and local seasonal produce.
  • vegetarian friendly • vegan friendly • alcohol • tables • wait staff

🏛 **From I-240E**, take exit 4B toward Downtown onto Patton Ave over ½ mile to Otis St. Turn left onto Otis and right onto Wall St 1 block to restaurant on right at Battery Park Ave. **From I-240W**, take exit 5C for Montford Ave onto Cherry St, turn left onto Hayward St, right onto N French Broad St, left onto Otis and left onto Wall to restaurant.

Earth Fare 🛍 🍴   ♿

66 Westgate Pkwy. ℂ 28-253-7656 ⏰ Daily 7-10
  • organic produce • vegetarian friendly • fresh juice • salad bar • cafe • deli • bakery •
  counter • tables • self-service • take-out

🏛 **From I-40**, I-26 or US 23/70, merge onto I-240 to exit 3B onto Westgate Pkwy to store on right just past exit.

Earth Fare 🛍 🍴

1856 Hendersonville Rd. ℂ 828-210-0100 ⏰ Daily 7-10
  • organic produce • vegetarian friendly • salad bar • cafe • deli • tables • self-service • take-out

🏛 **From I-26**, take exit 37 toward Skyline onto Long Shoals Rd (left from I-26E, right from I-26W) about 2 miles to Hendersonville Rd. Turn left onto Hendersonville about 1¼ miles to store on right.

French Broad Co-op 🛍

90 Biltmore Ave. ℂ 828-255-7650 ⏰ M-Sat 8-9, Sun 11-7
  • organic produce • co-op

🏛 **From I-240** take exit 5A south on Merriman Ave (left at fork, right onto Woodfin St and left from I-240E, merge onto Elm St and left from I-240W) about ½ mile (becomes Biltmore Ave) to store on left.

Greenlife Grocery 🛍 🍴

70 Merrimon Ave. ℂ 828-254-5440 ⏰ Daily 7-10
  • organic produce • vegetarian friendly • fresh juice • salad bar • cafe • deli • tables •
  self-service • take-out

1. Asheville
2. Beaufort
3. Black Mountain
4. Boone
5. Brevard
6. Carrboro
7. Cary
8. Chapel Hill
9. Charlotte
10. Concord
11. Durham
12. Elizabeth City
13. Fayetteville
14. Gastonia
15. Goldsboro
16. Greensboro
17. Hendersonville
18. Hickory
19. Kingston
20. Kitty Hawk
21. Morganton
22. Morrisville
23. Pittsboro
24. Raleigh
25. Roanoke Rapids
26. Salisbury
27. Sylva
28. Wilmington
29. Winston-Salem

From I-240 take exit 5A north on Merriman Ave (right at fork and right from I-240E, merge onto Elm St and right from I-240W) 1 block to store on left.

Haywood Road Community Co-op

771 Haywood Rd. © 828-225-4445 ① Daily 9-9
· organic produce · co-op

From I-240, take exit 2 toward W Asheville west on US26/US19/Haywood Rd (right from I-240W, onto Hanover St and left from I-240E) ¾ mile to store on right at Vermont Ave.

Laughing Seed Cafe

40 Wall St. © 828-252-3445 ① M, W-Th 11:30-9, F-Sat 11:30-10, Sun 10-9
Varied international menu.
· vegetarian · vegan friendly · organic focus · fresh juice · alcohol · tables · wait staff

From I-240E, take exit 4B toward Downtown onto Patton Ave over ½ mile to Otis St. Turn left onto Otis and right onto Wall St about 1 block to restaurant on right. **From I-240W,** take exit 5C for Montford Ave onto Cherry St, turn left onto Hayward St, right onto N French Broad St, left onto Otis and left onto Wall to restaurant.

Rosetta's Kitchen

111 Broadway St. © 828-232-0738 ① M-Th 10-11, F-Sat 10-3am, Sun 10-3pm
· vegetarian · vegan friendly · alcohol · tables · wait staff

From I-240, take exit 5A toward Merriman Ave/US-25. **From I-240E,** keep left at fork and turn right onto Woodfin St 1 block to Broadway St. Turn right onto Broadway o restaurant. **From I-240W,** merge onto Elm St and turn left onto Merrimon past hwy to restaurant.

The Green Sage

5 Broadway St. © 828-252-4450 ① M-W 7:30-9, Th 7:30-10, F 7:30-11, Sat 8-11, Sun 8-9
Eco-oriented eatery with a vegetarian version of just about everything on the menu.
· vegetarian · vegan friendly · organic focus · fresh juice · alcohol · tables · self-service · take-out

From I-240, take exit 5A toward Merrimon Ave/US-25. **From I-240E,** keep left at fork and turn right onto Woodfin 1 block to Broadway St. Turn left onto Broadway 2 blocks to restaurant on left after College St. **From I-240W,** merge onto Elm and turn left onto Merrimon about ½ mile to restaurant.

BEAUFORT

Coastal Community Market 🛍
606 Broad St. ✆ 252-728-2844 ⏰ M-Tues 11-6, W-F 11-7, Sat 9-5
  • organic produce
🍎 **From US 70/Cedar St**, go south on Queen St across tracks 1 block to Broad St. Turn left onto Broad to store on right.

BLACK MOUNTAIN

Black Mountain Natural Foods 🛍
108 Black Mountain Ave. ✆ 828-669-9813 ⏰ M-F 9-7, Sat 10-7, Sun 12-5
  • organic produce
🍎 **From I-40**, take exit 64 (NC 9) toward Black Mtn north on Broadway St (left from I-40E, right from I-40W) 3 blocks to Mitchell Ave. Turn left onto Mitchell 1 block to Black Mtn Ave. Turn right onto Black Mtn 1 block to store on right before tracks.

Greenlight Cafe 🍴
205 W. State St. ✆ 828-669-2444 ⏰ Tues-Th 10-7, F-Sat 9-8, Sun 10-2
  • vegetarian • vegan friendly • alcohol • tables • wait staff
🍎 **From I-40**, take exit 64 (NC 9) toward Black Mtn north on Broadway St (left from I-40E, right from I-40W) about ½ mile to Main St. Turn left onto Main (US 70) about 3 blocks to restaurant on right between N Dougherty St & New Bern Ave.

BOONE

Bare Essentials Natural Market 🛍
273 Boone Heights Drive ✆ 828-262-5592 ⏰ M-Sat 9-7, Sun 12-6
  • organic produce
🍎 **From NC 105/221/321 intersection**, go southeast on Blowing Rock Rd about ¾ mile to Boone Heights Rd. Turn left onto Boone Heights to store on left.

Earth Fare 🛍🍴
178 W. King St. ✆ 828-263-8138 ⏰ M-Th, Sun 8-9
  • organic produce • vegetarian friendly • salad bar • cafe • deli • tables • self-service
🍎 **From NC 105/US 221/321 intersection**, go north on Blowing Rock Rd about 1 mile to E King St. Turn left onto E King (becomes W King) about ½ mile to store on left.

BREVARD

Healthy Harvest 🛍
410 N. Broad St. ✆ 828-885-2599 ⏰ M-F 10-6, Sat 10-5
🍎 **From US 64/US 276/NC 80 intersection**, go south on US 276/Asheville Pkwy about 3 miles to store in College Plaza (across from Brevard College).

Poppies Gourmet Farmers' Market 🛍🍴
1 Market St. ✆ 828-885-5494 ⏰ M-Sat 8-8, Sun 10-6
  • organic produce • vegetarian friendly • alcohol • salad bar • cafe • deli • bakery • tables • self-service • take-out
🍎 **From US 64/US 276/NC 80 intersection**, go south on US 276/ Asheville Pkwy 1½ miles store on right after main Straus Park entrance.

Weaver Street Market 🛍
101 E. Weaver St. ✆ 919-929-0010 ⏰ M-F 7:30-9, Sat-Sun 8-9
  • organic produce • vegetarian friendly • deli • bakery • take-out • co-op
🍎 **From I-40**, take exit 266 south on Rt 86 about 2⅓ miles to Estes Dr exit. Turn right onto Estes (toward Carrboro) to end. Turn left onto Greensboro St and left at first light onto Weaver St to store in Carr Mill Mall.

CARY

Bright Palace ⛩
1207-J Kildaire Farm Rd. ✆ 919-468-7188 ◷ M-Th, Sun 11-3, 5-9, F-Sat 11-3, 5-10
Japanese/Chinese vegetarian menu.
 • vegetarian • vegan friendly • tables • wait staff • take-out
🚗 **From US 1**, take exit 99 north on SE Cary Pkwy (left from US 1N, right from US 1S) about 1 mile to High Meadow Dr. Turn right onto High Meadow under ½ mile to Kildaire Farm Rd. Turn right onto Kildaire Farm to restaurant on right.

Cool Breeze ⛩
740 E. Chatham St. ✆ 919-463-9130 ◷ Tues-Th 12-3, 6-10, F-Sun 12-10
Vegetarian Indian with a lunch buffet.
 • vegetarian • vegan friendly • tables • self-service • wait staff
🚗 **From I-40**, take exit 290 toward Cary west onto Chapel Hill Rd (right from I-40E, left from I-40W) about 1 mile to NE Maynard Rd. Turn left onto Maynard ¼ mile to E Chatham Rd. Turn right onto E Chatham to restaurant on left in Chatham Sq.

Once in a Blue Moon Bakery & Cafe ⛩
115-G W. Chatham St. ✆ 919-319-6554 ◷ M-F 7-6, Sat. 7:30-5
 • vegetarian • bakery • tables • self-service • take-out
🚗 **From I-40E**, take exit 287 toward Cary right onto N Harrison Ave about 3½ miles to W Chatham St. Turn left onto W Chatham to restaurant in Ashworth Village.
From I-40W, take exit 291 toward Cary right onto Farm Gate Rd 1 mile (becomes Cary Towne Blvd) to end at Walnut St. Turn right onto Walnut 1 mile to Kildaire Farm Rd. Turn right onto Kildaire Farm and make next right onto S Academy St about ¼ mile to W Chatham. Turn left onto W Chatham to restaurant.

Udipi Cafe ⛩
590 E. Chatham St. ✆ 919-465-0898 ◷ Daily 11:30-3, 5-9:30
Indian vegetarian with a lunch buffet.
 • vegetarian • vegan friendly • tables • self-service • wait staff
🚗 **From I-40**, take exit 290 toward Cary west on Chapel Hill Rd (right from I-40E, left from I-40W) about 1 mile to NE Maynard Rd. Turn left onto Maynard ¼ mile to E Chatham Rd. Turn right onto E Chatham ¼ mile to restaurant.

Whole Foods Market 🛒⛩   ♿
102B New Waverly Place ✆ 919-816-8830 ◷ Daily 7:30-9
 • organic produce • vegetarian friendly • salad bar • cafe • self-service • take-out
🚗 **From I-40/440**, take exit 293 toward Sanford onto US 64W/1S about 1 mile to Cary Pkwy exit. Follow left fork and turn left onto SE Cary Pkwy about ¾ mile to Tryon Rd. Turn right onto Tryon about ¾ mile to store at Kildare Farm Rd in Waverly Place Shopping Ctr.

CHAPEL HILL

Evos Fresh & Healthy ⛩
1800 E. Franklin St. ✆ 919-929-5867 ◷ Daily 11-10
Healthy fast-food concept with soyburgers, veggie patties, whole wheat wraps, organic greens, vegan chili, veggie corn dogs, natural meat, "airfriesTM", smoothies and such.
 • vegetarian friendly • tables • self-service • take-out
🚗 **From I-40**, take exit 270 toward Chapel Hill onto Rt 15S/501S under 1½ miles to E Franklin St. Veer right onto E Franklin under ½ mile to restaurant on left.

Sage Vegetarian Cafe ⛩   ♿
1129 Weaver Dairy Rd. ✆ 919-968-9266 ◷ Lunch M-Sat 11:30-2:30 Dinner M-Th 5-9, F-Sat 5-10
 • vegetarian • alcohol • tables • wait staff
🚗 **From I-40**, take exit 266 toward Chapel Hill/Carrboro south on NC 86 (right from I-40E, left from 1-40W) ½-⅔ mile to Weaver Dairy Rd. Turn left onto Weaver Dairy about ¼ mile to restaurant in Timberlyne Shoppping Ctr.

Weaver Street Market 🛍️
716 Market St. ✆ 919-929-2009 🕐 Daily 7-9
- organic produce • co-op

🚗 **From I-40,** take exit 270 onto Rt 15S/501S (becomes Fordham Blvd) about 7 miles to Main St. Turn right onto Main and right onto Market St to store.

Whole Foods Market/Wellspring Cafe 🛍️ 🍴   ♿
81 S. Elliott Rd. ✆ 919-968-1983 🕐 Daily 8-9 Cafe 7:30-9
- organic produce • vegetarian friendly • salad bar • cafe • self-service • take-out

🚗 **From I-40,** take exit 270 onto Rt 15S/501S 1½ miles to fork at E Franklin St. Go straight onto Franklin ½ mile to S Elliot Rd. Turn left onto Elliot to store on left.

CHARLOTTE

Berrybrook Farm Natural Foods Pantry 🛍️
1257 East Blvd. ✆ 704-334-6528 🕐 M-Th 9-7, F-Sat 9-6 Juice bar M-Sat 9-4 Hot food M-Sat 11-3:30
No indoor seating but a couple of swings on the porch.
- organic produce • vegetarian • fresh juice • deli • take-out

🚗 **From I-77,** take I-277 (Brookshire Fwy) to exit 2A and go south on Kenilworth Ave 1 mile to East Blvd. Turn right on East to store on corner.

Earth Fare 🛍️ 🍴
12235 N. Community House Rd. ✆ 704-926-1201 🕐 M-Sat 7-10, Sun 8-9
- organic produce • vegetarian friendly • salad bar • cafe • deli • tables • self-service • take-out

🚗 **From I-485E,** take exit 61 left at fork toward Johnston Rd/US 261. Turn left onto Johnston ½ mile to N Community House Rd. Turn right onto N Community House to store on right. **From I-485W,** take exit 61A onto Johnston about ¼ mile to N Community House and follow directions above.

Earth Fare 🛍️ 🍴
721 Governor Morrison St., Ste. 110 ✆ 704-749-5042 🕐 M-Sat 7-10, Sun 8-9
- organic produce • vegetarian friendly • salad bar • cafe • deli • tables • self-service • take-out

🚗 **From I-77,** take exit 5 east on Tyvola Rd (left from I-77S, right from I-77N) continuing onto Fairview Rd almost 4 miles total to Sharon Rd. Turn left onto Sharon over ½ mile to Lloyd Church Rd. Turn left onto Lloyd Church 1 block to roundabout and make first right onto Gov Morrison St to store on right.

Home Economist Natural Gourmet Market 🛍️   ♿
5410 E. Independence Blvd. ✆ 704-536-4663 🕐 M-Sat 8-8, Sun 10-6
- organic produce

🚗 **From I-77,** take I-277 (Brookshire Fwy) to exit 2B toward Independence Blvd. Take 74E (Independence Blvd) about 5 miles to store (before Idlewild Rd).

Talley's Green Grocery 🛍️ 🍴
1408-C East Blvd. ✆ 704-334-9200 🕐M-Sat 8:30-8, Sun 10-7
Store's Cafe Verde serves five daily entrees. Three are vegetarian.
- organic produce • vegetarian friendly • salad bar • cafe • deli • tables • self-service • take-out

🚗 **From I-77,** take I-277 (Brookshire Fwy) to exit 2A and go south on Kenilworth Ave 1 mile to East Blvd. Turn left onto East to store on right in Dilworth Garden Shopping Ctr.

Udipi Pure Vegetarian Cuisine 🍴
9510 University City Blvd. ✆ 704-549-0600 🕐 M, W-Th, Sun 11:30-3, 5-9:30, F-Sat 11:30-3, 5-10:30
Vegetarian Indo-Chinese. Daily lunch buffet.
- vegetarian • vegan friendly • alcohol • tables • self-service • wait staff

🚗 **From I-85N,** take exit 42 left at fork onto US 49/29/N Tryon Ave almost 1 mile to University City Blvd. Veer right onto University City 2⅓ miles to restaurant on right after E Mallard Creek Church Rd. **From I-85S,** merge onto I-485S to exit 33 (Hwy 49) toward Harrisburg. Turn right onto University City about ¾ mile to restaurant on left.

Woodland's Pure Vegetarian

7128-A Albemarle Rd. ℰ 704-569-9193 ⏰ M-F 11:30-3, 5-9:30, Sat-Sun 11:30-10
South Indian vegetarian.
- vegetarian • vegan friendly • alcohol • tables • wait staff • take-out

🚗 **From I-77,** take I-277 (Brookshire Fwy) to exit 2B onto US 74E (Independence Blvd) about 4 miles to Albemarle Rd. Turn left onto Albemarle about 3 miles to restaurant.

CONCORD

Natural Harvest Food Store

16 Union St. S. ℰ 704-795-5500 ⏰ Tues Sat 10-10
Store's Sweet Pea cafe serves organic vegetarian, vegan and raw foods.
- organic produce • vegetarian • vegan friendly • organic focus • alcohol • cafe • tables
- self-service • wait staff • take-out

🚗 **From I-85,** take exit 58 for 29S/601S onto Concord Pkwy N ¾-1 mile to Davidson Dr. Turn left onto Davidson and right onto Church St under 2 miles to Means Ave SE (before Corbarn Ave). Turn right onto Means 1 block to Union St S. Turn right onto Union 1 block to store on left.

DURHAM

Durham Co-op Grocery

1101 W. Chapel Hill St. ℰ 919-490-0929 ⏰ M-Sat 10-8, Sun 11-8 Winter M-F 1-7, Sat 9-7, Sun 11-8
- organic produce • co-op

🚗 **From I-40,** take exit 279B toward Durham onto Durham Fwy (NC 147N) about 8⅓ miles to exit 13. Turn right onto Chapel Hill St 3 blocks to store on left at Carroll St.

George's Garage

737 9th St. ℰ 919-286-4131 ⏰ Daily 11:30-10
Salad bar, sandwich station, hot and cold stations and more.
- vegetarian friendly • salad bar • alcohol • counter • tables • self-service • take-out

🚗 **From I-40,** take exit 279B toward Durham onto Durham Fwy (NC 147N) 9 miles to Swift Ave exit. Turn right onto Swift to light at Main St. Turn left onto Main 2 blocks to 9th St. Turn right onto 9th to restaurant on left at Hillsborough Rd. **From I-85,** take exit 175 south on Guess Rd (right from I-85N, left from I-85S) to Broad St. Turn right onto Broad about 1 mile to Hillsborough. Turn right onto Hillsborough 2 blocks to 9th. Turn right onto 9th to restaurant on right.

Whole Foods Market/Wellspring Cafe

621 Broad St. ℰ 919-286-2290 ⏰ Daily 7:30-10
- organic produce • vegetarian friendly • salad bar • cafe • self-service • take-out

🚗 **From I-40,** take exit 279B toward Durham onto Durham Fwy (NC 147N) 9 miles to Swift Ave exit. Turn right onto Swift across tracks and past Main St (becomes Broad St) to store on left. **From I-85,** take exit 175 south on Guess Rd to Broad. Turn right onto Broad about 1 mile to store on right.

ELIZABETH CITY

Soho Organic Market

406 S. Griffen St. ℰ 252-338-8378 ⏰ M-Sat 9-6
- organic produce

🚗 **From US 17/158 intersection,** go west 1 block on US 158 (Elizabeth) and turn right onto N Griffin St about ½ mile to store on left after tracks.

For listing changes, updates and travel resources, go to HealthyHighways.com

FAYETTEVILLE

Apple Crate Food Store 🛍

5430 Camden Rd. ✆ 910-423-8800 🕐 M-F 9-7, Sat 9-5

🚗 **From I-95S**, take Raeford Rd/US 401 exit right onto NC 59/S Main St about 4 miles to Camden Rd. Turn right onto Camden to store on left. **From I-95N**, merge onto 95N to US 301 service road to NC 59/Chickenfoot Rd. Turn left onto NC 59 and follow directions above.

Apple Crate Food Store 🛍

2711 Raeford Rd., #110 ✆ 910-426-7777 🕐 M-F 9-7, Sat 9-5
• organic produce

🚗 **From I-95S**, take exit 46 toward Fayetteville onto NC 87N 5½ miles to Robeson St. Turn left onto Robeson almost 2 miles to Raeford. Turn left onto Raeford to store on left. **From I-95N**, merge onto 95N and follow ramp onto NC 87 almost 1½ miles to Robeson. Turn left onto Robeson and follow directions above.

GASTONIA

Organic Marketplace 🛍

1012 S. New Hope Rd. ✆ 704- 864-0605 🕐 M-F 8-7, Sat 9-6
• organic produce • fresh juice

🚗 **From I-85**, take exit 20 south on New Hope Rd (right from I-85N, left from I-85S) about 1¼ miles to store on left.

GOLDSBORO

Healthabit Natural Foods 🛍

606 N. Spence Ave. ✆ 919-751-0300 🕐 M-Sat 10-6
• organic produce

🚗 **From US 70E**, exit right onto Cuyler Best Rd/NC-1565/N Spence Ave almost 1 mile to store on left after E Mall Rd. **From US 70W**, veer left onto E Ash St (signs for 70Bus/Goldsboro) about 2½ miles to Spence. Turn right onto Spence to store on right after Cashwell Dr.

GREENSBORO

A&S Natural Health 🛍   ♿

435C Dolley Madison Rd. ✆ 336-855-6500 🕐 M- Sat 10-7, Sun 1-6

🚗 **From I-40**, take exit 213 north on Guilford College Rd (left from I-40E, right from I-40W) about 2 miles (becomes College Rd after 1 mile) to Tomahawk Dr. Turn right onto Tomahawk and left to store in Guilford Village Shopping Ctr.

Boba House Vegetarian Restaurant 🍴

332 S. Tate St. ✆ 336-379-7444 🕐 M-F 11:30-3, 5-9:30, Sat 12-9:30
Bistro atmosphere, Asian orientation and many mock meat offerings.
• vegetarian • vegan friendly • alcohol • tables • wait staff

🚗 **From I-40W,** take exit 41 toward US 29N/US 220N right onto E Lee St 4 miles to S Tate St. Turn right onto S Tate under ½ mile to restaurant on left at UNC. **From I-40E,** take exit 216 toward Greensboro onto Hwy 6E/Patterson St 2 miles to NC 6/High Point. Turn left onto High Point ((becomes W Lee) 1½ miles to S Tate. Turn left onto under ½ mile to restaurant.

Deep Roots Market Natural Foods Co-op 🛍   ♿

3728 Spring Garden St. ✆ 336-292-9216 🕐 M-Sat 9-8, Sun 12-7
• organic produce • co-op

🚗 **From I-40**, take exit 214 (214B from I-40W) right onto Wendover Ave about 2 miles to Spring Garden St exit. Turn left off ramp to store on left.

Earth Fare ♿

2965 Battleground Ave. ✆ 336-369-0190 ⏱M-Sat 8-10, Sun 8-9
• organic produce • vegetarian friendly • fresh juice • salad bar • cafe • deli • bakery • tables • self-service • take-out

🚗 **From I-40**, take exit 214 (214B from I-40W) right onto Wendover Ave about 5 miles to Westover Terrace. Turn left onto Westover and merge onto Battleground Ave about 2 miles (past Cornwallis Ave & Cone Blvd) to store on left in Battleground Village Shopping Ctr.

Synergy Health

613 Dolley Madison Rd. ✆ 336-218-7099 ⏱M-F 10-7, Sat 10-6
• organic produce • fresh juice

🚗 **From I-40E**, veer right onto US 141 and take exit 24 about ¾ mile to merge onto Future I 840E 1 mile to exit 2. Turn right onto W Friendly Ave about 1¾ miles to Dolley Madison Rd. Turn right onto Dolley Madison to store on right. **From I-40W**, take exit 212A toward Bryan Blvd, merge onto Future I 840E and follow directions above.

HENDERSONVILLE

Hendersonville Community Co-op & Blue Mountain Deli ♿

715 Old Spartanburg Hwy. ✆ 828-693-0505 ⏱ M-Sat 8-7, Sun 11-6
• organic produce • vegetarian friendly • fresh juice • alcohol • cafe • tables • self-service • take-out • co-op

🚗 **From I-26**, take exit 22 west on Upward Rd 4-5 lights to Hwy 176/Spartanburg Hwy. Turn right onto Spartanburg 4 lights to Old Spartanburg Hwy. Turn right onto Old Spartanburg to store on left.

HICKORY

Health Hut

2432 N. Center St. (Hwy 127) ✆ 828-322-2523 ⏱ M-F 9-6, Sat 9-5
• organic produce

🚗 **From I-40E**, take exit 123A-B for US-321 toward Hickory/Lincolnton/US-70/State Hwy 127/Lenoir and follow 123B onto 321N about 1½ miles to 13th St SW. Turn right onto 13th and right onto 2nd Ave SW 1½ miles to NC 127/N. Turn left onto 127 2½ miles to store on left. **From I-40W**, take exit 125 for Hickory right onto Lenore Rhyne Blvd SE 1⅓ miles to 1st Ave SE. Turn left onto 1st almost ½ mile to NC 127. Turn right onto 127 2½ miles to store.

KINGSTON

Healthabit Natural Foods

601 N. Queen St. ✆ 252-523-8222 ⏱ M-Sat 10-6
• organic produce

🚗 Store is in town on east side of US 70/Queen St at Washington St.

KITTY HAWK

Health-A-Rama ♿

3712 N. Croatan Hwy. 158 ✆ 252-261-9919 ⏱ M-F 9-6, Sat 10-5, Sun 12:30-3:30
• organic produce • fresh juice

🚗 Store is on US 158 at mile marker 4¾ on west side (between Tateway Rd & Beacon Dr).

MORGANTON

Nature's Bounty

2145 S. Sterling St. ✆ 828-433-7325 ⏱ M-F 9-6, Sat 10-5

🚗 **From I-40**, take exit 105 for Hwy 18 toward Morganton/Shelby right onto S Sterling Rd over ½ mile to store on right.

MORRISVILLE

Tower Restaurant 🍴
144 Morrisville Square Way ✆ 919-465-2326 🕐 Lunch M-F 11:30-2:30, Sat-Sun 11:30-3:30 Dinner M-Th, Sun 5:30-9:30, F-Sat 5-10
Vegetarian Indian.
• vegetarian • vegan friendly • tables • wait staff

🍎 **From I-40**, take exit 285 toward Morrisville/Airport south on Aviation Pkwy (right from I-40E, left from I-40W) 2½-2¾ miles (becomes Morrisville Carpenter Rd). Continue under ¼ mile to Morrisville Sq Way and turn left to restaurant.

PITTSBORO

Chatham Marketplace 🛍️🍴
480 Hillsboro St. ✆ 919-542-2643 🕐 M-Th, Sat-Sun 8-8, F 8-9
• organic produce • vegetarian friendly • salad bar • cafe • deli • tables • self-service • take-out • co-op

🛒 NC 64 and US 501/15 intersect at the traffic circle in Pittsboro. Store is on US 501/15 (aka Hillsboro St) 3 blocks north of traffic circle on east side.

RALEIGH

Earth Fare 🛍️🍴
10341 Moncreiffe Rd. ✆ 919-433-1390 🕐 M-Sat 8-10, Sun 9-9
• organic produce • vegetarian friendly • salad bar • cafe • deli • tables • self-service • take-out

🍎 **From I-540**, take exit 3 north on Lumley Rd (right from I-540W, left from I-540E) ⅓-½ mile to Brier Creek Pkwy. Turn left onto Brier Creek to store in Brierdale Shopping Ctr.

Harmony Farms 🛍️
5653 Creedmoor Rd. ✆ 919-782-0064 🕐 M-F 10-7, Sat 10-6, Sun 1-6
• organic produce

🍎 **From I-40E**, take exit 283 onto I-540 (Wake Expwy) to exit 9 (NC 50). Go south on Creedmoor (aka 50) almost 4 miles to store in Creedmoor Cross Shopping Ctr. **From I-40W**, merge onto I-440E via exit 301 about 10 miles to exit 7B (Glenwood Ave). Merge onto Glenwood Ave/70W about 1 mile (past Crabtree Valley Mall) to Creedmoor Rd. Turn right onto Creedmoor about 1 mile to store.

Third Place Coffeehouse 🍴   ♿
1811 Glenwood Ave. ✆ 919-834-6566 🕐 M-F 6am-12am, Sat-Sun 7am-12am
A casual hang out.
• vegetarian • vegan friendly • tables • self-service

🍎 **From I-40E**, merge onto I-440N to exit 7. **From I-440**, take exit 7 onto US 70E (Glenwood Ave) about 2¾ miles to restaurant at 5 Points intersection. **From US 40W**, take exit 298B toward Raleigh/Downtown onto US 401N/NC 50N under 3 miles to US 70W. **From US 70W (Wade Ave)**, take Glenwood Ave N ramp onto Glenwood under ½ mile to restaurant.

Triangle Nutrition 🛍️
8801 Leadmine Rd., Ste. 117 ✆ 919-847-8498 🕐 M-F 10-6:30, Sat 10-6, Sun 1-5
🍎 **From I-540**, take exit 11 south onto Six Forks Rd about ½ mile to Lead Mine Rd. Turn right onto Lead Mine ⅓ mile to store on right.

Whole Foods Market/Wellspring Cafe 🛍️🍴   ♿
3540 Wade Ave. ✆ 919-828-5805 🕐 Daily 8-9 Cafe from 7:30
• organic produce • vegetarian friendly • salad bar • cafe • self-service • take-out

🍎 **From I-440**, take exit 4A (off outer loop from north, inner loop from south) onto Wade Ave to store on left at Ridge Rd in Ridge Wood Shopping Ctr. **From I-40E**, take exit 289 (Wade Ave) about 3 miles east to store.

ROANOKE RAPIDS

Nature's Manna Kitchen 🛍️
1168 Julian Allsbrook Hwy. ✆ 252-533-0003 🕐 M-Sat 10-6

• organic produce

🍎 **From I-95**, take exit 173 towards Roanoke Rapids west on US 158/Julian Allsbrook Hwy (right from I-95S, left from I-95N) about 1 mile to store on right.

SALISBURY

Simply Good Natural Foods 🛍
128 E. Innes St. ✆ 704-636-0889 ⏰ M-Sat 9-6
• organic produce

🍎 **From I-85,** take exit 76 toward Salisbury northwest on E lnnes St (left from I-85N, right from I-85S) almost 1 mile to store on right at N Main St.

SYLVA

Annie's Naturally Bakery 🍴
506 W. Main St. ✆ 828-586-9096 ⏰ Tues-Th 7-5, F 7-6, Sat 8-5 Lunch 11-3
Baked goods from organic grains plus a few vegetarian sandwiches, salads and soup.
• vegetarian friendly • alcohol • bakery • tables • self-service • take-out

🍎 **From US 74E (Great Smokey Mt Expy),** take exit 81A onto US 23S/US 441S about ½ mile to Haywood Rd. Turn left onto Haywood under 2 miles (becomes Main St) to restaurant between Spring & Evalina St. **From US 23W/74W**, take US 23 Bus exit left onto US 23/Ashville Hwy about 1½ miles to W Main. Turn right onto W Main under 1 mile (becomes Mill St) and make sharp left onto W Main about 4 blocks to restaurant.

WILMINGTON

Lovey's Natural Foods & Cafe 🛍 🍴
1319 Military Cutoff Rd. ✆ 910-509-0331 ⏰ M-F 9-7, Sat 9-6, Sun 11-5
• organic produce • vegetarian friendly • fresh juice • salad bar • cafe • tables • self-service • take-out

🍎 **From I-40E where hwy ends,** continue onto Hwy 117/132S (N College Rd) 1 mile to MLK Jr Pkwy/US 74. Turn left onto MLK Jr (becomes Eastwood Rd) 3¼ miles to Military Cutoff Rd. Turn left onto Military Cutoff 1 block to store on right in Landfall Shopping Ctr.

Tidal Creek Cooperative Food Market 🛍 🍴   ♿
5329 Oleander Drive ✆ 910-799-2667 ⏰ M-Sat 8-8, Sun 9-8
• organic produce • vegetarian friendly • fresh juice • salad bar • cafe • deli • bakery • tables • self-service • take-out • co-op

🍎 **From I-40E where hwy ends,** continue onto Hwy 117/132S (N College Rd) about 4½ miles to Oleander Drive (Hwy 76). Turn left onto Oleander about 1⅓ miles to store on left.

WINSTON-SALEM

Mary's, of Course! Cafe 🍴
301 Brookstown Ave. ✆ 336-725-5764 ⏰ Tues-F 9:30-3, Sat 10-3, Sun 10-2
Tofu and tempeh, vegetarian sausage and vegan burgers along with typical meat choices.
• vegetarian friendly • vegan friendly • tables • wait staff

🍎 **From I-40,** take exit 193B north on US 311/52 about 2½ miles to exit 109B for I-40 Bus and merge onto US 158W ¾ mile to exit 5C. Turn right onto Cherry St, left onto W 1st St and left onto SW Marshall St 2 blocks (past hwy) to Brookstown Ave. Turn left onto Brookstown 1 block to restaurant on left at S Cherry.

Whole Foods Market 🛍 🍴   ♿
41 Miller St. ✆ 336-722-9233 ⏰ Daily 8-9
• organic produce • vegetarian friendly • salad bar • cafe • self-service • take-out

🍎 **From I-40**, take exit 188 onto US 421S about 2½ miles to exit 3B. Turn left onto Stratford Rd to first light (Miller Rd). Turn right onto Miller 1 block to store on left.

NORTH DAKOTA

NORTH DAKOTA

1. Bismarck
2. Fargo
3. Grand Forks
4. Minot

BISMARCK

Terry's Health Products

801 E. Main Ave. © 701-223-1026 ⏰ M-F 9-6, Sat 9-3

🏠 **From I-94,** take exit 159 onto Hwy 83S/ND 1804S 2 miles (turns left onto N 7th St) to Main Ave. Turn left onto Main to store on right.

FARGO

Swanson Health Products

109 N. Broadway © 701-293-9842 ⏰M-F 9-6, Sat 9-5
· organic produce

🏠 **From I-94,** take exit 351 toward Downtown Fargo onto 81Bus N (University Dr). Follow 81Bus N (turns right onto 13th Ave and left onto 10th St S) 2 miles to NP Ave. Turn right onto NP to Broadway. Turn left onto Broadway to store on left. **From I-29,** take exit 65 (US 10) toward Downtown east on Main Ave (left from I-29S, right from I-29N) about 2½ miles to Broadway. Turn left onto Broadway to store.

Tochi Products

1111 2nd Ave. N. © 701-232-7700 ⏰ M-W, F-Sat 10-6, Th 10-8
organic produce seasonally.

🏠 **From I-94,** take exit 351 toward Downtown Fargo onto 81Bus N (University Dr). Follow 81Bus N (turns right onto 13th Ave and left onto 10th St S) 2⅔ miles to 2nd Ave N. Turn left onto 2nd 1 block to store on right. **From I-29,** take exit 65 (US 10) toward Downtown east on Main Ave (left from I-29S, right from I-29N) under 1 mile to 25th St NW. Turn left onto 25th and right onto 1st Ave under 1 mile to 14th St N. Turn left onto 14th and right onto 2nd 3 blocks to store.

GRAND FORKS

Amazing Grains Natural Food Market

214 DeMers Ave. © 701-775-4542 ⏰M-F 9-8, Sat 9-6, Sun 12-6
· organic produce · vegetarian friendly · bakery · take-out · tables · self-service · take-out · co-op

🏠 **From I-29,** take exit 140 right (east) onto DeMers Ave about 3¼ miles to store on left.

MINOT

The Magic Mill

115 S. Main St. © 701-852-4818 ⏰M-F 9:30-5, Sat 10-2

🏠 **From Hwy 83,** go east on 1st Ave SE 2 blocks to Main St. Turn right onto Main to store.

1. Akron	14. Fremont	27. Sylvania
2. Beavercreek	15. Kent	28. Tallmadge
3. Berlin	16. Lakewood	29. Toledo
4. Bowling Green	17. Lancaster	30. University Heights
5. Canton	18. Mason	31. Westerville
6. Centerville	19. Middleburg Heights	32. Westlake
7. Cincinnati	20. N.W. Canton	33. Willoughby
8. Cleveland	21. Newton Falls	34. Woodmere
9. Cleveland Heights	22. Niles	35. Wooster
10. Columbus	23. Oxford	36. Yellow Springs
11. Cuyahoga Falls	24. Parma Heights	37. Zanesville
12. Dayton	25. Solon	
13. Englewood	26. Stow	

AKRON

Mustard Seed Market & Cafe 🛍️ 🍴   ♿

3885 W. Market St. ℂ 330-666-7333 ⏰ M-Th 9-9, F-Sat 9-10, Sun 10-6 Cafe M-Th 11-8, F-Sat 11-9, Sun 10:30-3

Cafe offers everything from wheat grass and carrot juice to champagne and scotch!
   • organic produce • vegetarian friendly • fresh juice • alcohol • salad bar • cafe • deli •
   bakery • cafe • counter • tables • self-service • wait staff • take-out

🍎 **From I-77**, take exit 137A toward Fairlawn onto Rt 18E about ⅓ mile to store on left in West Market Plaza (next to Old Navy).

VegeTerranean 🍴

21 Furnace St. ✆ 330-374-5550 ⏱ M-F 7:30-3, 5-10, Sat 8-3, 5-10
Founded by rock musician Chrissie Hynde. Baked goods and beverages until lunch begins at 11.
 • vegan • organic focus • alcohol • tables • wait staff

🚗 **From I-77S/76E**, take exit 21C toward downtown north on OH 59 about 2¼ miles to N Howard St. Turn left onto N Howard 1 block to Furnace St. Turn right onto Furnace to restaurant on left. **From I-76W**, take exit 26B toward Cayuhoga Falls north on OH 8 1 mile to Perkins St/OH 59 exit. Turn left onto Perkins ½ mile to N Summit St. Turn right onto N Summit past tracks to Furnace. Turn left onto Furnace to restaurant on right. **From I-77N**, merge onto OH 8 and follow directions above.

BEAVERCREEK

Healthy Alternatives 🛍

2235 N. Fairfield Rd. ✆ 937-426-7772 ⏱ M-F 10-8, Sat 10-6, Sun 12-5
 • organic produce

🚗 **From I-675**, take exit 17 south on N Fairfield Rd (left from I-675S, merge right from I-675N) 1½ miles to store on right after Kemp Rd.

BERLIN

Nature's Food Market 🛍

4860 E. Main St. ✆ 330-893-2006 ⏱ M-Sat 8-7
 • organic produce

🚗 **From OH Tpke**, take exit 118 for US 250S and merge onto Milan Rd heading south 2¼ miles to Church St. Turn left onto W Church 5⅓ miles to Berlin Rd. Turn left onto Berlin 1½ miles to W Main St. Turn right onto W Main about ½ mile to store.

BOWLING GREEN

Squeaker's Vegetarian Cafe & Health Food Store 🛍🍴 ♿

175 N. Main St. ✆ 419-354-7000 ⏱ M-Sat 10-9, Sun 11-8
 • organic produce • vegan • organic focus • fresh juice • bakery • cafe • tables • wait staff • take-out

🚗 **From I-75**, take exit 181 for OH-64/OH-105 toward Pemberville/Bowling Green west on E Wooster St (right from I-75S, left from I-75N) almost 2 miles to N Main St. Turn right onto Main 1 block to store on left.

CANTON

Raisin Rack 🛍

4629 Cleveland Ave. N.W. ✆ 330-966-1515 ⏱ M-F 9-8, Sat 9-6, Sun 12-5
 • organic produce

🚗 **From I-77S,** take exit 109 toward Whipple Ave left onto Evehard Rd about 1¾ miles to S Main St. Turn right onto Main (becomes Cleveland Ave) about ⅔ mile to store between 47th & 46th St. **From I-77N,** take exit 107B toward Alliance onto US 62E under 1 mile to Cleveland Ave exit. Follow exit around to right onto Cleveland about 1½ miles to store.

CENTERVILLE

Health Food Unlimited 🛍

2250 Miamisburg-Centerville Rd. ✆ 937-433-5100 ⏱ M-F 10-9, Sat 10-6, Sun 12-5
 • organic produce

🚗 **From I-695**, take exit 2 onto Hwy 725W/Miamisburg-Centerville Rd (merge onto Leona Ln and right from I-695S, left from I-695N) about ½ mile to store on left in S Towne Ctr. **From I-75**, take exit 44 toward Centerville east on Miamisburg-Centerville Rd (left from I-75S, right from I-75N) about 1 mile to store on right.

CINCINNATI

Cincinnati Natural Foods
9268 Colerain Ave. ✆ 513-385-7000 ⏱ M-F 10-8, Sat 10-6, Sun 12-5
• organic produce

🍎 **From I-275**, take exit 33 south on Colerain Ave (left from I-275W, right from I-275E) almost 1½ miles (past Northgate Mall) to store on left at Round Top Rd.

Cincinnati Natural Foods
6911 Miami Ave. ✆ 513-271-7777 ⏱ M-F 10-8, Sat 10-6, Sun 12-5
• organic produce

🍎 **From I-71**, take exit 12 east on Montgomery Rd (left from I-71S, right from I-71N) to Hosbrook Rd. Turn right onto Hosbrook to Euclid Ave. Turn left onto Euclid to Miami Ave. Turn right onto Miami across tracks to store on right.

Clifton Natural Foods
169 W. McMillan St. ✆ 513-961-6111 ⏱ M-Sat 9-8, Sun 11-5
• organic produce

🍎 **From I-71S**, take exit 3 right onto Taft St (becomes Calhoun St) over 1 mile to end at Clifton Ave. Turn left onto Clifton 1 block to McMillan St. Turn left onto McMillan 2 blocks to store on right corner. **From I-75**, take exit 3 left onto Hopple St and veer left onto Martin Luther King Dr W about 1 mile (past light at Dixmyth) to Clifton. Turn right onto Clifton ½ mile to McMillan. Turn left onto McMillan to store.

Melt 🍴
4165 Hamilton Ave. ✆ 513-681-6358 ⏱ M-Sat 11-10, Sun 11-8
Deli sandwiches and "melts" made with tofu, tempeh or seitan as well as meat.
• vegetarian friendly • vegan friendly • tables • self-service • take-out

🍎 **From I-74E**, take exit 18 for Colerain Ave left onto Beekman St under ½ mile. Make first right onto Colerain and veer left at Blue Rock St under ½ mile to Hamilton Ave. Turn left onto Hamilton about ⅓ mile to restaurant on left. **From I-74W**, take exit 19 toward Elmore St/Spring Grove Ave onto Powers St, turn left onto Spring Grove and left onto Hamilton about ⅓ mile to restaurant. **From I-75**, merge onto I-74W and follow directions above.

Myra's Dionysus Restaurant 🍴
121 Calhoun St. ✆ 513-961-1578 ⏱ M-Th 11-10, F-Sat 11-11, Sun 5-10
A healthy option near the University. Lots of ethnic variety.
• vegetarian friendly • alcohol • tables • wait staff • take-out

🍎 **From I-75**, take exit 3 left onto Hopple St and veer left onto Martin Luther King Dr W about 1 mile to Clifton Ave. Turn right onto Clifton ½ mile to McMillan St. Turn left onto McMillan about ½ mile to Vine St. Turn left onto Vine and left onto Calhoun St to restaurant on left. **From I-71S**, take exit 3 right onto Taft Rd (becomes Calhoun) under 1 mile to restaurant. **From I-71N**, take exit 2 north on Reading St under 1 mile to Taft. Turn left onto Taft about ¾ mile to restaurant.

Spatz Natural Life Health Food 🛍
607 Main St. ✆ 513-621-0347 ⏱ M-F 9-4:30

🍎 **From I-71S**, take exit 2 and follow Gilbert Ave ramp onto US 22W (continues left onto 8th St) over ½ mile to Sycamore St. Turn left onto Sycamore and first right onto 6th St 2 blocks to store at Main St. **From I-75N**, take 5th St exit right onto 5th ½ mile to Main. Turn left onto Main 2 blocks to store.

Susan's Natural World 🛍 🍴
8315 Beechmont Ave. ✆ 513-474-4990 ⏱ M-F 10-8, Sat 10-6, Sun 12-5
• organic produce • vegetarian friendly • fresh juice • deli • counter • take-out

🍎 **From I-275S**, take exit 65 for Beechmont Ave/Hwy 25 toward Amelia right onto Ohio Pike (becomes Beechmont Ave) 1⅓ miles to store on left after 8 Mile Rd. **From I-275E**, take exit 69 left onto 5 Mile Rd 1 mile to Beechwood. Turn right onto Beechwood 1½ miles to store on right.

The Loving Cafe 🍴   ♿

6227 Montgomery Rd. ✆ 513-731-2233 ⏱ Tues-Sat 11-7
Veggie "meat" dishes and an eco-friendly outlook.
• vegan • organic focus • tables • self-service • take-out

🚗 **From I-71S,** take exit 12 right onto Montgomery Rd about 2 miles to restaurant on right (next to library). **From I-71N,** take exit 8C onto Ridge Ave almost 1½ miles to Montgomery. Turn right onto Montgomery 2 blocks to restaurant on left.

Udipi Cafe 🍴

7633 Reading Rd. ✆ 513-821-2021 ⏱ M-Th 11-2:30, 5:30-9:30, F 11-2:30, 5:30-10, Sat-Sun 11:30-3, 5:30-10
South Indian vegetarian with a weekday lunch buffet.
• vegetarian • vegan friendly • tables • self-service • wait staff

🚗 **From I-75,** take exit 15 east on Sharon Rd (left from I-75S, right from I-75N) 1½ miles to Reading Rd. Turn right onto Reading to restaurant on left. **From I-275,** take exit 46 toward Sharonville south on US 42/Cincinnati-Columbus Rd (right from I-275E, left from I-275W) about 1½ miles to Reading. Veer right onto Reading under ½ mile to restaurant on left after Sharon.

What's for Dinner? 🍴   ♿

3009 O'Bryon St. ✆ 513-321-4404 ⏱ M-F 10-8, Sat 10-4
Eat-in or carry-out entrees, sides and salads, about half vegetarian or vegan.
• vegetarian friendly • tables • self-service • take-out

🚗 **From I-71S,** take exit 5 left onto Dana Ave about ½ mile to Madison Rd. Turn right onto Madison about ½ mile to restaurant at O'Bryon St (look for dancing eggplant). **From I-71N,** take US 50E about 3 miles to Torrence Pkwy. Turn left onto Torrence over ½ mile (almost to end) to Grandin Rd. Turn left onto Grandin 1 block to restaurant at O'Bryon & Madison.

Wild Oats Market 🛒 🍴   ♿

2693 Edmondson Rd. ✆ 513-531-8015 ⏱ M-Sat. 8-10, Sun. 9-9
• organic produce • vegetarian friendly • salad bar • cafe • self-service • take-out

🚗 **From I-71,** take exit 6 (Smith Rd/Edwards Rd). **From I-71N,** turn right off exit and right at light to store in Rockwood Commons. **From I-71S,** turn right off exit and left at light onto Edmonston Rd back over hwy. Turn right at light to store.

CLEVELAND

Food Co-op 🛒

11702 Euclid Ave. ✆ 216-791-3890 ⏱ M-Sat 9-8, Sun 10-6
• organic produce, co-op

🚗 **From I-90,** take exit 173B onto Chester Ave/322E about 3 miles to Euclid Ave. Turn left onto Euclid about ¾ mile to store. **From I-77 or I-71,** merge onto I-90 and follow directions above.

Shtick's Vegetarian Kitchen 🍴   ♿ 💳

11065 East Blvd., Gund Law School ✆ 216-231-0922 ⏱ M-Th 7:30-6:30, F 7:30-4
Note: hours may change with school calendar
In Gund Law School at Case Western Reserve. Israeli/Arab mostly vegetarian menu.
• vegetarian friendly • tables • self-service • take-out

🚗 **From I-90,** take exit 173B east on Chester Ave about 3 miles to Euclid Ave. Turn left onto Euclid and veer left onto East Blvd about ⅓ mile to restaurant at Gund Law School.

CLEVELAND HEIGHTS

Tommy's 🍴

1824 Coventry Rd. ✆ 216-321-7757 ⏱ M-Th, Sun 9-9, F-Sat 9-10
Standard meat-and-white bread fare to a surprising vegetarian selection including tempeh, tofu, seitan, falafel, vegetable pies, toasted cheese sandwiches and more.
• vegetarian friendly • vegan friendly • tables • wait staff • take-out

🍴 **From I-90**, take exit 173B east on US 322 (Chester Ave, becomes Mayfield Rd) about 5 miles to Coventry Rd. Turn right onto Coventry to restaurant. **From I-271,** take exit 35 west on Mayfield Rd (322) about 5 miles to Coventry. Turn left onto Coventry to restaurant.

COLUMBUS

Benevolence 🍴
41 W. Swan St. ✆ 614-221-9330 🕐 M-F 11-8, Sat 8:30-8
Fresh soups, salads and homemade bread.
  • vegetarian • vegan friendly • tables • self-service

🍴 **From I-71S**, take exit 109A onto I-670W about 1⅔ miles to US 33W/Goodale St exit toward Neil Ave. Take the 4th St ramp right onto W Goodale, right onto N Park St and left onto W Swan St to restaurant. **From I-71N,** merge onto 315N about 2 miles to Grandview Heights exit toward Goodale St. Turn left onto Goodale Neil Connector (becomes Vine St) ¾ mile to N Park. Turn left onto N Park and right onto W Swan to restaurant.

Bexley Natural Market 🛒
508 N. Cassady Ave. ✆ 614-252-3951 🕐 M-F 10-8, Sat 10-6, Sun 11-5
  • organic produce • co-op

🍴 **From I-71**, take exit 109 toward Airport onto I-670E about 3 miles to exit 7 (5th Ave) toward 62W. Turn right onto 5th about ⅓ mile to light at Cassady Ave. Turn right onto Cassady to store.

Clintonville Community Market 🛒
200 Crestview Rd. ✆ 614-261-3663 🕐 M-Sat 7-10, Sun 8-10
  • organic produce • co-op

🍴 **From I-71**, take exit 113 onto Silver Rd to Weber Rd. Turn west onto Weber (left from I-71N, right from I-71S) and cross tracks. At second light (about ⅔ mile) turn left onto Calumet St 3 blocks to store on right at Crestview Rd.

Dosa Corner 🍴
1077 Old Henderson Rd. ✆ 614-459-5515 🕐 M 5-9, Tues-Sat 11-9, Sun 12-8
Southern Indian food on disposable dishes in a small, simple setting.
  • vegetarian • vegan friendly • tables • self-service • take-out

🍴 **From I-71**, take exit 115 west on E Cooke Rd (left onto Overlook Dr, right onto Indianola Ave and left onto E Cooke from I-71N, right onto Overlook, right onto Indianola and right onto Cooke from I-71S) 1 mile to E Henderson Rd. Veer right onto E Henderson under 2 miles to Kenny Rd. Turn left onto Kenny 1 block to Old Henderson Rd. Turn left onto Old Henderson to restaurant on right.

Dragonfly 🍴
247 King Ave. ✆ 614-298-9986 🕐 Tues-Th 5-10, F 5-11, Sat 11:30-3, 5-11
Live music, poetry and art on display.
  • vegan • organic focus • alcohol • tables • wait staff

🍴 **From I-71**, take exit 110A west onto 5th Ave about 1⅓ miles to Forsythe Ave. Turn right onto Forsythe to King Ave. Turn right onto King 1 block to restaurant at Neil Ave. **From I-70**, take I-670 to Grandview Heights exit north on Olentangy River Rd about 1¼ miles to King St. Turn right onto King under ¾ mile to restaurant.

Mad Mex 🍴
1542 N. High St. ✆ 614-586-4007 🕐 Daily 11-12
Mexican with vegan options including tofu and vegan cheese and sour cream.
  • vegetarian friendly • vegan friendly • alcohol • counter • tables • wait staff

🍴 **From I-71S**, take exit 112 right onto E Hudson St about ⅓ mile to Summit St. Turn left onto Summit under ½ mile to Chittenden Ave. Turn right onto Chittenden ⅓ mile to High St. Turn left onto High to restaurant on left. **From I-71N**, take exit 110B left onto 11th Ave over ⅓ mile to N Grant Ave. Turn right onto N Grant 1 block to Chittenden. Turn left onto Chittenden over ½ mile to High. Turn left onto High to restaurant.

Udipi Cafe 🍴
2001 E. Dublin Granville Rd. ℂ 614-885-7446 ◷ Daily 11:30-9:30
Vegetarian Indian with a weekday lunch buffet.
• vegetarian • vegan friendly • alcohol • tables • self-service • wait staff
🚗 **From I-71,** take exit 117 east on E Dublin Granville Rd (right from I-71N, left from I-71S) about 1 mile to Beechcroft Rd. Jog right onto Beechcroft and left back onto E Dublin Granville to restaurant on right. **From I-270,** take exit 30B toward New Albany west on OH 161 (left from I-270N, right from I-270S) 3½ miles (becomes E Dublin Granville) to Beechcroft. Turn left onto Beechcroft and right onto E Dublin Granville to restaurant.

Whole Foods Market 🛍🍴 &
1555 W. Lane Ave. ℂ 614-481-3400 ◷ M-Sat 8-9, Sun 8-8
• organic produce • vegetarian friendly • salad bar • cafe • self-service • take-out
🚗 **From Rt 315,** (access off I-270 from north of Columbus, I-670, I-70 or I-71N from south of Columbus) take Lane Ave exit toward Ohio State U west on Lane (right from 315S, left from 315N) to store at third light on left.

Whole Foods Market 🛍🍴
3670 W. Dublin Granville Rd. ℂ 614-760-5556 ◷ M-Sat 8-10, Sun 8-9
• organic produce • vegetarian friendly • salad bar • cafe • self-service • take-out
🚗 **From I-270,** take exit 20 south on Sawmill Rd S (right from I-270E, left from I-270W) under 1 mile to W Dublin Granville. Turn right onto W Dublin Granville to store. **From I-71,** take exit 119 (119B from I-71S) onto I-270W and follow directions above.

Whole World Pizza 🍴
3269 N. High St. ℂ 614-268-5751 ◷ Tues-Th 11-8, F-Sat 11-9, Sun 10-8
Whole wheat pizza, sloppy Joes, burgers, quesadillas, quiche..
• vegetarian • vegan friendly • tables • wait staff • take-out
🚗 **From I-71,** take exit 114 west on E Broadway St (right from I-71S, left from I-71N) about ⅔ mile to Clinton Heights Rd. Turn left onto Clinton Heights under ½ mile High St. Turn left onto High about 2 blocks to restaurant.

CUYAHOGA FALLS

New Earth Natural Foods 🛍
1605 State Rd. ℂ 330-929-2415 ◷ M-F 9-8, Sat 10-6
Juice bar makes fresh carrot juice and smoothies.
🚗 **From OH 8N (access off I-77N from south of Cuyahoga Falls),** take exit toward Talmadge Ave onto Gorge Blvd and left onto Tallmadge about ½ mile to N Main St. Turn right onto Main (becomes State Rd) under 1¾ miles to store. **From OH 8S (access off I-271 from north of Cuyahoga Falls),** turn right onto Broad Blvd about 1⅓ miles to State. Turn left onto State about ½ mile to store.

DAYTON

Christopher's Restaurant & Catering 🍴 &
2318 E. Dorothy Lane ℂ 937-299-0089 ◷ M-Sat 7:30am-9pm
All-American menu includes veggie breakfast patties, vegetarian biscuits with gravy, multi-grain pancakes, falafel, mushroom stroganoff and meatless lasagna.
• vegetarian friendly • tables • wait staff • take-out
🚗 In Dayton's Kettering suburb. **From I-675,** take exit 10 toward Dorothy Ln west on Indian Ripple Rd (left from I-675N, right from I-675S) about 1½ miles (becomes E Dorothy) to restaurant on left in Woodlane Plaza Ctr. **From I-75,** take exit 52B toward Xenia onto Rt 35E over 4½ miles to Woodman Dr exit. Turn right onto Woodman about 3 miles to Dorothy. Turn left onto Dorothy to restaurant on right. **From I-70W,** merge onto I-675 and follow directions above. **From I-70E,** merge onto I-75S and follow directions above.

Healthy Alternatives 🛍
8258 N. Main St. ℂ 937-890-8000 ⏱ M-F 10-8, Sat 10-6, Sun 12-5
  • organic produce
🚗 **From I-70,** take exit 29 (Englewood) south on Main St (left from I-70W, right from I-70E) about 1½ miles to store.

ENGLEWOOD
Artisan's Cafe 🍴
725 W. Wenger Rd. ℂ 937-832-1176 ⏱ M-Th 10:30-8, F-Sat 8-8
Diner-style menu with vegan, vegetarian and carnivorous choices.
  • vegetarian friendly • vegan friendly • tables • wait staff • take-out
🚗 **From I-70,** take exit 29 toward Englewood onto Hwy 48/S Main St (left from I-70E, right from I-70W) under ½ mile to W Wenger Rd. Turn left onto W Wenger 1⅓ miles to restaurant on right before Union Rd.

FREMONT
Naturally Yours 🛍
401 S. Front St. ℂ 419-332-0353 ⏱ M-F 9:30-5:30, Sat 9:30-1
🚗 **From OH Tpke,** take exit 91 south on OH 53 about 3 miles continuing onto Rawson Ave almost 1 mile to W State St. Turn left onto W State ½ mile to N Front St. Turn right onto S Front 4 blocks to store on left.

KENT
Kent Natural Foods Co-op 🛍
151 E. Main St. ℂ 330-673-2878 ⏱ M, Tues, Th-Sat 10-6:30, W 10-7
  • organic produce • co-op
🚗 **From I-76,** take exit 33 toward Kent north on Rt 43 (left from I-76E, right from I-76W) under 3½ miles to Main St. Turn right onto Main across bridge to store on left as you go up hill (dark green awning).

LAKEWOOD
Nature's Bin 🛍
18120 Sloane Ave. ℂ 216-521-4600 ⏱ M-F 9-8, Sat 9-7, Sun 9-6
Store is a vocational training site giving people with disabilities a real, hands-on experience.
  • organic produce • vegetarian friendly • deli • bakery • take-out
🚗 **From I-90,** take exit 164 north on Riverside Dr (right onto Niagara Dr, right onto Lakewood Heights Blvd and right onto Riverside from I-90E, merge onto N Marginal Dr, left onto Hilliard Rd and right onto Riverside from I-90W) over 1 mile to Sloan Ave. Turn left onto Sloan to store on right.

LANCASTER
Hand in Hand 🛍
639 N. Pierce Ave. ℂ 740-687-0306 ⏱ M-Sat 10-6
🚗 **From US 22E/US 33N intersection,** go east on US 22 3 miles to Cedar Hill Rd. Turn left onto Cedar Hill under ½ mile to S Pierce Ave. Turn right onto S Pierce ½ mile to store on left. **From US 22W,** turn right onto Cedar Hill and follow directions above. **From US 33S,** turn left onto Lancaster Circleville Rd 3 miles (becomes Cedar Hill) to S Pierce. Turn left onto S Pierce ½ mile to store.

Call Ahead
We suggest you call first if possible before visiting a location. Stores and restaurants have a habit of moving (and closing), and hours, services, etc. change more often than you might expect.

MASON

Basilico 🍴 &

6176 Tylersville Rd. ✆ 513-374-3447 ⊙ M-Th, Sun 7am-10pm, F-Sat 7am-11pm
A Certified Organic Restaurant.
• vegetarian friendly • organic focus • alcohol • tables • self-service

🍎 **From I-75**, take exit 22 towards Mason east on Tylersville Rd (right from I-75N, left from I-75S) 2-2¼ miles to restaurant on left between Nicholas Way & Snider Rd. **From I-71N**, take exit 24 left onto Western Row Rd under 1 mile continuing onto Tylersville 2¾ miles to restaurant on right past Snider Rd. **From I-71S**, take exit 25 towards Mason left onto Kings Mill Rd 2½ miles to E Main St. Turn left onto E Main ⅓ mile to Reading Rd. Turn left onto Reading under 1 mile to Tylersville. Turn right onto Tylersville about ¾ mile to restaurant on right.

Whole Foods Market 🛒 🍴

5805 Deerfield Blvd. ✆ 513-398-9358 ⊙ M-Sat 8-10, Sun 9-9
• organic produce • vegetarian friendly • salad bar • cafe • self-service • take-out

🍎 **From I-71**, take exit 19 north on S Mason Montgomery Rd (right from I-71S, merge onto Governors Way and left from I-71N) about 1 mile to Deerfield Blvd. Turn left onto Deerfield about ⅓ mile to store on left in Deerfield Towne Ctr.

MIDDLEBURG HEIGHTS

American Harvest 🛒 🍴

13387 Smith Rd. ✆ 440-888-7727 ⊙ M-Sat 10-8, Sun 12-6
• organic produce • vegetarian friendly • deli • tables • self-service • take-out

🍎 **From I-71S**, take exit 235 toward Middleburg Hts left onto Bagley Rd 1 mile to Pearl Rd. Turn left onto Pearl under 1 mile to Smith Rd. Turn right onto Smith to store on right in Southland Shopping Ctr. **From I-71N**, take exit 234 toward Parma Hts right onto Pearl about 2 miles to Smith. Turn right onto Smith to store.

N.W. CANTON

Mulligan's Restaurant & Pub 🍴

4118 Belden Village St. ✆ 330-493-8239 ⊙ M-Th 11-11, F-Sat 11-12, 11-10
A pub/barbecue joint offering bar-style vegetarian options.
• vegetarian friendly • alcohol • counter • tables • wait staff

🍎 **From I-77S**, take exit 109 (Everhard Rd/Whipple Ave) left at Belden Village Mall ½ mile to Belden Village St NW. Turn left onto Belden Village to restaurant on right. **From I-77N**, take exit 109B toward Everhard, merge onto Whipple and u-turn at Everhard heading south on Whipple ⅓ mile to Belden Village. Turn right onto Belden Village to restaurant on left.

NEWTON FALLS

Healthy Treasures 🛒

40 W. Broad St. ✆ 330-872-1119 ⊙ M-F 8:30-7, Sat 9-5
Organic produce in season.

🍎 **From I-80**, take exit 209 right at fork onto OH 5 about 1½ miles to Ridge Rd. Turn left onto Ridge about 1 mile to W Broad St. Turn left onto W Broad to store on right between N Canal & N Center St.

NILES

Cindy's Health and Vitality Center 🛒 🍴

56 Youngstown-Warren Rd. ✆ 330-652-8284 ⊙ M-F 9-8, Sat 9-6
• organic produce • vegetarian friendly • fresh juice • deli • tables • self-service • take-out

🍎 **From I-80**, take exit 227 toward Girard north on US 422/S State St (left from I-80E, right from I-80W) about 2½ miles (becomes Youngstown-Warren Rd) to store on left after Robbins Ave.

OXFORD

Kona Bistro

31 W. High St. ✆ 513-523-0686 ⏱ M-W, Sun 11-9, Th-Sat 11-10

Several creative vegetarian choices and an exemplary kids menu.

· vegetarian friendly · alcohol · tables · wait staff

🚌 US 27 is the main road into Oxford. Restaurant is on US 27 (aka High St) 2½ blocks west of Miami of Ohio U between Main & Beech St on south side.

PARMA HEIGHTS

Udupi Cafe

6339 Olde York Rd. ✆ 440-743-7154 ⏱ Daily 11:30-9:45

Indian vegetarian with a lunch buffet.

· vegetarian · tables · self-service · wait staff

🚌 **From I-480**, take exit 15 south on Ridge Rd (right from I-480E, left from I-480W) over ½ mile to Pearl Rd. Turn right onto Pearl 2 miles to Olde York Rd. Turn left onto Olde York to restaurant on left. **From I-71N**, take exit 234 right at fork toward Parma Heights onto Pearl/US 42 4 miles to Olde York. Turn right onto Olde York to restaurant. **From I-71S**, take exit 245 right onto W 25th St/US 42S (becomes Pearl) about 5½ miles to Olde York. Turn left onto Olde York to restaurant.

SOLON

Mustard Seed Market & Cafe

6025 Kruse Drive ✆ 440-519-3663 ⏱ M-Sat 9-9, Sun 10-6 Cafe M 11-3, Tues-Th 11-8, F-Sat 11-9, Sun 10:30-3

Cafe offers everything from wheat grass and carrot juice to champagne and scotch!

· organic produce · vegetarian friendly · fresh juice · alcohol · salad bar · cafe · deli · bakery · counter · tables · self-service · wait staff · take-out

🚌 **From Rt 422E**, take Rt 91/Solon exit right off exit ramp to light at Solon Rd. Turn right onto Solon and first right onto Kruse Dr to store on right in Uptown Solon Shopping Ctr. **From Rt 422W**, take Rt 91/Solon exit left, pass under fwy to second light, turn right onto Solon and right onto Kruse to store.

STOW

Cappabianca's Natural Foods

4946 Darrow Rd. ✆ 330-650-1588 ⏱ M-Th 10-7, F-Sat 10-6

🚌 **From OH 8N**, take Graham Rd exit toward Silver Lake right onto Graham about 1½ miles to Darrow Rd. Turn left onto Darrow 2⅓ miles to store on left. **From OH 8S**, take OH 303 exit toward Hudson left onto 303 ⅓ mile to Terex Rd. Turn right onto Terex 3 miles to Darrow. Turn right onto Darrow 1¼ miles to store.

SYLVANIA

Claudia's Natural Food Store

5644 Monroe St. ✆ 419-534-3343 ⏱ M-F 7:30-9, Sat 7:30-8, Sun 8:30-7

· organic produce · vegetarian friendly · fresh juice · deli · tables · self-service · take-out

🚌 **From I-475W**, take exit 18A onto Monroe St/Hwy 51W about 3½ miles to store on right. **From I-475N**, continue onto US 23N about ½ mile to Monroe St exit. Turn right onto Monroe/Hwy 51E about ¾ mile to store on left. **Coming from MI on US 23S**, take Monroe St exit and follow directions above.

TALLMADGE

Seven Grains Natural Market 🛍
92 West Ave. ℂ 330-633-9999 ⏲ M-Sat 9-8, Sun 10-6
• organic produce • vegetarian friendly • deli • take-out

🍎 **From OH 8N,** take Tallmadge Ave onto Gorge Blvd to E Tallmadge Ave. Turn right onto Tallmadge almost 3 miles to store at West Ave. **From OH 8S,** take OH 532 exit left onto Broad Blvd (becomes Broad Ave, then Talmadge) about 1¼ miles to Northwest Ave. Continue on Northwest about 1¾ miles to roundabout. Take first exit onto West about ¼ mile to store.

TOLEDO

Bassett's Health Foods 🛍
3344 Secor St. ℂ 419-531-0334 ⏲ M-F 9-9, Sat 9-8, Sun 11-5

🍎 **From I-475,** take exit 17 south on Secor Rd (left from I-475W, right from I-475E) about ⅔ mile to store on right at Central Ave in West Gate Shopping Ctr.

Bassett's Health Foods 🛍
4315 Heatherdowns Blvd. ℂ 419-382-4142 ⏲ M-Sat 9:30-8, Sun 11:30-5:30

🍎 **From I-80/90,** take exit 59/4 toward I-475 north on Reynolds Rd to Heatherdowns Blvd. Turn right onto Heatherdowns about 1 mile to store on right.

Phoenix Earth Food Co-op 🛍
1447 W. Sylvania Ave. ℂ 419-476-3211 ⏲ M-F 9-8, Sat 9-7, Sun 11-5
• organic produce • co-op

🍎 **From I-75,** take exit 205A onto Jeep Pkwy to Willys Pkwy. Turn north onto Willys (right from I-75S, left from I-75N) about ⅔ mile to W Sylvania Ave. Turn left onto W Sylvania about ¼ mile to store.

UNIVERSITY HEIGHTS

Whole Foods Market 🛍 🍽
13998 Cedar Rd. ℂ 216-371-5320 ⏲ Daily 8-9
• organic produce • vegetarian friendly • salad bar • cafe • self-service • take-out

🍎 **From I-271S,** take exit 32 west on Cedar Rd (right onto Brainard Rd and first right from I-271S, loop around left from I-271N) over 3 miles to store on right at Warrensville Ctr Rd.

WESTERVILLE

Raisin Rack 🛍 🍽
2545 Schrock Rd. ℂ 614-882-5886 ⏲ M-Sat 8-9, Sun 10-6
• organic produce • vegetarian friendly • fresh juice • salad bar • cafe • tables • self-service • take-out

🍎 **From I-270,** take exit 27 toward OH 710/Schrock Rd onto Cleveland Ave about ½ mile to store at Schrock Rd.

WESTLAKE

The Web of Life Natural Foods Market 🛍 🍽   ♿
25923 Detroit Rd. ℂ 440-899-2882 ⏲ M-Sat 9-9, Sun 10-6
• organic produce • vegetarian • vegan friendly • organic focus • fresh juice • cafe • deli • counter • tables • self-service • wait staff • take-out

🍎 **From I-90,** take exit 159 south on Columbia St (right from I-90E, left from I-90W) to Detroit Rd. Turn right onto Detroit about 1 mile to store in Williamsburg Sq.

WILLOUGHBY

Danny's Organic Marketplace 🛍️

37111 Euclid Ave. ✆ 440-946-2743 ⏰ M-F 9-7, Sat 9-6
• organic produce

🚗 **From I-93W**, take exit 193 for Hwy 306 toward Mentor right onto Broadmoor Rd/OH 306 under 1 mile to Mentor Ave. Turn left onto Mentor 1¾ miles to Erie St/Euclid Ave. Turn left onto Erie 1⅓ miles to store on right at Hamann Pkwy. **From OH-93E**, take exit 189 toward Willoughby right onto OH 91N/Som Center Rd 1¾ miles to Euclid. Turn right onto Euclid 1 mile to store on left at Hamann.

WOODMERE

Wild Oats Market 🛍️ 🍴   ♿

27249 Chagrin Blvd. ✆ 216-464-9403 ⏰ Daily 7-9
• organic produce • vegetarian friendly • salad bar • cafe • self-service • take-out

🚗 **From I-271**, take Chagrin Blvd exit. **From I-271N**, go east to store on left. **From I-217S**, go west over interstate overpass to store.

WOOSTER

Wooster Natural Foods 🛍️

138 E. Liberty St. ✆ 330-264-9797 ⏰ M-F 10-6, Sat 10-5
• organic produce

🚗 **From US 30E**, take OH 3S exit and turn right onto Columbus Rd ½ mile to W Liberty St. Turn right onto W Liberty under ½ mile to store on left after Market St. **From US 30W**, take OH 302 exit toward Madison right onto S Bever St ½ mile to E Liberty St. Turn left onto E Liberty 2 blocks to store on right. **From OH 83S**, take Rt 30E exit right onto Lincoln Way (becomes Pittsburg Ave then E Liberty) under 1½ miles to store.

YELLOW SPRINGS

Sunrise Cafe 🍴   ♿

259 Xenia Ave. ✆ 937-767-7211 ⏰ M, W-F 7:30-2, 5-9, Sat-Sun 8-2, 5-9
Eco-friendly with biodegradable take-out containers and composting of food waste.
• vegetarian friendly • vegan friendly,oganic focus • tables • wait staff • take-out

🚗 **From I-675**, take exit 20 right onto DaytonYellow Springs Rd over 5½ miles to Limestone St. Turn right onto Limestone about ½ mile to US 68 (Xenia Ave). Turn left onto Xenia about 2 blocks to restaurant on left. **From I-70**, take exit 52A toward Xenia onto Rt 68S (becomes Xenia Ave) over 7 miles to restaurant on right.

ZANESVILLE

Sweet Meadows 🛍️

2782 Maple Ave. ✆ 740-452-9151 ⏰ M-F 10:30-5:30, Sat 10-2
• organic produce

🚗 **From I-70E**, take exit 155 for 7th St toward Hwy 146E/60S, merge onto Elberon Ave and turn right onto OH 60 (Underwood St, becomes Adair Ave then Maple Ave) 2½ miles to store on right. **From I-70W**, take exit 153 onto Maple 2 miles to store on right.

OKLAHOMA

Map of Oklahoma with numbered location markers.

1. Ardmore
2. Bartlesville
3. Chickasha
4. Davis
5. Durant
6. Enid
7. Norman
8. Oklahoma City
9. Stillwater
10. Tahlequah
11. Tulsa

ARDMORE

Veggies Health Advantage Center 🛍️🍴

1202 Brookview Drive ✆ 580-226-2424 ⏲ M-F 9-7, Sun 12-5 Cafe M-F 11-3
· organic produce · vegan · salad bar · cafe · tables · self-service · take-out

🚘 **From I-35**, take ext 32 toward 12th St east on 12th Ave NW (onto Michelin Rd and left from I-35S, onto Holiday Dr and left from I-35N) 1 mile to Brookview Dr. Turn left onto Brookview to store on right.

BARTLESVILLE

Billie's Health Food Center 🛍️

313 S. Osage Ave. ✆ 918-336-8609 ⏲ M-F 9-5:30, Sat 10-4

🚘 **From US 60W**, turn right onto S Cherokee Ave 1 block to E 6th St. Turn left onto E 6th 1 block to S Osage Ave. Turn right onto S Osage 3 blocks to store on left. **From US 60E**, turn left onto S Dewey Ave 3 blocks to E 4th St. Turn right onto E 4th 1 block to S Osage. Turn left onto S Osage 1 block to store on left.

CHICKASHA

Natural Health Food Center 🛍️

1742 S. 4th St. ✆ 405-224-1854 ⏲ M 10-5, Tues-W, F 10-5:30, Th 10-6, Sat 10-2

🚘 **From I-44**, take exit 80 toward Duncan/Chickasha north on US 81/S 4th St ½-¾ mile to store on left after Southland Shopping Ctr.

DAVIS

Brocci-Flower Country Health Foods 🛍️

309 E. Benton Ave. ✆ 580-369-3434 ⏲ W-Th 11-5:30, F 11-2

🚘 **From I-35**, take exit 55 toward Davis east on OK 7 (left from I-35S, right from I-35N) about 3 miles (becomes Main St) to N 2nd St. Turn left onto N 2nd 1 block to E Benton St Turn right onto E Benton 1 block to store on right at N 3rd St.

DURANT

Family Health Food Store 📁

1020 W. Main St. ✆ 580-924-3214 ⏰ M-F 9-6, Sat 9-5
🏪 Store is on US 70 (aka Main St) just west of 10th St on the north side.

ENID

Pearson's Natural Food Center 📁   ♿

131 W. Garriott Rd. ✆ 580-234-5000 ⏰ M-F 9-5:30, Sat 9-1
Organic produce seasonally.

🏪 **From US-81**, take Hwy 412W (Garriot Rd) over ½ mile to store on right at Independence St.

NORMAN

Earth Natural Foods 📁 🍴   ♿

309 S. Flood Ave. ✆ 405-364-3551 ⏰ M-F 9-8, Sat 9-6, Sun 11-5
• organic produce • vegetarian friendly • fresh juice • cafe • deli • counter • tables • self-service • take-out

🏪 **From I-35**, take exit 109 toward Downtown east on W Main St (follow loop off exit from I-35S, right from I-35N) about 2 miles to the 4-way light. Turn right onto S Flood Ave to store in little cottage on left.

Native Roots Market 📁

132 W. Main St. ✆ 405-310-6300 ⏰ M-F 9-9, Sat 9-6, Sun 11-5
• organic produce

🏪 **From I-35**, take exit 109 toward Downtown east on W Main St (follow loop off exit from I-35S, merge right from I-35N) 2½ miles to store on right.

OKLAHOMA CITY

Akins Natural Foods Market 📁 🍴   ♿

2924 N.W. 63rd St. ✆ 405-843-3033 ⏰ M-Sat 8-9, Sun 9-9
• organic produce • vegetarian friendly • fresh juice • deli • tables • self-service • take-out

🏪 **From I-44W**, take exit 125C on left onto Northwest Expwy over 1½ miles to northbound May Ave ramp. Merge onto May about ⅔ mile to store on left in Mayfair Place Shopping Ctr. **From I-44E**, merge onto OK 3W/74N about 8½ miles to NW 50th St exit. Turn right onto NW 50th about ½ mile to May. Turn left onto May about 1 mile to store.

Akin's Natural Foods Market 📁

2370 W. Memorial Rd. ✆ 405-418-4305 ⏰ M-Sat 8-9, Sun 9-9
• organic produce

🏪 On John Kilpatrick Tpke about 1½ miles east of Hwy 74 (take Memorial Rd exit) and 3 miles west of US 77 (exit toward Penn Ave) on south side in Quail Springs Marketplace.

Health Food Center 📁 🍴

7301 S. Penn Ave., Ste. D ✆ 405-681-6060 ⏰ M-Sat 9-8, Sun 12-6
• organic produce • fresh juice • counter • take-out

🏪 **From I-44**, take exit 115 onto I-240E about 1 mile to exit 1C toward S Penn Ave. Merge onto SW 74th St and turn left onto Penn under ¼ mile to store on left in Walnut Square Shopping Ctr.

Nutritional Food Center 📁

1022-32 Classen Blvd. ✆ 405-232-8404 ⏰ M-Sat 8-6
• organic produce • fresh juice

🏪 **From I-40W**, take exit 149B and follow ramp onto Claussen Blvd N about 10 blocks to store at 10th St. **From I-40E**, take exit 149A (Reno Ave) toward Western Ave and follow ramp left for Sheridan Ave. Veer right onto Sheridan 2 blocks to Claussen. Turn left onto Claussen to store at 10th. **From I-35 or I-44**, merge onto I-40 and follow directions above from E or W as appropriate.

STILLWATER

Nature's Supply 🛍
211 N. Perkins Rd. ✆ 405-762-6240 ⏱ M-W, F-Sat 10-6, Th 10-8
• organic produce
🏠 Store is 1 block east of US 177 at E Hall of Fame Rd in Pioneer Sq.

TAHLEQUAH

The Oasis Health Food Store 🛍
111 N. Muskogee Ave. ✆ 918-456-1414 ⏱ M-F 9-5:30, Sat 9-3
• organic produce
🏠 Store is on OK 62 (aka Muskogee Ave) on west side at Delaware St.

TULSA

Akin's Natural Foods Market 🛍   ♿
7807 E. 51st St. ✆ 918-663-4137 ⏱ Daily 8-9
• organic produce
🏠 From I-44, take exit 231 toward Muskeegee/Broken Arrow onto US 64E/OK 51E
about ⅔ mile to Memorial Dr exit. Turn right onto Memorial about 1¼ miles to
E 51st St. Turn right onto E 51st to store on NW corner in Fontana Shopping Ctr.
From Hwy 169, exit at E 51st and go west about 1½ miles to store at Memorial.

Akin's Natural Foods Market 🛍
3321 E. 31st St. ✆ 918-742-6630 ⏱ Daily 8-9
• organic produce
🏠 From I-44E, take exit 228 toward Harvard Ave. Take E 51st ramp and turn left
onto Harvard about 2 miles to store at 31st St on NE corner in Newport Square
Shopping Ctr. From I-44W, take exit 231 toward Sand Spring onto US 64W/OK
51W almost 1½ miles to 31st St exit toward Fairgrounds/Expo Sq/Drillers Stadium.
Turn left onto E 31st about 1 mile to store at Harvard.

Be Le Vegetarian Restaurant 🍴
6634 S.Lewis Ave. ✆ 918-499-1414 ⏱ M-F 11-2:30, 5-9, Sat 11-9
Chinese/Vietnamese vegetarian.
• vegetarian • vegan friendly • tables • wait staff
🏠 From I-44, take exit 227 south on Lewis Ave (merge onto E 51st St and right from
I-44E, merge onto E Skelly Dr and left from I-44W) over 1½ miles to restaurant
on right after E 66th Pl.

Whole Foods Market 🛍🍴   ♿
1401 E. 41st St. ✆ 918-712-7555 ⏱ Daily 8-10
• organic produce • vegetarian friendly • salad bar • cafe • self-service • take-out
🏠 From I-44, take exit 226B north on Peoria Ave (right from I-44E, left from
I-44W) about 1 mile to E 41st St. Turn right onto E 41st to store.

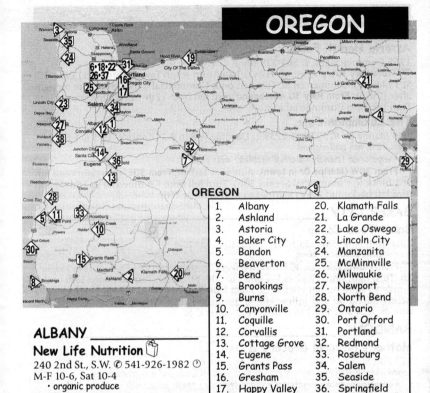

OREGON

OREGON

1.	Albany	20.	Klamath Falls
2.	Ashland	21.	La Grande
3.	Astoria	22.	Lake Oswego
4.	Baker City	23.	Lincoln City
5.	Bandon	24.	Manzanita
6.	Beaverton	25.	McMinnville
7.	Bend	26.	Milwaukie
8.	Brookings	27.	Newport
9.	Burns	28.	North Bend
10.	Canyonville	29.	Ontario
11.	Coquille	30.	Port Orford
12.	Corvallis	31.	Portland
13.	Cottage Grove	32.	Redmond
14.	Eugene	33.	Roseburg
15.	Grants Pass	34.	Salem
16.	Gresham	35.	Seaside
17.	Happy Valley	36.	Springfield
18.	Hillsboro	37.	Tigard
19.	Hood River	38.	Waldport

ALBANY

New Life Nutrition

240 2nd St., S.W. ✆ 541-926-1982 ⏲ M-F 10-6, Sat 10-4
· organic produce

🛍 **From I-5S**, take exit 234B toward Albany onto Hwy 99E/Pacific Blvd SE 2 miles onto Lyon St S ramp. Turn left onto 3rd Ave SW, right onto SE Broadalban St and right onto 2nd Ave SW to store on left. **From I-5N**, take exit 233 right at fork towards Albany onto Hwy 20/Santiam Hwy SE (becomes Pacific Blvd SE) and follow directions above.

ASHLAND

Ashland Food Co-op 🛍 🍴   ♿

237 N. 1st St. ✆ 541-482-2237 ⏲ Daily 7-9
· organic produce · vegetarian friendly · fresh juice · salad bar · deli · bakery · tables · self-service · take-out · co-op

🛍 **From I-5S,** take exit 19 toward Ashland right onto Valley View Rd to end at OR 99. Turn left onto OR 99 about 2½ miles (into town) to 1st St. Turn left onto 1st to store on l after B St. **From I-5N**, take exit 14 left at stop sign onto Hwy 66 1⅓ miles to end at Siskiyou Blvd (OR 99) Turn right onto Siskiyou 1⅓ miles to 1st. Turn right onto 1st to store on left .

ASTORIA

Astoria Co-op 🛍

1389 Duane St. ✆ 503-325-002 ⏲ M-Sat 9-7, Sun 11-5
· organic produce · co-op

🛍 **From Hwy 101**, go east on Hwy 30 and turn south (away from river) onto 8th St 1 block to Commercial St. Turn left onto Commercial 6 blocks to 15th St. Turn right onto 15th 1 block to Duane St. Turn right onto Duane 1 block to store on right at 14th St. **From Hwy 30 westbound**, turn left onto 15th St 2 blocks to Duane. Turn right onto Duane 1 block to store.

Astoria Health Foods 🛍

1255 Commercial St. ✆ 503-325-6688 ⏱ M-F 9-5:30, Sat 9-5

🚗 **From Hwy 101**, go east on Hwy 30 and turn south (away from river) onto 8th St 1 block to Commercial St. Turn left onto Commercial 4 blocks to store on right after 12th St. **From Hwy 30 westbound**, turn left onto 12th 1 block to Commercial. Turn left onto Commercial to store.

The Columbian Cafe 🍴

1114 Marine Dr. ✆ 503-325-2233 ⏱ Daytime W-Sun 8-2 Dinner W-Th 5-8, F-Sat 5-9
Vegetarian, fish and seafood.
  • vegetarian friendly • alcohol • tables • wait staff

🚗 **From 30W (Marine Dr in town)**, store is at 11th St. **From 30E**, turn right onto 8th St 1 block to Commercial St (aka 30E). Turn left onto Commercial to 16th St and turn left back onto 30W (Marine) to restaurant at 11th.

BAKER CITY

Baker Food Co-op 🛍

2816 10th St. ✆ 541-523-6281 ⏱ M-F 10-6, Sat 10-4
  • organic produce • co-op

🚗 **From I-84E**, take exit 303 toward Baker City right onto OH 86 ¾ mile to Hughes Ln. Turn right onto Hughes 1¼ miles to 10th St/US 30. Turn left onto 10th under 1 mile to store on left after D St. **From I-84W**, take exit 306 toward Haines onto Access Rd/US 30 and follow US 30 3½ miles (onto Elm St, Bridge St, Main St, Broadway St and 10th) to store on right after C St.

BANDON

Mother's Natural Grocery & Deli 🛍 🍴

975 2nd St. S.E. ✆ 541-347-4086 ⏱ M-Sat 9-6
Styled like a traditional country grocery with natural foods and a vegetarian deli.
  • organic produce • vegetarian • vegan friendly • fresh juice • deli • tables • self-service • take-out

🚗 Bandon is along the OR coast and store is on Hwy 101 (2nd St in town) before Rt 42 intersection.

BEAVERTON

New Seasons Market/Cedar Hills Crossing 🛍 🍴

3495 Cedar Hills Blvd. ✆ 503-641-4181 ⏱ Daily 8-10
  • organic produce • salad bar • deli • bakery • tables • self-service • take-out

🚗 **From OR 217S (Beaverton Tigard Fwy)**, take exit 1 west on SW Walker Rd (right from OR 217N, left from OR 217S) under 1 mile to SW Cedar Hills Blvd. Turn left onto SW Cedar Hills to store on right in Cedar Hills Crossing.

BEND

Cafe Yumm! 🍴

325 S.W. Powerhouse Drive, Ste 130 ✆ 541-318-9866 ⏱ M-Sat 10-9, Sun 11-7
The signature dish in this franchise is rice, beans and various accoutrements topped with wheat-free vegan Yumm! sauce.
  • vegetarian friendly • vegan friendly • alcohol • tables • self-service

🚗 **From Hwy 97N**, take exit 139 left onto SW Reed Market Rd under ½ mile to SW Chamberlain St. Turn right onto SW Chamberlain continuing onto SW Powerhouse Dr about ½ mile total to restaurant on left. **From Hwy 97S**, turn right onto SE Truman Ave 2 blocks to SW Hill St. Turn left onto SW Hill 1 block to SW Wilson Ave. Turn left onto SW Wilson 1 block to SW Bond St. Turn right onto SW Bond about ⅓ mile to SW Powerhouse. Turn left onto SW Powerhouse to restaurant on right.

Devore's Good Food Store 🛍

1124 N.W. Newport Ave. ✆ 541-389-6588 ⏱ M-Sat 8-7, Sun 10-6
  • organic produce • vegetarian friendly • deli • take-out

From Hwy 97, go west on Greenwood Rd (Hwy 20) and follow signs to Central OR Community College and Mt. Bachelor about 1 mile (through downtown and across river where Greenwood becomes Newport Ave) to store between NW 11th & 12th St.

Nature's General Store

1900 N.E. 3rd St. © 541-382-6732 ⏱ M-F 9-9, Sat-Sun 9-8
• organic produce • vegetarian friendly • fresh juice • deli • tables • self-service • take-out

From Hwy 97, take exit 137 toward Downtown east on NE Revere Ave (left from 97S, right from 97N) 3 blocks to NE 3rd St. Turn left onto NE 3rd 1 block to store on right in Wagner Payless Mall.

Wild Oats Market

2610 N.E. Hwy. 20 © 541-389-0151 ⏱ Daily 8-10
• organic produce • vegetarian friendly • salad bar • cafe • self-service • take-out

From Hwy 97S, merge onto US 20E toward Business District through downtown past Pilot Butte Park to store at SE 27th St. From Hwy 97N, take Knott Rd ramp toward Baker Rd. Turn right onto Knott about 7½ miles (becomes SE 27th St) to US 20. Turn left onto US 20 to store.

BROOKINGS

Brookings Natural Food Co-op

630 Fleet St. © 541-469-9551 ⏱ M-Th 9-5, F 9-5:30, Sat 9-4, Sun 10-2
• organic produce • co-op

Brookings is on Hwy 101 about 5 miles north of CA border. Store is on 101 in town in yellow bldg across from municipal parking lot.

BURNS

Simple Foods

85 W. Washington St. © 541-573-787 ⏱ M-Sat 10-5

From US 395/OR 78 intersection (Monroe St), go north on US 395 (N Broadway Ave) 4 blocks and turn left (west) onto W Washington St 1 block to store on left.

CANYONVILLE

Promise Natural Foods & Bakery

503 S. Main St. © 541-839-4167 ⏱ M-F 9:30-6, Sat 10-5
On-site organic bakery makes whole grain baked goods and pizza on Friday.
• organic produce • bakery

From I-5N, take exit 98 toward Canyonville right onto SW 5th St 2 blocks to store at Main St (peace symbol on bldg). From I-5S, take exit 98 left onto Canyonville Riddle Rd 2 blocks to Main. Turn right onto Main 4 blocks to store at 5th.

COQUILLE

Eden Valley

99 E. 1st St. © 541-396-4823 ⏱ M-F 10-6, Sat. 12-5
• organic produce • vegetarian friendly • deli • take-out

From Rt 42, turn onto N Adams St 1 block to store at 1st St.

CORVALLIS

Fireworks

1115 S.E. 3rd St. © 541-754-6958 ⏱ M-Th 11-2:30, 4-9:30, F-Sat 11-2:30, 5-11:30, Sun 10-2:30-4-9:30
Vegetarian, vegan, local seafood, natural poultry and meat, pizza from a wood-fired oven.
• vegetarian friendly • vegan friendly • organic focus • alcohol • tables • wait staff

From I-5, take exit 228 onto Hwy 34W about 11 miles (bypass Corvallis) to exit 99W on right. Restaurant is on left in Chapman Place (next to First Alternative Coop). From downtown Corvallis, go south on 3rd St, pass under Hwy 34 and over Mary's River to restaurant.

First Alternative Natural Foods Coop 🛍️ 🍴   ♿

1007 S.E. 3rd St. ☎ 541-753-3115 ⏰ Daily 9-9
  • organic produce • vegetarian friendly • organic focus • salad bar • deli • bakery •
  tables • self-service • take-out • co-op

🚗 **From I-5**, take exit 228 onto Hwy 34W about 11 miles (bypass Corvallis) to
exit 99W on right. Store is on left in Chapman Place. **From downtown Corvallis,** go
south on 3rd St, pass under Hwy 34 and over Mary's River to store.

First Alternative Natural Foods Coop 🛍️   ♿

2855 N.W. Grant Ave. ☎ 541-452-3115 ⏰ Daily 7-9
Grab-and-go meals and baked goods.
  • organic produce • bakery • co-op

🚗 **From I-5**, take exit 228 onto Hwy 34W about 10 miles. Continue straight onto
NW Harrison Blvd to NW 5th St. Turn right onto NW 5th and follow as it curves
left and becomes NW Buchanan Ave for about 1¼ miles to NW Kings Blvd. Turn
right onto NW Kings about ¼ mile to NW Grant Ave. Turn left onto NW Grant
almost ½ mile to store on left before NW 29th St.

Interzone 🍴   ♿ 🚲

1563 N.W. Monroe Ave. ☎ 541-754-5965 ⏰ M-F 7am-12am, Sat-Sun 8am-12am
Coffeehouse serving omelets, sandwiches, burritos and such.
  • vegetarian • vegan friendly • organic focus • tables • wait staff

🚗 **From I-5**, take exit 228 onto Hwy 34W about 10 miles. Continue straight onto
NW Harrison Blvd 2 blocks NW 6th St. Turn left onto NW 6th 3 blocks to NW
Monroe Ave. Turn right onto NW Monroe ½ mile to restaurant on right after 15th
St (across from OR State).

Nearly Normals 🍴   ♿

109 N.W. 15th St. ☎ 541-753-0791 ⏰ M-W 8-8, Th-F 8-9, Sat 9-9
Vegetarian and vegan world cuisine. Seating indoors and out.
  • vegetarian • vegan friendly • organic focus • alcohol • tables • self-service

🚗 **From I-5**, take exit 228 onto Hwy 34W about 10 miles. Continue straight onto
NW Harrison Blvd about ½ mile to NW 15th St. Turn left onto NW 15th ¼ mile
to restaurant.

COTTAGE GROVE_____

Sunshine General Store 🛍️

824 W. Main St. ☎ 541-942-8836 ⏰ M-Sat 10-7
  • organic produce

🚗 **From I-5**, take exit 174 toward Cottage Grove right onto E Cottage Grove Conn (becomes
Hwy 99) about 1 mile to Main St. Turn right onto Main about ⅓ mile to store on right.

EUGENE _____

Cafe Yumm! 🍴   ♿

130 Oakway Center ☎ 541-465-9866 ⏰ M-Sat 10-6, Sun 11-5
See Bend location for description.
  • vegetarian friendly • vegan friendly • alcohol • tables • self-service

🚗 **From I-5**, take exit 194B onto I-105W about 1⅓ miles to exit 2 (OR 99S/Coburg
Rd) toward Downtown. Take Coburg Rd ramp onto Oakway Rd to restaurant in
Oakway Ctr.

Cafe Yumm! 🍴   ♿

1801 Willamette St. #140 ☎ 541-686-9866 ⏰ M-Sat 10-9, 11-5
See Bend location for description.
  • vegetarian friendly • vegan friendly • alcohol • tables • self-service

🚗 **From I-5S**, take exit 194B onto I-105W 3½ miles to exit 1 toward Fairgrounds.
Turn left onto Jefferson St about 1 mile to W 18th Ave. Turn left onto 18th almost
½ mile to Willamette St. Turn right onto Willamette to restaurant on SE corner.
From I-5N, take exit 189 west on 30th Ave (becomes Amazon Pkwy) 4½ miles to

E 19th Ave. Turn left onto E 19th, right onto Oak St, left onto E 18th and left onto Willamette to store on SE corner at 18th.

Cafe Yumm! ⅋ &

730 E. Broadway © 541-344-9866 ⏰ Daily 10-9
See Bend location for description.
　• vegetarian friendly • vegan friendly • alcohol • tables • self-service
　🛍 **From I-5N,** take exit 192 right at fork onto OR 99/Franklin Blvd (becomes E Broadway) over 1½ miles to restaurant on right. **From I-5S,** take exit 191 right onto Glenwood Dr, right onto Glenwood Blvd and take the ramp onto I-5N to exit 192 and follow directions above.

Cafe Yumm! ⅋ &

1005 Green Acres Rd. © 541-684-9866 ⏰ M-F 10-8, Sun 11-5
See Bend location for description.
　• vegetarian friendly • vegan friendly • alcohol • tables • self-service
　🛍 **From I-5,** take exit 195 west on Belt Line Hwy (195B from I-5S, 195AB toward Belt Line W/Florence/Junction City from I-5N) 2¼-2¾ miles to Delta Hwy exit toward Downtown. Turn right onto Delta N 1 block to Green Acres Rd. Turn right onto Green Acres to restaurant on left.

Capella Market 🛍 ⅋ &

2489 Willamette St. © 541-345-1014 ⏰ Daily 8-10
Limited indoor seating plus outdoor seating weather permitting.
　• organic produce • vegetarian friendly • deli • tables • self-service • take-out
　🛍 **From I-5,** take exit 189 toward S Eugene west on E 30th Ave (left from I-5N, straight onto McVay Hwy then right from I-5S) about 3¼ miles until it becomes Amazon Pkwy. Turn right onto Amazon about ½ mile to Willamette St. Turn right onto Willamette to store on right.

Friendly Foods & Deli 🛍 ⅋

2757 Friendly St. © 541-683-2079 ⏰ M-Sat 8-10, Sun 9-10
　• organic produce • vegetarian • vegan friendly • deli • tables • self-service • take-out
　🛍 **From I-5,** take exit 189 toward S Eugene west on E 30th Ave (left from I-5N, straight onto McVay Hwy then right from I-5S) about 3¼ miles until it becomes Amazon Pkwy and zig zag onto 29th Ave over ½ mile to Lincoln St. Turn right onto Lincoln and left onto 28th Ave under ½ mile to Friendly St. Turn right onto Friendly to store on right.

Govinda's Vegetarian Buffet ⅋ &

1030 River Rd. © 541-461-0093 ⏰ M-Sat 11:30-2, 5-7:30
Buffet run by the Hare Krishna.
　• vegetarian, vegan friendly • salad bar • tables • self-service
　🛍 **From I-5S,** take exit 195B onto Belt Line Hwy W about 3¾ miles to exit 8 toward Santa Clara. Turn left onto River Rd under 1½ miles to restaurant on right. **From I-5N,** take exit 192 right at fork onto Hwy 99 under 3 miles to Jefferson St. Turn right onto Jefferson under ½ mile to W 1st St. Turn left onto W 1st continuing onto Railroad Blvd and NW Expwy 1 mile to River. Turn right onto River about 1 mile to restaurant on left.

Holy Cow Cafe ⅋

EMU Student Union/U OR © 541-345-2562 ⏰ M-Th 10-7, F 10-3 Summer 11-3
Best to call for current schedule
Organic vegetarian (mostly vegan) cafeteria in the U OR student union.
　• vegetarian • vegan friendly • organic focus • salad bar • tables • self-service • take-out
　🛍 **From I-5S,** take exit 194B onto Hwy 105W about 1⅓ miles to exit 2 (OR 99S/Coburg Rd). Take 99S and merge onto E Broadway heading east (becomes Franklin Blvd) to Agate St. Turn right onto Agate to 15th Ave (at Hayward Field). Turn right onto 15th and take first or second entrance on right (before street dead ends at University St) to visitor parking behind Student Union. Restaurant is on main floor of Student Union in food court. **From I-5N,** take exit 192 toward Eugene/Hwy 99 onto Franklin about 1⅓ miles to Agate. Turn left onto Agate to 15th and follow directions above.

Keystone Cafe 🍴

395 W. 5th Ave. © 541-342-2075 ⏰ M-Th- 7-2, F-Sat 7-3, Sun 8-3
Extensive breakfast menu with many healthy choices and an environmental attitude. Mostly vegetarian and vegan. Kid friendly.
• vegetarian friendly • vegan friendly • organic focus • tables • wait staff
🏠 **From I-5**, take exit 194B onto Hwy 105W over 3 miles to Hwy 126W/99S exit to Madison Ave. Turn right onto Madison 1 block to W 5th Ave. Turn right onto 5th 3 blocks (across I-5) to restaurant on left at Lawrence St.

Kiva 🛍️

125 W. 11th Ave. © 541-342-8666 ⏰ M-Sat 9-8, Sun 10-6
• organic produce • vegetarian friendly • deli • take-out
🏠 **From I-5S**, take exit 194B onto Hwy 105W about 3½ miles to Jefferson St/OR 99S exit. Take 99S ramp toward City Center/Mall left onto W 7th Ave. Turn left onto W 7th about ⅓ mile to Olive St. Turn right onto Olive about ⅓ mile to store at 11th Ave. **From I-5N**, take exit 192 toward Eugene onto OR 99N/126 Bus W about 1⅔ miles to 11th. Turn left onto 11th about 1 mile to store at Olive.

Laughing Planet Cafe 🍴

760 Blair Blvd. © 541-868-0668 ⏰ M-Sat 11-10, Sun 11-9
House specialty is burritos. Mostly vegetarian with vegan sauces. Chicken added on request.
• vegetarian friendly • vegan friendly • fresh juice • alcohol • tables • self-service
🏠 **From I-5**, take exit 194B toward Eugene onto I-105W about 3½ miles onto Jefferson St to W 8th Ave. Turn right onto W 8th 2 blocks to Monroe St. Turn right onto Monroe and left onto Blair Blvd to restaurant on right.

Lotus Garden 🍴

810 Charnelton St. © 541-344-1928 ⏰ M, W-F 11:30-2:30, 4:30-8:30, Sat 12-8:30
Vegetarian Chinese featuring faux meat dishes.
• vegetarian • vegan friendly • tables • wait staff
🏠 **From I-5S**, take exit 194B onto Hwy 105W about 3½ miles to Jefferson St/OR 99S exit. Take 99S ramp toward City Center/Mall left onto W 7th Ave. Turn left onto W 7th about ¼ mile to Charnelton St. Turn right onto Charnelton 1 block to restaurant at W 8th Ave. **From I-5N,** take exit 192 toward Eugene onto OR 99N/126 Bus W (becomes E Broadway) about 2½ miles to Olive St. Turn right onto Olive 1 block to 8th Ave. Turn left onto 8th 1 block to restaurant at Charnelton.

Morning Glory 🍴   ♿ ▨

450 Willamette St. © 541-687-0709 ⏰ Daily 7:30-3:30
Breakfast, lunch and all-vegan baked goods.
• vegetarian • vegan friendly • organic focus • fresh juice • bakery • tables • wait staff
🏠 **From I-5S**, take exit 194B toward Eugene onto I-105W about 1⅓ miles to exit 2 (OR 99S/Coburg Rd) toward Downtown. Take Coburg ramp and follow Coburg almost 1 mile to High St. Turn right onto High 1 block to 5th Ave. Turn left onto 5th (past 5th St Market) 3 blocks to Willamette St. Turn right onto Willamette to restaurant at end on left. **From I-5N**, take exit 192 toward Eugene onto OR 99N/126 Bus W almost 2½ miles until it becomes E 6th Ave. Follow E 6th left 1 block to High. Turn right onto High and follow directions above.

New Frontier Market 🛍️

1101 W. 8th Ave. © 541-345-7401 ⏰ M-F 7am-12am, Sat 8-12, Sun 8-11
• organic produce
🏠 **From I-5**, take exit 194B onto Hwy 105W about 3½ miles to Jefferson St/OR 99S exit. Merge onto Jefferson to W 8th Ave. Turn right onto 8th about ⅓ mile to store at Van Buren St.

Pizza Research Institute 🍴   ♿

1328 Lawrence St. © 541-343-1307 ⏰ Daily 5-9:30
Far beyond typical pizza. Home-smoked cheese as well as tofu.
• vegetarian • vegan friendly • organic focus • alcohol • tables • self-service • wait staff • take-out

🚗 **From I-5**, take exit 194B onto I-105W 3½ miles and merge left at end onto Jefferson St ½ mile to W 13th Ave. Turn left onto W 13th under ¼ mile to Lawrence St. Turn right onto Lawrence to restaurant on right.

Ratatouille 🍴

1530 Willamette St. ✆ 541-344-0203 ⏰ Tues-Sat 5-10
· vegetarian · organic focus · alcohol · tables · wait staff

🚗 **From I-5N**, take exit 192 toward Eugene right at fork onto Or 99/Or 126/Franklin Blvd 2¼ miles (becomes E Broadway) to Willamette St. Turn left onto Willamette ½ mile to restaurant on right after E 15th St. **From I-5S**, take exit 194B onto US 105W about 3½ miles and veer left onto Jefferson St ½ mile to W 13th Ave. Turn left onto W 13th ½ mile to Willamette. Turn right onto Willamette 2 blocks to restaurant.

Red Barn 🛍️ 🍴

357 Van Buren St. ✆ 541-342-7503 ⏰ Daily 8-10
· organic produce · vegetarian friendly · deli · tables · self-service · take-out

🚗 **From I-5**, take exit 194B toward Eugene onto I-105W about 3½ miles to OR 99N/OR 126 exit. Turn right onto W 6th Ave about 4 blocks to Blair Blvd. Turn right onto Blair about ¼ mile to Van Buren St. Turn right onto Van Buren to store.

Sam Bond's Garage 🍴   ♿

407 Blair Blvd. ✆ 541-431-6603 ⏰ Daily 4-closing (1am or beyond)
A no-smoking bar (except in courtyard) with a vegetarian organic menu, local beer and music.
· vegetarian · vegan friendly · organic focus · alcohol · tables · self-service

🚗 **From I-5**, take exit 194B toward Eugene onto I-105W about 3½ miles to OR 99N/OR 126 exit. Turn right onto W 6th Ave about 4 blocks to Blair Blvd. Turn right onto Blair about ¼ mile to restaurant at 4th Ave.

Sundance Natural Foods 🛍️

748 E. 24th Ave. ✆ 541-343-9142 ⏰ Daily 7-11 Salad/Food Bar Daily 11-9
· organic produce · vegetarian · vegan friendly · salad bar · tables · self-serve · take-out

🚗 **From I-5**, take exit 189 toward S Eugene west on E 30th Ave (left from I-5N, straight onto McVay Hwy then right from I-5S) about 3¼ miles to light at Hilyard St. Turn right onto Hilyard about ⅔ mile (park will be on left) to light at 24th Ave. Turn right onto 24th Ave to store.

GRANTS PASS_____

Farmer's Market 🛍️

603 Rogue River Hwy. ✆ 541-474-0252 ⏰ M-Sat 8:30-6:30, Sun 10-5
· organic produce

🚗 **From I-5**, take exit 55 (US 199/Redwood Hwy) toward Crescent City onto Grants Pass Pkwy about 1⅔ miles to Parkdale Dr. Turn left onto Parkdale about ¼ mile to Rogue River Hwy. Turn right onto Rogue River to store.

Sunshine Natural Food Market 🛍️ 🍴

128 S.W. H St. ✆ 541-474-5044 ⏰ M-F 9-6, Sat 9-5:30
Salad bar weekdays only.
· organic produce · vegetarian friendly · fresh juice · salad bar · tables · self-service
· take-out

🚗 **From I-5**, take exit 55 (US 199/Redwood Hwy) toward Crescent City. Take Redwood Hwy/199 Spur about 2 miles to NW 6th St. Turn left onto 6th to H St. Turn right onto H to store.

GRESHAM_____

Whole Foods Market 🛍️ 🍴   ♿

2077 N.E. Burnside Rd. ✆ 503-674-2827 ⏰ Daily 8-10
· organic produce, vegetarian friendly, salad bar, cafe, self-service, take-out

🚗 **From I-84**, take exit 16 toward Wood Village south on NE 238th Dr (left from I-84W, right from I-84E) over 3 miles (becomes NE 242nd Dr, NE 242nd Ave, NE Hogan Dr) to NE Burnside Rd. Turn left onto NE Burnside past first light to store.

HAPPY VALLEY

New Seasons/Happy Valley Town Center 🛍️ 🍴
15861 S.E. Happy Valley Town Center Drive ✆ 503-558-9214 ⏲ Daily 8-10
• organic produce • salad bar • deli • bakery • tables • self-service • take-out

🍎 **From I-205**, take exit 14 east on SE Sunnyside Rd (left at fork and left from I-205S, right from I-205N) about 3¼ miles to SE 157th Ave. Turn left onto SE 157th and right onto Happy Valley Town Ctr Dr to store on left.

HILLSBORO

New Seasons Market/Orenco Station 🛍️   ♿
1453 NE 61st Ave. ✆ 503-648-6968 ⏲ Daily 8-10
• organic produce • vegetarian friendly • salad bar • deli • bakery • take-out

🍎 **From Hwy 26**, take exit 64 south on NW 185th (left from 26W, right from 26E) about ½ mile to NW Cornell Rd. Turn right onto NW Cornell about 2½ miles to store at NE 61st Ave.

Whole Foods 🛍️ 🍴   ♿
19440 N.W. Cornell Rd. ✆ 503-645-9200 ⏲ Daily 9-10
• organic produce • vegetarian friendly • salad bar • cafe • self-service • take-out

🍎 **From Hwy 26**, take exit 64 south on NW 185th (left from 26W, right from 26E) about ½ mile to NW Cornell Rd. Turn right onto NW Cornell ½ mile to store on left.

HOOD RIVER

Mother's Marketplace 🛍️ 🍴
106 Hwy. 35 ✆ 541-387-2202 ⏲ M-Th, Sun 10-7, F 10-3
• organic produce • vegetarian • vegan friendly • organic focus • fresh juice • deli • counter • tables • self-service • take-out

🍎 From I-84, take exit 64 south on US 35 under ¼ mile to store on right.

KLAMATH FALLS

Night Fire Natural Foods 🛍️
919 Klamath Ave. ✆ 541-850-1100 ⏲ M-F 9-7, Sat 10-6
• organic produce • fresh juice

🍎 **From US 97**, turn right onto Main St and right onto Klamath Ave under 1 mile to store on left.

LA GRANDE

Nature's Pantry 🛍️
1907 4th St. ✆ 541-963-7955 ⏲ M-Th 9-6, F 9-5, Sun 12-4
• organic produce

🍎 **From I-84**, take exit 261 toward La Grande/Elgin left onto OR 82/Island Ave about 1 mile to Adams Ave. Turn right onto Adams ½ mile to 4th St. Turn left onto 4th to store on left.

LAKE OSWEGO

New Seasons Market/Mountain Park 🛍️ 🍴
3 SW Monroe Pkwy. ✆ 503-496-1155 ⏲ Daily 8-10
• organic produce • vegetarian friendly • salad bar • deli • bakery • tables • self-service • take-out

🍎 **From I-5S,** take exit 297 onto SW Barbur Blvd and turn right onto SW Terwilliger Blvd 1⅓ miles to SW Boones Ferry Rd. Veer right onto SW Boones Ferry 2 miles to SW Monroe Pkwy. Turn right onto SW Monroe to store on right. **From I-5N**, take exit 295 right at fork and right onto SW 35th Dr continuing onto SW 35th Ave and SW Walking Woods Dr under 2 miles total to SW McNary Pkwy. Turn left onto SW McNary ½ mile to SW Monroe. Turn left onto SW Monroe about ⅓ mile to store on left before Boones Ferry.

LINCOLN CITY

Aunt Mary's 🍴

1347 N.W. Hwy. 101 ✆ 541-996-2390 ⏰ M-Tues, Sun 12-6, W-Th 12-10, F-Sat 12-12
Vegan with cheese available. In addition to food they sell "adult" toys; you must be 18 to enter.
• vegetarian friendly • vegan • alcohol • counter • tables • wait staff
⬒ On southwest corner of Hwy 101 at 14th St.

Trillium Natural Foods 🛍

♿

1026 S.E. Jetty Ave. ✆ 541-994-5665 ⏰ M-Sat 9:30-7, Sun 11-6
• organic produce
⬒ **From Hwy 101 in Lincoln City**, go east on W Devils Lake Rd (right from 101N, left from 101S) 1 block to SE Jetty Ave. Turn right onto Jetty to store (across from factory outlet).

MANZANITA

Mother Nature's Natural Foods 🛍

298 Laneda Ave. ✆ 503-368-5316 ⏰ Daily 10-7
• organic produce
⬒ **From Hwy 101**, go west (toward the ocean) on 29th St (becomes Laneda Ave) about ⅓ mile to store on south side at 3rd St.

MCMINNVILLE

Harvest Fresh Grocery & Deli 🛍🍴

251 N.E. 3rd St. ✆ 503-472-5740 ⏰ M-F 8-8, Sat 8-7, Sun 10-7
• organic produce • vegetarian friendly • fresh juice • deli • counter • tables • self-service • take-out
⬒ **From OR 99W (Baker St in town)**, go east on NE 3rd St 1 block to store on north side.

MILWAUKIE

Bob's Red Mill Natural Foods Mill Outlet & Bakery 🍴

5000 S.E. International Way ✆ 503-654-3215 ⏰ M-F 6-6, Sat 7-5
Bob's Red Mill flours, hot cereals, beans and more along with coffee and baked goods.
• bakery • counter • tables • self-service
⬒ **From I-205,** take exit 13 for Milwaukie onto Hwy 224W about 2⅓ miles to SE Freeman Way. Turn right onto Freeman 1 block to International Way. Turn right onto International to first left onto Mallard Way. Take first driveway on left to store.

NEWPORT

Oceana Natural Foods Co-op 🛍🍴

♿

159 S.E. 2nd St. ✆ 541-265-3893 ⏰ M-F 8-7, Sat 8-6, Sun 10-6 Hot food/Salad bar M-F 10:30-6
Vegetarian except for tuna with many vegan choices.
• organic produce • vegetarian friendly • vegan friendly • organic focus • fresh juice • salad bar • cafe • deli • bakery • tables • self-service • take-out • co-op
⬒ **From Hwy 101 in Newport**, turn east onto Hwy 20 (right from 101N, left from 101S) 2 blocks to Benton St. Turn right onto Benton 2 blocks store at SE 2nd St.

NORTH BEND

Coos Head Food Store 🛍

1960 Sherman Ave. ✆ 541-756-7264 ⏰ M-F 9-7, Sat 10-6, Sun 12-5
• organic produce • co-op
⬒ In North Bend Hwy 101S is Sherman Ave. Store is 1 block south of library.

ONTARIO

Oregon Natural Market 🛍

373 S.W. 1st St. ✆ 541-889-8714 ⏰ M-Sat 9-6
• organic produce

🚗 **From I-84**, take exit 376A toward Ontario west on US 30/E Idaho Ave (right from I-84E, loop around right from I-84W) about ¾ mile to N Oregon St. Turn left onto N Oregon 3 blocks to SW 3rd Ave. Turn right onto SW 3rd 1 block to SW 1st St. Turn left onto SW 1st 1 block to store on right.

PORT ORFORD

Seaweed Natural Grocery & Cafe 🛍🍴

832 Hwy. 101 ✆ 541-332-3640 ⏰ M-Sat 11-5
• organic produce • vegetarian friendly • cafe • bakery • tables • self-service • take-out

🚗 On southern OR coast on Hwy 101 at mile post 301.

PORTLAND

Alberta Cooperative Grocery 🛍

1500 N.E. Alberta St. ✆ 503-287-4333 ⏰ Daily 9-10
• organic produce • co-op

🚗 **From I-5S**, take exit 304 for Rosa Parks Way left onto N Portland Blvd 1 mile to NE MLK Jr Blvd. Turn right onto NE MLK ½ mile to NE Killingsworth St. Turn left onto NE Killingsworth ½ mile to NE 15th Ave. Turn right onto NE 15th 3 blocks to store on right at NE Alberta St. **From I-5N**, take exit 303 for Killingsworth St onto N Missouri Ave and right onto NE Killingsworth about 1½ miles to NE 15th. Turn right onto NE 15th 3 blocks to store.

Bay Leaf 🍴

4768 S.E. Division St. ✆ 503-232-7058 ⏰ M-Sat 11-10, Sun 12-9:30
Predominantly vegan with a strong Asian influence.
• vegetarian • vegan friendly • tables • wait staff

🚗 **From I-205**, take exit 19 west on Division St (left from I-205N, right from I-205S) about 2⅓ miles to restaurant on left after SE 42nd Ave. **From I-84W**, take exit 9 onto I-205S and follow directions above. **From I-84E**, take exit 3 toward 58th Ave left onto NE Glisan St and turn right onto NE 60th Ave about 1½ miles (jog left after ½ mile at Stark to stay on 60th) to Division. Turn right onto Division about ½ mile to restaurant. **From I-5**, take exit 300 (300B from I-5S) onto MLK Blvd heading south about ½ mile to SE Mill St. Turn right onto SE Mill, left onto SE 3rd Ave and right onto SE Division 2½ miles to restaurant on right.

Blue Moose Cafe 🍴

4936 N.E. Fremont St. ✆ 503-548-4475 ⏰ M-F 11-8, Sat-Sun 9-8
• vegetarian • vegan friendly • alcohol • tables • wait staff

🚗 **From I-84E**, take exit 1 left onto NE 33rd Ave 1 mile to NE Fremont St. Turn right onto NE Fremont about 1 mile to restaurant on right between NE 49th & 50th Ave. **From I-84W**, merge onto I-205N. **From I-205**, take exit 23 (B from I-205N, A from I-205S) for US 30 toward Killingsworth St left at fork toward Sandy Blvd W and merge onto NE Sandy Blvd about 1¾ miles to NE Fremont. Veer right onto NE Fremont 1 mile to restaurant on left after NE 50th.

Bye and Bye 🍴

1011 N.E. Alberta St. ✆ 503-281-0537 ⏰ M-Th 4-9, F 2-9, Sat-Sun 12-9
Bar with all vegan menu. Food ends at 9 pm but bar goes late.
• vegan • alcohol • counter • tables • self-service

🚗 **From I-5S**, take exit 304 for Rosa Parks Way left onto N Portland Blvd 1 mile to NE MLK Jr Blvd. Turn right onto NE MLK ¾ mile to NE Alberta St. Turn left onto NE Alberta 6 blocks to restaurant after NE 10th Ave. **From I-5N**, take exit 303 for Killingsworth St onto N Missouri Ave and right onto NE Alberta about 1 mile to restaurant.

Cafe Diablo 🍴

2839 N.W. St. Helens Rd. ✆ 503-222-6600 ⊕ M-Sat 2pm-2:30am
Smoke-free, vegan club with exotic dancers and Mexican-style food.
  • vegan • alcohol • tables • wait staff

🚌 **From I-5S**, merge onto I-405S and take exit 3 (after crossing Fremont Bridge) onto US 30W 2 miles to NW 35th Ave. Turn left onto NW 35th over ½ mile to end at NW St Helens Rd. Turn right onto NW St Helens under ¼ mile to restaurant on left. **From I-5N**, merge onto I-405N to exit 3 on left onto US 30W and following directions above.

Caffe Destino 🍴

1339 N.E. Fremont St. ✆ 503-284-9455 ⊕ M-F 6:30-3, Sat-Sun 7-3
Breakfast, sandwiches, soups, salads.
  • vegetarian • vegan friendly • alcohol • counter • tables • self-service

🚌 **From I-5S**, take exit 304 left onto N Portland Blvd 1 mile to NE MLK Jr Blvd. Turn right onto MLK 1½ miles to NE Fremont St. Turn left onto Freemont ½ mile to restaurant between NE 13th &14th Ave. **From I-5N**, take exit 303 for Killingsworth St right onto NE Alberta St ½ mile to N Vancouver Ave. Turn right onto Vancouver ¾ mile to Fremont. Turn left onto Freemont over ¾ mile to restaurant.

Chaos Cafe 🍴 ♿

2026 Powell St. ✆ 503-546-8112 ⊕ M-Sat 9-9, Sun 9-8
Casual dining in a music/art space.
  • vegetarian • vegan friendly • fresh juice • alcohol • tables • wait staff

🚌 **From I-5**, take exit 299A onto US 26E (left onto SW Hood Ave, right onto SW Whitaker St, right onto SW Kelly Ave and right from I-5N, merge onto SW Hood, right onto SW Gaines St, right onto SW Kelly and right from I-5S) across Ross Island Bridge about 1½ miles to restaurant on right after SE 20th Ave.

Dreamers Cafe Food Cart 🍴

S.W. 5th Ave. (near S.W. Oak & S.W. Stark St.) ⊕ M-F 11-2:30
Vegetarian street cart.
  • vegetarian • take-out

🚌 **From I-5N**, merge onto I-405N to exit 2A for Salmon St. Turn right onto SW Salmon 3 blocks to SW 10th Ave. Turn left onto SW 10th 6 blocks to SW Stark St. Turn right onto SW Stark 5 blocks to SW 5th Ave. Turn left onto SW 5th to cart. **From I-5S,** take exit 300B and follow signs across Morrison Bridge onto SW Washington St under ½ mile to SW 4th Ave. Turn right onto SW 4th 1 block to Oak St. Turn left onto Oak 1 block to SW 5th. Turn left onto SW 5th to cart.

Earthbound Vegan Cuisine 🍴

S.E. 41st St. & Hawthorne Blvd. ✆ 503-221-4598 ⊕ Tues-F 11-6, Sat-Sun 12-6
Vegan street cart with soups, salads, sandwiches and Thai brown rice bowls.
  • vegan • take-out

🚌 **From I-5S**, take exit 300B toward Oregon City onto SE Belmont St under ½ mile to SE 11th Ave. Turn right onto SE 11th 5 blocks to SE Hawthorne Blvd. Turn left onto SE Hawthorne 1¾ miles to cart at 41st Ave. **From I-5N**, take exit 300 for I-84 E right at fork onto SE Yamhill St, right onto SE Water St, right onto SE Hawthorne, left onto SE Madison and sharp right onto SE Hawthorne 2⅓ miles to cart at 41st.

Food Front Co-op 🛍

2375 N.W. Thurman St. ✆ 503-222-5658 ⊕ Daily 8-9
  • vegetarian friendly • deli • take-out • co-op

🚌 **From I-405**, take exit 3 onto Rt 30W to Vaughn St exit. Turn left onto NW 23rd Ave 1 block to store on right at NW Thurman St.

Garden Cafe 🍴   ♿

10123 S.E. Market St. ✆ 503-251-6125 ⏰ M-F 6:30-6:30
Vegetarian cafe in the Seventh-day Adventist Medical Center.
  • vegetarian • vegan friendly • tables • self-service
🍎 **From I-205**, take exit 19 east on SE Division St (left from I-205S, right from I-205N) about ⅓ mile to SE 101st Ave. Turn left onto 101st ½ mile to SE Market St. Turn right onto Market to restaurant on ground floor in Adventist Medical Ctr.

India Chaat House 🍴

804 S.W. 12th Ave. ✆ 503-241-7944 ⏰ M-F 11-7, Sat 11-4
Street cart with an attached seating area selling vegetarian Indian food.
  • vegetarian • vegan friendly • tables • self-service • take-out
🍎 **From I-405S**, take exit 2A for Couch St toward Burnside Ave onto NW 15th Ave 1 block to SW Adler Ave. Turn left onto SW Adler 4 blocks to SW 11th Ave. Turn right onto SW 11th 3 blocks to SW Taylor St. Turn right onto SW Taylor 1 block to SW 12th Ave. Turn right onto SW 12th 1 block to cart at Yamhill St. **From I-405N**, take exit 2A right onto SW Salmon St 2 blocks to SW 12th. Turn left onto SW 12th 2 blocks to cart.

Laughing Planet Cafe 🍴   ♿

3320 S.E. Belmont St. ✆ 503-235-6472 ⏰ M-Sat 11-10, Sun 11-9
See Eugene location for description.
  • vegetarian friendly • vegan friendly • fresh juice • alcohol • tables • self-service
🍎 **From I-84**, take exit 2 to 39th Ave (straight from I-84E, left onto Halsey St from I-84W). Go south on 39th (right from I-84E, left from I-84W) about 1¼ miles (through first roundabout) to Belmont St. Turn right onto Belmont 5 blocks to restaurant at 33rd Ave. **From I-5N**, take exit 300 onto SE Yamhill St to 3rd Ave. Turn left onto 3rd 1 block to Belmont. Turn right onto Belmont 1½ miles to restaurant. **From I-5S**, take exit 300B and take ramp toward OR City left at fork onto SE Belmont St about 1½ miles to restaurant. **From downtown Portland**, go across Morrison Bridge onto Belmont about 2 miles to restaurant.

Laughing Planet Cafe 🍴

3765 N. Mississippi Ave. ✆ 503-467-4146 ⏰ M-Th, Sun 11-9, F-Sat 11-10
See Eugene location for description.
  • vegetarian friendly • vegan friendly • fresh juice • alcohol • tables • self-service
🍎 **From I-5N**, take exit 303 left at fork (signs for Interstate) onto N Going St across hwy to N Maryland Ave. Turn left onto N Maryland 2 blocks to N Skidmore St. Turn right onto N Skidmore ⅓ mile (back across hwy) to N Mississippi Ave. Turn right onto N Mississippi ⅓ mile to restaurant on right after N Failing St. **From I-5S**, take exit 302A right at fork (signs for City Center) onto N Broadway St to N Flint Ave. Turn right onto N Flint under ½ mile to N Russell St. Turn left onto N Russell continuing onto N Kerby Ave 1 block to N Graham St. Turn left onto N Graham about ¼ mile to N Mississippi. Turn right onto N Mississippi ½ mile to restaurant on left after N Beech St.

Laughing Planet Cafe 🍴

922 N.W. 21st Ave. ✆ 503-445-1319 ⏰ M-Sat 11-10, Sun 11-9
See Eugene location for description.
  • vegetarian friendly • vegan friendly • fresh juice • alcohol • tables • self-service
🍎 **From I-405S**, take exit 3 onto US 30W under ½ mile to NW Vaughn St exit. Make sharp left onto NW Vaughn about ¼ mile to NW 21st Ave. Turn right onto NW 21st ½ mile to restaurant on left after NW Lovejoy St. **From I-405N**, take exit 2B onto NW 14th Ave under ½ mile to NW Lovejoy. Turn left onto NW Lovejoy under ½ mile to NW 21st. Turn left onto NW 21st to restaurant.

Laughing Planet Cafe 🍴

4110 S.E. Woodstock Blvd. ✆ 503-788-2921 ⏰ M-W, Sun 11-9, Th-Sat 11-10
See Eugene location for description.
  • vegetarian friendly • vegan friendly • fresh juice • alcohol • tables • self-service

From **I-205S**, take exit 17 onto S Foster Rd about 1 mile to SE 82nd Ave. Turn left onto SE 82nd about ¼ mile to SE Woodstock Ave. Turn right onto SE Woodstock 2 miles to restaurant on left after SE 42nd Ave. **From I-205N**, take exit 16 left onto Johnson Creek Blvd under ½ mile to SE 82nd. Turn right onto SE 82nd about 1½ miles to SE Woodstock Ave. Turn left onto SE Woodstock 2 miles to restaurant.

Lion's Den Cafe

S.W. 9th Ave. & Adler St. ✆ 503-314-9606 ⊕ M-F 10-4
Vegan food cart with a loosely African theme.
  • vegan • tables • self-service • take-out

From **I-405S**, take exit 2A for Couch St toward Burnside Ave onto SW 15th Ave to SW Adler St. Turn left onto SW Adler 6 blocks to cart at SW Adler & SW 9th Ave. **From I-405N**, take exit 2A toward Salmon St left at fork onto SW 14th Ave to SW Adler. Turn right onto SW Adler 5 blocks to cart.

Los Gorditos

S.E. 50th Ave & S.E. Division St. ✆ 503-875-2615 ⊕ Winter M-Sat 11-8 Summer M-Sat 11-10:30
Vegan tacos from a truck with patio seating.
  • vegan • tables • take-out

From **I-205N**, take exit 19 left onto SE Powell Blvd ¾ mile to SE 82nd Ave. Turn right onto SE 82nd ½ mile to SE Division St. Turn left onto SE Division 1½ miles to truck at SE Division & SE 50th Ave. **From I-205 S**, take exit 19 right onto SE Division 2¼ miles to truck at SE 50th.

New Seasons Market/Arbor Lodge

6400 N. Interstate Ave. ✆ 503-467-4777 ⊕ Daily 8-10
  • organic produce • vegetarian friendly • salad bar • deli • bakery • tables • self-service
  • take-out

From **I-5**, take exit 304 west on N Rosa Parks Way (right from I-5S, left from I-5N) a few blocks to N Maryland Ave. Turn left onto N Maryland 1 block to N Holman St. Turn right onto N Holman 1 block to N Interstate Ave. Turn right onto N Interstate to store on right.

New Seasons Market/Concordia

5320 N.E. 33rd Ave. ✆ 503-288-3838 ⊕ Daily 8-10
  • organic produce • vegetarian friendly • salad bar • deli • bakery • tables • self-service
  • take-out

From **I-84E**, take exit 1 left onto 33rd Ave about 2 miles to store. **From I-84W**, merge onto I-205N via exit 9. **From I-205**, take exit 23 (B from 205N, A from 205S) west on US 30 Bypass about 3⅓ miles to 33rd Ave. Turn left onto NE 33rd about ¾ miles to store.

New Seasons Market/Raleigh Hills

7300 S.W. Beaverton Hillsdale Hwy. ✆ 503-230-4949 ⊕ Daily 8-10
  • organic produce • vegetarian friendly • salad bar • deli • bakery • tables • self-service
  • take-out

From **Hwy 26W (I-405 exit 1D)**, take exit 71B (Sylvan) left onto Skyline Blvd (becomes SW Scholls Ferry Rd) about 2 miles to Beaverton Hillsdale Hwy. Veer right onto Beaverton Hillsdale Hwy to store.

New Seasons Market/Sellwood

1214 S.E. Tacoma St. ✆ 503-230-4949 ⊕ Daily 8-10
  • organic produce • vegetarian friendly • salad bar • deli • bakery • tables • self-service
  • take-out

From **I-5N**, take exit 297 right onto SW Terwilliger Blvd about ½ mile to SW Taylors Ferry Rd. Turn left onto Taylors Ferry 1 mile to Macadam Ave. Turn right onto Macadam ½ mile to Sellwood Bridge. Turn left onto Sellwood Bridge (becomes SE Tacoma St) to store ⅓ mile past bridge. **From I-5S,** take exit 299A toward Lake Oswego right onto on SW Hood Ave (becomes Macadam) about 2 miles to Sellwood Bridge and follow directions above.

New Seasons Market/Seven Corners 🛒 🍴
1954 S.E. Division St. ✆ 503-445-2888 ⊕ Daily 8-10
• organic produce • vegetarian friendly • salad bar • deli • bakery • tables • self-service • take-out

🚽 **From I-5S,** take exit 300B onto SE Belmont Ave and take ramp onto SE MLK Jr Blvd ½ mile to SE Mill St. Turn right onto SE Mill 1 block and turn left onto SE 3rd Ave continuing onto SE Division St 1 mile to store on right after SE 18th Ave. **From I-5N,** take exit 300 right at fork and merge onto SE Yamhill Ave ⅓ mile to SE MLK. Turn right onto SE MLK and follow directions above.

Nhut Quang 🍴
3438 N.E. 82nd Ave. ✆ 503-775-7900 ⊕ Tues-Sun 10-8
Inexpensive vegan Thai in a spartan atmosphere.
• vegan • tables • wait staff • take-out

🚽 **From I-84E,** take exit 5 toward 82nd Ave/Hwy 213 right onto NE Multnomah St and right onto NE 82nd 1 mile to restaurant on right between NE Klickitat & NE Fremont St. **From I-84W,** merge onto I-205N. **From I-205,** take exit 23 (B from I-205N, A from I-205S) for US 30 toward Killingsworth St left at fork toward Sandy Blvd W and merge onto NE Sandy Blvd about 1 mile to NE 82nd. Turn left onto NE 82nd about ⅓ mile to restaurant on left after NE Fremont.

Old Wives' Tales 🍴   ♿
1300 E. Burnside St. ✆ 503-238-0470 ⊕ M-Th, Sun 8am-9pm, F-Sat 8am-10pm
Extensive breakfast menu, many vegan choices and very kid friendly.
• vegetarian • vegan friendly • alcohol • tables • wait staff

🚽 **From I-5N,** follow exit 300 to Water St. Turn right onto Water 1 block to SE Taylor St. Turn right onto Taylor about ¼ mile to SE Grand Ave. Turn left onto Grand ½ mile to E Burnside St. Turn right onto Burnside about ⅓ mile to restaurant between 12th & 14th Ave. **From I-5S,** take exit 300B and take ramp toward OR City left at fork onto S Belmont Ave to SE Grand. Turn left onto Grand under ½ mile to E Burnside. Turn right onto Burnside about ⅓ mile to restaurant. **From I-84W,** take exit 1 and follow ramp toward Grand Ave left onto 12th Ave almost ½ mile to Burnside. Turn left onto Burnside to restaurant.

Papa G's Vegan Organic Deli 🍴
2314 S.E. Division St. ✆ 503-235-0244 ⊕ Daily 10-10
• vegan • organic focus • tables • self-service • take-out

🚽 **From I-205,** take exit 19 west on Division St (left from I-205N, right from I-205S) about 3¾ miles to restaurant on right after SE 24th Ave. **From I-84W,** take exit 9 onto I-205S and follow directions above. **From I-84E,** take exit 2 right onto NE 39th Ave almost 2 miles to Division. Turn right onto Division about 1 mile to restaurant on left. **From I-5,** take exit 300 (300B from I-5S) onto MLK Blvd south about ½ mile to SE Mill St. Turn right onto SE Mill, left onto SE 3rd Ave and right onto SE about 1 mile to restaurant.

Paradox Cafe 🍴
3439 S.E. Belmont St. ✆ 503-232-7508 ⊕ M-W 8-9, Th-Sat 8-9:30, Sun 8-3
Vegetarian except for a beef burger and chicken sausage.
• vegetarian friendly • vegan friendly • organic focus • alcohol • tables • wait staff

🚽 **From I-84,** take exit 2 to 39th Ave (straight from I-84E, left onto Halsey St from I-84W). Go south on 39th (right from I-84E, left from I-84W) about 1¼ miles (through first roundabout) to Belmont St. Turn right onto Belmont 3 blocks to restaurant between 35th & 34th Ave. **From I-5N,** take exit 300 onto SE Yamhill St to 3rd Ave. Turn left onto 3rd 1 block to Belmont. Turn right onto Belmont 1½ miles to restaurant between 34th & 35th Ave. **From I-5S,** take exit 300B and take ramp toward OR City left at fork onto SE Belmont St about 1½ miles to restaurant. **From downtown Portland,** go across Morrison Bridge onto Belmont about 2 miles to restaurant.

People's Food Co-op 🛍

3029 S.E. 21st Ave. ✆ 503-232-9051 ◔ Daily 8-10
On Wednesday the co-op hosts a farmers' market.
  • organic produce, co-op

🍽 **From I-5**, take exit 299A (OR 43/Macadam Ave) toward US 26E/Ross Island Bridge onto SW Hood Ave (veer right from I-5N, straight ahead from I-5S) 2 blocks to Whittaker St. Turn right onto Whittaker, left onto Kelly Ave and veer left onto ramp toward US 26E/Ross Island Bridge. Turn right onto US 26 about 1½ miles (across bridge) to SE 21st Ave. Turn left onto SE 21st 1 block to store at SE Tibbets St.

Proper Eats 🛍 🍴

8638 N. Lombard St. ✆ 503-445-2007 ◔ M-Th 8-10, F-Sat 8-12, Sun 8-8
Largely vegan with raw food options. Live music.
  • organic produce • vegetarian • vegan friendly • alcohol • deli • cafe • tables • wait staff • take-out

🍽 **From I-5S**, take exit 305 toward Interstate Ave left onto OR 99W/N Denver Ave about 1½ miles to N Lombard St. Turn left onto NE Lombard 3¾ miles to store on left after N Philadelphia Ave. **From I-5N**, take exit 305B onto N Lombard 4¼ miles to store.

Red and Black Cafe 🍴

400 S.E. 12th Ave. ✆ 503-231-3899 ◔ M-F 7:30am-11 pm, Sat-Sun 8am-11pm
Worker owned vegan cafe with live music and community events.
  • vegan • organic focus • tables • self-service

🍽 **From I-5**, take exit 300 (300B from I-5S) east on SE Belmont St (merge left from I-5S, right at fork onto SE Yamhill St, left onto SE 3rd Ave and right onto SE Belmont from I-5N) about ½ mile to SE 12th Ave. Turn left onto SE 12th about 5 blocks to restaurant on right at SE Oak St.

Sweet Lemon Vegetarian Bistro 🍴

4888 N.W. Bethany Blvd., K6 ✆ 503-617-1419 ◔ M-F 11-8, Sat 12-8
Run by followers of Supreme Master Ching Hai.
  • vegetarian • vegan friendly • organic focus • tables • self-service

🍽 **From US 26**, take exit 65 north on NW Bethany Blvd (right from US 26W, left from US 26E) 2 miles to restaurant on right in Bethany Village.

Sweet Pea Baking 🍴

1205 S.E. Stark St. ✆ 503-477-5916 ◔ M-F 7-8, Sat-Sun 9-8
Vegan baked goods, light breakfast and lunch.
  • vegan • tables • self-service

🍽 **From I-5,** take exit 300 (300B from I-5S) east on SE Belmont St (merge left from I-5S, right at fork onto SE Yamhill St, left onto SE 3rd Ave and right onto SE Belmont from I-5N) about ½ mile to SE 12th Ave. Turn left onto SE 12th about 4 blocks to SE Stark St. Turn right onto SE Stark to restaurant on left.

The Blossoming Lotus Cafe 🍴

925 N.W. Davis St. ✆ 503-228-0048 ◔ M-Th 8-9, F-Sat 8-10
World fusion cuisine with vegan and live foods. Breakfast to candlelight dinner.
  • vegan • organic focus • fresh juice • alcohol • tables • self-service • wait staff

🍽 **From I-405N**, take exit 2B toward Everett St onto NW 14th Ave. Turn right onto Everett 3 blocks to NW 11th Ave. Turn right onto NW 11th 1 block. Turn left onto NW Davis to restaurant on left inside Yoga Pearl. **From I-405S**, take exit 2A for Couch St onto Burnside St. Turn left onto NW Couch, left onto NW 14th and right onto NW Davis 4 blocks to restaurant.

*Please tell these businesses
that you found them in Healthy Highways*

The Farm ⑪

10 SE 7th Ave. ℰ 503-736-FARM ⏱ Daily 5-11:30
Vgetarian, vegan and local fish.
  • vegetarian friendly • vegan friendly • alcohol • tables • wait staff

🚌 **From I-5S**, take exit 300B toward Oregon City onto SE Belmont about ¼ mile to SE Grand Ave. Turn left onto SE Grand under ½ mile to SE Ankenny St. Turn right onto SE Ankenny 2 blocks to SE 7th Ave. Turn left onto SE 7th 1 block to restaurant on right at E Burnside Ave (in a restored Victorian home). **From I-5N**, keep right at fork onto SE Yamhill St, right onto SE 3rd Ave, right onto SE Taylor St and left onto SE Grand ½ mile to SE Ankenny. Turn right onto SE Ankenny and follow directions above. **From I-84W**, take exit 1 left onto NE Lloyd Blvd and left onto NE 12th Ave about 6 blocks to E Burnside. Turn left onto E Burnside 5 blocks to SE 7th. Turn left onto SE 7th to restaurant on left.

The SuperBowl ⑪

4409 S.E. Hawthorne ℰ 503-757-2695 ⏱ M-Sat 11:30-7
Cart selling a beans/brown rice/avocado/cheese bowl in a special Tali Sauce.
  • vegetarian • take-out

🚌 **From I-5S**, take exit 300B toward Oregon City onto SE Belmont St under ½ mile to SE 11th Ave. Turn right onto SE 11th 5 blocks to SE Hawthorne Blvd. Turn left onto SE Hawthorne about 1¾ miles to cart between 44th & 45th Ave. **From I-5N**, take exit 300 for I-84E right at fork onto SE Yamhill St, right onto SE Water St, right onto SE Hawthorne, left onto SE Madison and sharp right to go east on SE Hawthorne 2½ miles to cart.

The Whole Bowl Cart ⑪

100 N.W. Glisan St. ℰ 503-757-2695 ⏱ Tues-F 11ish-2:30ish
See The SuperBowl for description.
  • vegetarian • take-out

🚌 **From I-405S**, take exit 2B toward Everett St onto NW 16th Ave and make first right onto NW Everett ⅓ mile (across hwy) to NW 10th Ave. Turn left onto NW 10th 2 blocks to NW Glisan. Turn left onto NW Glisan past NW 11th to cart. **From I-405N**, take exit 2B toward Everett onto NW 14th Ave under ¼ mile to NW Hoyt St. Turn right onto NW Hoyt 3 blocks to NW 11th Ave. Turn right onto NW 11th 1 block to NW Glisan. Turn right onto NW Glisan to cart.

The Whole Bowl Cart ⑪

S.W. 9th Ave. & Adler St. ℰ 503-757-2695 ⏱ M-F 11-3
See The SuperBowl for description.
  • vegetarian • take-out

🚌 **From I-405S**, take exit 2A for Couch St toward Burnside Ave onto SW 15th Ave to SW Adler St. Turn left onto SW Adler 6 blocks to cart at SW 9th Ave. **From I-405N**, take exit 2A toward Salmon St left at fork onto SW 14th Ave to SW Adler. Turn right onto SW Adler 5 blocks to cart.

Van Hahn Vegetarian Restaurant ⑪

8446 S.E. Division St. ℰ 503-788-0825 ⏱ M, W-Sun 10-9
Vietnamese food, run by Buddhist nuns. Profits support nearby temple.
  • vegan • tables • wait staff

🚌 **From I-205N**, take exit 19 left onto SE Powell Blvd to first right onto SE 92nd Ave ½ mile to SE Division St. Turn left onto SE Division about ⅓ mile to restaurant on left after SE 85th Ave. **From I-205 S**, take exit 19 right onto SE Division ½ mile to restaurant.

Vege Thai ⑪

3272 S.E. Hawthorne Blvd. ℰ 503-234-2171 ⏱ M-F 11:30-3, 5-9, Sat-Sun 12-9
Mostly vegan Thai. Brown rice available.
  • vegetarian • vegan friendly • tables • wait staff

🚌 **From I-5S**, take exit 300B toward Ocean City onto SE Belmont St under ½ mile to SE 11th Ave. Turn right onto SE 11th 5 blocks to SE Hawthorne Blvd. Turn left onto SE Hawthorne over 1 mile to restaurant on right between SE 32nd & 33rd

Ave. **From I-5N**, take exit 300 right at fork onto SE Yamhill St and right onto SE Water St 5 blocks to SE Hawthorne. Turn right onto SE Hawthorne, left onto SE Madison St and sharp left back onto SE Hawthorne almost 2 miles to restaurant.

Vegetarian House 🍴
22 N.W. 4th Ave. ✆ 503-274-0160 ⏱ Daily 11-9
Chinese vegetarian. Weekday lunch buffet option.
• vegetarian • vegan friendly • tables • self-service • wait staff
🍴 **From I-405N**, take exit 2A toward Salmon St and follow signs to merge onto SW 14th Ave to SW Adler St. Turn right onto SW Adler ½ mile to SW 4th Ave. Turn right onto SW 4th ⅓ mile to restaurant on right at Couch St. **From I-104N,** take exit 2A toward Burnside St and merge onto SW 15th Ave to SW Adler. Turn left onto SW Adler and follow directions above.

Vita Cafe 🍴   ♿
3024 N.E. Alberta St. ✆ 503-335-8233 ⏱ M-F 9-10, Sat-Sun 8-10
Mostly vegetarian/vegan menu has four sections: Italian, Asian, Mexican and American (with meatless versions of traditional comfort food).
• vegetarian friendly • vegan friendly • organic focus • alcohol • tables • wait staff
🍴 **From I-84E**, take exit 1 left onto 33rd Ave about 1¾ miles to NE Alberta St. Turn left onto Alberta about 5 blocks to restaurant (before 30th Ave). **From I-84W**, merge onto I-205N via exit 9. **From I-205**, take exit 23 (B from I-205N, A from I-205S) west on US 30 Bypass about 3⅓ miles to 33rd Ave. Turn left onto NE 33rd under 1 mile to Alberta. Turn right onto Alberta about 4 blocks to restaurant.

Whole Foods Market 🛍 🍴   ♿
2825 E. Burnside St. ✆ 503-232-6601 ⏱ Daily 8-10
• organic produce • vegetarian friendly • salad bar • cafe • self-service • take-out
🍴 **From I-84**, take exit 2 to 39th Ave (straight from I-84E, left onto Halsey St from I-84W). Go south on 39th (right from I-84E, left from I-84W) about ¾ mile (through first roundabout) to E Burnside St. Turn right onto Burnside about ⅔ mile to store at 28th Ave. **From I-5N**, follow exit 300 to Water St. Turn right onto Water 1 block to SE Taylor St. Turn right onto Taylor about ¼ mile to SE Grand Ave. Turn left onto Grand ½ mile to E Burnside. Turn right onto Burnside about 1 mile to store. **From downtown Portland**, go across Burnside Bridge onto E Burnside about 1¼ miles to store.

Whole Foods Market 🛍 🍴   ♿
3535 N.E.15th Ave. ✆ 503-288-3414 ⏱ Daily 8-10
• organic produce • vegetarian friendly • salad bar • cafe • self-service • take-out
🍴 **From I-405,** turn left onto N Cook St ¼ mile to NE Rodney Ave. Turn left onto Rodney 2 blocks to NE Fremont St. Turn right onto NE Fremont about ⅔ mile to store at NE 15th Ave. **From I-5N**, take exit 302A toward Rose Quarter/Broadway right onto NE Weidler St about ¾ mile to NE 15th Ave. Turn left onto 15th about 1 mile to store at NE Fremont. **From I-5S**, take exit 302B left onto N Fremont under 1½ miles to store at 15th Ave.

Whole Foods Market 🛍 🍴   ♿
1210 N.W. Couch St. ✆ 503-525-4343 ⏱ Daily 8-10
• organic produce • vegetarian friendly • salad bar • cafe • self-service • take-out
🍴 **From I-405S**, take exit 2A toward Burnside St left onto NW Couch St 3 blocks to store at NW 12th Ave. **From I-405N**, take exit 2B toward Everett St left onto NW 14th Ave, right onto NW Everett and right onto NW 13th Ave 2 blocks to NW Couch. Turn left onto Couch 1 block to store.

REDMOND

Cornucopia Natural Foods 🛍
111 N.W. 6th St. ✆ 541-548-5911 ⏱ M-F 9-6, Sat 10-6
• vegetarian friendly • deli • take-out
🍴 US 97 and OR 126 intersect in Redmond. Store is on US 97 (aka NW 6th Ave) north of 126 at Antler Ave.

ROSEBURG

New Day Quality Grocery 🛍️

210 S.E. Jackson St. © 541-672-0275 ⏱ M-F 9:30-6:30, Sat 9:30-5
• organic produce • co-op

🏠 **From I-5**, take exit 124 toward City Center onto OR-138E ½ mile to SE Stephens St. Turn right onto SE Stephens ⅓ mile to NE Diamond Lake Blvd. Turn right onto NE Diamond Lake 1 block to SE Jackson St. Turn right onto SE Jackson to store on right.

SALEM

Life Source Natural Foods 🛍️ 🍴

2649 Commercial St. S.E. © 503-361-7973 ⏱ M-Sat 8-9, Sun 9-8
• organic produce • vegetarian • vegan friendly • salad bar • deli • tables • self-service • take-out

🏠 **From I-5S**, take exit 260A onto OR 99E Bus S (Salem Pkwy, becomes Commercial St NE) 5 miles to Commercial St SE. Turn right onto Commercial SE over 1½ miles to store at Culver Ln. **From I-5N**, take exit 249 and take ramp toward Salem right onto Commercial about 4 miles to store.

Marco Polo Global Restaurant 🍴

300 Liberty St. S.E. © 503-364-4833 ⏱ M-Th 11-2, 4-9, F 11-2, 4-10, Sat 12-10, Sun 11-8
Four menus: vegetarian (with over 80 options), Chinese, European and gluten-free.
• vegetarian friendly • vegan friendly • organic focus • alcohol • counter • tables • wait staff

🏠 **From I-5**, take exit 253 toward Detroit Lake/Bend west on Mission St SE (right from I-5S, left from I-5N) almost 3 miles to Liberty St SE. Turn right onto Liberty about ½ mile to restaurant in Pringle Park Plaza.

SEASIDE

Seaside Heath Foods 🛍️

144 N. Roosevelt Drive © 503-738-3088 ⏱ M-F 9:30-5:30, Sat 9:30-5
🏠 Store is on Hwy 101 on west side between 1st & 2nd Ave.

SPRINGFIELD

Cafe Yumm! 🍴

3346 Gateway Rd. © 541-747-9866 ⏱ M-Sat 8-9, Sun 10-6
See Bend location for description.
• vegetarian friendly • vegan friendly • alcohol • tables • self-service

🏠 **From I-5**, take exit 195A for Belt Line Hwy E right onto Gateway St about ½ mile to restaurant on left.

TIGARD

Whole Foods Market 🛍️ 🍴

7380 S.W. Bridgeport Rd. © 503-639-6500 ⏱ Daily 8-10
• organic produce • vegetarian friendly • salad bar • cafe • self-service • take-out

🏠 **From I-5**, take exit 290 toward Durham onto Bridgeport Rd (right from I-5S, left from I-5N) about ⅓ mile to store on left.

WALDPORT

Natural Selection 🛍️

185 N.W. Hwy. 101 © 541-563-6101 ⏱ M-Sat 9-6, Sun 12-5
🏠 Store is on SE corner at intersection of Hwy 101 & 34 (2 blocks south of Alsea Bay Bridge).

<u>STANDARD SERVING SIZES</u>

BREADS/CEREALS/GRAINS
(6-11 servings daily)

1 serving =	1-ounce slice bread (*CD case*)
"	1 tortilla or 3-inch pancake (*compact disc*)
"	½ small muffin, English muffin or bagel
"	½ cup cooked cereal, rice, pasta (*cupcake liner*)
2 servings =	1 cup pasta (*half grapefruit*)

MEAT AND NONMEAT PROTEINS
(2-3 servings daily)

1 serving =	2 to 3 ounces meat, poultry (*cassette tape*)
"	2 to 3 ounces fish (*checkbook*)
"	1 cup cooked beans (*baseball*)
"	4 to 6 ounces tofu (*deck of cards*)
"	2 eggs
"	¼ cup roasted soybeans/soynuts (*2 ping pong balls*)
"	½ cup nuts or seeds (*modest handfull*)
"	4 tablespoons nut butter(*2 ice cubes*)

MILK AND DAIRY PRODUCTS
(2-3 servings daily; 4 servings ages 9-18 or over 51)

1 serving =	1 cup milk or yogurt
"	1½ ounces hard cheese, chunk (*3 dominoes*)
"	1½ ounces hard cheese, slice (*computer disc*)

VEGETABLES
(2-5 servings daily, but more vegetables is always better)

1 serving =	1 cup raw leafy greens (*man's fist*)
"	½ cup vegetables, cooked or raw (*light bulb*)
"	1 medium potato (*computer mouse*)
"	¾ cup vegetable juice

FRUIT
(2-4 servings daily)

1 serving =	1 medium fruit (*tennis ball*)
"	½ cup cut-up fruit (*7 cotton balls*)
"	¼ cup dried fruit (*small egg*)
"	¾ cup fruit juice

PENNSYLVANIA

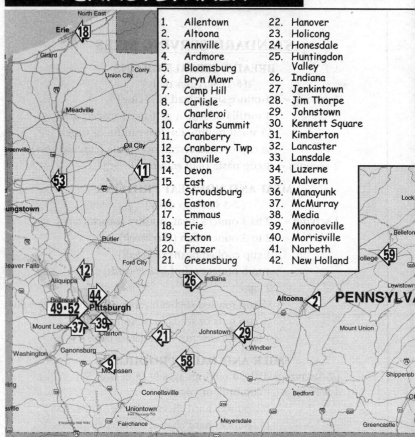

1. Allentown
2. Altoona
3. Annville
4. Ardmore
5. Bloomsburg
6. Bryn Mawr
7. Camp Hill
8. Carlisle
9. Charleroi
10. Clarks Summit
11. Cranberry
12. Cranberry Twp
13. Danville
14. Devon
15. East Stroudsburg
16. Easton
17. Emmaus
18. Erie
19. Exton
20. Frazer
21. Greensburg
22. Hanover
23. Holicong
24. Honesdale
25. Huntingdon Valley
26. Indiana
27. Jenkintown
28. Jim Thorpe
29. Johnstown
30. Kennett Square
31. Kimberton
32. Lancaster
33. Lansdale
34. Luzerne
35. Malvern
36. Manayunk
37. McMurray
38. Media
39. Monroeville
40. Morrisville
41. Narbeth
42. New Holland

ALLENTOWN

Garden Gate Natural Foods 📇

17 S. 9th St. ✆ 610-433-8891 🕐 M-F 9-6:30, Sat 10-4:45, Sun 11-5
• organic produce • vegetarian friendly • deli • take-out

📖 **From Rt 22**, merge onto PA 145S toward 7th St (right from 22E, left from 22W) about 1¾ miles to Linden St. Turn right onto Linden 2 lights to N 9th St. Turn left onto 9th 1½ blocks to store on right.

Sign of the Bear Natural Foods 📇

514 N. Saint Cloud St. ✆ 610-439-8575 🕐 M-F 9:30-6, Sat 9:30-4
• organic produce • vegetarian friendly • deli • take-out

📖 **From Rt 22**, take 15th St exit toward Allentown onto Mauch Chunk Rd (right from 22E, left from 22W) to 15th. Bear right onto 15th ¾ mile to Tilghman St. Turn right onto Tilghman about ¼ mile to Saint Cloud St. Turn left onto Saint Cloud to store.

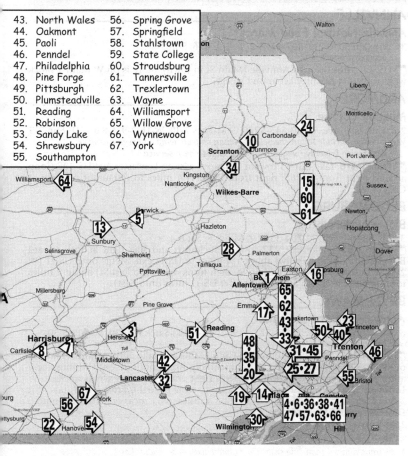

43. North Wales	56. Spring Grove
44. Oakmont	57. Springfield
45. Paoli	58. Stahlstown
46. Penndel	59. State College
47. Philadelphia	60. Stroudsburg
48. Pine Forge	61. Tannersville
49. Pittsburgh	62. Trexlertown
50. Plumsteadville	63. Wayne
51. Reading	64. Williamsport
52. Robinson	65. Willow Grove
53. Sandy Lake	66. Wynnewood
54. Shrewsbury	67. York
55. Southampton	

Syb's West End Deli 🍴

2151 Liberty St. ☎ 610-434-3882 ⏰ Tues-F 8-3, Sat 8-2, Sun 8-1
· vegetarian friendly · tables · wait staff · take-out

🚗 **From Rt 22E,** take PA 309S towards Quakertown 1 mile to Tilghman St E ramp. Merge onto W Tilghman 2⅔ mile to St Lucas St. Turn right onto St Lucas under ¼ mile to Liberty St. Turn right onto Liberty past first block to restaurant (before 22nd St). **From Rt 22W,** take 15th St exit toward Scherersville/Ballietsville onto Mauch Chunk Rd to Stanley St. Turn left onto Stanley 4 blocks to 19th St. Turn right onto 19th 1 mile to Tilghman. Turn right onto Tilghman about ¼ mile to Albright Ave. Turn left onto Albright about ¼ mile to Liberty. Turn right onto Liberty to restaurant.

ALTOONA

Everything Under the Sun 🛍

3415 Pleasant Valley Blvd. ☎ 814-943-6330 ⏰ M-Sat 10-6, Sun 12-5
· organic produce

🚗 **From I-99,** take exit 32 toward PA 36 west on Frankstown Rd (left from I-99S, merge right from I-99N) about 4 blocks (past hwy) and U-turn at Pleasant Valley Blvd to store on right in Pleasant Valley Shopping Ctr.

ANNVILLE

Annville Natural Food Market 🛍️

37 W. Main St. ✆ 717-867-2773 ⏰ M-F 9:30-6, Sun 9-4
• organic produce

🚗 US 422 runs through Annville (Main St in town). Store is on W Main 1 block
west of PA 934 & Valley Lebanon College.

ARDMORE

Milkboy Coffee 🍴

2 E. Lancaster Ave. ✆ 610-645-5269 ⏰ M-Tues 7-10, W-Th 7-9, F-Sat 7-11, Sun 7-5
Vegan choices include seitan cheesesteak, seitan chipolte wrap and vegan scrapple.
• vegetarian friendly • vegan friendly • tables • self-service

🚗 From I-476, take exit 13 toward Villanova east on Lancaster Ave/US 30E (loop
around right from I-476S, right from I-476N) 4 miles to restaurant on right at
Cricket Ave.

BLOOMSBURG

Bloom Naturally 🛍️

330 E. Fifth St. ✆ 570-784-3357 ✆ M-F 8-6, Sat 8-4

🚗 From I-80E, take exit 232 toward Buckhorn and stay right at fork toward
Bloomsburg onto Mall Blvd about 1¾ miles to US 11 exit. Merge onto US 11 (W
2nd St, becomes W Main, E Main St, then turns right onto East St) about 2 miles
to store on right at 5th St (4 blocks after US 11 turns onto East).

BRYN MAWR

Arrowroot Natural Foods 🛍️

834 W. Lancaster Ave. ✆ 610-527-3393 ⏰ M-F 9-7, Sat 9:30-6:30, Sun 10-5:30
• organic produce

🚗 From I-76E, take exit 330 toward Gulph Mills and take ramp toward Villanova
onto PA 320 almost 2 miles to Montgomery Ave. Continue onto Montgomery
almost 1½ miles to N Merion Ave. Turn right onto N Merion across tracks to W
Lancaster Ave. Turn left onto W Lancaster to store on right. From I-76W, take exit
339 on left onto E City Ave/Rt 1S about 2¾ miles to E Lancaster. Turn right onto E
Lancaster over 4 miles to store on left.

Milkboy Coffee 🍴

824 W. Lancaster Ave. ✆ 610-527-0690 ⏰ M-Th 8-10, F 8-12, Sat 9-12, Sun 9-10
More limited menu than "big sister" in Ardmore with only sandwiches.
• vegetarian friendly • vegan friendly • tables • self-service

🚗 From I-76E, take exit 330 toward Gulph Mills and take ramp toward Villanova
onto PA 320 almost 2 miles to Montgomery Ave. Continue onto Montgomery
almost 1½ miles to N Merion Ave. Turn right onto N Merion across tracks to W
Lancaster Ave. Turn left onto W Lancaster to restaurant on right. From I-76W, take
exit 339 on left onto E City Ave/Rt 1S about 2¾ miles to E Lancaster. Turn right
onto E Lancaster over 4 miles to restaurant on left.

CAMP HILL

The Healthy Grocer 🛍️

3800 Trindle Rd. ✆ 717-737-5123 ⏰ M-F 9-9, Sat 10-6, Sun 11-5
• organic produce • vegetarian friendly • fresh juice • deli • take-out

🚗 From I-76E (PA Tpke), take exit 236 for Gettysburg Pike and follow signs for
Harrisburg onto US 15N about 3¾ miles to Trindle Rd. Turn left onto Trindle
about ¾ mile to store on right at S 38th St. From I-76W, take exit 242 onto I-83N
2½ miles to exit 41A toward Camp Hill. Merge onto PA 541W (Harrisburg Expwy)
about 3½ miles to exit 4 for PA 641 toward Mechanicsville. Turn left onto PA 641/
Trindle Rd about ⅓ mile to store on left. From I-83S, merge onto PA 541W and
follow directions above.

CARLISLE

Appalachian Whole Foods Market 🛍️
100 W. High St. ✆ 717-241-6982 ⏰ M-Sat 10-6
  • organic produce

🍎 **From PA Tpke,** take exit 226 toward I-81N/Harrisburg south on US 11/Carlisle 3 miles to High St. Turn right onto High 2 blocks to store on left. **From I-81S** take exit 49 right onto PA 641/High /Trindle Rd 1¾ miles to store after US 11/Holly Pike. **From I-81N**, take exit 47 left onto Holly Pike/S Hanover 1 mile to High. Turn left onto W High to store.

Good Life Cafe 🍴
26 N. Hanover St. ✆ 717-249-8747 ⏰ Tues-W 11-9, Th-Sat 11-10
Dinner more vegetarian friendly than lunch. BYOB. Live jazz at night.
  • vegetarian friendly • organic focus • counter • tables • wait staff • take-out

🍎 **From PA Tpke**, take exit 226 toward I-81 N/Harrisburg south on US 11/Carlisle/Harrisburg Pike almost 3 miles to restaurant on right after Louther St. **From I-81S** take exit 49 right onto PA 641/High St/Trindle Rd 1½ miles to Hanover St. Turn right onto N Hanover 2 blocks to restaurant on left. **From I-81N**, take exit 47 left onto Holly Pike/S Hanover over 1 mile to restaurant.

CHARLEROI

Yareck's Health Foods 🛍️
2 McKean Ave. ✆ 724-489-9261 ⏰ M-F 10-6, Sat 10-4
🍎 **From I-70**, take exit 40 toward Allenport/Charleroi left onto PA 88 (becomes McKean Ave) ½-1 mile to store on right.

CLARKS SUMMIT

Everything Natural 🛍️🍴   ♿
426 S. State St. ✆ 570-586-9684 ⏰ M-Sat 9-8
  • organic produce • vegetarian friendly • tables • self-service • take-out

🍎 **From I-476N (PA Tpke)**, take US 6W/US 11N exit toward Clarks Summit onto 6W/11N about 1⅓ miles (past 6 lights) to store on left. **From I-81**, take exit 194 (PA Tpke) toward Clarks Summit onto I-476N and follow directions above.

CRANBERRY

God's Little Garden 🛍️
80 Regina Drive # 9 ✆ 814-676-8660 ⏰ M-Th 10-7, F 10-4, Sun 12-5
Bible-based mainly vegan store.
  • organic produce

🍎 Store is one block south of PA 322 opposite Cranberry Mall. Go south onto Kimberly Ln and follow around until it becomes Regina Dr to store left.

CRANBERRY TWP

Mad Mex 🍴
20510 Perry Hwy. ✆ 724-741-5656 ⏰ M-Th 11-11, F-Sat 11-12, Sun 11-10
Mexican with vegan options including tofu and vegan cheese and sour cream.
  • vegetarian friendly • vegan friendly • alcohol • counter • tables • wait staff

🍎 **From I-79S**, take exit 78 toward US 19 right onto Rt 228 under ½ mile to US 19. Turn right onto US 19 1 mile to restaurant in Village Shoppes of Cranberry. **From I-79N**, take exit 76 on left and merge onto US 19 2 miles to restaurant.

DANVILLE

Brews N Bytes Internet Cafe & Eatery 🍴
20 Lower Mulberry St. ✆ 570-275-8666 ⏰ Tues-Sat 9-9
  • vegetarian friendly • vegan friendly • tables • wait staff • take-out

🍎 **From Rt 11**, go south on Mill St (right from Rt 11W, left from Rt 11E) and left onto Lower Mulberry St to restaurant on right.

DEVON

Whole Foods Market 🛍️ 🍴

821 Lancaster Ave. ✆ 610-688-9400 🕐 Daily 8-9
• organic produce • vegetarian friendly • salad bar • cafe • self-service • take-out

🏬 Store is on Rt 30 (aka Lancaster Rd) on north side under ½ mile west of Sugartown & east of Valley Forge Rd.

EAST STROUDSBURG

Kreative Kuisine 🍴

214 N. Courtland St. ✆ 570-476-1229 🕐 M, F 11-2, Tues-Th 11-6
In addition to "vegetarian Mondays" there is always vegetarian soup and quiche.
• vegetarian friendly • organic focus • tables • self-service

🏬 **From I-80E**, take exit 305 right onto Hwy 309/Main St about 1¾ miles to Brown St. Veer right onto Brown to S Courtland St. Veer left onto Courtland under 1 mile to restaurant on left past W Broad St at Vine St. **From I-80W**, take exit 308 right onto Prospect St about ¾ mile to Analomink St. Turn left onto Analomink across tracks to S Courtland. Turn right onto Courtland under ½ mile to restaurant.

EASTON

Nature's Way Market 🛍️

143 Northampton St. ✆ 610-253-0940 🕐 M-Th 9-6, F 9-8, Sat 9-5, Sun 12-4
🏬 **From Rt 22E**, take 4th St exit onto PA 248 past light (becomes PA 611/Larry Holmes Dr) and make forced right to light at bridge. Turn right onto Northampton St to store on right. **From Rt 22W**, take first exit after Delaware River Toll Bridge (Rt 611), stay right under bridge, then stay left to stop sign. Turn left onto 611 1 block to Northampton. Turn right onto Northampton to store.

EMMAUS

Balasia 🍴

500 Chestnut St. ✆ 484-330-6405 🕐 Lunch Tues-F 12-4, Sun 11:30-4 Dinner Th-Sat 5-11
Dinner by reservation only.
• vegan • organic focus • tables • wait staff

🏬 **From I-78W**, take exit 58 onto W Emmaus Ave 1 mile continuing onto Harrison Ave 1 mile to Lehigh St. Turn left onto Lehigh/N 5th St under ½ mile to Chestnut St. Turn left onto Chestnut to restaurant on left. **From I-78E**, take exit 55 right at fork toward Emmaus onto S Cedar Crest Blvd 3 miles to Chestnut. Turn left onto Chestnut 1 mile to restaurant on right at 5th.

ERIE

Whole Foods Co-op 🛍️ 🍴   ♿

1341 W. 26th St. ✆ 814-456-0282 🕐 M-Sat 9-8, Sun 12-6
• organic produce • vegetarian friendly • fresh juice • cafe • counter • tables • self-service • take-out • co-op

🏬 **From I-79**, take exit 182 onto US 20E/W 26th St (right from I-79N, left from I-79S) about 1½ miles to store on right at Brown Ave (4th light). **From I-90,** take exit 22B onto I-79N and follow directions above.

EXTON

Devi 🍴

151 W. Lincoln Hwy. ✆ 610-594-9250 🕐 M-Th 11:30-2:30, 5:30-9:30, F-Sat 11:30-2:30, 5:30-10, Sun 11:30-2:30, 5:30-9
South Indian vegetarian with a lunch buffet.
• vegetarian • vegan friendly • alcohol • tables • self-service • wait staff

🏬 **From US 30**, take Hwy 11 exit north on Pottstown Pike (left from US 30E, right from US 30W) about ½ mile to Lincoln Hwy/PA 30. Turn left onto W Lincoln to restaurant on right in Whiteland Towne Ctr.

FRAZER
Oasis Cafe 🛍🍴
134 Lancaster Ave. (Rte. 30) ✆ 610-647-9797 ⏰ M, Sat 11-3, Tues-F 11-5:30
Cafe serves raw foods, vegetarian and antibiotic-free meat and poultry.
  • vegetarian friendly • vegan friendly • cafe • tables • self-service • take-out
🚗 **From US 202S**, take Hwy 29N under ½ mile to Swedesford Rd. Turn left onto Swedesford under ½ mile to Morehall Rd. Turn right onto Morehall about ½ mile. Veer right onto Lancaster Ave ½ mile to restaurant on left after Conestoga Rd. **From US 202N,** take Hwy 30 exit right onto Lancaster about 2¾ miles to restaurant on right after Malin Rd.

GREENSBURG
Nature's Way Market 🛍
796 Highland Ave. ✆ 724-836-3524 ⏰ M-Tues, Th-F 9-6, W 9-7, Sat 9-5
Fresh sandwiches and salads in the cooler.
  • organic produce
🚗 **From US 30 (Lincoln Hwy) & US 19 (Main St in Greensburg) intersection**, go north on US 19 about ¾ mile to Mt Pleasant St and make sharp right onto Mt Pleasant across tracks to S Highland Ave. Make sharp left onto S Highland to store on left.

HANOVER
Allen's Natural Foods 🛍
1150 Carlisle St. ✆ 717-637-7230 ⏰ M-F 9-6, Sat 9-4
  • organic produce
🚗 **From Rt 30,** take Rt 94/Carlise Pike south almost 4 miles to store on right in Value City Mall.

HOLICONG
Earth Foods 🛍
4950 York Rd. ✆ 215-794-5311 ⏰ M-F 10-6, Sat 10-5, Sun 11-3
🚗 Store is on Rt 202 (aka York Rd) on east side ½ mile north of Durham Rd and about 1¾ miles south of the factory outlet mall.

HONESDALE
Nature's Grace Health Food & Deli 🛍   ♿
947 Main St. ✆ 570-253-3469 ⏰ M-Th 10-6, F 10-7, Sat 10-5
  • organic produce • vegetarian friendly • fresh juice • deli • bakery • take-out
🚗 **From Rt 6E,** turn right onto Main St (aka Rt 6) to store on east side between 10th & Chapel St.

HUNTINGDON VALLEY
All Ways Cafe 🍴
634 Welsh Rd. ✆ 215-914-2151 ⏰ M-Sat 11-7:30
Vegetarian, fish and chicken.
  • vegetarian friendly • tables • self-service
🚗 **From PA 232/Huntingdon Pike & PA 63 intersection**, restaurant is just west on Welsh Rd (aka PA 63) on south side.

INDIANA
Back to Nature 🛍
2520 Warren Rd ✆ 724-349-1772 ⏰ M-F 9-7, Sat 9-5
  • organic produce
🚗 **From US 422W/Ben Franklin Hwy**, take Oakland Ave exit towards Indiana left from US 422E, right from US 422W under 1 mile to Ben Franklin Rd S. Turn left onto Ben Franklin continuing onto Indian Springs Rd under ½ mile to Warren Rd. Turn left onto Warren 1 block to store on left.

JENKINTOWN

Whole Foods Market ⬚ ⑪   ♿

1575 The Fairway ✆ 215-481-0800 ⏲ M-Sat 8-10, Sun 8-9
• organic produce • vegetarian friendly • salad bar • cafe • self-service • take-out

⬚ **From I-276 (PA Tpke),** take exit 343 toward Willow Grove onto PA 611S about 4½ miles to The Fairway. Turn left onto The Fairway to store on left in Baederwood Shopping Ctr.

JIM THORPE

Cafe Origins ⑪

107 Broadway ✆ 570-325-8776 ⏲ April-Dec Call for seasonal hours
Mainly vegetarian/vegan gourmet Mediterranean menu with a few seafood options.
• vegetarian friendly • vegan friendly • alcohol • tables • wait staff

⬚ In the Poconos. **From I-476,** take exit 74 toward Interchange Rd/Rt 209 and follow signs for Lehighton/Jim Thorpe to merge onto Interchange Rd/Rt 209 about 6 miles to restaurant on left between Race & Broadway St.

JOHNSTOWN

The Healthy Way ⬚

508 Luray Ave. ✆ 814-266-2828 ⏲ Tues-F 9-5, Sat 10-4
⬚ **From US 219**, go north on Hwy 56/Scalp Ave (right from US 219S, loop around right from US 219N) about ¾ mile to Luray Ave. Turn left onto Luray 2 blocks to store on left.

KENNETT SQUARE

Spring Run Natural Foods ⬚

909 E. Baltimore Pike ✆ 610-388-0500 ⏲ M-Sat 9-7, Sun 11-5
• organic produce

⬚ Store is on US 1 (aka Baltimore Pike) ½ mile west of RT 52 just south of Longwood Gardens.

KIMBERTON

Kimberton Whole Foods ⬚ ⑪

2140 Kimberton Rd. ✆ 610-935-1444 ⏲ M-F 8-8, Sat 9-6, Sun 10-6
• organic produce • vegetarian friendly • cafe • tables • self-service • take-out

⬚ **From I-76 (PA Tpke)**, take exit 327 (King of Prussia) toward Valley Forge onto PA 363 (N Gulph Rd) about 1⅔ miles to PA 23 (Port Kennedy Rd). Turn left onto 23W about 7 miles (through Phoenixville) to PA 113. Turn left onto 113/Kimberton Rd about 1¼ miles and bear right to stay on Kimberton about 1 mile to store on left.

LANCASTER

Rhubarb's Market ⬚

1521 Lititz Pike ✆ 717-390-3001 ⏲ M-F 9-8, Sat 9-6
⬚ **From Rt 30**, take Lititz Pike (Rt 501) south about ⅓ mile to store on left.

LANSDALE

Arnold's Way ⬚ ⑪

319 W. Main St. ✆ 215-361-0116 ⏲ M, W, Th, Sat 10-6, Tues, F 10-7, Sun 11-6
Vegan raw foods deli.
• organic produce • vegan • fresh juice • deli • tables • self-service • take-out

⬚ **From I-476**, take exit 31 toward Lansdale onto Rt 63 (left from I-476S, right from I-476N). Follow 63 (Sumneytown Pike) as it turns left onto Forty Foot Rd after about ¼ mile, right onto Welsh Rd after another 1⅔ miles and continue on 63 (becomes Main St) about 2 miles more (about 4 miles total) to store.

North Penn Health Food Center 🛍

1313 N. Broad St. ✆ 215-855-1044 ⏱ M-Sat 10-6

🍎 **From I-476**, take exit 31 toward Lansdale onto Rt 63 (left from I-476S, right from I-476N). Follow 63 (Sumneytown Pike) as it turns left onto Forty Foot Rd after about ¼ mile, right onto Welsh Rd after another 1⅔ miles and continue on 63 (becomes Main St) about 2 miles more about 4 miles (total) to N Broad St. Turn left onto N Broad 1 mile to store on right.

LUZERNE

House of Nutrition 🛍 ♿

50 Main St. ✆ 570-714-0436 ⏱ M, Th, F 9-8, Tues, W 9-6, Sat 10-6, Sun 12-5
• organic produce

🍎 **From I-81,** take exit 170B onto RT 309N about 4½ miles to exit 6 toward Luzerne. Turn right at light onto Union St, right at light onto Buckingham St and after Vaughn St veer right onto Main St to store on right.

Mill Hollow Cafe 🍴

50 Main St. ✆ 570-714-3841 ⏱ Tues-Sat 9:30am-3pm, alternate F 5:30pm-8pm
Breakfast and lunch plus dinner alternating Fridays. Dinner reservations required and entree (vegetarian, vegan or fish) must be ordered ahead. BYOB.
• vegetarian friendly • vegan friendly • organic focus • tables • wait staff

🍎 **From I-81,** take exit 170B onto RT 309N about 4½ miles to exit 6 toward Luzerne. Turn right at light onto Union St, right at light onto Buckingham St and after Vaughn St veer right onto Main St to restaurant on right.

MALVERN

Su Tao Cafe 🍴

81 Lancaster Avenue ✆ 610-651-8886 ⏱ M-Th 11:30-9:30, F-Sat 11:30-10, Sun 12:30-9:30
Mostly Asian with mock meat and lunch buffet option.
• vegan • tables • self-service • wait staff • take-out

🍎 **From Rt 202,** take Rt 29 south about 2½ miles to Lancaster Pike. Turn right to restaurant in Great Valley Shopping Ctr.

MANAYUNK

Machismo Burrito Bar 🍴

4330 Main St. ✆ 215-508-3333 ⏱ Daily 11-9
Build-your-own burrito: vegetarian beans and "meat," vegan cheese and sour cream, brown rice.
• vegetarian friendly • vegan friendly • tables • self-service • take-out

🍎 **From I-76,** take exit for Belmont Ave toward Green Ln across the Schuykill on Belmont and turn right onto Main St under ¼ mile to restaurant on right between Grape & Cotton St.

Mugshots Coffeehouse & Cafe 🍴

110 Cotton St. ✆ 215-482-3964 ⏱ Tues-F 6-4, Sat-Sun 8-4
Environmentally sensitive outlook.
• vegetarian friendly • vegan friendly • organic focus • fresh juice • tables • self-service

🍎 **From I-76,** take exit for Belmont Ave toward Green Ln across the Schuykill on Belmont and turn right onto Main St about ⅓ mile to Cotton St. Turn left onto Cotton 1 block to restaurant on left.

**For listing changes, updates and travel resources,
go to HealthyHighways.com**

MCMURRAY

Sunny Bridge Natural Foods 🛍

130 Gallery Drive ✆ 724-942-5800 ⏰ M-Th 10-8, F 10-6, Sat 9-5, Sun 11-4
• organic produce

🍎 **From I-79,** take exit 48 toward Hendersonville east on PA 1032/Southpointe Blvd (left from I-79S, right from I-79N) about ½ mile to Morganza Rd. Turn left onto Morganza about ½ mile to Georgetown/Hahn Rd. Turn right onto Georgetown and continue onto Hahn then Maple Ln 2½ miles to Washington St. Veer left onto Washington and make second left onto Gallery Dr to store on right.

MEDIA

Selene Whole Foods Co-op 🛍

305 W. State St. ✆ 610-566-1137 ⏰ M 11-6, Tues 10-6, W-F 10-7, Sat 10-5
• organic produce • co-op

🍎 **From I-476,** take exit 3 toward Media west on E Baltimore Pike (left from I-476N, right from I-476S) about 1 mile to Rt 252 (N Providence Rd). Turn right onto 252 to first light (State St). Turn left onto State past 4 lights to store on right at Orange St. **From I-95,** take exit 7 onto I-476N almost 3 miles to exit 3 and follow directions above.

MONROEVILLE

Mad Mex 🍴

4100 William Penn Hwy. ✆ 412-349-6767 ⏰ M-Th 11-11, F-Sat 11-12, Sun 11-10
See Cranberry Twp location for description.
• vegetarian friendly • vegan friendly • alcohol • counter • tables • wait staff

🍎 **From the PA Tpke,** merge onto I-376W. **From I-376W,** take US 22 exit on left toward Monroeville onto US 22/Wm Penn Hwy ½ mile to restaurant on left in Miracle Mile Plaza. **From I-376E,** take exit 14A onto Haymaker Rd and turn right onto US 22 under ½ mile to restaurant.

Udipi Cafe 🍴

4141 Old William Penn Hwy. ✆ 412-373-5581 ⏰ M, W-Th, Sun 11:30-9, F-Sat 11:30-9:30
Indian vegetarian.
• vegetarian • vegan friendly • tables • wait staff

🍎 **From the PA Tpke,** merge onto I-376W. **From I-376W,** take US 22 exit toward Monroeville onto US 22/Wm Penn Hwy under 1 mile to Duff Rd. Turn right onto Duff ⅓ mile to Old Wm Penn Hwy. Turn left onto Old Wm Penn under 1 mile to restaurant on right. **From I-376E,** take exit 10B toward Monroeville onto US 22. Turn left onto Rodi Rd and right onto Old Wm Penn 2½ miles to restaurant on left.

MORRISVILLE

Big Bear Natural Food 🛍

332 W. Trenton Ave. ✆ 215-736-0553 ⏰ M-F 9-8, Sat 10-7, Sun 12-5
• organic produce • vegetarian friendly • fresh juice • deli • take-out

🍎 **From US 1N,** take US 13S exit toward Bristol to Lower Morrisville Rd exit and follow exit back onto 13N over 1 mile to W Trenton Ave. Turn right onto Trenton about ½ mile to store a few blocks past Pennsbury Shopping Ctr. **From US 1S,** take N Pennsylvania Ave exit right onto S Pennsylvania about ¾ mile to W Trenton. Turn left onto Trenton about ¼ mile to store (before Pennsbury Shopping Ctr).

Greenlight 🍴

27 E. Bridge St. ✆ 215-736-8668 ⏰ M-Sat 11:30-7
• vegan • take-out

🍎 **From US 1N,** take the Pennsylvania Ave exit toward Morrisville left at fork for Pennsylvania Ave N and turn left onto S Pennsylvania past tracks to E Bridge St. Turn right onto E Bridge to restaurant on right. **From NJ on I-195W,** merge onto

Rt 29N 3 miles to US 1S exit toward Morrisville. Take US 1S across the water into PA about ½ mile to N Pennsylvania Ave exit toward Morrisville. Merge onto S Pennsylvania Ave and turn right onto E Bridge to restaurant.

NARBETH

Narbeth Natural Foods & Vegetarian Cafe 🛍 🍴

231 Haverford Ave. ℂ 610-667-7634 ⏱ Store Tues-Sat 10-5:30 Cafe Tues-Sat 10:30-3 *Cafe is vegetarian except for tuna. High tea served after 3.*
• organic produce • vegetarian friendly • vegan friendly • fresh juice • cafe • tables • wait staff • take-out

🍎 **From I-76**, take exit 339 unto US 1S about 2½ miles to E Wynnewood Rd. Turn right onto E Wynnewood 1 mile to Chestnut Ave. Turn right onto Chestnut 3 blocks to S Narbeth. Turn left onto S Narbeth 3 blocks (across tracks) to E Haverford Ave. Turn left onto E Haverford to store on right.

NEW HOLLAND

Community Natural Foods Store 🛍

12 S. Railroad Ave. ℂ 717-355-0921 ⏱ M-W 8-6, Th-F 8-8, Sat 9-4
• organic produce

🍎 **From US 322E**, turn right onto Railroad Ave about 3⅓ miles to store. **From 322W**, turn left onto Main St 1⅓ miles to Railroad. Turn left onto Railroad to store.

NORTH WALES

Whole Foods Market 🛍 🍴

1210 Bethlehem Pike ℂ 215-646-6300 ⏱ Daily 8-9
• organic produce • vegetarian friendly • salad bar • cafe • self-service • take-out

🍎 **From I-76 (PA Tpke)**, take exit 339 (Fort Washington) onto Rt 309N about 6½ miles to Rt 63. Turn west onto 63 to store on corner in Gwynedd Crossing Shopping Ctr.

OAKMONT

Today's Market 🛍

612 Allegheny River Blvd ℂ 412-828-4244 ⏱ M, Th 10-8, Tues-W, F, Sat 10-6, Sun 11-4
• organic produce

🍎 **From I-76 (PA Tpke)**, take exit 48 toward Pittsburgh/New Kensington onto Freeport Rd/Rowe St about 1½ miles to Hulton Bridge. Cross bridge and onto Hulton Rd 2 blocks to Allegheny River Blvd. Turn right onto Allegheny River under ½ mile to store on left between Pennsylvania & Maryland Ave.

PAOLI

Arrowroot Natural Market 🛍

83 E. Lancaster Ave. ℂ 610-640-2720 ⏱ M-F 9-6, Sat 9:30-6, Sun 10-4
• organic produce

🍎 **From I-76 (PA Tpke),** take exit 328 toward W Chester onto Rt 202S about 3¼ miles to Rt 252. Merge onto 252S about 2½ miles to E Lancaster Ave/US 30. Turn right to store on right. **From I-476**, take exit 13 (St David's) onto US 30W about 7 miles to store after Rt 252 intersection.

PENNDEL

The Natural Foods Store 🛍

131 Hulmeville Ave. ℂ 215-752-7268 ⏱ M-Th 10-6:30, F 10-7:30, Sat 10-5:50
• vegetarian friendly • deli • take-out

🍎 **From I-95**, take exit 44 southwest on PA 1 Bus/W Lincoln Hwy (right at fork toward Penndel from I-95S, left at fork and left from I-95N) 1 mile to Hulmeville Ave. Turn left onto Hulmeville to store on left.

PHILADELPHIA

A Full Plate Cafe 🍴
1009 N. Bodine St. ✆ 215-627-4068 ⏱ M-Th 11-9, F 11-10, Sat 10-10, Sun 10-3
Southern cooking including vegan pulled "pork" and "meat" loaf. BYOB.
 • vegetarian friendly • vegan friendly • tables • wait staff
🚗 **From I-95S**, take exit 23 toward Girard Ave/Lehigh Ave onto Aramingo Ave and veer right onto E Girard about 1 mile to N 2nd St. Turn left onto N 2nd past Germantown Rd to W George St. Turn right onto W George 2 blocks to N Bodine St. Turn left onto N Bodine to restaurant on left. **From I-95N,** take exit 22 on left for Callowhill St right onto N 3rd St over ½ mile to W Widley St. Turn right onto W Widley 1 block to N Bodine. Turn left onto N Bodine to restaurant on right.

Azure 🍴
931 N. 2nd St. ✆ 215-629-0500 ⏱ M-Th 11:30-11, F 11:30-12, Sat 11-3, 4-12, Sun 11-3, 4-11
Several seitan dishes.
 • egetarian friendly • vegan friendly • alcohol • tables • wait staff
🚗 **From I-95S**, take exit 23 toward Girard Ave/Lehigh Ave onto Aramingo Ave and veer right onto E Girard about 1 mile to N 2nd St. Turn left onto N 2nd about 3 blocks to restaurant on right after W Laurel St. **From I-95N,** take exit 22 on left for Callowhill St right onto N 3rd St over ½ mile to W Widley St. Turn right onto W Widley 3 blocks to N 2nd St. Turn right onto N 2nd about 1 block to restaurant.

Basic Four Vegetarian Snack 🍴
1136 Arch St. ✆ 215-440-0991 ⏱ M-F 9-5, Sun 9-4
Light fare at a stand in the Reading Terminal Market.
 • vegetarian • vegan friendly • tables • self-service • take-out
🚗 **From I-676W**, take left fork to exit onto N 8th St and turn left onto N 8th ⅓ mile to Arch. Turn right onto Arch 4 blocks to restaurant. **From I-676E**, take exit toward Broad St onto Vine St to N 10th St. Turn right onto N 10th under ¼ mile to Arch. Turn right onto Arch 2 blocks to restaurant.

Brown Sugar Bakery & Cafe 🍴
219 S. 52nd St. ✆ 215-472-7380 ⏱ M-W 9-10, Th-Sat 9-11, Sun 9-8
A neighborhood Caribbean eatery with many vegetarian options.
 • vegetarian friendly • vegan friendly • tables • self-service
🚗 **From I-76E**, take exit 346B onto University Ave continuing onto S 38th St about 1 mile total to Walnut St. Turn left onto Walnut about 1½ miles to S 52nd St. Turn left onto S 52nd to restaurant on left at Chancellor St.

Charles Plaza 🍴   ♿
234 N. 10th St. ✆ 215-829-4383 ⏱ M-Th 11:30-10, F 11:30-12, Sat 1-12, Sun 1-10:30
"Natural health" Chinese restaurant. No meat but chicken and seafood.
 • vegetarian friendly • vegan friendly • organic focus • tables • wait staff • take-out
🚗 In Philadelphia's Chinatown. **From I-676W**, take Vine St exit and follow signs onto Vine to N 10th St. Turn left onto N 10th to restaurant on right corner. **From I-676E**, take exit for Broad St onto Vine ½ mile to N 10th. Turn right onto N 10th to restaurant.

Essene Market & Cafe 🛍🍴
719 S. 4th St. ✆ 215-922-1146 ⏱ M-Tues, Th-Sun 9-8, W, F 9-9
 • organic produce • vegan • organic focus • cafe • deli • bakery • tables • self-service • take-out
🚗 **From I-95N**, take exit 16 (Columbus Blvd/Washington Ave) left onto Columbus to first light (Washington Ave). Turn left onto Washington to third light (3rd St). Turn right onto 3rd to Monroe St. Turn left onto Monroe 1 block to store at 4th St. **From I-95S**, take exit 16 right onto Columbus to first light (Christian St). Turn right onto Christian 3 blocks to 3rd and follow directions above.

Gianna's Grille 🍴
507 S. 6th St. ℂ 215-829-4448 ⊙ M-Th, Sun 12-9, F-Sat 12-10
Sandwiches, salads, pizza, soy cheese lasagna, vegetarian "meat" options, vegan desserts.
　• vegetarian friendly • vegan friendly • tables • self-service
🚌 **From I-676,** take Independence Mall/6th St exit south on 6th to restaurant between Lombard & South St.

Govinda's Cafe 🍴
1408 South St. ℂ 215-985-9303 ⊙ Th-Sat 5-11, Sun 2-10
Dinner buffet or table service. An eclectic menu of vegetarian "continental" food.
　• vegetarian • vegan friendly • tables • self-service • wait staff
🚌 **From I-95,** take exit 20 west on Washington Ave about 1 mile to Broad St. Turn right onto Broad about ½ mile to South St to restaurant on left. (By car continue 1 block to Lombard St and turn left onto Lombard, left onto 15th St and left onto South.) **From I-76,** take exit 346A onto South St across the water (right from I-76W, left from I-76E) about 1¼ miles to restaurant between 15th & Broad.

Govinda's Gourmet to Go 🍴
1400 South St. ℂ 215-545-5452 ⊙ M-Th 11:30-11, F-Sat 11:30-12, Sun 11:30-10
Mainly take-out with a few tables.
　• vegetarian • vegan friendly • tables • self-service • take-out
🚌 **From I-95,** take exit 20 west on Washington Ave about 1 mile to Broad St. Turn right onto Broad about ½ mile to South St to restaurant on left. (By car continue 1 block to Lombard St and turn left onto Lombard, left onto 15th St and left onto South to restaurant.) **From I-76,** take exit 346A onto South St across the water (right from I-76W, left from I-76E) about 1¼ miles to restaurant at corner.

Honey Sit 'n' Eat 🍴　　　　　　　　　　　　　　♿ 📷
800 N. 4th St. ℂ 215-925-1150 ⊙ M-F 8-10, Sat 8-9, Sun 8-4:30
Rustic diner atmosphere. All-day breakfast.
　• vegetarian friendly • vegan friendly • tables • wait staff
🚌 **From I-95S,** take exit 23 toward Girard Ave/Lehigh Ave onto Aramingo Ave and veer right onto E Girard 1 mile to N 4th St. Turn left onto N 4th under 1 mile to restaurant on right at Brown St. **From I-95N,** take exit 22 on left right onto Callowhill St about 3 blocks to N 5th St. Turn right onto N 5th over ½ mile to Popular St. Turn right onto Poplar and second right onto N 4th 1 long block to restaurant.

Horizons 🍴
611 S. 7th St. ℂ 215-923-6117 ⊙ Tues-Th 6-10, F-Sat 6-11
Dinner in the intimate dining room or soups, small plates and drinks in the lounge.
　• vegan • alcohol • tables • wait staff
🚌 **From I-95,** take exit 20 for Washington Ave onto S Columbus Blvd/S Delaware Ave onto Washington about ¾ mile to S 7th St. Turn right onto S 7th under ½ mile to restaurant on right between Bainbridge & South St.

Kingdom of Vegetarians Restaurant 🍴
129 N. 11th St. ℂ 215-413-2290 ⊙ Daily 11:30-11
Chinese vegetarian.
　• vegetarian • vegan friendly • tables • wait staff • take-out
🚌 In Philadelphia's Chinatown. **From I-676W,** take left fork to exit onto N 8th St and turn left onto N 8th ⅓ mile to Arch St. Turn right onto Arch 3 blocks to N 11th St. Turn right onto N 11th 2 blocks to restaurant on right at Cherry St. **From I-676E,** take exit toward Broad St onto Vine St to N 10th St. Turn right onto N 10th under ¼ mile to Arch. Turn right onto Arch 1 block to N 11th. Turn right onto N 11th 1 block to restaurant.

Mad Mex 🍴
3401 Walnut St. ✆ 215-382-2221 ⏰ M-Sat 11:30-12 or 1am, Sun 11:30-11
See Cranberry Twp location for description.
• vegetarian friendly • vegan friendly • alcohol • counter • tables • wait staff
🍎 **From I-76E**, take exit 345 right onto Arch St continuing onto N 30th St and left onto Market St 2 blocks to Schuykill Ave. Turn right onto Schuykill (across river) 2 blocks to Walnut St. Turn right onto Walnut over ½ mile to restaurant on right after S 34th St. **From I-76W**, take exit 345 right onto Chestnut St about ¼ mile to S 23rd St. Turn right onto S 23rd about 3 blocks to Walnut. Turn right onto Walnut (back across river) under 1 mile to restaurant.

Magic Carpet Foods 🍴
Spruce St. and 36th St. ✆ 215-735-9211 ⏰ M-F 10:30-3
Cart at U Penn. Falafel, spinach pie, pita sandwiches, tofu, tempeh, seitan peppersteak and more.
• vegetarian • take-out
🍎 **From I-76**, take exit 346B onto University Ave (right at fork from I-76E, merge onto S 34th St and left from I-76W) about ¾ mile to Spruce St. Turn right onto Spruce 2 blocks to cart at S 36th St (on U Penn Campus).

Magic Carpet Foods 🍴
34th St. and Walnut St. ✆ 215-735-9211 ⏰ M-F 11-4
See Spruce St location for description.
• vegetarian • vegan friendly • take-out
🍎 **From I-76E**, take exit 345 for 30th St/Market St right onto Arch St, left onto JFK Blvd and right onto Market 3 blocks to S 34th St. Turn left onto S 34th 4 blocks to cart at Walnut Ave. **From I-76W**, take exit 345 for 30th right onto Chestnut St (across water) 2 blocks to S 23rd St. Turn right onto S 23rd 2 blocks to Walnut. Turn right onto Walnut back across water and 5 blocks to cart at S 34th.

Mama's Vegetarian 🍴
18 S. 20th St ✆ 215-751-0477 ⏰ M-Th 11-7:30, F 11-3, Sun 12-7
Small eatery with a Middleastern menu.
• vegetarian • vegan friendly • kosher • counter • tables • self-service • take-out
🍎 **From I-76W**, take 30th St exit right onto Chestnut St under ½ mile to S 20th St. Turn left onto S 20th 1 block to restaurant on left between Ludlow & Ranstead St. **From I-76E**, merge onto I-676 and take the 23rd St exit. Turn right onto N 23rd ⅓ mile to Market St. Turn left onto Market 2 blocks to S 21st. Turn right onto 21st 2 blocks to Chestnut. Turn left onto Chestnut 1 block to 20th. Turn left onto 20th 1 block to restaurant.

Maoz Vegetarian 🍴
248 South St. ✆ 215-625-3500 ⏰ M-Th, Sun 11am-1am, F-Sat 11am-3am
Falafel, salads and fries.
• vegetarian • vegan friendly • fresh juice • tables • self-service • take-out
🍎 **From I-95S**, take exit 20 on left right onto S Columbia Blvd (signs for Washington Ave) ⅓ mile to Christian St. Turn right onto Christian ⅓ mile to S 3rd St. Turn right onto S 3rd ⅓ mile to South St. Turn right onto South to restaurant on right. **From I-95N**, take exit 20 left onto S Columbia about ⅓ mile to Washington. Turn left onto Washington ⅓ mile to S 3rd. Turn right onto S 3rd ½ mile to South and follow directions above.

Maoz Vegetarian 🍴
1115 Walnut St. ✆ 215-922-3409 ⏰ M-Th, Sun 10-10, F-Sat 10am-3am
Falafel, salads and fries.
• vegetarian • vegan friendly • fresh juice • tables • self-service • take-out
🍎 **From I-95S**, take exit 22 toward I-626W/Central Philadelphia onto N 2nd St ½ mile to Market St. Turn right onto Market about ¼ mile to S 4th St. Turn left onto S 4th about ¼ mile to Walnut St. Turn right onto Walnut over ½ mile to restaurant on right after S 11th St. **From I-95N**, take exit 20 toward Washington Ave left onto S Columbus Blvd/S Delaware Ave 1 mile to Dock St. Turn right onto Dock, left onto Front St and left onto Walnut about 1 mile to restaurant.

Memphis Taproom 🍴

2331 E. Cumberland St. ✆ 215-425-4460 ⏰ M-F 11:30-12, Sat-Sun 11-12
Creative vegetarian/vegan options: Tempura Zucchini with Poblano Coconut Curry, Tofu Tzatziki, BBQ Seitan, Buckwheat and White Bean Chili.
  • vegetarian friendly • alcohol • counter • tables • self-service • wait staff
🍎 **From I-95S**, take exit 25 toward Castor Ave right onto E Allegheny and left onto Richmond St under 1 mile to E Lehigh Ave. Turn right onto E Lehigh ½ mile to Memphis St. Turn left onto Memphis about ⅓ mile to E Cumberland St. Turn left onto E Cumberland to restaurant on left. **From I-95N**, take exit 23 toward Girard Ave/Lehigh Ave onto N Delaware Ave continuing onto Aramingo Ave about ½ mile to E Huntingdon St. Turn left onto E Huntingdon 3 blocks to Memphis. Turn left onto Memphis 4 blocks to E Cumberland. Turn left onto E Cumberland to restaurant.

Mi Lah 🍴

218 S. 16th St. ✆ 215-732-8888 ⏰ M-Sat 11-3, 5-10, Sun 11-3
Creative vegan menu. BYOB.
  • vegan • fresh juice • counter • tables • wait staff
🍎 **From I-676**, take exit for Central Philadelphia/Broad St south on N 15th St (loop around right from I-676W, right from I-676E) about ¾ mile to Latimer St. Turn right onto Latimer 1 block to S 16th St. Turn right onto S 16th about 2 blocks to restaurant on left before Walnut St. **From I-76S or I-95S**, merge onto I-676 and follow directions above. **From I-76N**, take exit 345 right onto Chestnut St about ¾ mile to S 17th St. Turn right onto S 17th about ¼ mile to Locust. Turn right onto Locust and left onto S 16th to restaurant.

Mugshots Coffeehouse & Juicebar 🍴

2100 Fairmont St. ✆ 267-514-7145 ⏰ M-Th 7-9, F-Sun 7-6
Environmentally sensitive outlook.
  • vegetarian friendly • vegan friendly • organic focus • fresh juice • tables • self-service
🍎 **From I-76 or I-676**, go north on N 22nd St (right from I-676W, left from I-76) ½ mile to Fairmont Ave. Turn right onto Fairmont 1 block to restaurant on right at 21st St.

Natural Goodness Market & Cafe 🛍 🍴

2000 Walnut St. ✆ 215-977-7749 ⏰ M-F 9-7, Sat 11-3:30 Cafe closes 1 hour earlier
  • organic produce • vegetarian friendly • organic focus • fresh juice • cafe • tables • self-service
🍎 **From I-95S**, take exit 22 toward I-626W/Central Philadelphia onto Vine Expwy W about 1 mile to Central Philadelphia/Broad St exit. Merge onto N 15th St about ¾ mile to Walnut St. Turn right onto Walnut about 5 blocks (past Rittenhouse Sq) to store on left. **From I-95N**, take exit 20 toward Washington Ave left onto S Columbus Blvd/S Delaware Ave 1 mile to Dock St. Turn right onto Dock, left onto Front St and left onto Walnut about 1¾ miles to store.

New Harmony Vegetarian Restaurant 🍴

135 N. 9th St. ✆ 215-627-4520 ⏰ Daily 11:30-10:30
Chinese Buddhist menu. Brown rice available.
  • vegan • fresh juice • kosher • tables • wait staff • take-out
🍎 In Philadelphia's Chinatown. **From I-676W,** take left fork to exit onto N 8th St and turn left onto N 8th 2 blocks to Cherry St. Turn right onto Cherry 1 block to N 9th St. Turn right onto N 9th to restaurant on right. **From I-676E**, take exit for 8th St right onto N 8th and follow directions above.

Call Ahead

We suggest you call first if possible before visiting a location. Stores and restaurants have a habit of moving (and closing), and hours, services, etc. change more often than you might expect.

Old City Coffee 🍴
221 Church St. © 215-629-9292 ① M-W 6:30-6, Th-F 6:30-7, Sat 7-7, Sun 7-6
Breakfast, soups, sandwiches, baked goods. Vegetarian except for fish soup on Friday.
• vegetarian • tables • self-service
🚻 **From I-95S**, take exit 22 for Callowhill St toward I-676 onto N 2nd St ½ mile to Market St. Turn right onto Market 1 block to N 3rd St. Turn right onto N 3rd 1 block and right onto Church Christ Walkway to restaurant on left. **From I-95N**, take exit 20 toward Washington Ave left onto S Columbus Blvd/S Delaware Ave about 1½ miles to Market. Veer right toward Market then left onto Market 2 blocks to N 3rd and follow directions above.

Royal Tavern 🍴
937 E. Passyunk Ave. © 215-389-6694 ① M-F 12pm-1am, Sat-Sun 10pm-1am
"Gastro pub" with vegetarian and vegan choices.
• vegetarian friendly • vegan friendly • alcohol • tables • wait staff
🚻 **From I-95**, take exit 20 onto S Columbus Blvd (signs for Washington Ave) about ¼ mile to Washington. Turn west onto Washington (right from I-95S, left from I-95N) ¾ mile to E Passyunk Ave. Turn right onto Passyunk to restaurant on right.

Singapore Kosher Vegetarian Restaurant 🍴
1006 Race St. © 215-922-3288 ① M-Th, Sun 11:30-10:30, F-Sat 11:30-11
Southeast Asian vegan kosher. Brown rice available.
• vegan • kosher • tables • wait staff • take-out
🚻 In Philadelphia's Chinatown. **From I-676E**, take exit toward Broad St onto Vine St to N 12th St. Turn right onto N 12th to second right onto Race St 2 blocks to restaurant on right at N 10th St. **From I-676W**, take Vine St exit and follow signs onto Vine to N 12th. Turn left onto N 12th and follow directions above.

Su Xing House 🍴
1508 Sansom St. © 215-564-1419 ① M-Th 11-10:30, F-Sat 11-11, Sun 12-10
Chinese vegetarian. Brown rice available.
• vegetarian • vegan friendly • tables • wait staff • take-out
🚻 **From I-76W**, take exit 345 and go across the Schulykill on Chestnut St about 1 mile to S 15th St. Turn right onto S 15th 1 block to Sansom St. Turn right onto Sansom to restaurant on left. **From I-76E**, merge onto I-676. **From I-676**, take exit toward Central Philadelphia south on N 15th St almost 1 mile to Sansom. Turn right onto Sansom to restaurant on left.

The Flower Cafe 🍴
48 Maplewood Mall © 215-991-6514 ① M-W 11-4, Th-F 11-6
Vegetarian, raw food, poultry and fish options.
• vegetarian friendly • vegan friendly • tables • wait staff • take-out
🚻 **From I-76E**, take exit for US 1N left at fork onto 1N under 2 miles to N Germantown Ave exit. Merge onto W Roberts Ave and turn left onto Wayne Ave 1 mile to W Maplewood Ave. Turn right onto W Maplewood, left onto Greene St and right onto Maplewood Mall to restaurant on right. **From I-76W**, take exit 240B onto US 1N and follow directions above.

The Nile Cafe 🍴   ♿
6008 Germantown Ave. © 215-843-6453 ① Tues-Sat 11-8, Sun 2-6
Southern soul food with meat analogs, whole wheat wraps and hoagies, vegan "ice cream."
• vegan • tables • self-service • take out
🚻 **From I-76E**, take exit 340A onto East City Ave continuing onto Lincoln Dr about 2 miles total to W Harvey St. Veer right onto W Harvey under 1 mile to Germantown Ave. Turn left onto Germantown to restaurant on left. **From I-76W**, take exit 340B onto US 1N under 2 miles to Germantown exit. Merge onto W Roberts Ave continuing onto W Berkeley St ½ mile total to Germantown. Turn left onto Germantown 1½ miles to restaurant.

Weaver's Way Co-op

559 Carpenter Lane ℂ 215-843-2350 ⦿ M-F 9-8, Sat-Sun 9-6
• organic produce • vegetarian friendly • deli • take-out • co-op

From I-76, take exit 340A toward Lincoln Dr onto City Ave to Lincoln. Turn left onto Lincoln about 3 miles to Greene St. Turn left onto Greene 2 blocks to Carpenter Ln. Turn right onto Carpenter to store on right.

White Dog Cafe

3420 Sansom St. ℂ 215-386-9224 ⦿ M-Sat 11:30am-1am, Sun 10:30am-12am
A Certified Green Restaurant with live music and community events.
• vegetarian friendly • alcohol • tables • wait staff

From I-95N (and I-76), take I-76W (Schuylkill Expwy) to exit 346A and turn left onto South St to first right onto 33rd St to Market St. Turn left onto Market and left onto 34th St 1½ blocks to Sansom St (sign says Sansom Row). Turn right onto Sansom to restaurant. **From I-95S (and I-676),** take I-676W to 76E (Schuylkill Expwy) toward airport. Take exit 345 (30th St Station) around station to second light and turn right onto Market 4 blocks to 34th. Turn left onto 34th 1½ blocks to Sansom St (sign says Sansom Row). Turn right onto Sansom to restaurant.

Whole Foods Market

2001 Pennsylvania Ave. ℂ 215-557-0015 ⦿ Daily 8-10
• organic produce, vegetarian friendly, salad bar, cafe, self-service, take-out

From I-95, take I-676W to Museum exit (exit past Broad St). Take ramp toward Ben Franklin Pkwy/Art Museum and turn left onto N 22nd St, cross over Ben Franklin Pkwy and turn right onto Hamilton St (light with Best Western on far corner). At first stop sign turn right onto N 21st St ½ block to Pennsylvania Ave. Turn left onto Pennsylvania to store. **From I-76,** take exit 344 onto Vine St Expwy/I-676E/US 30E. Take 676E to 23rd St exit toward Ben Franklin Pkwy and follow directions above.

Whole Foods Market

929 South St. ℂ 215-733-9788 ⦿ Daily 8-10
• organic produce • vegetarian friendly • salad bar • cafe • self-service • take-out

From I-95, take exit 20 west on Washington about ¾ mile to 11th St. Turn right onto 11th under ½ mile to South St. Turn right onto South about 4 blocks to store at 9th St. **From I-76,** take exit 349 onto PA 611N/Broad St (circle around and left onto Broad across hwy from I-76E, exit onto Pollack St and right onto Broad from I-76W) about 2 miles to South St. Turn right onto South under ½ mile to store.

PINE FORGE

Gracie's 21st Century Cafe

1534 Manatawny Rd. ℂ 610-323-4004 ⦿ W-Sat from 5:30
Upscale dining with ample vegetarian choices, wild fish and organic chicken and meat.
• vegetarian friendly • organic focus • fresh juice • alcohol • tables • wait staff

From US422/Rt 100 intersection in Pottstown, go north on Rt 100 to first light (King St). Turn right onto King to first light (Manatawny St). Turn left onto Manatawny almost 3½ miles to restaurant on left.

PITTSBURGH

Brillobox

4104 Penn Ave. ℂ 412-621-4900 ⦿ Kitchen Tues-Sat 5-12, Sun 8-12 Starving Artist Dinner Sun 6
Restaurant/bar/performance venue. All-vegetarian starving artist dinner lasts until food runs out.
• vegetarian friendly • alcohol • tables • self-service

From I-579N, take Bigelow Blvd exit almost 2 miles to Bloomfield Bridge. Follow Bloomfield ½ mile to Main St. Turn left onto Main under ¼ mile to Penn Ave. Turn right onto Penn to restaurant. **From I-579S,** take 7th Ave exit, follow signs onto Bigelow Blvd and follow directions above.

Double Wide Grill 🍴

2339 E. Carson St. © 412-390-1111 ⏱ M-Th, Sun 11-10, F-Sat 11-11

Unusual vegetarian/vegan choices: seitan wings, tofu with chimichurri sauce, potato tacos and more.

• vegetarian friendly • alcohol • tables • wait staff • take-out

🚗 **From I-376W**, take exit 3A for Hwy 885S toward Glenwood right onto Bates St, right onto 2nd Ave and left across Hot Metal Bridge onto Hot Metal St 3 blocks to E Carson St. Turn right onto E Carson under 1 mile to restaurant on right after S 24th St. **From I-70**, merge onto I-376E. **From I-376E**, take exit 1C on left onto Grant St and turn right onto 2nd Ave ½ mile to Armstrong Tunnel. Turn right and go across 10th St Bridge onto 10th St 3 blocks to E Carson. Turn left onto E Carson 1 mile to restaurant on left past S 23rd St.

Evgefstos! 🍴

Carnegie Mellon U., 2nd Fl. University Center © 412-268-2139 ⏱ M-F 11-2, 5-8

• vegetarian • vegan friendly • tables • self-service • take-out

🚗 **From I-376W**, take exit 5 toward Homestead left onto Forward Ave ⅓ mile to Murray Ave. Turn left onto Murray about ½ mile to Forbes Ave. Turn left onto Forbes over 1 mile to Carnegie Mellon Campus. Restaurant is on 2nd floor of University Center. **From I-376E**, take exit 2A onto Forbes Ave toward Oakland 2 miles to Carnegie Mellon Campus.

Hoi Polloi Vegetarian Cafe & Coffeehouse 🍴

1100 Galveston Ave. © 412-586-4567 ⏱ M-Th 6am-9pm, F 6-10, Sat 7-10, Sun 1-9

• vegetarian • vegan friendly • tables • self-service

🚗 **From I-279S**, take exit 7A toward North Shore onto Reedsdale St and turn right onto Ridge Ave 1 block to Galveston Ave. Turn left onto Galveston about ⅓ mile to restaurant on right after W North Ave. **From I-279N**, veer left onto PA 65N and take the US 19S exit right at fork and merge onto W End Bridge. Turn right onto Western Ave about ⅓ mile to Allegheny Ave. Turn left onto Allegheny 4 blocks to W North. Turn right onto W North 1 block to Galveston. Turn left onto Galveston to restaurant.

Mad Mex 🍴

370 Atwood St. © 412-681-5656 ⏱ Daily 11am-1am

See Cranberry Twp location for description.

• vegetarian friendly • vegan friendly • alcohol • counter • tables • wait staff

🚗 **From I-376E**, take exit 2A onto Forbes St toward Oakland 1 mile to Meyran Ave. Turn right onto Meyran ⅓ mile to Bates St. Turn left onto Bates 2 blocks to Atwood St. Turn left onto Atwood to restaurant on left. **From I-376W**, take exit 3B onto Bates ½ mile to Atwood and follow directions above.

Mad Mex 🍴

7905 McKnight Rd. © 412-366-5656 ⏱ M-Th 11-11, F-Sat 11-12, Sun 11-10

See Cranberry Twp location for description.

• vegetarian friendly • vegan friendly • alcohol • counter • tables • wait staff

🚗 **From I-279**, take exit 14 right onto Union Ave (signs for W View) continuing onto Gass Rd about ¼ mile to Highland Ave. Turn right onto Highland about ¾ mile to US 19/Perryville Ave. Turn right onto US 19 about 1½ miles to Third Degree Rd. Turn right onto Third Degree continuing onto Babcock Blvd about 1 mile total to McKnight Rd. Turn right onto McKnight to restaurant on right.

Mad Mex 🍴

2101 Greentree Rd. © 412-279-0200 ⏱ M-Th 11-11, F-Sat 11-12, Sun 11-10

See Cranberry Twp location for description.

• vegetarian friendly • vegan friendly • alcohol • counter • tables • wait staff

🚗 **From I-79**, take exit 55 onto Washington Pike Connector and turn left onto Washington Pike about 1 mile to Greentree Rd. Turn left onto Greentree about 1 mile to restaurant on right in Scott Towne Ctr. **From I-279**, take exit 2 toward Carnegie onto Lydia St ⅓ mile to PA 50/Washington Ave. Turn left onto Washington 1 mile to Hope Hollow Rd. Turn left onto Hope Hollow under 1 mile to Swallow Hill Rd. Turn left onto Swallow Hill and right onto Greentree to restaurant.

Maggie's Organic Cafe 🍴
300 S. Craig St. ✆ 412-621-8200 ⏱ M-Sat 10-8
Organic vegan and raw foods in a deli setting.
   • vegan • organic focus • tables • self-service • take-out
🚗 **From I-376E**, take exit 2A onto Forbes St toward Oakland about 1½ miles to Craig St. Turn left onto Craig 2 blocks to restaurant on left at Winthrop St. **From I-376W**, take exit 3B (PA 885) toward Oakland. Merge onto Bates Pl under ½ mile to McKee Pl. Turn left onto McKee to second right (⅓ mile) at Forbes. Turn right onto Forbes ¾ mile to Craig. Turn left onto Craig 2 blocks to restaurant.

Make Your Mark Artspace and Coffeeshop 🍴
6736 Reynolds St. ✆ 412-365-2117 ⏱ M-F 7-7, Sat 8-7
Soups, salads and sandwiches.
   • vegetarian • vegan friendly • tables • self-service
🚗 **From I-376W**, take exit 8 for Hwy 8N toward Wilkinsburg onto Ardmore Blvd about 2½ miles to S Dallas Ave. Turn left onto S Dallas 1 block to Reynolds St. Turn right onto Reynolds about ⅓ mile to restaurant on left. **From I-376E**, take exit 2A toward Oakland onto Forbes Ave about 2 miles to Beeler St (at end of Carnegie Mellon campus). Veer left onto Beeler and right onto Wilkins Ave about ¾ mile to Linden Ave. Turn left onto Linden ½ mile to Reynolds. Turn left onto Reynolds about 3 blocks to restaurant.

Milky Way 🍴
2120 Murray Ave. ✆ 412-421-3121 ⏱ M-Th, Sun 11-8, F 11-2 pm, Sat 1 hour after sundown-11:30
Vegetarian pizza, pasta and Middleastern dishes plus fish.
   • vegetarian friendly • vegan friendly • kosher • tables • self-service
🚗 **From I-376**, take exit 5 and follow ramp toward Squirrel Hill/Homestead to Forward Ave. Turn left onto Forward ⅓ mile to Murray Ave. Veer left onto Murray about ¼ mile to restaurant on left between Douglas & Hobart St.

Sree's Foods 🍴
2103 Murray Ave. ✆ 412-860-9181 ⏱ M-F 11:30-2:30, 5-9
Vegan and chicken Indian boxed lunch and dinner.
   • vegan friendly • tables • self-service • take-out
🚗 **From I-376,** take exit 5 and follow ramp toward Squirrel Hill/Homestead to Forward Ave. Turn left onto Forward ⅓ mile to Murray Ave. Veer left onto Murray ⅓ mile to restaurant on right at Hobart St.

Sree's Foods 🍴
701 Smithfield St. ✆ 412-288-9992 ⏱ M-F 11:30-3
Vegan and chicken Indian boxed lunch and dinner.
   • vegan friendly • tables • self-service • take-out
🚗 **From I-376W,** take exit 1D onto 2nd Ave, turn right onto Bigelow Blvd and left onto 3rd Ave ⅓ mile to Smithfield St. Turn right onto Smithfield under ½ mile to restaurant on left at 7th Ave. **From I-279**, take exit 6C on left onto Fort Duquesne Blvd about ¼ mile to Stanwick St. Turn right onto Stanwick about ¼ mile to Liberty Ave. Turn left onto Liberty under ½ mile to 7th. Turn right onto 7th 1 block to restaurant on left at Smithfield.

Sree's Lunch 🍴
Tech St. ⏱ M-F 11-3
Indian vegan and chicken lunch from a street trailer at Carnegie Mellon U.
   • vegan friendly • take-out
🚗 **From I-376W**, take exit 5 toward Squirrel Hill/Homestead to Forward Ave. Turn left onto Forward ⅓ mile to Murray Ave. Veer left onto Murray about ½ mile to Forbes Ave. Turn left onto Forbes about 1 mile to Margaret Morrison St. Turn left onto Margaret Morrison (Carnegie Mellon campus) about ¼ mile to Tech Ave. Turn left onto Tech to red trailer. **From I-376E**, take exit 2A toward Oakland onto Forbes St about 1½ miles to Schenly Dr. Turn right onto Schenly and follow about ½ mile to Frew St. Turn left onto Frew ⅓ mile to Tech. Turn left onto tech to trailer.

The East End Food Co-op 🛍️ 🍴
7516 Meade St. ℭ 412-242-3598 ⏱ Daily 8-9
 • vegetarian • salad bar • cafe • deli • tables • self-service • co-op

🛍 **From I-376**, take exit 8B onto PA 8N about 2¼ miles to Braddock Ave. Turn right onto Braddock 1 block to Meade St. Turn left onto Meade to store on lower level in The Factory.

The Good Life Market 🛍️
3141 Banksville Rd. ℭ 412-531-1895 ⏱ M-W, F 10-7, Th 10-8, Sat 10-5, Sun 12-5
 • organic produce

🛍 **From I-79**, take exit 59A onto I-1279N toward Pittsburgh. **From I-279N**, take exit 4A onto Greentree Rd 1⅓ miles to McMonagle Ave. Turn right onto McMonagle ¾ mile to Banksville Rd. Turn right onto Banksville to store on right. **From I-179S**, take exit 5A onto Rt 19/Banksville Rd 2 miles to store on left before McMonagle.

The Quiet Storm Coffeehouse & Restaurant 🍴
5430 Penn Ave. ℭ 412-661-9355 ⏱ M-F 8-9, Sat 10-9, Sun 10-8
 • vegetarian • vegan friendly • counter • tables • wait staff

🛍 **From I-376**, take exit 8 for Hwy 8N toward Wilkinsburg onto Ardmore Blvd 2¾ miles to Penn Ave. Continue onto Penn about 1½ miles to restaurant on left.

Whole Foods Market 🛍️ 🍴   ♿
5880 Centre Ave. ℭ 412-441-7960 ⏱ Daily 8-10
 • organic produce • vegetarian friendly • salad bar • cafe • self-service • take-out

🛍 **From downtown Pittsburgh, take PA 380E (Baum Blvd)** about ¾ mile to Liberty Ave. Turn right onto Liberty 1 block to Centre Ave. Turn left onto Centre Ave about ½ mile to store. **From I-376**, take exit 8B onto PA 8N about 3¾ miles to Penn Ave (PA 380). Keep straight onto Penn almost 1 mile to S Highland Mall. Turn left onto S Highland and right onto 380 (Penn Cir S, becomes Centre St) about ¼ mile to store.

Zenith Tea Room 🍴   ♿
86 S. 26th St. ℭ 412-481-4833 ⏱ Th-Sat 11:30-8:30, Sun 11-2:30
In a large industrial space with an antique store and art gallery.
 • vegetarian • vegan friendly • tables • wait staff • take-out

🛍 **From I-376W**, take exit 3A and cross bridge on Hot Metal St to E Carson St. Turn right onto E Carson about ¼ mile to 26th St. Turn left onto 26th to restaurant. **From downtown**, take Birmingham Bridge across river and turn left onto E Carson over ½ mile to 26th. Turn right onto 26th to restaurant.

PLUMSTEADVILLE _____

Plumsteadville Natural Foods 🛍️
Rte. 611 ℭ 215-766-8666 ⏱ M-F 9:30-6, Sat 9:30-5
 • organic produce

🛍 **From I-276 (PA Tpke)**, take exit 343 and follow PA 611 ramp toward Doylestown/ Willow Grove Naval Air station onto 611N about 13 miles to store in Plumstead Shopping Ctr.

READING _____

Nature's Garden Natural Foods 🛍️
4290 Perkiomen Ave. ℭ 610-779-3000 ⏱ M-F 9-8, Sat 10-7, Sun 11-5
Thursday delivery of fresh vegetarian food to go.
 • organic produce

🛍 **From US 422E**, take Mt Penn exit left onto E Neversink Rd over ½ mile to Perkiomen Ave. Turn right onto Perkiomen (422 Bus E) ⅓ mile to store in Reading Mall. **From US 422W** take the 422 Bus exit toward Mt Penn. Follow 422 Bus W and make first left onto 422 Bus E to store.

ROBINSON

Mad Mex

2 Park Manor Drive © 412-494-5656 ℗ M-Th, Sun 11-11, F-Sat 11-12
See Cranberry Twp location for description.
• vegetarian friendly • vegan friendly • alcohol • counter • tables • wait staff

🍎 **From I-79N,** take exit 59B onto US 22W/30W about 3½ miles and take the PA 60S exit left onto Campbells Run Rd ⅓ mile to PA 60N/Steubenville Pike. Turn left onto Steubenville about ¼ mile to Park Manor Dr. Turn right onto Park Manor and make first left into Robinson Plaza to restaurant on left. **From I-79S,** take exit 60B onto PA 60N about 3 miles to Park Manor and follow directions above. **From PA 60S,** take exit 1B onto US 22E/30E about ¼ mile to Park Manor. Turn left onto Park Manor and follow directions above.

SANDY LAKE

Organics and More

3273 S. Main St . © 724-376-5076 ℗ M, W, F 11-6, Sat 9-2
• organic produce

🍎 **From I-79,** take exit 130 for PA 358 toward Sandy Lake east on PA 358/Sandy Lake Greenville Rd (right from I-79N, left from I-79S) about 4¾ miles to S Main St. Turn right onto S Main to store on right.

SHREWSBURY

Saubel's Market

65 E. Forrest Ave. © 717-235-3891 ℗ M-Sat 7-9, Sun 8-7
Family-owned grocery with a big natural/organic section at this location.
• organic produce • vegetarian friendly • deli • take-out

🍎 **From I-83,** take exit 4 toward Shrewsbury west on E Forrest Ave (right from I-83S, left from I-83N) about ½ mile to store on right.

SOUTHAMPTON

Blue Sage Vegetarian Grill   ♿

772 Second St. Pike © 215-942-8888 ℗ Lunch Tues-Sat 11:30-3, Dinner Tues-Th 4:30-9, F-Sat 4:30-10
Intriguing dishes you probably haven't seen elsewhere. BYOB.
• vegetarian • vegan friendly • organic focus • tables • wait staff • take-out

🍎 **From I-276 (PA Tpke),** take exit 351 onto US 1S toward Philadelphia under 1 mile to E St Rd exit. Take E St Rd about 5 miles to 2nd St Pike. Turn right onto 2nd St Pike under ¼ mile to restaurant on left in 2-store shopping center.

Bunn's Natural Foods

1007 Street Rd., © 215-355-1165 ℗ M, Th-F 9-6, Tues-Wed 9-8, Sat 9-5, Sun 11-3
• organic produce

🍎 **From I-276 (PA Tpke),** take exit 351 onto US 1S toward Philadelphia to E St Rd exit. Take E St Rd about 4¾ miles to store between Cushmore & Churchville Rd.

SPRING GROVE

Sonnewald Natural Foods   ♿

4796 Lehman Rd. © 717-225-3825 ℗ Tues-Th 10-6, F 10-9, Sat 8-5
Most of the produce is grown on their 60-acre organic farm and two greenhouses. On-site flour mill.
• organic produce

🍎 **From Rt 30 west of York,** go south on Rt 616 2½ miles to light in New Salem. Turn right onto New Salem Rd (becomes Stoverstown Rd) 2⅓ miles to Lehman Rd (cemetary on corner). Turn right onto Lehman to store on left.

SPRINGFIELD

Martindale's Natural Market 🛍️

1172 Baltimore Pike © 610-543-6811 ① M-F 8-9, Sat 9-9
• organic produce

🍎 **From I-476**, take exit 3 toward Swarthmore east on Baltimore Pike (left from I-476S, right from I-476N) about ¾ mile to store on left in Olde Sproul Shopping Ctr.

STAHLSTOWN

Maggie's Mercantile 🛍️ 🍴   ♿

1262 Rte. 711 © 724-593-5056 ① Tues-F 10-6, Sat 12-8, Sun 12-6
Fine dining first Friday of month from 7-9pm and Saturday buffet 5-8. Reservations required.
• organic produce • vegan • organic focus • fresh juice • cafe • deli • bakery • counter • tables • self-service • take-out

🍎 **From I-70/76 (PA Tpke)**, take exit 9 (Donegal) and follow onto Rt 31E to Rt 711N. Turn left onto 711N 2½ miles to store on right.

STATE COLLEGE

Mad Mex 🍴

240 S. Pugh St. © 814-272-5656 ① M-W, Sun 11-11, Th-Sat 11-12
See Cranberry Twp location for description.
• vegetarian friendly • vegan friendly • alcohol • counter • tables • wait staff

🍎 **From US 220**, take exit 73 onto US 322E about 1⅓ miles to Hwy 26 exit for State College. Turn right onto Hwy 26/E College Ave 2 miles to S Pugh St. Turn left onto S Pugh to restaurant on right adjoining the Days Inn Hotel.

Nature's Pantry 🛍️   ♿

1350 E. College Ave. © 814-861-5200 ① M, W, F 10-6, Tues, Th 10-8, Sat 10-4
🍎 **From US 220**, take exit 73 onto US 322E about 1⅓ miles to Hwy 26 exit for State College. Turn right onto Hwy 26/E College Ave to store on left.

The Granary 🛍️   ♿

2766 W. College Ave. © 814-238-4844 ① M-W, F-Sat 10-6, Th 10-8
🍎 **From US 220**, take exit 73 onto US 322E about 1⅓ miles to Hwy 26 exit for State College. Turn right onto Hwy 26/E College Ave under 5 miles (becomes W College) to store on left.

STROUDSBURG

Earthlight Natural Foods 🛍️

829 Ann St. © 570-424-6760 ① M-Sat 9:30-6, Sun 11-5
• organic produce

🍎 **From I-80W**, take exit 307 right onto PA 191N to first left (Ann St.) Turn left onto Ann ⅓ mile to store. **From I-80E**, take exit 307 left onto Park Ave ¼ mile to Ann. Turn left onto Ann about 1 block to store.

Everybody's Cafe 🍴

905 Main St. © 570-424-0896 ① M-Th, Sun 11-8, F-Sat 11-9:30
Dinner menu offers 30 vegetarian/vegan entrees and 50-60 tapas items. Lunch is burgers (including nonmeat versions). In a renovated mansion.
• vegetarian friendly • vegan friendly • alcohol • tables • wait staff

🍎 **From I-80W**, take exit 307 right onto PA 191N and make second left onto US 209 Bus (W Main St) under ½ mile to restaurant. **From I-80E**, take exit 305 and follow ramp toward Rt 209 Bus right onto W Main under 1 mile to restaurant.

TANNERSVILLE

Earthlight Natural Foods 🛍️

1632 Fountain Springs E. © 570-619-6592 ① M-Sat 9:30-6
• organic produce

🍴 **From I-80W,** take exit 299 toward Tannersville onto Rt 715 about ¼ mile to Rt 611. Turn right onto 611 about 2 miles to store on left. **From 80E,** take exit 299 right onto 715 over ½ mile, merge south onto Rt 611 and follow directions above.

TREXLERTOWN

Healthy Alternatives 🛍

7150 Hamilton Blvd. ✆ 610-366-9866 ⏲ M-W 9:30-6, Th 9:30-7, F 9:30-8, Sat 10-5
• organic produce • vegetarian friendly • organic focus • deli • take-out

🍴 **From I-78,** take exit 49A toward Trexlertown onto PA 100S about 2½ miles to US 222 (Hamilton Blvd). Turn left onto Hamilton under ½ mile to store on right in Trexlertown Shopping Ctr.

WAYNE

Whole Foods Market 🛍 🍴   ♿

821 Lancaster Ave. ✆ 610-688-9400 ⏲ Daily 8-9
• organic produce, vegetarian friendly, salad bar, cafe, self-service, take-out

🍴 **From I-476,** take exit 13 toward St Davids left off ramp onto Rt 30W (E Lancaster Ave) about 2½ miles (through town) to light at Berkley Rd. Turn right onto Berkley to store in Devon Sq. **From Rt 202,** take Devon exit south on Valley Forge Rd (left past light and bear left at fork from 202S, right at light and bear left at fork from 202N) about 1½ miles to Conestoga Rd. Turn left onto Conestoga ½ mile to bend and bear right onto Old Conestoga Rd, under overpass and right into store lot.

WILLIAMSPORT

Freshlife Whole Food Market & Cafe 🛍 🍴   ♿

2300 E. 3rd St. ✆ 570-322-8280 ⏲ M-F 9-8, Sat 9-5
• organic produce • vegetarian friendly • cafe • deli • bakery • counter • tables • self-service • take-out

🍴 **From I-180,** take exit 23B onto E 3rd St about ¼ mile to store on left. **From 220N/I-180E,** take exit 25 (Faxon) onto Northway Rd to E 3rd. Turn right onto E 3rd under 1 mile to store on right.

WILLOW GROVE

Nature's Harvest 🛍   ♿

101 E. Moreland Rd. ✆ 215-659-7705 ⏲ M-Sat 10-8, Sun 11-6
• organic produce

🍴 **From I-276 (PA Tpke),** take exit 343 toward Willow Grove onto Rt 611S almost 2 miles to store at intersection 611 & Rt 63 in Moreland Plaza.

WYNNEWOOD

Whole Foods Market 🛍   ♿

339 E. Lancaster Ave. ✆ 610-896-3737 ⏲ Daily 8-9
• organic produce • vegetarian friendly • salad bar • deli • bakery • take-out

🍴 **From I-76,** take exit 339 (City Line Ave) onto Rt 1S (right from I-76E, left from I-76W) about 2¾ miles to Rt 30/East Lancaster Ave. Turn right onto Lancaster under 2 miles to Wynnewood Rd. At next light turn right into store parking lot.

YORK

Allen's Natural Foods 🛍

350 S. Richland Ave. ✆ 717-845-8085 ⏲ M-F 9-6, Sat 9-4
• organic produce

🍴 **From US 30, take PA 74 (Carlisle Rd)** toward W York (merge straight from 30E, left off ramp from 30W) over 1 mile to Linden Ave. Turn right onto Linden 1 bock to Richland Ave. Turn left onto Richland ½ mile to store. **From I-83S,** merge onto 30W via exit 22 and follow directions above. **From I-83N,** take exit 15 toward S George St onto 83 Bus N 2 miles to Country Club Rd. Turn left onto Country Club 1 mile to Richland. Turn right onto Richland ¾ mile to store.

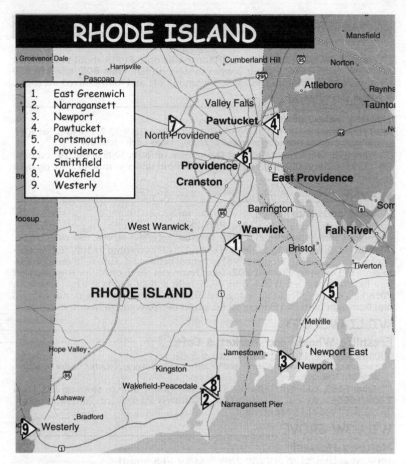

EAST GREENWICH

Back to Basics Natural Food Grocery 🛍
500 Main St. ✆ 401-885-2679 ⏲ M-F 9-7, Sat 9-6, Sun 12-5
 • organic produce

🛏 **From I-95S,** veer left onto Rt 4S under ½ mile to exit 8 toward E Greenwich. Follow Division Rd ramp and turn right onto Rt 401 about 2¼ miles (becomes 1st Ave) to Main St. Turn left onto Main to store on right. **From I-95N,** take exit 8A onto Quaker Ln, turn left onto 401/Division Rd and follow directions above.

NARRAGANSETT

Crazy Burger Cafe & Juice Bar 🍴
144 Boon St. ✆ 401-783-1810 ⏲ M-Th, Sun 8-9, F-Sat 8-10
The attraction here is the six vegan burgers.
 • egetarian friendly • vegan friendly • fresh juice • tables • wait staff

🛏 **From Rt 1S,** take Rt 108S exit toward Narragansett left onto Kingstown Rd and at rotary take second exit onto Rt 1A/Kingstown Rd about 1¼ miles to Caswell St. Turn right onto Caswell 2 blocks to Central St. Turn left onto Central 1 block to Boon St. Turn right onto Boon to restaurant on left. **From Rt 1N,** take exit for Narragansett right onto Rt 1A/Woodruff Ave (becomes S Pier Rd) under 1½ miles to Gibson Ave. Turn left onto Gibson under ¼ mile to restaurant on right after Rodman St.

Food for Thought 🛍

140 Point Judith Rd. #32 © 401-789-2445 ⏰ M, W-Sat 9-6, Tues 9-7
🍎 **From Rt 1S**, take Rt 108S exit right onto Woodruff Ave and right onto Point Judith Rd about ½ mile to store on left in Mariner Square Mall. **From Rt 1N**, take Narragansett exit right onto Woodruff and follow directions above.

NEWPORT

A Market Natural Foods 🛍

181 Bellevue Ave. © 401-846-8137 ⏰ M-Sat 8-8, Sun 9-7
• organic produce
🍎 **From the Newport Bridge**, take RI 238S exit right onto JT Connell Rd continuing onto Farewell St about ⅓ mile to Americas Cup Ave. Take right fork onto Americas Cup under 1 mile and veer left onto Memorial Blvd W ⅓ mile to Bellevue Ave. Turn right onto Bellevue to store on right in Bellevue Garden Shopping Plaza.

Lucia Italian Restaurant 🍴

186B-190B Thomas St. © 401-846-4477 ⏰ M-Tues 5:30-10, Th 12-3:30, 5:30-10, F 12-3:30, 5:30-10:30, Sat 12-11, Sun 12-10
Italian menu with vegetarian section including seitan dishes. BYOB.
• vegetarian friendly • vegan friendly • tables • wait staff
🍎 **From the Newport Bridge**, take RI 238S exit right onto JT Connell Rd continuing onto Farewell St under ½ mile to Thames St. Veer right onto Thames under ½ mile to restaurant on left across from Brick Market Place.

PAWTUCKET

Garden Grille 🍴

727 East Ave. © 401-726-2826 ⏰ M-Th 11-9:30, F-Sat 11-10, Sun 10-3, 5-9:30
• vegetarian • vegan friendly • organic focus • fresh juice • alcohol • counter • tables • wait staff
🍎 **From I-95N,** take exit 25 (N Main St) right off ramp to light at N Main (US 1N). Turn left onto N Main about ½ mile to Lafayette St. Turn right onto Lafayette about 3 blocks to end. Restaurant is on left in Blackstone Plaza. **From I-95S**, take exit 27 for downtown Pawtucket toward US 1. Turn left at light onto George St about ⅓ mile to light at East Ave. Bear left onto East under 1 mile to restaurant on right.

PORTSMOUTH

The Green Grocer 🛍

934 E. Main Rd. © 401-683-0007 ⏰ M-Sat 9-8, Sun 10-5
Homemade soups and locally made prepared foods available.
• organic produce
🍎 **From the Newport Bridge,** turn left and continue on Rt 138 (becomes W Main then E Main Rd) over 4½ miles to store on left before Union St.

PROVIDENCE

Julian's 🍴   ♿

318 Broadway © 401-861-1770 ⏰ M-F 9-11, Sat-Sun 9-2:45, 5-11
A variety of tofu and tempeh options.
• vegetarian friendly • alcohol • tables • wait staff
🍎 **From I-95**, take exit 21 west on Broadway (left from I-95N, onto Service Rd and right from I-95S) about ½ mile to restaurant on left after Vinton St.

*Please tell these businesses
that you found them in Healthy Highways*

Taqueria Pacifica at AS220 Cafe 🍴   ♿

115 Empire St. ✆ 401-621-8785 ☉ Tues-Sat 10-10
Tofu burritos, vegan sour cream, local vegetables. Alcohol after 5 pm.
  • vegetarian friendly • organic focus • alcohol • tables • self service
🍎 **From I-95S**, take exit 21 left onto Atwells Ave across hwy, left onto Broadway and left onto Empire St 1 block to restaurant on left after Washington St. **From I-95N**, take exit 21 right onto Broadway and follow directions above.

Whole Foods Market 🛍 🍴   ♿

601 N. Main St. ✆ 401-621-5990 ☉ Daily 8-10
  • organic produce • vegetarian friendly • salad bar • cafe • self-service • take-out
🍎 **From I-195**, take exit 24 onto Branch Ave (left from I-195S, right from I-195N) to first light (N Main St). Bear right onto N Main about 3 blocks to store on left.

Whole Foods Market 🛍   ♿

261 Waterman St. ✆ 401-272-1690 ☉ Daily 8-10
  • organic produce • vegetarian friendly • salad bar • deli • bakery • take-out
🍎 **From I-195**, take exit 3 right onto Gano St to third light (Waterman St). Turn right onto Waterman 3 blocks to store on right. **From I-95N**, take exit 20 onto I-195E and follow directions above. **From I-95S**, take exit 22C-B-A toward downtown and make two lefts off ramp onto US 6E/Memorial Dr about ¼ mile to Washington Pl. Turn left onto Washington (becomes Waterman) about 1¼ miles to store.

SMITHFIELD

Foodworks 🛍

9 Cedar Swamp Rd. ✆ 401-232-2410 ☉ M-Sat 9-8, Sun 10-6
  • organic produce
🍎 **From I-295**, take exit 7B toward Greenville onto RI 44W/Putnam Pike about 1¼ miles (third light) to Cedar Swamp Rd. Turn right onto Cedar Swamp to store on right in Apple Valley Plaza.

WAKEFIELD

Alternative Food Cooperative 🛍

357 Main St. ✆ 401-789-2240 ☉ M-F 9-8, Sat 9-6, Sun 10-5
  • organic produce • vegetarian • deli • take-out • co-op
🍎 **From Rt 1S**, take first Wakefield exit right onto Old Tower Hill Rd (becomes Main St) about 1 mile (past 3 lights and then ⅓ mile) to store on right (across from Kenyon Ave). **From Rt 1N**, take Pond St exit left onto Pond about ¾ mile to Main. Turn right onto Main ⅓ mile to store on left.

WESTERLY

Allen's Health Food 🛍

62 Franklin St. ✆ 401-596-5569 ☉ M-Tues 9-5:30, W-Th, Sat 9:30-5:30, F 9-6
🍎 **From I-95**, take exit 92 onto Rt 2S (right from I-95N, onto Rt 617 and left from I-95S) about 1¼ miles to Rt 78. Merge onto 78E 4½ miles to Rt 1S exit. Turn right onto Rt 1 (aka Franklin St) about ½ mile to store on right in Ocean Plaza.

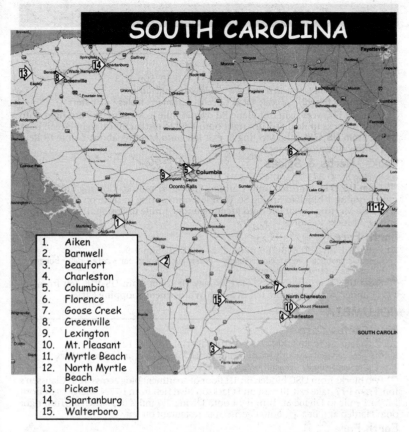

SOUTH CAROLINA

1. Aiken
2. Barnwell
3. Beaufort
4. Charleston
5. Columbia
6. Florence
7. Goose Creek
8. Greenville
9. Lexington
10. Mt. Pleasant
11. Myrtle Beach
12. North Myrtle Beach
13. Pickens
14. Spartanburg
15. Walterboro

AIKEN

Magnolia Natural Market 🛍 🍽

210 York St. S.E. ✆ 803-649-3339 🕐 M-F 10-6
• organic produce • vegetarian friendly • vegan friendly • fresh juice • cafe • deli • tables • self-service • wait staff • take-out

💬 Aiken is about 5 miles south of I-20 exit 18 on SC 19. **From SC 19, US 1 and US 78 intersection**, store is 3 blocks southeast on Richland Ave and 1 block southwest (right coming from SC 19, left coming north on US 78) on left side of York St.

BARNWELL

The Genesis Store 🛍

214 Main St. ✆ 803-541-6109 🕐 M-Th 10-7, F 10-3
💬 **From US 278**, merge onto Dunbarton Blvd from US 278S (turn right onto Dunbarton from US 278N) and circle around Main St to store on right.

BEAUFORT

It's Only Natural 🛍

95 Sea Island Pkwy. ✆ 843-986-9595 🕐 M-F 8-5:30, Sat 9-5
• organic produce • vegetarian friendly • organic focus • fresh juice • cafe • deli • tables • self-service • take-out

💬 **From the mainland or Port Royal Island on SC 21**, store is on right between Sunset Blvd & Youmans Dr. **From Port Royal on SC 802 (aka Ladys Island Dr)**, turn left onto SC 21/Sea Island Pkwy under ½ mile to store on left after Youmans.

CHARLESTON

Alluette's Cafe 🍴

80A Reid St. ℰ 843-577-6926 ⏰ M-Sat 11-4, 5-8:30, Sun 11-3
Geechee-Gullah soul food with a new age, wholefoods sensibility.
  • vegetarian friendly • organic focus • alcohol • counter • tables • wait staff

🍎 **From US 17E,** veer right onto Line Rd over ½ mile to Meeting St. Turn right onto Meeting 4 bocks to Reid St. Turn right onto Reid to restaurant on right (small pink bldg). **From US 17W,** take Meeting St exit left onto Meeting about 1 mile to Reid and follow directions above.

Books, Herbs & Spices 🛍

63 Spring St. ℰ 843-722-4747 ⏰ M-F 10-6, Sat 9:30-6

🛍 **From US 17E**, continue onto Cannon St over ½ mile to Coming St. Turn left onto Coming 1 block to Spring St. Turn left onto Spring to store on left. **From US 17W,** take Meeting St exit left onto Meeting under 1 mile to Spring. Turn right onto Spring 3 blocks to store.

Earth Fare 🛍 🍴   ♿

74 Follly Rd. Blvd. ℰ 843-769-4800 ⏰ M-Sat 8-10, Sun 9-9
  • organic produce • vegetarian friendly • fresh juice • salad bar • cafe • deli • bakery • tables • self-service • take-out

🍎 **From US 17**, go south on SC 171/Wesley Dr (right from US 12E, left from US 17W) under ¼ mile to store left in South Windermere Shopping Ctr.

COLUMBIA

Blue Cactus Cafe 🍴

2002 Greene St. ℰ 803-929-0782 ⏰ Tues-F 11-3, 5-9, Sat 12-9
Korean plus burritos, variously spiced "beans & rice," sandwiches and other surprises.
  • egetarian friendly • vegan friendly • tables • wait staff

🍎 Two blocks from USC hidden on 1st floor of apartment bldg across from Claussen's Inn. **From I-77,** take exit 10 west on Ft Jackson Blvd (left from I-77N, merge right from I-77S) 1 mile to Divine St. Turn right onto Divine 2½ miles to Harden St. Turn right onto Harden and first left onto Greene St to restaurant on left.

Earth Fare 🛍 🍴   ♿

3312 B Devine St. ℰ 803-799-0048 ⏰ Daily 8-10
  • organic produce • vegetarian friendly • fresh juice • salad bar • cafe • deli • bakery • tables • self-service • take-out

🍎 **From I-77**, take exit 10 west on Fort Jackson Blvd (left from I-77N, merge right from I-77S) 1 mile to end at Devine St (US 76). Turn right onto Devine about 2 blocks to store on left.

Rosewood Market & Deli 🛍 🍴   ♿

2803 Rosewood Dr. ℰ 803-765-1083 ⏰ M-Sat 9-8:30, Sun 10-7
Vegetarian, vegan and macrobiotic selections.
  • organic produce • vegetarian friendly • vegan friendly • cafe • deli • bakery • counter • tables • self-service • take-out

🍎 **From I-77S**, take exit 10 onto Ft Jackson Blvd ½ mile and take left fork onto Wildcat Rd continuing onto Rosewood Dr about 2 miles total to store on right at S Maple St. **From I-77N,** take exit 5 left at fork onto SC 48W/Bluff Rd toward Columbia 2½ miles to Rosewood. Turn right onto Rosewood almost 1½ miles to store on left.

FLORENCE

The Healthy Food Store 🛍

2191 W. Evans St. ℰ 843-629-9204 ⏰ M-Sat 9-6
Limited produce selection.

🍎 **From I-95S**, take exit 160A for I-20E toward Florence onto David H McLeod Blvd E about 2 miles to W Evans St. Turn left onto W Evans 1 block to store on left.

GOOSE CREEK
Vitamins Plus 🛍️
119 N. Goose Creek Blvd. ✆ 843-797-3200 ⏰ M-Sat 10-7
• organic produce

🍎 **From I-26S**, take exit 206B for US 78E toward Goose Creek onto University Blvd 1½ miles to Goose Creek Rd. Veer left onto Goose Creek ½ mile and take ramp onto Goose Creek Blvd about 2¼ miles to store on left. **From I-26W,** take exit 209B-A toward Goose Creek 2 miles to US 78/Rivers Ave. Turn left onto US 78 under 1 mile and veer left onto US 52/Goose Creek Blvd 2½ miles to store.

GREENVILLE
Earth Fare 🛍️ 🍴   ♿
3620 Pelham Rd. ✆ 864-527-4220 ⏰ M-Sat 8-9, Sun 9-9
• organic produce • vegetarian friendly • fresh juice • salad bar • cafe • deli • bakery
• counter • tables • self-service • take-out

🍎 **From I-85**, take exit 54 northwest on Pelham Rd (left from I-85N, merge right from I-85S) 1-1⅓ miles to store on left.

SWAD 🍴
1421A Laurens Rd. ✆ 864-233-2089 ⏰ M-Sat 11:30-9
Vegetarian Indian.
• vegetarian • vegan friendly • tables • wait staff • take-out

🍎 **From I-85**, take exit 48B toward Greenville onto Laurens Rd (right from I-85S, loop around right from I-85N) about 2½ miles to restaurant.

Whole Foods Market 🛍️ 🍴
1140 Woodruff Rd. ✆ 864-335-2300 ⏰ M-Th, 8-9, F-Sat 8-10, Sun 9-9
• organic produce • vegetarian friendly • salad bar • cafe • self-service • take-out

🍎 **From I-85**, take exit 51 for I-385S and take exit 51A southeast on Woodruff Rd (left from I-85S, merge right from I-85N) to store on right. **From I-385**, take exit 65 northwest on Woodruff about ¾ mile to store on left.

LEXINGTON
14 Carrot Whole Foods 🛍️
5300 Sunset Blvd. ✆ 803-359-2920 ⏰ M-Sat 9-7, Sun 1-6
• organic produce

🍎 **From I-20W**, take exit 61 toward Lexington/Lake Murray Dam onto US 378W (Sunset Blvd) under 3 miles to store. **From I-20E**, take exit 55 toward Lexington/ Lake Murray Dam left onto SC 6 2⅔ miles to US 378. Continue straight onto 378E about 1½ miles to store.

MT. PLEASANT
Whole Foods Market 🛍️ 🍴
923 Houston Northcutt Blvd. ✆ 843-971-7240 ⏰ Daily 8-9
• organic produce • vegetarian friendly • salad bar • cafe • self-service • take-out

🍎 Store is 3 miles east of Charleston and 2⅓ miles west of I-526 exit 30 just south of US 17 on west side of Houston Northcutt Blvd in Patriots Plaza Shopping Ctr.

MYRTLE BEACH
New Life Natural Foods 🛍️ 🍴
1209 38th Ave. N. ✆ 843-448-0011 ⏰ M-Sat 9-8, Sun 12-6
• organic produce • vegetarian friendly • fresh juice • deli • tables • self-service • take-out

🍎 **From Hwy 501**, take 17N/Byp toward N Myrtle Beach about 3 miles to 38th Ave N. Turn right onto 38th to store.

NORTH MYRTLE BEACH

New Life Natural Foods 🛍️

556 Hwy. 17 N. ℂ 843-272-4436 ⏰ M-Sat 9-7, Sun 12-6
• vegetarian friendly • deli • take-out

🚗 **From Rt 22/Veteran's Hwy**, take Hwy 31N 7½ miles to Hwy 9 toward N Myrtle Beach. Merge onto 9S ½ mile to store. **From the coast**, go inland at Sea Mtn Rd about 1¾ miles to store at Little River Neck Rd.

PICKENS

Bee Well Honey & Natural Market 🛍️

205 Hampton Ave. (Hwy. 8) ℂ 864-898-5122 ⏰ M-F 9-7, Sat 9-5
Fresh raw honey and homegrown organic vegetables in season.

🚗 **From US 178/SC 83 intersection**, store is 3 blocks east on SC 83/Jewell St and 1 block south on SC8/Hampton St on east side.

SPARTANBURG

Garner's Natural Foods 🛍️ 🍴

1855 E. Main St. ℂ 864-585-1021 ⏰ M-Sat 9-6
• vegetarian friendly • cafe • tables • self-service • take-out

🚗 **From I-26N**, take exit 21B onto US 29N (E Main St) about 7 miles to store on right in Hillcrest Specialty Row. **From I-85N**, take exit 72 toward Spartanburg onto US 176E about 3⅓ miles (becomes N Pine St). Follow N Pine almost 2 miles to E St John St (US 29). Turn left onto 29 (E Main St) about 2¼ miles to store on right. **From I-85S**, take exit 83 toward SC 110/Cowpens right onto Horry Rd, left onto Dewberry Rd and left onto SC 110/Battleground Rd 2 miles to US 29. Turn right onto 29 (N Main) 6 miles to store on left.

WALTERBORO

No Junk Julie's 🛍️

281 Cooler's Dairy Rd. ℂ 843-538-8809 ⏰ Tues-Sat 10-6
• organic produce

🚗 **From I-95**, take exit 57 onto SC 64 (Bells Hwy) toward Waterboro. Turn left at second light onto Robertson Blvd, go two lights and turn left onto Wichman St (Cottageville Hwy/12-A) about 3 miles (look for Circle M Ranch sign on left). Turn left onto Cooler's Dairy Rd about ¼ mile to store on left.

SYMBOLS & DESCRIPTIONS

The symbols and standard list of features we employed are explained below. Because not all establishments responded in full to our questionnaire, some details will inevitably be missing.

 natural food store

 restaurant

  natural food store with an eating area

♿ handicap restrooms

🚫 no credit cards accepted

alcohol indicates beer, wine and/or hard liquor is served.

bakery denotes baked goods made on site.

cafe signifies a store with an eating area.

co-op refers to ownership.

counter and **tables** refer to seating options.

deli implies a display case with freshly made food.

fresh juice signifies that fresh juice is made on the premises.

kosher is for kitchens that have been so certified.

organic focus means a significant portion of the menu incorporates organic ingredients.

organic produce is noted where we have been able to verify a reasonable selection. These stores may also sell conventional produce.

salad bar is just what it says.

self-service includes buffets, cafeterias, salad bars, and venues where orders are placed at the counter (even if the food is brought to your table).

take-out is noted when we know it to be a significant feature.

vegan means no animal products at all are served.

vegan-friendly signifies attention to providing animal-free choices.

vegetarian means no animal flesh is served.

vegetarian-friendly signifies fish, poultry or meat may also be served.

wait staff denotes full table service. When both self-service and wait staff appear, orders are taken at the table and there is also either a buffet or salad bar option.

SOUTH DAKOTA

1. Aberdeen
2. Brookings
3. Mitchell
4. Pierre
5. Rapid City
6. Sioux Falls
7. Spearfish

ABERDEEN

Natural Abundance Food Coop

125 S. Main St. ✆ 605-229-4947 ◷ M-F 9-7, Sat 9-6
• organic produce • co-op

🛍 **From Hwy 12**, go north on Main St 4 blocks to store at 2nd Ave.

BROOKINGS

Nature's Paradise

1455 6th St. ✆ 605-697-7404 ◷ M-Sat 10-5:30
• organic produce

🛍 **From I-29**, take exit 132 onto Hwy 14W (right from I-29S, left from I-29N) 1 mile (past 3 lights) to store (across from pool).

MITCHELL

Wayne & Mary's Nutrition Center

1313 W. Havens St. ✆ 605-996-9868 ◷ M-F 9-7, Sat 9-5

🛍 **From I-90**, take exit 330 north on 90 Bus (right from I-90W, left from I-90E) about ⅔ mile to first light and turn right onto W Havens to store on right at west end of mall.

PIERRE

Main Street Market

540 S. Garfield Ave. ✆ 605-224-9909 ◷ M-F 10-6, Sat 10-5
🛍 Store is just north of Hwy 34 on the east side of S Garfield Ave.

RAPID CITY

Breadroot Natural Food Co-op

130 Main St. ✆ 605-348-3331 ◷ M-Sat 10-6, Sun 12-5
• organic produce • co-op

🛍 **From I-90E**, take exit 57 onto I-190S about 1⅓ miles to W Omaha St. Turn

left onto W Omaha about 1 mile to 1st St. Turn right onto first across tracks to Main St. Turn right onto Main to store on right. **From I-90W,** take exit 60 left at fork toward E North St, veer left onto E North 2½ miles and continue onto E Blvd N about ¼ mile to Main. Turn right onto Main 1 block to store.

Main Street Market
512 Main St. ℂ 605-341-9099 ⏱ M-F 9-6, Sat 9-5

From I-90, take exit 58 south on Hains Ave (left from I-90W, right from I-90E) about 1½ miles (becomes N 5th St) to Main St. Turn right onto Main to store on right.

Staple and Spice Market
601 Mt. Rushmore Rd, ℂ 605-343-3900 ⏱ M-F 9-6, Sat 9-5
 • organic produce

From I-90, take exit 57 onto I-190S (West Blvd) 1½ miles to St Joseph St. Turn left onto St Joseph 2 blocks to store at Mt Rushmore Rd.

SIOUX FALLS

Meadowsweet Market
3801 W. 34th St., Ste. 109 ℂ 605-361-5526 ⏱ M-F 9-8, Sat 9-5, Sun 12-5
 • organic produce

From I-29, take exit 78 southwest on W 26th St (left from I-29S, right from I-29N) continuing onto S Louise Ave over ½ mile to store on left at W 34th St.

The Co-op Natural Foods Cooperative
2504 S. Duluth Ave. ℂ 605-339-9506 ⏱ M-F 9-7, Sat 9-6, Sun 12-5
 • organic produce • co-op

From I-29, take exit 77 west on W 41st St (left from I-29S, right from I-29N) under 2½ miles to S Duluth Ave. Turn left onto S Duluth ½ mile to store on right between W 35th & W 33rd St.

SPEARFISH

Bay Leaf Cafe
126 W. Hudson St. ℂ 605-642-5462 ⏱ Winter M-W 11-2:30, Th-Sat 11-8:30 Memorial to Labor Day M-Sat 11-9, Sun 4-9
 • egetarian friendly • alcohol • tables • wait staff

From I-90, take exit 12 toward Spearfish/Black Hills State U west on Jackson Blvd (left from I-90W, right from I-90E) about ½ mile to Main St. Turn left onto Main 2 blocks to W Hudson St. Turn right onto Hudson to restaurant.

Good Earth Natural Foods
638 Main St. ℂ 605-642-7639 ⏱ M-Sat 9-5:30
 • organic produce

From I-90, take exit 12 toward Spearfish/Black Hills State U west on Jackson Blvd (left from I-90W, right from I-90E) about ½ mile to Main St. Turn left onto Main to store on left.

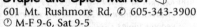

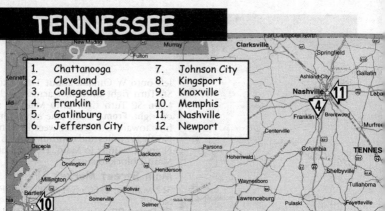

TENNESSEE

1. Chattanooga
2. Cleveland
3. Collegedale
4. Franklin
5. Gatlinburg
6. Jefferson City
7. Johnson City
8. Kingsport
9. Knoxville
10. Memphis
11. Nashville
12. Newport

CHATTANOOGA

Country Life Vegetarian Restaurant & Bakery 🍴

809 Market St. ✆ 423-634-9925 ✆ M-F, Sun 11-2:30
Run by laymen from the Seventh-day Adventist church.
  • vegan • tables • self-service

🍴 **From I-24**, take exit 178 left at fork and merge onto US 27N about 1 mile to exit 1A for ML King Blvd. Turn right onto W MLK 3 blocks to Market St. Turn left onto Market to restaurant on left before 8th St.

Greenlife Grocery 🛒 🍴   ♿

301 Manufacturer's Rd. ✆ 423-702-7300 ✆ M-Sat 8-9, Sun 9-9
  • organic produce • vegetarian friendly • fresh juice • salad bar • cafe • deli • tables •
  self-service • take-out

🍴 **From I-24**, take exit 178 left at fork and merge onto US 27N about 2½ miles to Manufacturers Rd. Turn right onto Manufacturers about ⅓ mile to store on left.

CLEVELAND

Abundant Living 🛒

855 Keith St. N.W. ✆ 423-614-7885 ✆ M-F 9-7, Sat 9-6
  • organic produce

🍴 **From I-75**, take exit 25 for TN 60 toward Cleveland east on 25th St NW (left from I-75N, right from I-75S) about 1¼ miles to Keith St NW. Turn right onto Keith about 1¼ miles to store on right in Keith St Plaza.

COLLEGEDALE

Village Market 🛒 🍴   ♿

5002 University Dr. ✆ 423-236-2300 ✆ M-Th 7-8, F 7-4, Sun 9-6 Hot bar M-F 10:30-2
  • organic produce • vegetarian • vegan friendly • salad bar • deli • tables • self-service
  • take-out

🍴 **From I-75**, take exit 11 (Ooletewah) east on Lee Hwy (right from I-75N, left from I-75S) about ⅓ mile to Little Debbie Pkwy. Turn right onto Little Debbie 1¾ miles to end at Apison Pike. Turn left onto Apison over 1½ miles to 4-way stop at University Dr. Veer right onto University to store on left in Fleming Plaza (across from Southern Adventist U).

FRANKLIN

Wild Oats Market 🛒 🍴

1735 Galleria Blvd. ✆ 615-778-1910 ✆ M-Sat 7-10, Sun 9-10
  • organic produce • vegetarian friendly • salad bar • cafe • self-service • take-out

🍴 **From I-65**, take exit 69 south on Galleria Blvd (left from I-65S, left onto Moores Ln and left from I-65N) to store on right.

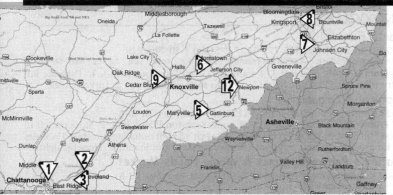

GATLINBURG

Whole Earth Grocery 🛍️ 🍴

446 E. Pkwy., Ste. 4 ✆ 865-436-6967 ⏰ M-F 10-6, Sat 10-5, Sun 11-3
Produce is seasonal and local. Lunch weekdays from 11-3.
• organic produce • vegetarian friendly • vegan friendly • tables • self-service, take-out
🍴 On the northern edge of the Great Smoky Mts. Store is on Hwy 321 about ¼ mile east of Hwy 441 between Spruce & Poplar Ln.

JEFFERSON CITY

Hill's Health Hut 🛍️

107 E. Old Ajay Hwy. ✆ 865-475-2993 ⏰ M-F 9:30-5:30, Sat 10-3
🍴 **From I-40W**, take exit 417 north on TN 92N (right from I-40W, left from I-40E) over 7 miles (at over 6 miles 92 turns right onto George Ave, right onto College St, and left onto S Banner Ave) to Old Andrew Johnson (Ajay) Hwy. Turn left onto Ajay Hwy to store.

JOHNSON CITY

Natural Food Market 🛍️

3211 People's St., Ste. 74 ✆ 423-610-1000 ⏰ M-Sat 10-9, Sun 1-5
• organic produce
🍴 **From I-26**, take exit 19 for State Hwy 381 toward Bristol/State of Franklin Rd south on Oakland (right from I-26E, left from I-26W) ⅓ mile to Green Line Ave/W Oakland. Turn left onto Green Line 1 block to Peoples St. Turn left onto Peoples about ¼ mile to store on left.

The Health Barn 🛍️

3116 E. Oakland Ave. ✆ 423-283-4719 ⏰ M-Sat 10-8
• organic produce
🍴 **From I-26E**, take exit 19 for State Hwy 381 toward Bristol/State of Franklin Rd left on Oakland Ave under ¼ mile to Browns Mill Rd. Jog right onto Browns Mill continuing onto Oakland under ½ mile to store on left after Kingsport Hwy. **From I-26W**, take exit 20A and merge onto N Roan St ½ mile to E Oakland. Turn left onto E Oakland 1 block to store on right.

KINGSPORT

Good Food Grocery 🛍️

1425 E. Center St. ✆ 423-246-3663 ⏰ M-F 8-7, Sat 8-6, Sun 1-5
🍴 **From I-81**, take exit 59 onto TN 36N (Center St in Kingsport) about 5½ miles to store.

KNOXVILLE

Earth Fare 🛒🍴
10903 Parkside Dr. ✆ 865-777-3837 ◷ M-Sat 8-10, Sun 9-9
• organic produce • vegetarian friendly • salad bar • cafe • deli • tables • self-service
🍎 **From I-75/40**, take exit 374 south on Lovell Rd about ½ mile to Parkside Rd. Turn right onto Parkside about ½ mile to store in the Shops at Turkey Creek.

Natural & Organic 🛒
7025 Kingston Pike ✆ 865-584-8422 ◷ M 10-8, Tues-Th 10-6
🍎 **From I-75/40E**, take exit 380 left onto Kingston Pike 1 mile to store on left in West Hill Shopping Ctr. **From I-40W**, take exit 383 left onto Papermill Dr 1¼ miles to Kingston Pike. Turn right onto Kingston Pike about ⅓ mile to store on right.

Nature's Pantry Gourmet & Whole Foods Market 🛒
6600 Kingston Pike ✆ 865-584-4714 ◷ M-Sat 10-8, Sun 12-6
• organic produce
🍎 **From I-40**, take exit 383 (Papermill Dr) onto Northshore Dr (straight from I-40E, 2 lefts from I-40W) about ½ mile to Kingston Pike. Turn right onto Kingston Pike to store about 1 mile up hill on left.

Organic Roots Cafe 🍴
6600 Kingston Pike ✆ 865-584-6728 ◷ M-Sat 11-6
• vegan • organic focus • fresh juice • tables • wait staff • take-out
🍎 **From I-40**, take exit 383 (Papermill Dr) onto Northshore Dr (straight from I-40E, 2 lefts from I-40W) about ½ mile to Kingston Pike. Turn right onto Kingston Pike to restaurant about 1 mile up hill on left.

Three Rivers Market 🛒
937 N. Broadway ✆ 865-525-2069m◷ Daily 9-9
• organic produce • co-op
🍎 **From I-40W**, take exit 389A and at Broadway turn around to head south about 1 mile to store on right between Glenwood & Gill Ave. **From I-40E**, take exit 388 (Henley St) toward Downtown and follow exit ramp toward TN 62 for Western Ave. Turn left onto Western to Broadway. Turn left onto Broadway 1 mile to store on left between Gill & Glenwood.

MEMPHIS

RP Tracks 🍴
3547 Walker Ave. ✆ 901-327-1471 ◷ Daily 11am-2am
Barbecued tofu, vegan nachos and more along with traditional pub food.
• vegetarian friendly • vegan friendly • alcohol • counter • tables • wait staff
🍎 A few blocks from U of Memphis. **From I-40W,** continue on Sam Cooper Blvd W 3½ miles and take exit 7 left onto N Highland 2¼ miles to Walker Ave. Turn left onto Walker to restaurant on right. **From I-240W**, take exit 20 right onto Gatewell Rd under 2 miles to Park Ave. Turn left onto Park 1 mile to S Highland. Turn right onto S Highland about ½ mile to Walker. Turn right onto Walker to restaurant. **From I-240E**, take exit 21 onto Lamar Ave and turn right onto S Prescott St under 2 miles to Radford Rd. Turn right onto Radford 3 blocks and turn left onto S Highland under 1 mile to Walker. Turn right onto Walker to restaurant. **From I-55**, merge onto I-240E and follow directions above.

Wild Oats Market 🛒🍴   ♿
5022 Poplar Ave. ✆ 901-685-2293 ◷ M-Sat 8-10, Sun 9-9
• organic produce • vegetarian friendly • salad bar • cafe • self-service • take-out
🍎 **From I-240**, take exit 15 (15B from I-240E) onto US 78W/Poplar Ave (right from I-240W, left from I-240E) about 1⅓ miles to store on right at Mendenhall/Mt Moriah Rd.

NASHVILLE

Grins Vegetarian Cafe 🍴   ♿
2421 Vanderbilt Place ✆ 615-322-8571 ◷ M-Th 10:30-8, F 10:30-2

On the Vanderbilt U campus but open to all.
• vegetarian • kosher • tables • self-service

🍎 **From I-40W**, take exit 209A onto 13th Ave N to Broadway. Turn left onto Broadway about 1 mile (stay right when road forks onto West End Ave) to light at 25th Ave. Turn left onto 25th 2 blocks to restaurant at Vanderbilt Place (in Schulman Center). **From I-40E**, merge onto I-440E and take exit 1 toward West End Ave/US70S E left onto Murphy Rd and left onto West End about 1 mile to light at 25th. Turn right onto 25th 2 blocks to restaurant.

Produce Place 🛍️
4000 Murphy Rd. ✆ 615-383-2664 ⏰ M-F 9-6:30, Sat 8-6
• organic produce

🍎 **From I-440**, take exit 1 toward West End Ave onto Murphy Rd. Turn west onto Murphy (right from I-440E, left from I-440W) about ½ mile to store at 40th St.

The Turnip Truck Natural Market 🛍️ 🍴
970 Woodland St. ✆ 615-650-3600 ⏰ M-Sat 8-8, Sun 10-7
• organic produce • vegetarian friendly • deli • counter • self-service • take-out

🍎 **From I-24E**, take exit 48 toward James Robertson Pkwy onto Interstate Dr and turn left onto Main St about ¾ mile to S 9th St. Turn right onto S 9th 1 block to Woodland Ave. Turn left onto Woodland 2 blocks to store on right before S 10th St. **From I-24W**, take exit 49 for Shelby Ave right onto Summer Pl and left onto 5th St 3 blocks to Woodland. Turn right onto Woodland under 1 mile to store.

Veggie Cafe 🍴
1601 Riverside Drive ✆ 615-495-8888 ⏰ Tues-Sat 10:30-7, 1st Sun 10-2
Soups, sandwiches, wraps, hot specials and nondairy smoothies.
• vegetarian • vegan friendly • organic focus • tables • self-service • take-out

🍎 **From I-65S**, take exit 90A for Hwy 155W/Briley Pkwy left at fork onto US 31E S 3 miles to Trinity Ln exit. Turn right onto E Trinity about ¾ mile to Gallitin Pike. Turn right onto Gallitin ½ mile to Cahal Ave. Turn left onto Cahal 1 mile to Porter Rd. Veer right onto Porter and veer left onto Riverside Dr to restaurant on right. **From I-24W**, take exit 47A toward Ellington Pkwy and veer right onto Spring St to Main St. Turn left onto Main 1 mile continuing onto Gallitin about 1⅓ miles to Cahal. Turn right onto Cahal and follow directions above.

Whole Foods Market 🛍️ 🍴
4021 Hillsboro Pike ✆ 615-440-5100 ⏰ M-Sat 7-10, Sun 8-9
• organic produce • vegetarian friendly • salad bar • cafe • self-service • take-out

🍎 **From I-440**, take exit 3 south on Hillsboro Pike (right from I-440E, loop around right from I-440W) about 1¾ miles to store on right.

Woodlands 🍴
3415 West End Ave. ✆ 615-463-3005 ⏰ M-F11:30-2:45, 5-10, Sat-Sun 11:30-10
Vegetarian Indian with a lunch buffet.
• vegetarian • vegan friendly • tables • self-service • wait staff

🍎 **From I-440W**, take exit 1A for US 70S E onto West End Ave to restaurant on right just off hwy on lower level of the Continental Condominiums Bldg. **From I-440E**, take exit 1 for Murphy Rd toward West End left onto Murphy to other side of hwy and turn right onto West End to restaurant on left.

NEWPORT
The Mustard Seed Health Foods 🛍️
331 Cosby Hwy. ✆ 423-623-4091 ⏰ M-Th 9:30-6, F 9:30-4
• organic produce

🍎 **From I-40**, take exit 435 toward Newport onto Hwy 321N (left from I-40E, right from I-40W) over 1 mile (past 3 lights) to store on left in The Village Shopping Ctr. **From I-81**, merge onto I-40E and follow directions above.

TEXAS

1. Abilene	14. Fredericksburg	27. Pearland
2. Acton	15. Ft. Worth	28. Plano
3. Amarillo	16. Georgetown	29. Richardson
4. Arlington	17. Highland Park	30. Roanoke
5. Austin	18. Houston	31. S. Padre Island
6. Beaumont	19. Kerrville	32. San Antonio
7. Blanco	20. Longview	33. Sherman
8. Bryan	21. Lubbock	34. Sugar Land
9. Colleyville	22. Lufkin	35. Sulphur Springs
10. Corpus Christi	23. McAllen	36. Temple
11. Dallas	24. Midland	37. Tyler
12. Denton	25. Nacogdoches	38. Waco
13. El Paso	26. Nassau Bay	39. Wichita Falls

ABILENE

Natural Food Center 🛍 🍴

2534 S. 7th St. ✆ 325-673-2726 ⊙ M-F 10-6, Sat 10-5 Lunch M-F 11-2:30, Sat 11-2
• vegetarian friendly • counter • self-service • take-out

🏠 **From I-20**, take exit 283A onto US 83S over 2½ miles and take exit toward S 7th St onto S Clack St and left onto S 7th about 2 miles to store on left.

Vitamins Plus 🛍

2550 Barrow St. ✆ 325-698-0512 ⊙ M-Sat 9-9, Sun 10-6
• organic produce

🏠 **From I-20**, take exit 283A onto US 83S about 4⅓ miles and take exit toward Southwest Dr onto S Clack St about 1 mile to S 27th St. Turn left onto S 27th ½ mile to Barrow St. Turn left onto Barrow to store on left.

ACTON

Health Nutts 🛍

3135 Fall Creek Hwy. ✆ 817-326-1483 ⊙ M-F 9-6:30, Sat 10-4

🏠 **From TX 377**, go south on Fall Creek Hwy/Farm-to-Market Rd167 about 2¾ miles to store on left after Cleburne Hwy.

AMARILLO

Eat-Rite Health Promotion Center 🛍 🍴   ♿

2425 I-40W ✆ 806-353-7476 ⊙ M-F 9-6, Sat 9-5
• organic produce • vegetarian friendly • fresh juice • salad bar • deli • bakery • counter • tables • self-service • take-out

🏠 **From I-40**, take exit 68B toward Georgia St. Store is just off hwy on SE corner.

Fountain of Health 🛍

3705 Olsen Blvd. ✆ 806-355-4011 ⊙ M 9-7, Tues-Sat 9-6
• organic produce

🏠 **From I-40**, take exit 67 south on S Western St (merge onto Frontage Rd and right from I-40E, merge onto Wolfin Ave and left from I-40W) under ½ mile to Olsen Blvd. Turn left onto Olsen 3 blocks to store on right after Hobbs Rd.

Natural Grocers by Vitamin Cottage 🛍️
400 S.W. 34th Ave. ✆ 806-463-5500 ⏰ M-F 9-8, Sat 9-7, Sun 11-5
 • organic produce

🛍️ **From I-40E,** take exit 64 onto Frontage Rd and right onto S Soncy Rd about ¾ mile to W 34th Ave. Turn right onto W 34th almost 1 mile to store on left in Summit Shopping Ctr. **From I-40W,** take exit 65 onto Frontage Rd and left onto S Coulter St about ¾ mile to W 34th. Turn right onto W 34th to store on right.

Nutrition House 🛍️
3404 N.E. 24th Ave. ✆ 806-374-9587 ⏰ M-Sat 1-5
 • organic produce

🛍️ **From I-40E,** take exit 70 onto US87N/60E 1 mile to US 60E/287N exit toward Pampa/Dumas. Merge onto Buchanan St almost 1½ miles to E Amarillo Blvd. Turn right onto E Amarillo over 1½ miles to N Seminole St. Turn left onto N Seminole 1 mile to NE 24th Ave. Turn right onto NE 24th to store on right. **From I-40W,** take exit 77 for Grand St onto I-40 Access Rd, turn right onto Tower Rd and right onto S Grand about 3 miles to NE 24th. Turn left onto NE 24th 1 block to store on left.

Vitamins Plus 🛍️
4210B S.W. 45th Ave. ✆ 806-352-6624 ⏰ M-Sat 9-9, Sun 10-6
 • organic produce

🛍️ **From I-40E,** take exit 67 onto Frontage Rd and turn right onto S Western Ave about 2 miles to W 45th Ave. Turn right onto W 45th to store on right. **From I-40W,** take exit 70 onto I-27S 3½ mile to exit 120B. Merge onto Canyon Ave and turn right onto W 45th about ¾ miles to store after S Western.

ARLINGTON

Whole Foods Market 🛍️ 🍴   ♿
801 E. Lamar Blvd. ✆ 817-461-9362 ⏰ Daily 8-10
 • organic produce • vegetarian friendly • salad bar • cafe • self-service • take-out

🍎 **From I-30W,** take exit 28 and follow FM 157N ramp onto Collins St under ¼ mile to Lamar Blvd. Turn left onto Lamar to store. **From I-30E,** take exit 27 left onto Cooper St and right onto Lamar about 1 mile to store.

AUSTIN

Bouldin Creek Coffeehouse 🍴
1501 S. 1st St. ✆ 512-416-1601 ⏰ M-F 7am-12am, Sat-Sun 9am-12am
All-day breakfast, salads, sandwiches and combo plates with beans and brown rice.
 • vegetarian • vegan friendly • alcohol • counter • self-service

🍎 **From I-35N,** take exit 232A (Oloff St/Live Oak) and follow S I-35 about ½ mile to Oloff. Turn left onto Oloff 1¼ miles to S 1st St. Turn right onto S 1st over ½ mile to restaurant at Elizabeth St. **From I-35S,** take exit 234A right onto Caesar Chavez St/E 1st St under ½ mile to Barzos St. Turn right onto Barzos, left onto 2nd St and left onto Congress Ave ⅓ mile (across river) to Barton Springs Rd. Turn right onto Barton Springs ¼ mile to S 1st. Turn left onto S 1st about ⅔ mile to restaurant.

Casa de Luz 🍴   ♿
1701 Toomey Rd. ✆ 512-476-2535 ⏰ Breakfast Daily 7-10 Lunch M-Sat 11:30-2, Sun 11-2 Dinner Daily 6-8:30
Restaurant and meeting place serving a set vegan/macrobiotic plate.
 • vegan • organic focus • tables • self-service

🍎 **From I-35,** take exit 233 west on Riverside Dr (left from I-35N, right from I-35S) about 2 miles to Lamar St. Turn left onto Lamar and make next right onto Toomey Rd 2 blocks to restaurant on left.

Madras Pavilion 🍴
9025 Research Blvd., Ste. 100 ✆ 512-719-5575 ⏰ M-F 11-3, 5-9:30, Sat-Sun 11-10
Vegetarian Indian with a lunch buffet.
 • vegetarian • vegan friendly • alcohol • tables • wait staff • self-service

From I-35N, take exit 240B onto US 183N to FM 1325 exit toward Burnet Rd. Bear left onto Research Blvd ⅓ mile to restaurant. **From I-35S**, take exit 241 toward Rundberg Ln and follow exit almost 1 mile to Rundberg. Turn right onto Rundberg about 2¼ miles to Metric Blvd. Turn left onto Metric ⅓ mile to Research. Turn right onto Research to restaurant.

Mother's Cafe & Garden 🍴
4215 Duval St. ✆ 512-451-3994 ⏱ M-F 11:15-10, Sat-Sun 10-10
 • vegetarian • vegan friendly • alcohol • tables • wait staff

From I-35, take exit 237A and follow Airport Blvd ramp onto E 45th St about ½ mile to Duval St. Turn left onto Duval almost 2 blocks to restaurant (before Park Blvd).

Mr. Natural 🛍 🍴
2414-A S. Lamar Blvd. ✆ 512-916-9223 ⏱ M-Sat 9-9
Unusual Mexican dishes, meat-substitute entrees, many vegan options.
 • vegetarian • vegan friendly • fresh juice • cafe • bakery • tables • self-service • take-out

From I-35, take exit 232A west onto E Oltorf St (merge onto I-35 Frontage Rd and right from I-35S, merge onto I-35 Frontage Rd and left from I-35N) 2 miles to Lamar Blvd. Turn left onto Lamar ½ mile to restaurant on left after Bluebonnet Ln.

Mr. Natural 🛍 🍴
1901 E. Cesar Chavez St. ✆ 512-477-5228 ⏱ M-Sat 8-8
See Lamar Blvd location for description.
 • vegetarian • vegan friendly • fresh juice • cafe • bakery • tables • self-service • take-out

From I-35, take exit 234A from I-35S, 234B from I-35N east onto E Cesar Chavez St (merge onto Service Rd and right from I-35N, left from I-35S) about ¾ mile to restaurant on right at Chicon St.

Sun Harvest Farms 🛍 🍴
4006 S. Lamar Blvd. ✆ 512-444-3079 ⏱ Daily 7-10
 • organic produce • vegetarian friendly • fresh juice • cafe • deli • tables • self-service • take-out

From I-35, take exit 230 (230B from 35S) left onto US 290W/TX 71W/W Ben White Blvd 2½ miles to Lamar Blvd exit. Turn right onto Lamar about ⅓ mile to store.

Sun Harvest Farms 🛍
2917 W. Anderson Lane ✆ 512-451-0660 ⏱ Daily 7-10
 • organic produce • vegetarian friendly • deli • take-out

From I-35N, take exit 240B toward Research Blvd onto 183N (W Anderson Ln) about 1 mile to exit toward Ohlen Rd/Peton Gin Rd. Follow onto Research Blvd and Anderson Sq and turn right onto W Anderson about 1⅓ miles to store. **From I-35S**, take exit 240A to 183N and follow directions above.

SWAD 🍴
9515 N. Lamar Blvd. ✆ 512-997-7923 ⏱ M, W-F 11:30-2:30, 5-9:30, Sat-Sun 11:30-9:30
Indian vegetarian.
 • vegetarian • vegan friendly • tables • wait staff

From I-35, take exit 241 west on Rundberg Ln (onto I-35 Service Rd and right from I-35S, onto I-35 Service Rd and left from I-35N) over ½ mile to N Lamar Blvd. Turn right onto N Lamar 1 block to restaurant on right.

Tom's Tabooley 🍴
2928 Guadalupe St. ✆ 512-479-7337 ⏱ M-F 7-7, Sat 11-7
Vegetarian/ vegan Middleastern menu except for lamb and beef gyros.
 • vegetarian friendly • vegan friendly • tables • self-serve • take-out

From I-35S, take exit 237A-236B toward Airport Blvd/38½ St onto I-35 Service Rd to E 41st St. Turn right onto 41st over ½ mile to Duval St. Turn left onto Duval 4 blocks to E 38th St. Turn right onto 38th over ½ mile to Guadalupe St. Turn left onto Guadalupe ½ mile to restaurant on right after W 30th St. **From I-35N**, take exit 235A toward 15th & MLK Blvd onto I-35 Service Rd N to E 15th St. Turn left onto 15th ½ mile to Congress Ave. Turn right onto Congress 4 blocks to MLK. Turn left onto MLK 3 blocks to Guadalupe. Turn right onto Guadalupe 1 mile to restaurant on left after W 29th St.

Veggie Heaven ♨
1914A Guadalupe St. ✆ 512-457-1013 ⏲ Daily 12-8:45
Asian vegetarian.
• vegetarian • vegan friendly • tables • wait staff • take-out
🚘 **From I-35**, take exit 235A toward 15th St/MLK Blvd/State Capitol. Turn west onto MLK (right from I-35S, left from I-35N) about 1 mile to Guadalupe St. Turn right onto Guadalupe 1 block to restaurant on left (across from Dobie Mall).

Wheatsville Co-op 🛍 ♨ &
3101 Guadalupe St. ✆ 512-478-2667 ⏲ Daily 9-11
• organic produce • vegetarian friendly • deli • bakery • tables • self-service • take-out • co-op
🚘 **From I-35**, take 38½ St exit west (becomes 38th St) under 2 miles to Guadalupe St. Turn left onto Guadalupe 7 blocks to store on left at 31st St.

Whole Foods Market 🛍 ♨ &
525 N. Lamar Blvd. ✆ 512-476-1206 ⏲ Daily 8-10
• organic produce • vegetarian friendly • salad bar • cafe • self-service • take-out
🚘 **From I-35S,** take exit 234B toward 8th-3rd St onto Service Rd/East Ave and turn right onto 6th St about 1¼ miles to N Lamar Blvd. Turn left onto N Lamar to store on left. **From I-35N,** take exit 234C toward 6th-12th St onto Service Rd, turn left onto 6th and follow directions above.

Whole Foods Market 🛍 ♨ &
9607 Research Blvd. # 300 ✆ 512-345-5003 ⏲ Daily 8-10
• organic produce • vegetarian friendly • salad bar • cafe • self-service • take-out
🚘 **From I-35N,** take exit 240B onto 183N about 4 miles to Gateway Loop 360 exit. Stay straight onto Research Blvd about ¼ mile to store on west side in Gateway Mkt. **From I-35S,** take exit 250 onto Mo Pac Expwy about 7½ miles to 183N ramp to Research Blvd. Turn right onto Research to store.

BEAUMONT

Basic Foods 🛍 ♨
229 Dowlen Rd. #7 ✆ 409-861-4424 ⏲ M-Sat 9-7
• organic produce • vegetarian friendly • deli • bakery • tables • self-service • take-out
🚘 **From I-10E**, take exit 851 toward US 90/Liberty onto I-10 and turn left onto College St about 2¼ miles to Dowlen Rd. Turn right onto Dowlen over ½ mile to store on left before Phelan Blvd. **From I-10W**, take exit 852A right onto Laurel St under ½ mile to N 23rd St. Turn right onto N 23rd 1 block to Phelan. Turn left onto Phelan under 2 miles to Dowlen. Turn left onto Dowlen to store on right.

BLANCO

Real Foods Market 🛍 ♨
410 Fourth St. ✆ 830-494-2781 ⏲ Tues-F 10-6, Sat 10-3
Housed in an historic hardware store.
• organic produce • vegetarian friendly • fresh juice • deli • tables • self-service • take-out
🚘 **From US 281 (aka Main St) in Blanco,** store is 1 block east on 4th St on north side.

BRYAN

Brazos Natural Foods 🛍
4303 S. Texas Ave. ✆ 979-846-4459 ⏲ M-F 9-6, Sat 9-2
• organic produce
🚘 **From TX 6**, take FM 60 exit onto University Dr E under 2 miles to Texas Ave S. Turn right onto Texas about ½ mile to store on right between N Rosemary & Inwood Dr.

COLLEYVILLE

The Healthy Approach Market 🛍
5100 Hwy. 121 ✆ 817-399-9100 ⏲ M-Sat 9-9

🍴 **From I-820**, take exit 22B (Airport Fwy) onto 183E/121N (stay left on 121N where road splits) about 8½ miles to Hall Johnson Rd exit. U-turn under 121S to store on right on service road.

CORPUS CHRISTI

Sun Harvest Farm 🛒
1440 Airline Rd. ✆ 361-993-2850 ⏰ Daily 7-10
• organic produce • vegetarian friendly • deli • take-out

🍴 **From I-37**, take exit 4A toward Padre Island Airport onto TX 358E about 10 miles to Airline Rd exit. Store is on corner Airline & S Padre Island Dr (aka TX 358).

DALLAS

Cosmic Cafe 🍴
2912 Oak Lawn Ave. ✆ 214-521-6157 ⏰ M-Sat 11-10, Sun 12-10
Indian with some southwest and Mediterranean influence.
• vegetarian • vegan friendly • alcohol • tables • wait staff

🍴 **From I-35E S**, take exit 430A toward Oak Lawn Ave onto N Stemmens Fwy ⅓ mile to Oak Lawn. Turn left onto Oak Lawn 1 mile to restaurant on right. **From I-30**, merge onto I-35 E N to exit 430A. Turn right onto Oak Lawn under 1 mile to restaurant.

Kalachandji's Restaurant & Palace 🍴
5430 Gurley Ave. ✆ 214-821-1048 ⏰ Lunch Tues-F 11:30-2, Sat 12-3 Dinner Tues-Sun 5:30-9
Vegetarian buffet. Adjacent spiritual palace open to the public.
• vegetarian • vegan friendly • salad bar • tables • self-service

🍴 **From I-30W**, take exit 48B toward Munger Blvd onto service road to Gurley Ave. Turn right onto Gurley past second block to restaurant/palace on right (before Graham Ave). **From I-30E**, take exit 48B onto service rd and turn left onto Munger, right onto Lindsley Ave 2 blocks to Henderson Ave, right onto Henderson 2 blocks to Gurley and left onto Gurley 2 blocks to restaurant.

Natural Grocers by Vitamin Cottage 🛒
7517 Campbell Rd. ✆ 972-735-9200 ⏰ M-F 9-8, Sat 9-7, Sun 11-6
• organic produce

🍴 **From US 75S**, take exit 28B onto George Bush Tpke W under 3 miles to Coit Rd. Turn left onto Coit 1½ miles to Campbell Rd. Turn right onto Campbell to store on right. **From US 75N**, take exit 8B onto Coit 5 miles to Campbell. Turn left onto Campbell to store.

Roy's Natural Market 🛒 🍴
130 Preston Royal Shopping Center ✆ 214-987-0213 ⏰ M-Th, Sun 9-10, F 9-6:30
• organic produce • vegetarian friendly • fresh juice • salad bar • tables • self-service • take-out

🍴 **From I-635E**, take exit 22D south on Dallas N Tollway S almost 2 miles to Royal Ln. Turn left onto Royal to store on left in Preston Royal Shopping Ctr. **From I-635W**, take exit 21D toward Preston Rd and merge onto LBJ Fwy ½ mile to Preston. Turn left onto Preston 2 miles to Royal. Turn right onto Royal to store on right.

Spiral Diner 🍴
1101 N. Beckley Ave. ✆ 214-948-4747 ⏰ Tues-Sat 11-10, Sun 11-5
Vegan burgers, sandwiches, salads and hot plates. A Certified Green Restaurant.
• vegan • organic focus • bakery • counter • tables • self-service • take-out

🍴 In Oak Cliff. **From I-30E**, take exit 44A toward Beckley Ave onto Dallas Ft Worth Tpke under ½ mile to Beckley. Turn right onto Beckley under 1 mile to restaurant on right at N Zang Blvd. **From I-30E,** merge onto I-35ES. **From I-35E**, take exit 427A right onto Colorado Blvd about ¾ mile to Beckley. Turn left onto Beckley 2 blocks to restaurant.

Whole Foods Market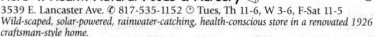

2218 Greenville Ave. © 214-824-1744 ⊕ Daily 8-10
• organic produce • vegetarian friendly • salad bar • cafe • self-service • take-out

From I-30, take exit 48B north on S Munger (right from I-30W, left from I-30E) about 1½ miles to end at Greenville Ave. Turn right onto Greenville about ¾ mile to store on right at Belmont Ave. **From US 75N (Central Expwy)**, take exit 2 right onto Willis Ave 1 mile to Greenville. Turn right onto Greenville 3 blocks to store on left after Belmont. **From US 75S,** take exit 3 right onto Mockingbird Ln ½ mile to Greenville. Turn right onto Greenville about 1½ miles to store.

Whole Foods Market

11700 Preston Rd. © 214-361-8887 ⊕ Daily 7-10
• organic produce • vegetarian friendly • salad bar • cafe • self-service • take-out

From I-635, take exit 21 toward Preston Rd onto LBJ Fwy and turn south onto Preston (right from I-635E, left from I-635W) over 1 mile to store on left after Forest Ln in Preston Ctr.

DENTON

Cupboard Natural Foods

200 W. Congress St. © 940-387-5386 ⊕ M-Sat 8-9, Sun 11-6
• organic produce • vegetarian friendly • salad bar • cafe • tables • self-service • take-out

From I-35, take exit 469 onto US 380E/W University Dr (right from I-35N, left from I-35S) under 3 miles to N Elm St (US 77). Turn right onto Elm (77S) about ¾ mile to Congress St. Turn right onto Congress store on corner.

Vitamins Plus

824 W. University Drive © 940-382-8816 ⊕ M-Sat 9-9, Sun 10-6
• organic produce

From I-35, take exit 469 onto US 380E/W University Dr (right from I-35N, left from I-35S) almost 2 miles to store on left in Denton Shopping Ctr.

EL PASO

Sun Harvest Farm

6100 N. Mesa St. © 915-833-3380 ⊕ Daily 7-10
• organic produce • vegetarian friendly • deli • take-out

From I-10, take exit 13 to Sunland Park Dr. Go north on Sunland Park (right from I-10W, left from I-10E) to N Mesa St. Turn left onto N Mesa to first light (Balboa Rd). Turn right onto Balboa to store on left in shopping plaza.

FREDERICKSBURG

The Peach Basket

334 W. Main St. © 830-997-4533 ⊕ M-F 9-6:30, Sat 9-5:30, Sun 12-5

US 290 and US 87 merge in town and become Main St. Store is on north side of W Main between Orange & Milan St.

FT. WORTH

Herb 'n Health Natural Foods & Nursery

3539 E. Lancaster Ave. © 817-535-1152 ⊕ Tues, Th 11-6, W 3-6, F-Sat 11-5
Wild-scaped, solar-powered, rainwater-catching, health-conscious store in a renovated 1926 craftsman-style home.
• organic produce

From I-30, take exit 18 south on Oakland Blvd (right from I-30E, left from I-30W) about 1¼ miles to Lancaster Ave. Turn right onto Lancaster 8 blocks to Perkins St. Turn right onto Perkins and immediately left onto circular drive to store.

Spiral Diner 🍴

1314 W. Magnolia Ave. ℂ 817-332-8834 ⊕ Tues-Sat 11-10, Sun 11-5
See Dallas location for description.
  • vegan • organic focus • bakery • counter • tables • self-service • take-out

🚗 **From I-30E**, take exit 13B toward Henderson St/Summit Ave onto W FwyW and right onto Summit continuing onto 8th Ave under 1 mile to Magnolia Ave. Turn right onto Magnolia 4 blocks to restaurant on left at 6th Ave. **From I-30W**, take exit 13B left onto Henderson St 1 mile to Magnolia. Turn right onto Magnolia 3 blocks to restaurant on right.

Sunflower Shoppe 🛍 🍴

5817 Curzon Ave. ℂ 817-738-9051 ⊕ M-Sat 9-9
  • organic produce • vegetarian friendly • cafe • deli • tables • self-service • take-out

🚗 **From I-30E**, take exit 9B onto Calmont Ave, right onto Horne St and left onto Camp Bowie Blvd 2 blocks to Curzon Ave. Turn left onto Curzon to store on right corner. **From I-30W**, take exit 9B onto Camp Bowie about 1 mile to Curzon. Turn left onto Curzon to store.

GEORGETOWN

The Herbery 🛍

2411-5 Williams Drive ℂ 512-863-6637 ⊕ M-F 9:30-6, Sat 9:30-3

🚗 **From I-35S**, take exit 262 toward FM 2338 onto I-35 about 1½ miles to Williams Dr. Turn right onto Williams about 1 mile to store on right between Golden Oaks & River Bend Dr. **From I-35N**, take exit 261A toward Andice/FM 2338 onto I-35 Frontage Rd about 1 mile to Williams. Turn left onto Williams 1 mile to store.

HIGHLAND PARK

Whole Foods Market 🛍 🍴   ♿

4100 Lomo Alto Drive ℂ 214-520-7993 ⊕ Daily 8-10
  • organic produce • vegetarian friendly • salad bar • cafe • self-service • take-out

🚗 **From I-35EN**, take exit 420A right onto Oak Lawn Ave about 1¼ miles to Lemmon Ave. Turn left onto Lemmon about 1 mile to store on right at Lomo Alto Dr. **From I-35ES**, take exit 432A left onto Inwood Rd about 2 miles to Lemmon. Turn right onto Lemmon about 1 mile to store on left. **From Dallas North Tollway**, take Lemmon Ave exit to store just east of tollway.

HOUSTON

A Moveable Feast 🛍 🍴

9341 Katy Fwy. ℂ 713-365-0368 ⊕ M-Sat 9-9 Cafe M-Sat 11-9
  • vegetarian friendly • cafe • bakery • alcohol • tables • self-service • take-out

🚗 **From I-10E**, take exit 758B toward Blalock Rd/Campbell Rd onto Katy Fwy to store. **From I-10W**, take exit 758A toward Bunker Hill Rd onto Katy Fwy and U-turn onto Katy Fwy heading east to store.

Baba Yega 🍴

2607 Grant St. ℂ 713-522-0042 ⊕ M-Th 11-9:30, F-Sat 11-10:30, Sun 10-9
The bread is whole wheat and the rice brown.
  • egetarian friendly • alcohol • tables • wait staff

🚗 **From I-10E**, take exit 767A toward Studemont St onto Katy Fwy to Studemont. Turn right onto Studemont 1 mile and continue straight onto Montrose Blvd 1 mile to Missouri St. Turn left onto Missouri 1 block to Grant St. Turn right onto Grant to restaurant on left. **From I-45N**, take exit 47A onto Allen Pkwy about 1 mile to Studemont. Turn left onto Studemont (immediately becomes Montrose) and follow directions above. **From I-10W**, merge onto I-45S. **From I-45S,** take exit 47D toward Dallas St/Fort Pierce St onto Heiner St ½ mile to Bagby St. Veer right onto Bagby ¾ mile to Westheimer Rd. Turn right onto Westheimer about ½ mile to Grant. Turn right onto Grant to restaurant.

Bombay Sweets ⑪

5827 Hillcroft Ave. ✆ 713-780-4453 ◷ Daily 10:30-9:30
Indian vegetarian with all-day buffet and a la carte.
• vegetarian • vegan friendly • tables • self-service • wait staff

🍎 **From I-610**, take exit 8A onto US 59S 2⅓ miles to exit toward Hillcroft Ave. Merge onto SW Fwy Access Rd and right onto Hillcroft under ¼ mile to restaurant on right.

Field of Greens ⑪

2320 W. Alabama St. ✆ 713-533-0029 ◷ M-Th 11-9, F 11-9:30, Sat-Sun 9-9:30
Mostly vegetarian/vegan with a few fish options. Vegan, sugar-free desserts.
• vegetarian friendly • vegan friendly • organic focus • tables • self-service

🚙 **From US 59**, take exit toward Kirby Dr onto Fwy Access Rd and go north on Kirby (left from US 59E, right from US 59W) about ½ mile to W Alabama St. Turn right onto W Alabama 2½ blocks to restaurant on left between Revere St & Greenbriar Dr.

Madras Pavilion ⑪

3910 Kirby Drive, Ste. 130 ✆ 713-521-2617 ◷ M-F 11:30-3, 5:30-9:30, Sat-Sun 11:30-10
Vegetarian Indian with a buffet available at lunch.
• vegetarian • vegan friendly • alcohol • tables • self-service • wait staff

🚙 **From I-610**, take exit 8A onto US 59N toward Downtown (left from I-610S, right from I-610N) about 2¼ miles to Kirby Dr exit. Follow exit onto SW Fwy to Kirby. Turn left onto Kirby to restaurant. **From I-45**, take exit 46B onto US 59S toward Victoria about 3½ miles to Kirby Dr exit. Follow exit to Lomitas St. Turn right onto Lomitas 1 block to Algerian Way. Turn left onto Algerian 1 block to restaurant at Kirby.

Nature's Market 🛍

10924 FM 1960 W. ✆ 281-469-7665 ◷ M, W, F 10-6, Tues, Th 10-8, Sat 10-5
🚙 **From US 290**, go northeast on FM 1960 (left from US 290E, right from US 290W) about 2 miles to store at Jones Rd.

Pepper Tree Veggie Cuisine ⑪

3821 Richmond Ave. ✆ 713-621-9488 ◷ Tues-F 11-9, Sat-Sun 11:30-9
Asian with a buffet weekdays from 11-2 and all day weekends.
• vegetarian • vegan friendly • tables • self-service • wait staff

🚙 **From US 59S**, take exit toward Edloe St/Weslayan Rd onto Fwy Access and turn right onto Edloe 3 blocks to Richmond Ave. Turn left onto Richmond 2½ blocks to restaurant on left after Cummins St. **From US 59N**, take exit for Newcastle DR/Weslayan Rd onto Fwy Rd and turn left onto Weslayan 3 blocks to Richmond. Turn right onto Richmond 1 block to restaurant on right.

Quan Yin Vegetarian Restaurant ⑪

10804 Bellaire Blvd. ✆ 281-498-7890 ◷ Tues-F 11-9, Sat-Sun 10-9
Chinese vegan with many mock meat dishes.
• vegan • tables • wait staff

🍎 **From I-10**, take exit 232 (232B from I-10W) and merge onto W Sam Houston Tollway S about 5 miles to Bellaire Blvd exit. Merge onto W Sam Houston Pkwy S and turn right onto Bellaire ¾ mile to restaurant on right before Wilcrest Dr.

Sandy's Market 🛍⑪

12171 Katy Fwy. ✆ 281-870-9999 ◷ Daily 7-7
Health-oriented breakfast and lunch buffet until 3:30.
• vegetarian friendly • organic focus • salad bar • tables • self-service • take-out

🚙 **From I-10E**, take exit 753B toward Dairy-Ashford Rd and merge onto Katy Fwy under ½ mile to store on right after Tully Rd. **From I-10W**, exit onto Katy Fwy/Old Katy Rd and turn left toward Katy Fwy and left onto Katy Fwy 1 block to store.

Shiv Sagar ⑪

6662 Southwest Fwy. ✆ 713-977-0150 ◷ Daily 11-9:30
Indian vegetarian.
• vegetarian • vegan friendly • tables • wait staff

🚙 **From I-610**, take exit 8A onto US 59S 3 miles to restaurant on right after Hillcroft Ave.

Sunfired Raw & Vegetarian Deli 📋 🍴

4915 MLK Blvd. ✆ 713-643-2884 ⏰ M-F 9:30-7, Sat 9:30-6:30
The deli is mostly raw food.
  • vegan • deli • tables • self-service • take-out

🍎 **From I-45S,** take exit 44B onto TX 5 about 1¼ miles to US 90/Old Spanish Trail. Turn right onto US 90 1 block to MLK Blvd. Turn left onto MLK to store on left in MacGregor Pl Shopping Ctr. **From I-45N,** take exit 41B onto Gulf Fwy about 1 mile to US 90/S Wayside Dr. Turn left onto US 90 1½ miles to MLK. Turn left onto MLK to store. **From I-610E,** take exit 36A onto S Loop E about ¾ mile and turn left onto MLK about 1½ miles to store on right. **From I-610W,** take exit 35 onto S Loop E over ½ mile and turn right onto MLK about 1½ miles to store.

Tri-Health Health Foods 📋

11025 Fuqua St. ✆ 713-947-7373 ⏰ M-F 9:30-7, Sat 9:30-6, Sun 12-6

🍎 **From I-45,** take exit 33 toward Fuqua St/Hwy 8 onto Gulf Fwy to Fuqua exit. Turn west onto Fuqua (right from I-45S, left from I-45N) under ¼ mile to store on right.

Whole Foods Market 📋 🍴   ♿

2955 Kirby Drive ✆ 713-520-1937 ⏰ Daily 8-10
  • organic produce • vegetarian friendly • salad bar • cafe • self-service • take-out

🍎 **From I-610,** take exit 8A onto US 59 toward Downtown (left from I-610S, right from I-610N) about 2¼ miles to Kirby Dr exit. Follow exit onto SW Fwy to Kirby. Turn left onto Kirby about ½ mile to store.

Whole Foods Market 📋 🍴   ♿

11145 Westheimer Rd. ✆ 713-784-7776 ⏰ Daily 8-10
  • organic produce • vegetarian friendly • salad bar • cafe • self-service • take-out

🍎 **From Beltway 8 (Sam Houston Tollway),** take Westheimer Rd west under 1 mile to store at Wilcrest Dr.

Whole Foods Market 📋 🍴   ♿

4004 Bellaire Blvd. ✆ 713-667-4090 ⏰ Daily 8-10
  • organic produce • vegetarian friendly • salad bar • cafe • self-service • take-out

🍎 **From I-610,** take exit 6 east on Bellaire Blvd (right from I-610N, left from I-610S) about 1 mile to store on left at Weslayan St. **From Rt 59,** go south on Weslayan about 1½ miles to store on right at Bellaire.

Whole Foods Market 📋 🍴   ♿

6401 Woodway #149 ✆ 713-789-4477 ⏰ Daily 8-10
  • organic produce • vegetarian friendly • salad bar • cafe • self-service • take-out

🍎 **From I-610,** take exit 10 onto W Loop Fwy to Woodway Dr. Turn right from I-610S, left from I-610N onto Woodway almost 3 miles to store. **From I-10E,** take exit 760 onto Katy Fwy to Voss Rd. Turn right onto Voss 2 miles to Woodway. Turn left onto Woodway about ¼ mile to store.

KERRVILLE

Kerrville Health Foods 📋   ♿

141 W. Water St. ✆ 830-896-7383 ⏰ M-Sat 9-6

🍎 **From I-10,** take exit 508 toward Kerrville onto TX 16S/Frederickburg Rd (left from I-10W, right from I-10E) almost 2½ miles to Main St. Turn right onto Main about ½ mile to store

LONGVIEW

Jack's Natural Food Store 📋 🍴

1614 Judson Rd. ✆ 903-753-4800 ⏰ M-F 9-5 Deli 9-3
  • vegetarian friendly • fresh juice • deli • tables • self-service

🍎 **From I-20E,** take exit 595A north on Estes Pkwy (becomes High St, then Judson Rd) about 7 miles to store on right. **From I-20W,** take exit 595 and follow access road to Estes Pkwy. Turn right onto Estes and follow directions above.

Jack's Natural Food Store 🛍 🍴

400 E. Loop 281 © 903-758-9777 ⊙ M-F 9-6, Sat 9-5 Deli M-F 11-3, Sat 11-2
• vegetarian friendly • fresh juice • deli • tables • self-service

🚐 **From I-20**, take exit 599 north on TX 281 Loop (right from I-20W, left from I-20E) about 8 miles to store at Airline Rd.

Jack's Natural Food Store 🛍 🍴

2199 Gilmer Rd. © 903-759-4262 ⊙ M-F 9-6, Sat 9-2 Deli M-F 11-2
• vegetarian friendly • fresh juice • deli • tables • self-service

🚐 **From US 80,** go north on Gilmer Rd (left from US 80E, right from US 80W) about 2 miles to store past W Loop 281 between Toler & Reed Rd.

Vitamins Plus 🛍

321 W. Loop 281 © 903-295-7716 ⊙ M-Sat 9-9, Sun 10-7
• organic produce

🚐 **From I-20E**, take exit 589 on left onto Hwy 61 6 miles, continuing onto N Spur 63½ mile to W 281 Loop. Turn right onto W 281 to store on left. **From I-20W,** take exit 599 right onto W 281 about 8½ miles to store on right.

LUBBOCK

Natural Health Market 🛍

4414 82nd St. © 806-788-1424 ⊙ M-Sat 9-6
• organic produce

🚐 **From I-27**, take exit 1A onto S Loop 289W 2½ miles to Quaker Ave. Go south on Quaker (left from 289W, right from 289E) under 1 mile to 82nd St. Turn right onto 82nd to store on right in Village Shopping Ctr.

Natural Health Market 🛍

3833 50th St., Ste. 4 © 806-796-1230 ⊙ M-Sat 9-6
• organic produce

🚐 **From I-27**, take exit 1C east on 50th St (right from I-27S, left from I-27N) about 3 miles to store on left past Memphis Ave. **From S Loop 289E**, turn left onto Quaker Ave about 1⅓ miles to 50th St. Turn right onto 50th past first block to store on right. **From S Loop 289W**, turn right onto Peoria Ave continuing onto Quaker and follow directions above.

The Alternative Food Company 🛍

2611 Boston Ave. © 806-747-8740 ⊙ M-Sat. 9-6
• organic produce

🚐 **From I-27S**, take exit 3 right onto US 62W/19th St about 1⅔ miles to University Ave. Turn left onto University about ½ mile (7 blocks) to 26th St. Turn right onto 26th 2 blocks to Boston Ave. Turn right onto Boston to store on right. **From I-27N**, take exit 2 left onto 34th St about 1¾ miles to Boston. Turn right onto Boston about ½ mile (8 blocks) to store.

Vitamins Plus 🛍

5109 82nd St. © 806-698-8612 ⊙ M-Sat 9-9, Sun 10-6
• organic produce

🚐 **From I-27S**, take exit 1A onto Hwy 289W about 3 miles to Slide Rd exit. Merge onto S Loop 289 and turn left onto Slide about 1 mile to 82nd St. Turn right onto 82nd to store on right. **From I-27N**, take exit 1 left onto Ave H about 4½ miles to store on left (before Slide).

Well Body Natural Foods 🛍 🍴

3708 34th St. © 806-793-1015 ⊙ M-F 8-8, Sat 8-6, Sun 9-5
• organic produce • vegetarian friendly • fresh juice • cafe • tables • self-service • take-out

🚐 **From I-27S**, take exit 3 onto US 62/W19th St about 2¾ miles to Indiana Ave. Turn left onto Indiana 1 mile to 34th St. Turn right onto 34th 3½ blocks to store on right between Louisville & Memphis Ave. **From I-27N**, take exit 2 left onto 34th St 3 miles to store.

LUFKIN

Morning Glory Natural Foods 🛍

124 S. First St. ℂ 936-637-7481 ⏱ M-F 9-6, Sat 9-1
🛒 Store is on US 59 (aka 1st St) 1 block south of Frank Ave on west side between E Lufkin & E Shepard Ave.

MCALLEN

Sun Harvest Farms 🛍

2008 N. 10th St. ℂ 956-618-5388 ⏱ Daily 8-9
• organic produce
🛒 **From US 281**, turn west onto W Ferguson St (becomes Pecan Blvd) about 3 miles to 10th St. Turn right onto 10th a few blocks to store on right.

MIDLAND

Natural Foods Market 🛍 🍴

2311 W. Wadley Ave. ℂ 432-699-4048 ⏱ M-F 9-7, Sat 9:30-7
• organic produce • vegetarian friendly • fresh juice • salad bar • cafe • tables • self-service • take-out
🛒 **From I-20W**, take exit 144 toward State Hwy 250/Midland onto I-20 about ½ mile and merge onto TX 250 about 7½ miles to N Garfield St exit. Turn to left onto N Garfield 1 mile (past Midland College) and turn left onto W Wadley Ave 1 block to store on left. **From I-20E**, take exit 131 toward Loop 250/State Hwy 158 W/ Midland onto I-20 and merge onto TX 250 over 7¾ miles to Garfield exit. Merge onto W Loop 250 N, turn right onto N Garfield and follow directions above.

NACOGDOCHES

Morning Glory Natural Foods 🛍

3500 North St. ℂ 936-564-0159 ⏱ M-F 9-7, Sat 9-5, Sun 12-5
• organic produce
🛒 **From US 59**, merge onto TX 59. Store is on TX 59 (aka North St) on west side at Lakewood St.

NASSAU BAY

Erma's Nutrition Center 🛍

18045 Upper Bay Rd. ℂ 281-333-4746 ⏱ M 10-7, Tues-F 10-6, Sat 9:30-4
Farmer's market onsite Saturdays 10-2.
• organic produce
🛒 **From I-45**, take exit 25 toward Alvin east on Hwy 1 (loop around right from I-45S, veer right from I-45N) 2¾-3¼ miles to Upper Bay Rd (across from Space Ctr). Turn left onto Upper Bay to store on left in Nassau Bay Shopping Village.

PEARLAND

Natural Rewards 🛍

3704 E. Broadway St. ℂ 281-412-3303 ⏱ M-F 9:30-6:30, Sat 9:30-5
🛒 **From I-45**, merge onto S Beltway 8 W/S Sam Houston Tollway W and take Telephone Rd/TX 35 south onto N Main St (signs for Pearland) 2½ miles to E Broadway St. Turn left onto E Broadway 3 blocks to store on right at Park Ave.

PLANO

Whole Foods Market 🛍 🍴   ♿

2201 Preston Rd. ℂ 972-612-6729 ⏱ Daily 8-10
• organic produce • vegetarian friendly • salad bar • cafe • self-service • take-out
🛒 **From Pres George Bush Tpke (TX 190),** take Preston Rd/TX 289N (left from 190E, right from 190W) about 1¼ miles to store on NW corner at Park Blvd.

RICHARDSON

Madras Pavilion 🍴

101 S. Coit Rd. ✆ 972-671-3672 ⏰ M-F 11:30-3, 5:30-10, Sat-Sun 11:30-10
Vegetarian Indian with a buffet available at lunch.
• vegetarian • vegan friendly • alcohol • tables • self-service • wait staff
🚻 **From I-635**, take exit 19 (B from I-635W, C from I-635E) and follow Coit Rd ramp onto LBJ Expwy about ¼ mile to Coit. Go north on Coit (right from I-635W, left from I-635E) under 2 miles to restaurant on left at Belt Line Rd in Dallas Metroplex. **From US 75S**, take exit 24 toward Belt Line and follow N Central Expwy to Belt Line. Turn right onto Belt Line 2 miles to Coit. Turn left onto Coit to restaurant.

Suma Veggie Cafe 🍴   ♿

800 E. Arapaho Rd. ✆ 972-889-8598 ⏰ M-F 11-2, 5-9, Sat 12-9
Vegan Chinese with a buffet available at lunch.
• vegan • tables • self-service • wait staff
🚻 **From I-635**, take exit 19A onto US 75N. **From US 75**, take exit 25 toward Arapaho Rd and follow expwy to Arapaho. Go east on Arapaho (right from 75N, left from 75S) over ¾ mile (3 lights) to restaurant at Bowser Rd.

Udipi Cafe 🍴

35 Richardson Heights Village ✆ 972-437-2858 ⏰ M, W-Th 11:30-9:30, F-Sun 11:30-10
Vegetarian Indian with a buffet available at lunch.
• vegetarian • vegan friendly • tables • self-service • wait staff
🚻 **From I-635**, take exit 19A onto US 75N. **From US 75**, take exit 24 and follow S Central Expwy to Belt Line Rd. Go west on Belt Line (left from 75N, right from 75S) and make first left into Richardson Heights Ctr to restaurant.

Veggie Garden 🍴   ♿

516 W. Arapaho Rd. ✆ 972-479-0888 ⏰ M-F 11-2:30, 5-9, Sat-Sun 11:30-3, 4-9
Vegan Chinese with a buffet available at lunch.
• vegan • tables • self-service • wait staff
🚻 **From I-635**, take exit 19A onto US 75N. **From US 75,** take exit 25 toward Arapaho Rd and follow S Central Expwy to Arapaho. Go west on Arapaho (sharp left from 75N, right from 75S) about ½ mile to restaurant.

Whole Foods Market 🛍🍴

60 Dal-Rich Village ✆ 72-699-8075 ⏰ Daily 8-10
• organic produce • vegetarian friendly • salad bar • cafe • self-service • take-out
🚻 **From I-635**, take exit 19 (B from I-635W, C from I-635E) and follow Coit Rd ramp onto LBJ Expwy about ¼ mile to Coit. Go north on Coit (right from I-635W, left from I-635E) about 1¾ miles to store on SE corner at Belt Line Rd. **From US 75N (Central Expwy)**, take exit 8B north on Coit about 3 miles to store. **From US 75S**, take exit 24 to Belt Line. Turn left onto Belt Line about 2½ miles to store at Coit.

ROANOKE

Abundant Life Health Food 🛍

500 E. Hwy. 377 ✆ 817-430-4624 ⏰ M-F 9-6:30, Sat 9-5
• organic produce
🚻 **From I-35WN**, take exit 72 toward Hwy 114/Dallas/Bridgeport right onto Hwy 114 3¼ miles to TX 377. Turn right onto TX 377 about ¾ mile to store in Towne W Shopping Ctr. **From I-35WS,** take exit 70 onto Frontage Rd about 1 mile to Hwy 114. Turn left onto 114 and follow directions above.

S. PADRE ISLAND

Naturally's Health Food Store & Cafe 🛍🍴

3109 Padre Blvd. ✆ 956-761-5332 ⏰ M-Sat 9-6, Sun 10-4

• vegetarian friendly • organic focus • fresh juice • alcohol • cafe • bakery • tables • wait staff • take-out

📦 **From TX 100/Queen Isabella Cswy**, turn left onto Padre Blvd about 1¼ miles to store on left between Ling & Pike St.

SAN ANTONIO

Green Vegetarian Cuisine & Coffee 🍴

1017 N. Flores St. © 210-320-5865 ⊘ M-Th 7-9, F 7-7, Sun 8-9
Emphasis is on "green" menu and restaurant practices.
• vegetarian • vegan friendly • tables • wait staff

📦 **From I-10E**, take exit 569B toward Frio St onto W Poplar St, left onto N Laredo St, right onto W Cypress St and right onto N Flores St about ⅓ mile to restaurant on right between Marshall St & Euclid Ave. **From I-10W**, merge onto I-35N. **From I-35N**, take exit 151A toward San Pedro Ave onto Quincy St, left onto San Pedro, left onto W Elmyra St and right onto N Flores about 1½ blocks to restaurant on left. **From I-35S**, take exit 157A onto E Elmyra ½ mile to N Flores and follow directions above.

Sun Harvest Farms 🛍

8101 Callaghan Rd. © 210-979-8121 ⊘ Daily 7-10
• organic produce • vegetarian friendly • deli • take-out

📦 **From I-10E**, take exit 562 left onto WI-10/87S/McDermott Fwy to I-10E/87S ramp toward Callaghan Rd. Turn left onto Callaghan to store. **From I-140 Loop**, take exit 16B onto WI-10/US 87N/McDermott Fwy about ⅓ mile to Callaghan. Turn right onto Callahan to store.

Sun Harvest Farms 🛍 🍴

17700 N. U.S. Hwy. 281 © 210-499-1446 ⊘ Daily 7-10
• organic produce • vegetarian friendly • deli • take-out

📦 **From N Loop 1604**, tgo south on San Pedro Ave (left from 1604W, right from 1604E) about ¾ tmile o Donella Dr. Turn left onto Donella and left onto San Pedro to store on east side.

Sun Harvest Farms 🛍

2502 Nacogdoches Rd. © 210-824-7800 ⊘ Daily 7-10
• organic produce • vegetarian friendly • deli • take-out

📦 **From I-410 Loop**, take exit 23 onto Nacogdoches Rd (left from I-410E, right from I-410W) under ¼ mile to store.

Whole Foods Market 🛍 🍴   ♿

255 E. Basse Rd., Ste. 130 © 210-826-4676 ⊘ Daily 8-10
• organic produce • vegetarian friendly • salad bar • cafe • self-service • take-out

📦 **From I-410E Loop,** take exit 21B onto US 281S about ½ mile to Jones-Maltsberger Rd exit. Turn left at light onto Jones-Maltsberger and go under hwy and over tracks. Turn right into Quarry Shopping Ctr and follow access road on right to store at south end. **From I-410W Loop**, take exit 23 onto Nacogdoches Rd 1½ miles to E Basse Rd. Veer right onto E Basse about 1 mile to store.

SHERMAN

Green Market Natural Foods & Vitamins 🛍 🍴

1909 Texoma Pkwy., Ste. F © 903-892-8667 ⊘ M-F 9-7, Sat 9-6, Sun 11-5
• organic produce • vegetarian friendly • fresh juice • cafe • counter • tables • self-service • take-out

📦 **From US 75N**, take exit 61 onto Texoma Pkwy about ¾ mile to store on right after N Grand Ave. **From US 75S**, take exit 60 for N Travis St onto N Sam Rayburn Fwy and make two lefts to cross hwy and continue on Sam Rayburn to Texoma Pkwy. Merge onto Texoma and follow directions above.

SUGAR LAND

Madras Pavilion ⑪

16260 Kensington Drive ⓒ 281-481-3672 ⏱ M-F 11:30-3, 5:30-9:30, Sat-Sun 11:30-10
Vegetarian Indian with a buffet available at lunch.
• vegetarian • vegan friendly • alcohol • tables • self-service • wait staff
⬤ **From SW Fwy/US 59**, take Lakeside Plaza Dr west (right from 59S, left from 59N) 1 block to Kensington Dr. Turn left onto Kensington to restaurant on right.

Udipi Cafe ⑪

3559 Hwy. 6 ⓒ 281-313-2700 ⏱ M, W-Sun 11-10
Vegetarian Indian with a lunch buffet.
• vegetarian • vegan friendly • tables • self-service • wait staff
⬤ **From SW Fwy/US 59**, go east on TX 6/Alvin-Sugarland Rd (left from US 59S, right from US 59N) 1½ miles to restaurant on left in Market at First Colony.

Whole Foods Market ⑪ ⑪

15900 Southwest Fwy. ⓒ 281-491-5577 ⏱ Daily 7-10
• organic produce • vegetarian friendly • salad bar • cafe • self-service • take-out
⬤ Store is on SW Fwy/US 59 at TX 6/Alvins-Sugerland Rd on west side.

SULPHUR SPRINGS

Korth Health Foods ⑪

1171 S. Broadway ⓒ 903-439-4727 ⏱ M-F 9-6, Sat 9-5
⬤ **From I-30**, take exit 124 toward Hwy 11 north on S Broadway (merge onto Industrial Dr E and right from I-30W, merge onto Shannon Rd W and left from I-30E) 2 blocks to store on left.

TEMPLE

Discover Natural Foods Inc. ⑪

1706 W. Ave M ⓒ 254-773-7711 ⏱ M-F 9-6, Sat 9-4
⬤ **From I-35N**, take exit 300 toward Ave H /49th-57th St right onto 57th St to W Ave M. Turn left onto M under 1 mile to store in Natural Medical Ctr. **From I-35S,** take exit 300 toward Ave H/49th-57th St left onto W Ave H about ¼ mile to S 35th St. Turn left onto S 35th about ⅓ mile to M. Turn right onto M to store.

TYLER

Vitamins Plus ⑪

5614 S. Broadway Ave ⓒ 903-534-3717 ⏱ M-Sat 9-9, Sun 10-6
• organic produce
⬤ **From TX 31W eastbound**, turn left onto S SE Loop 323 4½ miles to US 69. Turn left onto US 69/S Broadway Ave about 1 mile to store on right. **From TX 31E westbound,** turn right onto S SW Loop 323 about 4½ miles to US 69. Turn right onto US 69 about 1 mile to store.

Whole Health ⑪

4834 S. Broadway Ave. ⏱ 903-581-8811 ⏱ M-F 9-6, Sat 10-6
Farmers' market in parking lot Saturday 8am to noon.
• organic produce
⬤ **From TX 31W eastbound**, turn left onto S SE Loop 323 4½ miles to US 69. Turn left onto US 69/S Broadway Ave to store on right in Broadway Square. **From TX 31E westbound,** turn right onto S SW Loop 323 4½ miles to US 69. Turn right onto US 69 to store.

WACO

Terry and Jo's Food for Thought 🍴
1121 Speight Ave. ✆ 254-753-3998 ⏱ Daily 11-10
• vegetarian friendly • vegan friendly • organic focus • tables • self-service

🏠 **From I-35**, take exit 34 for 18-17th St. **From I-35S**, merge onto I-35 Service Rd, veer left toward Speight Ave and turn left onto Speight (across hwy) 4-5 blocks to restaurant on left between S 12th & 11th St. **From I-35N**, merge onto Service Rd and right onto Speight 4-5 blocks to restaurant.

Vitamins Plus 🛍
5900 Bosque Blvd. ✆ 254-776-7867 ⏱ M-Sat 9-9, Sun 10-6
• organic produce

🏠 **From I-35S**, take exit 333A onto service rd and right onto Spur 396/Valley Mills Dr about 3¾ miles to Bosque Blvd. Turn left onto Bosque to store on left. **From I-35N**, take exit 330 onto service rd and take ramp for TX 6N/Hwy 340N toward Meridian onto TX 6N 4 miles to exit 396. Merge onto TX 6 and turn right onto Bosque 1¼ miles to store on right.

WICHITA FALLS

Sunshine Natural Foods 🛍 🍴   ♿
2907 Bob Ave./Parker Square ✆ 940-767-2093 ⏱ M-F 9-6, Sat 10-5:30 Salad bar M-F 11-2
• organic produce • vegetarian friendly • salad bar • bakery • tables • self-service • take-out

🏠 **From US 287**, take US 82W over 2 miles to Kemp Blvd exit. Turn left onto Kemp to second light and turn left into Parker Square to store.

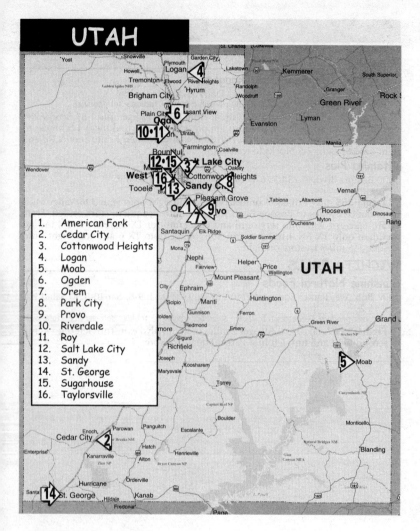

UTAH

1. American Fork
2. Cedar City
3. Cottonwood Heights
4. Logan
5. Moab
6. Ogden
7. Orem
8. Park City
9. Provo
10. Riverdale
11. Roy
12. Salt Lake City
13. Sandy
14. St. George
15. Sugarhouse
16. Taylorsville

AMERICAN FORK

Good Earth Natural Foods 🛍

336 W. Main St. ℭ 801-756-0233 ⏲ M-Sat 9-9
· organic produce

🗓 **From I-15**, take exit 279 toward American Fork east on W 8000 N/W Main St (left from I-15S, right from I-15N) under ¾ mile to store on left after N 350 W.

CEDAR CITY

Sunshine Nutrition 🛍

111 W. 535 S. ℭ 435-586-4889 ⏲ M-Sat 9-7
· organic produce

🗓 **From I-15**, take exit 59 east on W 200 N (loop around right off exit ramp from 15S, left from 15N) to Main St. Turn right onto Main to W 535 S. Turn right onto W 535 S to store on left.

COTTONWOOD HEIGHTS

Whole Foods Market 🕎 🍴
6390 S. Highland Drive ✆ 801-773-9455 ⏲ Daily 7:30-10
• organic produce • vegetarian friendly • salad bar • cafe • self-service • take-out
🚗 **From I-215**, take exit 8 south on Highland Dr (right from I-215E, left from I-215W) about ½ mile to store (before Fort Union Blvd).

LOGAN

Caffe Ibis 🍴
52 Federal Ave. ✆ 435-753-4777 ⏲ M-Th, Sat 6-6:30, Sat 6am-9pm, Sun 8-6
The focus is on fair-trade coffee. The food is mostly sandwiches and burritos.
• vegetarian friendly • tables • self-service • take-out
🚗 **From US 91**, turn east onto Federal Ave (right from 91N, left from 91S) 1 block to restaurant at Church St (½ block north of Tabernacle Park). **From UT 30E**, continue on E 200 N 1 bock past 91 to Church. Turn right onto Church 1 block to restaurant at Federal.

Shangri-La Health Foods 🕎
438½ N. Main St. ✆ 435-752-1315 ⏲ M-Sat 9-6
🚗 US 91, US 89 and UT 30 converge in Logan. Store is at corner Main St & 400 N (where 91 & 89 merge) in Albertson's shopping plaza. **From UT 30E**, continue on E 200 N to Main. Turn left onto Main ⅓ mile to store.

MOAB

Moonflower Market 🕎
39 E. & 100 N. ✆ 435-259-5712 ⏲ M-Sat 9-8, Sun 10-3
• organic produce
🚗 **From Rt 191**, go east on E 100 N (left from 191S, right from 191N) to store at 39 E.

OGDEN

Harvest Health Food 🕎
341 27th St. ✆ 801-621-1627 ⏲ M-F 9-6:30, Sat 9-5
🚗 **From I-15**, take exit 344A onto E 31st St (merge right from I-15N, loop around right from I-15S) about 1 mile to Wall Ave. Turn left onto Wall ½ mile to 27th St. Turn right onto 27th ⅓ mile to store.

OREM

Good Earth Natural Foods 🕎
500 S. State St. ✆ 801-765-1616 ⏲ M-Sat 9-9
• organic produce
🚗 **From I-15**, take exit 272 east on Center St (left from I-15S, right from I-15N) about 1½ miles to S State St. Turn right onto S State about ⅔ mile (past 400 S) to store.

PARK CITY

Fairweather Natural Foods 🕎 🍴
1270 Iron Horse Drive ✆ 435-649-4561 ⏲ M-F 9-7, Sat 10-6, Sun 12-6
• organic produce • vegetarian friendly • fresh juice • tables • self-service • take-out
🚗 **From I-80E**, take exit 145 toward Kimball Jct/Park City onto UT 224S about 5½ miles to Iron Horse Dr. Turn left onto Iron Horse to store on left (last driveway). **From I-80W**, take exit 148 toward Heber/Provo left onto Silver Creek Rd (becomes US 40E) 3½ miles to exit 4 (UT 248). Turn right onto 248 about 2½ miles to Bonanza Dr. Turn left onto Bonanza about ¼ mile to Iron Horse. Turn right onto Iron Horse to store on right. **From US 40W,** take exit 4 toward Park City left onto UT 248 about 2¾ miles to Bonanza. Turn left onto Bonanza about ¼ mile to Iron Horse. Turn right onto Iron Horse to store on right.

Morning Ray Cafe 🍴
255 Main St. © 435- 615-6951 ⏱ M-F 7am-1pm, Sat-Sun 7-2
All-day breakfast, soups, salads, whole grain pizzas, sandwiches. No meat but fish and poultry.
· vegetarian friendly · organic focus · alcohol · tables · wait staff
🍴 **From I-80E**, take exit 145 toward Kimball Jct/Park City onto UT 224S about 5¾ miles to Park Ave. Continue straight onto Park over 1 mile to 4th St. Turn left onto 4th 1 block to Main St. Turn right onto Main to restaurant in Treasure Mt Inn (mezzanine level). **From I-80W**, take exit 148 toward Heber/Provo left onto Silver Creek Rd (becomes US 40E) 3½ miles to exit 4 (UT 248). Turn right onto 248 about 2½ miles to Bonanza Dr. Turn left onto Bonanza ½ mile to Deer Valley Dr. Turn left onto Deer Valley over ½ mile to Main. Turn right onto Main over ½ mile to restaurant.

Whole Foods Market 🛒 🍴
1748 W. Redstone Center Dr. © 435-575-0200 ⏱ Daily 7:30-9
· organic produce · vegetarian friendly · salad bar · cafe · self-service · take-out
🍴 **From I-80**, take exit 145 south on Olympic Pkwy (right from I-80E, left from I-80W) about ⅓ mile to Unita Way. Turn left onto Unita, right onto Redstone Ave and left onto Redstone Ctr Dr to store on left.

PROVO _____

Good Earth Natural Foods 🛒
1045 S. University Ave. © 801-375-7444 ⏱ M-Sat 9-9
· organic produce
🍴 **From I-15**, take exit 266 onto UT 189N/University Ave (straight from I-15N, loop around right from I-15S) ½-1 mile to store.

RIVERDALE _____

Good Earth Natural Foods 🛒
1050 W. Riverdale Rd. © 801-334-5500 ⏱ M-Sat 9-8
· organic produce
🍴 **From I-15N**, take exit 342 toward I-84E/Riverdale onto UT 26/W Riverdale Rd about 1 mile to store. **From I-15S** merge onto I-84E. **From I-84**, take exit 81 onto UT 26/W Riverdale Rd (left from I-84E, right from I-84W) under ⅓ mile to store.

ROY _____

Down To Earth Natural Foods 🛒 🍴
5418 S.1900 W. © 801-728-0234 ⏱ M-Sat 9-8 Deli M-F 11-6, Sat 11-4
· organic produce · vegetarian friendly · deli · tables · self-service · take-out
🍴 **From I-15**, take exit 341 west on W 5600 S (left from I-15N, right from I-15S) to first right (S 1900 W). Turn right onto S 1900 W past first block to store.

SALT LAKE CITY _____

Evergreen House 🍴
755 S. State St. © 801-328-8889 ⏱ M-Th 12-6, F-Sat 12-9
Chinese vegan except for one dish that includes egg.
· vegan · tables · wait staff · take-out
🍴 **From I-15S**, take exit 305C-A left onto W1300S 1 mile to State St. Turn left onto State under 1 mile to restaurant on right between E800S & E700S. **From I-15N**, take exit 305D-A and follow signs for UT 270. Merge onto US 270 about 1⅓ miles to W900S. Turn right onto W900S 3 blocks to State. Turn left onto State 1½ blocks to restaurant. **From I-80W**, take exit 124 right onto State about 2½ miles to restaurant.

Liberty Heights Fresh 🛒
1290 S. 1100 E. © 801-583-7374 ⏱ M-Sat 8:30-8, Sun 10-7
· organic produce · vegetarian friendly · fresh juice · deli · take-out

🍴 **From I-80 coming from south**, take exit 126 right onto S1300E 1½ miles to E1300S. Turn left onto E1300S 1 block to S1100E. Turn right onto S1100E to store on left corner. **From I-80E or I-15S**, take 305C-A left onto W1300S 2½ miles to store at S1100E. **From I-15N**, take exit 305A-D right at fork (signs for I-15/I-800) about 1½ miles to W1300S, turn right onto W1300S and follow directions above.

Oasis Cafe 🍴
151 S. 500 E. ✆ 801-322-0404 ⏱ M-F 8-9, Sat-Sun 8-10
Menu includes seafood and chicken but all soups and sauces are vegetarian.
 • vegetarian friendly • vegan friendly • alcohol • counter • tables • wait staff
🍴 **From I-15**, take exit 307 east on W400S (left at fork toward W400S and turn left from I-15E, exit on left and turn right from I-15N) 2 miles to S500E. Turn left onto S500E 2½ blocks to restaurant on right.

One World Everybody Eats 🍴
41 S. 300 E. ✆ 801-519-2002 ⏱ Daily 11-9
Pay what you can afford, take what you can eat, get more if you like. Always a free meal for those without means.
 • vegetarian friendly • vegan friendly • organic focus • tables • self-service
🍴 **From I-15S**, take exit 307 left at fork and turn left onto W400S about 1½ miles to S State St. Turn left onto S State 3 blocks to E100S. Turn right onto E100S 2 blocks to S300E. Turn left onto S300E to restaurant on right. **From I-15N**, take exit 305D-A toward Valley Rd right at fork toward UT 270, then left at fork toward UT 270 for about ¾ mile and right at fork toward UT 270 to finally merge onto UT 270 1⅓ miles to W900S. Turn right onto W900S 3 blocks to S State. Turn left onto S State 1¼ miles to E100S and follow directions above.

Sage's Cafe 🍴
473 E. 300 S. ✆ 801-322-3790 ⏱ M-F 11:30-2:30, 5-9:0, Sat-Sun 10-9:30
Vegan with some raw foods choices and a monthly raw special night.
 • vegan • organic focus • alcohol • tables • wait staff • take-out
🍴 **From I-15**, take exit 307 east on W400S (left at fork toward W400S and turn left from I-15E, right from I-15N) almost 1½ miles to S State St. Turn left onto S State 1 block to E300S. Turn right onto E300S 4 blocks to restaurant on left.

Vertical Diner 🍴
2280 S.W. Temple ✆ 801-484-8378 ⏱ Daily 10-9
Diner fare with many faux meat choices and all-day breakfast.
 • vegan • alcohol • tables • wait staff
🍴 **From I-15**, exit onto I-80E. **From I-80E**, take exit 124 left onto S State St 2 blocks to E Truman Ave. Turn left onto E Truman 2 blocks to SW Temple Ave. Turn right onto SW Temple 1 block to restaurant on left. **From I-80W**, take exit 124 for State and veer right onto E2400S 2 blocks past S State to E Truman. Turn right onto E Truman and follow directions above.

Whole Foods Market 🛍🍴   ♿
645 E. 400 S. ✆ 801-355-7401 ⏱ Daily 7:30-10
 • organic produce • vegetarian friendly • salad bar • cafe • self-service • take-out
🍴 **From I-80**, take exit 125 north on 700E (left from I-80E, right from I-80W) almost 3 miles to E400S. Turn left onto E400S to store on right. **From I-15N**, merge onto I-80E and follow directions above. **From I-15S**, take exit 307 left at fork toward W 400S and turn left onto W400S 2⅓ miles to store on left before S 700 E.

Whole Foods Market 🛍🍴   ♿
1131 E. Wilmington Ave. ✆ 801-359-7913 ⏱ Daily 7:30-10
 • organic produce • vegetarian friendly • salad bar • cafe • self-service • take-out
🍴 **From I-80,** take exit 126 (UT 181/13th E) north on S1300E (left from I-80E, right from I-80W) about ¼ mile to Wilmington Ave. Turn left onto Wilmington about ¼ mile to store.

SANDY

Good Earth Natural Foods 🛍️
7905 S. 700 E. ✆ 801-562-2209 ⏰ M-Sat 9-9
• organic produce

🚗 **From I-215W**, take exit 9 right onto Union Park Ave 1 block to E6600S. Turn left onto E6600S and first left onto S900E (becomes S700E) under 2 miles to store on left. **From I-215E**, take exit 9 right at fork onto Union Park Ave over ½ mile to E6900S/E Ft Union Blvd. Veer right onto E Ft Union about ⅓ mile to S900E. Turn left onto S900E about 1 mile to store. **From I-15S**, merge onto I-215E and follow directions above. **From I-15N**, take exit 295 right at fork and turn right onto W900S under 1½ miles to S700E. Turn left onto S 700E 1⅓ miles to store on right.

Shirlyn's Natural Foods 🛍️
1922 E. 9400 S. ✆ 801-562-1118 ⏰ M-Sat 9-8
Mostly supplements but some food.

🚗 **From I-15**, take exit 295 for Hwy 209 left at fork (signs for Sandy) and veer left onto W9000S/Hwy 209 under 4 miles (becomes E9400S) to store on right at Highland Dr. **From I-15N**, take exit 293 toward Hwy 151 right at fork (signs for Sandy) and merge onto W10600S almost 1½ miles to UT 71/S700E. Turn right onto S700E 1½ miles to E9400S. Turn right onto E9400S 2 miles to store.

ST. GEORGE

Health Nut Natural Foods Market 🛍️
700 S. 100 W. ✆ 435-652-4372 ⏰ M-F 9-7, Sat 9-6
Two vegan sandwiches daily to go.
• organic produce • fresh juice

🚗 **From I-15**, take exit 6 onto Bluff St/15 Bus (right from I-15S, left from I-15N) ¾-1 mile to W700S. Turn right onto W700S 1 block to store at S100W.

SUGARHOUSE

Omar's Living Cuisine 🍴
2148 S. Highland Drive ✆ 801-486-0332 ⏰ M-Th 12-8, F-Sat 12-9
All raw food. Inside Herbs for Health.
• vegan • tables • wait staff

🚗 **From I-80E**, take exit 126 right onto S1300E, right onto E Pkwy Ave and right onto E Highland Dr under ½ mile to restaurant on left. **From I-80W**, take exit 126 right onto S1300E past park and left onto E2100S to first left onto E Highland to restaurant.

TAYLORSVILLE

Shirlyn's Natural Foods 🛍️
5578 S. Redwood Rd. ✆ 801-982-0305 ⏰ M-Sat 9-8
Mostly supplements but some food.

🚗 **From I-215**, take exit 13 for Redwood Rd/State Hwy 68 north on S Redwood (right from I-215N, left from I-215S) ¼-½ mile to store on left between W5600S & W5400S.

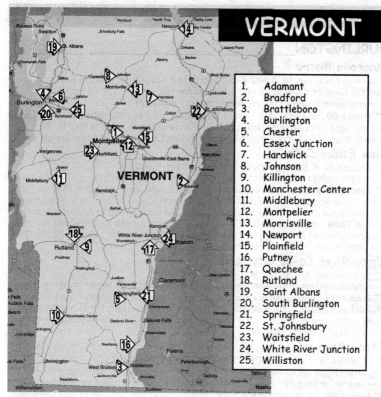

1.	Adamant
2.	Bradford
3.	Brattleboro
4.	Burlington
5.	Chester
6.	Essex Junction
7.	Hardwick
8.	Johnson
9.	Killington
10.	Manchester Center
11.	Middlebury
12.	Montpelier
13.	Morrisville
14.	Newport
15.	Plainfield
16.	Putney
17.	Quechee
18.	Rutland
19.	Saint Albans
20.	South Burlington
21.	Springfield
22.	St. Johnsbury
23.	Waitsfield
24.	White River Junction
25.	Williston

ADAMANT

Adamant Co-op

1313 Haggett Rd. © 802-223-5760 ⏱ M-F 9:30-6, Sat 9:30-3, Sun 10-1
• organic produce • co-op

🏠 **From I-89**, take exit 8 (Montpelier) onto Memorial Dr about 1 mile to light at Main St. Turn left onto Main through town to traffic circle. Take first right off traffic circle to continue on Main (becomes County Rd). At fork turn right onto Center Rd about 5 miles to store at crossroad in Adamant.

BRADFORD

South End Market

45 S. Main St. © 802-222-5701 ⏱ M-F 9-6, Sat 9-5
• organic produce

🏠 **From I-91**, take exit 16 toward Bradford (US 5/Bradford ramp) onto Rt 25E (right from I-91N, left from I-91S) to first left (Maple St). Turn left onto Maple about ⅓ mile to Mill St. Turn right onto Mill and merge right onto S Main St (25 Bus) about ⅓ mile to store on left.

BRATTLEBORO

Brattleboro Food Co-op

2 Main St. © 802-257-1841 ⏱ -Sat 8-9, Sun 9-9
• organic produce • vegetarian friendly • fresh juice • salad bar • cafe • deli • tables • self-service • take-out • co-op

🏠 **From I-91**, take exit 1 toward Brattleboro onto US 5/Canal St (right from I-91N, left from I-91S) over 1 mile (to where Canal becomes Main St) to store on left in Brookside Shopping Ctr.

BURLINGTON

Magnolia Bistro 🍴

1 Lawson Lane, Ste. 10 ✆ 802-846-7446 ⏱ M-F 7am-3pm, Sat-Sun 8-3
Certified Green breakfast/lunch eatery. Very kid friendly.
 • vegetarian friendly • organic focus • tables • wait staff
🍎 **From I-89**, take exit 14W toward Burlington unto Rt 2W (right from I-89S, loop around right from I-89N) about 1½ miles (becomes Main St) to St Paul St. Turn right onto St Paul 1 block to Lawson Ln. Turn left onto Lawson to restaurant on left.

New Ethics Cafe 🍴   ♿

260 North St. ✆ 802-540-2834 ⏱ Tues-Sat 11-9, Sun 11-7
 • vegan • tables • self-service
🍎 **From I-89S**, take exit 16 toward Winsooki right onto Rt 2/7 1 mile to traffic circle. Take second exit onto Main St and continue to follow Rt 7 (becomes N Winsooki Ave) 1¾ miles to North St. Turn right onto North to restaurant on right corner. **From I-89N**, take exit 14W toward Burlington onto Rt 2W about 1¼ miles (becomes Main) to Willard St. Turn right onto Willard over ½ mile to North. Turn left onto North ⅓ mile to restaurant on right after N Winsooki.

Onion River Co-op City Market 🛒 🍴

82 S. Winooski Ave. ✆ 802-863-3659 ⏱ Daily 7-11
 • organic produce • vegetarian friendly • cafe • deli • tables • self-service • take-out • co-op
🍎 **From I-89,** take exit 14W toward Burlington onto US 2W (right from I-89S, loop around right from I-89N) about 1½ miles (becomes Main St) to Winooski Ave. Turn right onto Winooski to store. **From Rt 7N**, turn left onto Main St ¼ mile to Winooski and follow directions above.

Stone Soup 🍴   ♿ 📷

211 College St. ✆ 802-862-7616 ⏱ M 7-7, Tues-F 7-9, Sat 9-7
Vegetarian/vegan hot buffet and salad bar. Sandwich menu includes free-range poultry.
 • vegetarian friendly • vegan friendly • alcohol • salad bar • tables • self-service
🍎 **From I-89**, take exit 14W toward Burlington onto US 2W (right from I-89S, loop around right from I-89N) about 1½ miles (becomes Main St) to Church St. Turn right onto Church 1 block to College St. Turn left onto College to restaurant. **From Rt 7N**, turn left onto Main St ⅓ mile to Church and follow directions above.

CHESTER

Moon Dog Cafe & Market 🛒 🍴

295 Main St. ✆ 802-875-4966 ⏱ M-Sat 9-7, Sun 10-5
 • organic produce • vegetarian friendly • fresh juice • cafe • bakery • tables • self-service • take-out
🍎 **From Rt 35, Rt 11 & Rt 103 intersection**, store is ⅓ mile west on Rt 11 (aka E Main St) on south side.

ESSEX JUNCTION

Sweet Clover Market 🛒

21 Essex Way, Ste. 418 ✆ 802-872-8288 ⏱ Daily 9-8
Features local products from small producers and family farms.
 • organic produce
🍎 **From VT 15 (aka Center Rd in town)**, go south on Essex Way (right from VT 15E, left from VT 15W) under ¼ mile to store in Essex Shoppes & Cinema.

HARDWICK

Buffalo Mountain Co-op 🛒

29 Main St. ✆ 802-472-6020 ⏱ M-F 9-7, Sat 9-6, F 9-7, Sun 10-4
 • organic produce • co-op
🍎 Take Rt 15 to Hardwick. Store is in town (where Rt 15 is Main St) on east side.

JOHNSON

Roo's Natural Foods 🛍
2 Lower Main St. E. ✆ 802-635-1788 ⏱ M-F 12-6, Sat 11-4
• organic produce

🍎 Take Rt 15 to Johnson. Store is in town (where Rt 15 is Main St) in large yellow house.

KILLINGTON

Hemingway's Restaurant 🍴
4988 Rte. 4 ✆ 802-422-3886 ⏱ Tues-Sun 6-10
Gourmet restaurant offering a 4-course vegetarian price-fixed meal. Vegan available with advance notice.
• vegetarian friendly • alcohol • tables • wait staff

🍎 On Rt 4 between junctions 100N & 100S.

MANCHESTER CENTER

Nature's Market 🛍
303 Center Hill Rd. ✆ 802-362-0033 ⏱ M-Sat 9-6, Sun 11-5
• organic produce

🍎 **From Rt 7**, take exit 4 toward Historic VT /7A west on VT 11 (right from 7S, left at fork in ramp from 7N) under 1 mile to Center Hill Rd. Turn right onto Center Hill to store.

New Morning Natural Foods 🛍
Rte. 11 & 30 ✆ 802-362-3602 ⏱ M-Sat 9-6:30, Sun 11-5
• organic produce

🍎 **From Rt 7**, take exit 4 toward Historic VT/7A west on VT 11 (right from 7S, left at fork in ramp from 7N) to store in red barn next to VFW.

MIDDLEBURY

Middlebury Natural Foods Co-op 🛍
9 Washington St. ✆ 802-388-7276 ⏱ Daily 8-7
• organic produce • co-op

🍎 Take Rt 7 to Middlebury. At traffic circle turn onto Washington St to store on left.

MONTPELIER

Hunger Mountain Co-op 🛍 🍴
623 Stone Cutters Way ✆ 802-223-8000 ⏱ Daily 8-8
• organic produce • vegetarian friendly • salad bar • cafe • deli • tables • self-service • take-out • co-op

🍎 **From I-89**, take exit 8 toward Montpelier/US 2 onto Memorial Dr over 1 mile to light at Main St (Rt 12). Turn left onto Main and make first right onto Stonecutter's Way to store on right.

MORRISVILLE

Appletree Natural Foods 🛍
30 Mountainview Plaza ✆ 802-888-8481 ⏱ M-Sat 9-6, Sun 10-5
🍎 Take Rt 15 to Morrisville. Turn onto Munsun Ave (on south side of Rt 15) to store on left in Mountainview Plaza.

Bee's Knees 🍴 ♿
82 Lower Main St. ✆ 802-888-7889 ⏱ Tues-Sun 7:30-10
Vegetarian plus local meat and poultry. Live music most nights.
• vegetarian friendly • organic focus • alcohol • tables • wait staff

🍎 Restaurant is on Rt 100 (aka Lower Main St) 1 block west of Rt 15A/Rt 100 intersection on north side.

NEWPORT

Newport Natural Foods 🛍 🍴

194 Main St. ℭ 802-334-2626 ⊕ M-Th 9-5:30, F 9-6, Sat 9-5, Sun 10:30-4
• organic produce • vegetarian friendly • organic focus • cafe • bakery • tables • self-service • take-out

🍎 **From I-91N**, take exit 27 toward Newport/VT 105 right onto VT 191 about 2¼ miles to end at US 5/VT 105. Turn left onto 5/105 about ½ mile (across water, becomes Main St) to store on right (2 blocks past light). **From I-91S,** take exit 28 toward Newport right onto US 5/VT 105 about 4 miles (across water) to store.

PLAINFIELD

Plainfield Co-op 🛍

153 Main St. ℭ 802-454-8579 ⊕ M-F 9-8, Sat-Sun 10-6
• organic produce • co-op

🍎 **From US Rt 2E**, turn right at blinking light in Plainfield and go down hill to village. **From Rt 2W,** turn left before blinking light and bear left. Cross bridge and bear left onto Main St to end. Store is on left behind fire station.

PUTNEY

Putney Food Co-op 🛍 🍴

8 Carol Brown Way ℭ 802-387-5866 ⊕ M-Sat 7:30-8
• organic produce • vegetarian friendly • deli • bakery • tables • self-service • take-out • co-op

🍎 **From I-91N**, take exit 4 toward Putney/US 5 left onto Putney Landing Rd and left across hwy to Rt 5. Turn right onto Rt 5/Main St and left onto Carol Brown Way to store on right. **From I-91S,** take exit 4 right onto Rt 5/Main St ⅓ mile to Carol Brown. Turn left on Carol Brown to store.

QUECHEE

Farmers Diner 🍴

5573 Woodstock Rd. (Rte. 4) ℭ 802-295-4600 ⊕ M-Tues, 6:30 am-3 pm, W-Sun 6:30-8
Featuring food from farmers and small-scale producers within 70 miles.
• vegetarian friendly • organic focus • alcohol • counter • tables • wait staff • take-out

🍎 **From I-89**, take exit 1 toward Woodstock west on Rt 4 (left from I-89N, right from I-89S) about 2½ miles to restaurant in Quechee Gorge Village.

RUTLAND

Rutland Area Food Co-op 🛍

77 Wales St. ℭ 802-773-0737 ⊕ M-Sat 9-7, Sun 10-5
• organic produce • co-op

🍎 **From Rt 7**, turn west onto Center St (right from 7S, left from 7N) 4 blocks to Wales St. Turn left onto Wales to store on right.

Sunshine Natural Market 🛍

42 Center St. ℭ 802-775-2050 ⊕ M-Sat 9-7, Sun 10-6
• organic produce

🍎 **From Rt 7**, turn west onto Center St (right from 7S, left from 7N) 4 blocks to store at Wales St.

SAINT ALBANS

Rail City Market 🛍

8 S. Main St. ℭ 802-524-3769 ⊕ M-Sat 9-6

🍎 **From I-89**, take exit 19 (VT 104) toward US 7/St Albans and follow Access Road (St Albans S State Hwy) west (left from I-89N, right from I-89S) under 1 mile to Rt 7. Turn right onto Rt 7 (S Main St) about ½ mile to store on left (across from south end of park).

SOUTH BURLINGTON

Healthy Living Natural Foods Market & Cafe 🛍 🍴   ♿

222 Dorset St. ✆ 802-863-2569 ⏰ Daily 8-9
• organic produce • vegetarian friendly • fresh juice • salad bar • cafe • deli • bakery • tables • self-service • take-out

🍎 **From I-89**, take exit 14E onto US 2E (right from I-89N, loop around right from I-89S) to first right (Dorset St). Turn right onto Dorset under ½ mile to store on left between Market St & San Remo Rd.

SPRINGFIELD

Springfield Food Co-op 🛍   ♿

335-1 River St. ✆ 802-885-3363 ⏰ M-W, F 8-6, Th 8-7, Sat 8-5, Sun 10-5
• organic produce • vegetarian friendly • deli • take-out

🍎 **From I-91**, take exit 7 toward Springfield onto Rt 11W about 4 miles to store on right after Rt 11 changes from Main to River St.

ST. JOHNSBURY

Natural Provisions 🛍   ♿

537 Railroad St. ✆ 802-748-3587 ⏰ M-F 9-6:30, Sat 9-5, Sun 10-4
In an old church with stained- glass windows and working steeple bell.
• organic produce

🍎 **From I-91**, take exit 20 (St Johnsbury) onto US 5N (Railroad St) about 1¼ miles to store in town in green church at Maple St. **From I-93N**, take exit 1 (St Johnsbury) right onto VA 18N about ⅓ mile to Rt 2W. Turn left onto 2W (becomes Portland St) 3 miles to Railroad St. Turn right onto Railroad 1 block to store.

St. J. Food Co-op 🛍   ♿

490 Portland St. ✆ 802-748-9498 ⏰ M-W, Sat 9-6, Th-F 9-7, Sun 11-4
• organic produce • co-op

🍎 **From I-91**, take exit 20 (St Johnsbury) onto US 5N (Railroad St) about 1¼ miles to Portland St. Turn right onto Portland about ½ mile to store. **From I-93N**, take exit 1 (St Johnsbury) right onto VA 18N about ⅓ mile to Rt 2W. Turn left onto 2W (becomes Portland St) about 3 miles to store.

WAITSFIELD

Sweet Pea Natural Foods 🛍

Village Square, Rte. 100 ✆ 802-496-7763 ⏰ M-Sat 10-7, Sun 11-6
• organic produce • vegetarian friendly • deli • take-out

🍎 **From Rt 89**, take exit 10 onto Rt 100S about 10 miles into Waitsfield. Store is in town in Village Square Shopping Ctr.

WHITE RIVER JUNCTION

Upper Valley Food Co-op 🛍 🍴

193 N. Main St. ✆ 802-295-5804 ⏰ M-Sat 9-8, Sun 11-5
• organic produce • vegetarian friendly • deli • tables • self-service • take-out

🍎 **From I-91N**, take exit 11 toward White River Junction onto Rt 5N about 1 mile to Main St. Stay straight onto Main to store. **From I-91S**, take exit 12 toward White River Junction/US 5 left onto Bugbee St to Rt 5S. Turn right onto 5S (Hartford St) about 1 mile to Main. Turn sharp left onto Main to store.

WILLISTON

Natural Provisions 🛍 🍴

329 Harvest Lane, Ste. 100 ✆ 802-876-1400 ⏰ M-Sat 8-8, Sun 8-6
• organic produce • vegetarian friendly • salad bar • cafe • deli • tables • self-service • take-out

🍎 **From I-89**, take exit 12 toward Williston north on VA 2A/Essex Rd (left from I-89S, right from I-89N) ⅓ mile to Marshall Ave. Turn left onto Marshall ⅓ mile to Harvest Ln. Turn right onto Harvest under ¼ mile to store on right.

VIRGINIA

1. Abingdon
2. Alexandria
3. Annandale
4. Arlington
5. Blacksburg
6. Bristol
7. Chantilly
8. Charlottesville
9. Dale City
10. Fairfax
11. Falls Church
12. Fredericksburg
13. Front Royal
14. Hamilton
15. Harrisonburg
16. Lexington
17. Lynchburg
18. Manassas
19. Norfolk
20. Portsmouth
21. Purcellville
22. Radford
23. Reston
24. Richmond
25. Roanoke
26. Springfield
27. Staunton
28. Sterling
29. Vienna
30. Virginia Beach
31. Warrenton
32. White Marsh
33. Yorktown

ABINGDON

Cardinal Corner Whole Health

611 E. Main St. ✆ 276-628-3170 ⏰ M-Sat 10-6

🍎 **From I-81**, take exit 19 toward Abingdon/Damascus onto US 11/E Main St (left from I-81N, right from I-81S) about 1⅓ miles to store on right.

ALEXANDRIA

Healthway Natural Foods

1610 Belle View Blvd. ✆ 703-660-8603 ⏰ M-W, F 10-7, Th 10-8, Sat 10-6, Sun 12-5
  • organic produce

🍎 **From I-495 (Capitol Beltway)**, take exit 177A south onto Richmond Hwy/US 1S about ⅔ mile to Huntington Ave. Turn left onto Huntington and right onto Fort Hunt Rd 1 mile to Belle View Blvd. Turn left onto Belle View to store.

MOM's Organic Market

3831 Mt. Vernon Ave. ✆ 703-535-5980 ⏰ M-Sat 9-9, Sun 10-8
  • organic produce

🍎 **From I-395**, take exit 7 (7A from I-395N) east on S Glebe Rd (left from I-395S, right from I-395N) and stay left at fork to continue on S Glebe about 1 mile to S Arlington Ridge Rd. Turn right onto S Arlington/Mt Vernon Ave about ⅓ mile to store on left.

WHOLE FOODS MARKET

1700 Duke St. ✆ 703-706-0891 ⏰ Daily 8-10
  • organic produce • vegetarian friendly • salad bar • cafe • self-service • take-out

🍎 **From I-495 (Capitol Beltway)**, take exit 176B from I-495W or 176B-A from I-495W toward Alexandria, veer right onto Telegraph Rd and take ramp onto Duke St under 1 mile to store on right.

ANNANDALE

Healthway Natural Foods

4113 John Marr Drive ✆ 703-354-7782 ⏰ M-W, F 10-7, Th 10-8, Sat 10-6, Sun 12-5
  • organic produce

🛏 **From I-495N (Capital Beltway)**, take exit 52A-B toward Annandale onto Little River Tpke/Rt 236E toward Annandale about 1½ miles to John Marr Dr. Turn left onto John Marr about ¼ mile to store on right at Columbia Pike.

ARLINGTON

Saran Foods 🍴

5157 N. Lee Hwy. © 703-533-3600 ⊘ Tues-Sun 11-9:30
Indian vegetarian with a daily lunch buffet option.
 • vegetarian • vegan friendly • tables • self-service • take-out

🛏 **From I-66W**, take exit 71 right onto VA 120N/Glebe Rd about ¾ mile to Lee Hwy/US 29. Turn left onto Lee ½ mile to restaurant on right in John Mason Shopping Ctr. **From I-66E**, take exit 69 onto Fairfax Dr and turn left onto Lee Hwy about 1¾ miles to restaurant on left.

Whole Foods Market 🛍 🍴   ♿

2700 Wilson Blvd. © 703-527-6596 ⊘ Daily 8-10:30
 • organic produce • vegetarian friendly • salad bar • cafe • self-service • take-out

🛏 **From I-395**, take exit 11B and follow signs onto US 50W. Take 50W (Arlington Blvd) 1 mile and merge to right onto Fairfax Dr under ½ mile to N Danville St. Turn right onto N Danville to store on left. **From I-66E**, take exit 72 left onto Lee Hwy/US 29S and U-turn at N Kenmore St onto 29N ½ mile to N Danville. Turn right onto N Danville about ⅓ mile to store.

BLACKSBURG

Annie Kay's Whole Foods 🛍

1531 S. Main St. © 540-552-6870 ⊘ M-F 9-7:30, Sat 9-6, Sun 12-6
 • organic produce

🛏 **From I-181S**, take exit 118C-B-A (US 11/US 460) toward Blacksburg and follow exit 118B onto US 460W 5½ miles to exit 5 AB/460 Bus toward Blacksburg. Keep left at fork and follow 460W onto S Main St 1¾ miles to store on right between Landsdowne & Ardmore St. **From I-181N**, take exit 118B onto 460W 6 miles to exit 5AB and follow directions above.

Eats Natural Foods 🛍 &♿

708 N. Main St. ✆ 540-552-2279 ⊙ M-F 10-8, Sat-Sun 10-6
• organic produce • co-op

🍎 **From I-181S,** take 118C-B-A (US 11/US 460) toward Blacksburg and follow exit 118B onto US 460W 5½ miles to exit 5AB/460 Bus toward Blacksburg. Keep left at fork and follow 460W onto S Main St about 3¼ miles to N Main St. Turn right onto N Main to store on left. **From I-181N,** take exit 118B onto 460W 6 miles to exit 5AB and follow directions above.

Gillies 🍴

153 College Ave. ✆ 540-961-2703 ⊙ M-F 8-9, Sat 8-2, 5-9, Sun 8-2
Vegetarian, vegan and fish.
• vegetarian friendly • vegan friendly • fresh juice • alcohol • tables • wait staff

🍎 **From I-181S,** take 118C-B-A (US 11/US 460) toward Blacksburg and follow exit 118B onto US 460W 5½ miles to exit 5AB/460 Bus toward Blacksburg. Keep left at fork and follow 460W onto S Main St about 3¼ miles. Just after College Ave turn right onto N Main, sharp left onto N Main and right onto College to restaurant on right. **From I-181N,** take exit 118B onto 460W 6 miles to exit 5AB and follow directions above.

BRISTOL

The Shouting Sprout 🛍

3170 Linden Drive ✆ 276-644-9111 ⊙ M-Sat 10-8
Smoothie bar with a counter and a few tables.
• organic produce

🍎 **From I-81,** take exit 7 north on Old Airport Rd (right from I-81S, left from I-81S) to first left onto Linden Dr to store on right.

CHANTILLY

Lotus Vegetarian Restaurant 🍴

13872 Metrotech Drive ✆ 703-378-6888 ⊙ M-Th, Sun 11-9:30, F-Sat 11-10
Chinese vegetarian plus sandwiches, organic salad and organic French fries.
• vegetarian • vegan friendly • fresh juice • tables • self-service • take-out

🍎 **From US 50/Jackson Memorial Hwy,** turn into Sully Plaza Shopping Ctr on Metro Tech drive to restaurant on right.

CHARLOTTESVILLE

Integral Yoga Natural Foods 🛍 &♿

923 H Preston Ave. ✆ 434-293-4111 ⊙ M-Sat 9-8, Sun 11-6
• organic produce • vegetarian • vegan friendly • organic focus • fresh juice • deli • bakery • take-out

🍎 **From I-64E,** take exit 120 left onto 5th St/VA 631N (becomes Ridge St) 2⅓ miles to Preston Ave. Turn left onto Preston about ½ mile to store in Preston Plaza. **From I-64W,** take exit 124 onto 250W almost 2 miles to 250 Bypass. Take 250 Bypass 1 mile to McIntire Rd. Turn left onto McIntire and follow onto Harris St about ⅔ mile to Preston (250 Bus). Turn right onto Preston to store. **From Rt 29S,** take 29 Bus S (Emmet St) almost ½ mile to Barracks Rd. Turn left onto Barracks ½ mile continuing onto Preston almost ⅔ mile to store.

Rebecca's Natural Food 🛍

1141 Emmet St. ✆ 434-977-1965 ⊙ M-F 9-8, Sat-Sun 10-6
• organic produce

🍎 **From I-64,** take 118B onto Rt 29N toward Charlottsville about 4 miles to Emmett St/US 29S exit. Merge onto Emmet St N ⅓ mile to store on right after Barracks Rd.

Whole Foods Market 🛍 🍴 &♿

300 Shoppers World Court ✆ 434-973-4900 ⊙ M-Sat 8-10, Sun 8-9

• organic produce • vegetarian friendly • salad bar • cafe • self-service • take-out

🍎 **From I-64E**, take 118B onto Rt 29N about 6¼ miles to store on west side (29S) in Shopper's World. **From I-64W**, take exit 124 onto Rt 250W almost 2 miles to Rt 250 Bypass. Follow 250 Bypass 2½ miles to Rt 29N (toward Washington). Turn right onto 29N (Emmet St) 1¾ miles to store on west side.

DALE CITY

The Natural Grocer 🍃
14453 Potomac Mills Rd. ✆ 703-494-7287 ⏰ M-F 10-8, Sat 10-6

🍎 **From I-95S**, take exit 156 (VA 784W) and follow ramp onto Potomac Mills Rd. Stay right at fork and right onto Potomac Mills to store in Potomac Festival Shopping Ctr (behind Day's Inn). **From I-95N**, take exit 156 onto Dale Blvd/VA 784W about 1½ miles to Gideon Dr. Turn right onto Gideon about ¾ mile to Opitz Blvd. Turn right onto Opitz and right onto Potomac Mills Rd to store.

FAIRFAX

Healthway Natural Foods 🍃   ♿
10360 Lee Hwy. ✆ 703-591-1121 ⏰ M-W, F 10-7, Th 10-8, Sat 10-6, Sun 12-5
• organic produce

🍎 **From I-66**, take exit 60 toward Fairfax onto VA 123S (Chain Bridge Rd) to Lee Hwy. Turn left onto Lee 1 block to store in Fairfax Shopping Ctr.

Woodlands 🍴
4078 Jermantown Rd. ✆ 703-385-1996 ⏰ M-F 11:30-3, 5-9:45, Sat 11:30-9:45, Sun 11:30-9:15
Vegetarian Indian with a buffet available at lunch.

• vegetarian • vegan friendly • tables • self-service • wait staff

🍎 **From I-66**, take exit 57A toward Fairfax onto US 50E about 1¼ miles to Jermantown Rd. Turn right onto Jermantown to restaurant.

FALLS CHURCH

Kennedy's Natural Foods 🍃 🍴
1051 W. Broad St. ✆ 703-533-8484 ⏰ M-Sat 11-7
• vegetarian friendly • deli • tables • self-service • take-out

🍎 **From I-66**, take exit 66 (66A from I-66W) right onto Rt 7E (Leesburg Pike) about 1 mile to store on right in West End Shopping Ctr. **From I-495**, take exit 47B toward Falls Church onto 7E about 2 miles to store.

Sunflower Vegetarian Restaurant 🍴   ♿
6304 Leesburg Pike ✆ 703-237-3888 ⏰ Daily 11:30-9:30
Mostly Asian vegetarian with American overtones.

• vegetarian • vegan friendly • tables • wait staff • take-out

🍎 **From I-66E**, take exit 66 right onto Rt 7E about 3 miles onto Rt 50E service rd. Turn right into parking lot behind the gas station to restaurant on right. **From Rt 7W**, restaurant is on right after Castle Rd.

Whole Foods Market 🍃 🍴   ♿
7511 Leesburg Pike ✆ 703-448-1600 ⏰ M-Sat 8-10:30, Sun 8-10
• organic produce • vegetarian friendly • salad bar • cafe • self-service • take-out

🍎 **From I-66**, take exit 66 (66B from I-66W) onto Rt 7W (Leesburg Pike) about ¼ mile to store on left.

FREDERICKSBURG

Healthway Natural Foods 🍃   ♿
4211 Plank Rd. ✆ 540-786-4844 ⏰ M-Th 10-7, F 10-8, Sat 10-6, Sun 12-5
• organic produce

🍎 **From I-95**, take exit 130B onto Rt 3W (Plank Rd) about 2 miles to store on right.

Pantry Shelf Natural Foods & Gourmet Grocery 🛍️
811 Sophia St. ✆ 540-373-2253 ⏰ M-Th, Sat 10-6, F 10-7
  • organic produce

🚗 **From I-95**, take exit 130A toward Fredericksburg onto Rt 3E about 1½ miles to Williams St (signs for Historic Downtown). Turn left onto Williams (3 Bus) 1 block to Hanover St. Turn right onto Hanover about 1¼ miles to Sophia St. Turn left on Sophia to store on right.

Sammy T's 🍴   ♿
801 Caroline St. ✆ 540-371-2008 ⏰ M-Th, Sun. 11-9, F-Sat 11-10 Nonsmoking room hours: M-F 11-3, 5-8, Sat-Sun 11-8
Sandwiches, soups, salads and hot entrees for every eating style.
  • vegetarian friendly • vegan friendly • alcohol • tables • wait staff

🚗 **From I-95**, take exit 130A toward Fredericksburg onto Rt 3E about 1½ miles to Williams St (signs for Historic Downtown). Turn left onto Williams St (3 Bus) 1 block to Hanover St. Turn right onto Hanover 1 mile to restaurant at Caroline St.

FRONT ROYAL

Better Thyme 🛍️
417 South St. ✆ 540-636-9209 ⏰ M-W 9-6, Th-Sat 9-8, Sun 12-5

🚗 **From I-66**, take exit 6 toward Front Royal/VA 55 onto US 340S (becomes 340E) almost 4 miles to VA 55. Turn left onto 55E (South St) to store in first shopping ctr on right. **From I-66W**, take exit 13 (VA 79) toward Front Royal/VA 55 left onto VA 49 about ¼ mile to VA 55. Turn right onto 55E about 5¼ miles to store on left before US 340.

HAMILTON

Natural Mercantile of Hamilton 🛍️
341 E. Colonial Hwy. ✆ 540-338-7080 ⏰ M-F 10-7, Sat 10-5
  • organic produce

🚗 **From VA 7**, take VA 204 exit toward Hamilton south on Hamilton Station Rd (loop around right from VA 7W, merge right from VA 7E) ½-¾ mile to VA 7/E Colonial Hwy. Turn right onto E Colonial to store on right.

HAMPTON

The Healthy Connection/Organic Food Depot 🛍️
2007 N. Armistead Ave. ✆ 757-826-6404 ⏰ M-F 10-6, Sat 10-5
Homegrown produce from Pungo Farm in Virginia Beach plus a smoothie bar.
  • organic produce

🚗 **From I-64E**, take exit 261B onto Hampton Rd Center Pkwy E under 2 miles to N Armstead Ave. Turn right onto N Armstead about 1¼ mile to store on right between Inglewood Dr & W Mercury Blvd. **From I-64W**, take exit 265B toward LaSalle Ave onto N Armstead about 1¼ miles to store on left after W Mercury.

HARRISONBURG

Kate's Natural Products 🛍️ 🍴   ♿
451 University Blvd. ✆ 540-433-2359 ⏰ M-Sat 9-6
  • organic produce • vegetarian friendly • deli • tables • self-service • take-out

🚗 **From I-81S**, take exit 247A toward Elkton onto E Market St under 1 mile to second light (University Blvd). Turn right onto University about ⅔ mile to store on right (before next light). **From I-81N**, take exit 245 right onto Port Republic Rd and left onto Forest Hills Dr (becomes University) about 1⅓ miles to store on left after light at Reservoir St.

Sue's Super Nutrition 🛍️
3060 S. Main St. ✆ 540-432-9855 ⏱ M-Sat 9-6
Small produce section and homemade soups in winter.

🚗 **From I-81**, take exit 243 toward Harrisonburg right onto Main St ½ mile to store on right.

The Little Grill 🍴
621 N. Main St. ✆ 540-434-3594 ⏱ Tues-F 7-9, Sat 7-3, Sun 9-2
Mostly vegetarian wholefoods menu. Closed Mondays to host the free community soup kitchen.
• vegetarian friendly • alcohol • tables • wait staff

🚗 **From I-81**, take exit 247B toward Harrisonburg onto US 33W under 2 miles to US 11N. Merge straight onto 11N (Main St) to restaurant.

LEXINGTON

Cool Spring Organic Market 🛍️
800 S. Main St. ✆ 540-463-6506 ⏱ M-Sat 8-7, Sun 9-5
• organic produce • vegetarian friendly • deli • take-out

🚗 **From I-81**, take exit 188B toward Lexington onto Rt 60W about 2¼ miles. Go under overpass and make immediate left onto Rt 11 under 1 mile to light at S Main St. Turn right onto S Main to store on right.

Healthy Foods Coop & Counter Culture Cafe 🛍️ 🍴   ♿
110 W. Washington St. ✆ 540-463-6954 ⏱ M-F 9-6, Sat 9-5 Cafe M-F 11-2
Vegetarian/vegan lunch weekdays, soup and sandwiches on Saturday.
• organic produce • vegetarian • organic focus • fresh juice • salad bar • cafe • deli • counter • tables • self-service • wait staff • take-out

🚗 **From I-81**, take exit 188B toward Lexington onto Rt 60W almost 3 miles to downtown Lexington (where 30 becomes Nelson St). At third light turn right onto Washington St to store on left after second light.

LYNCHBURG

Fresh Air Natural Foods 🛍️
2264 Lakeside Drive ✆ 434-385-9252 ⏱ M-F 9-8, Sat 9-6
• organic produce

🚗 Store is about ½ mile east of US 501/US 221 intersection on north side of US 221 (aka Lakeside Dr).

Health Nut Nutrition 🛍️
113B Tradewynd Drive ✆ 434-239-5170 ⏱ M-F 10-6, Sat 10-3

🚗 **From US 501N**, take exit 10B onto Timberlake Rd about 2¼ miles to Laxton Rd. Turn right onto Laxton ½ mile to Enterprise Dr. Turn right onto Enterprise about ¾ mile to Tradewynd Dr. Turn right onto Tradewynd to store at end on left. **From US 221**, go south on Enterprise (left from US 221W, right from US 221E) 1¼ miles to Tradewynd. Turn left onto Tradewynd to store.

MANASSAS

Healthway Natural Foods 🛍️   ♿
10778 Sudley Manor Drive ✆ 703-361-1883 ⏱ M-Th 10-7, F 10-8, Sat 10-6, Sun 12-5
• organic produce

🚗 **From I-66**, take exit 47A toward Manassas onto Sudley Rd/VA 234 BusS about 1 mile to Sudley Manor Dr. Turn right onto Sudley Manor to store in Bull Run Ctr.

NORFOLK

Amalfi Ristorante ⑪
2010 Colley Ave. © 757-625-1262 ⊙ M-Th, Sun 10:30-10, F-Sat 10:30-11
Italian market with vegetarian and vegan menus.
  • vegetarian friendly • vegan friendly • alcohol • counter • tables • wait staff • take-out

🚗 **From I-64E,** take exit 276 toward Naval Base onto Granby St/US 460W 4 miles
to E 21st St. Turn right onto E 21st about ¾ mile to Colley Ave. Turn left onto
Colley 1 block to restaurant on left. **From I-64W,** take exit 279A onto Norwood Ave
W ½ mile to Chesapeake Blvd. Veer left onto Chesapeake about 1⅓ miles to traffic
circle and take first exit onto Lafayette Blvd/US 247 to Colley. Turn left onto Colley
about ⅓ mile to restaurant on left after W 21st St. **From I-264W,** take exit 11B onto
E Brambleton Ave 2¼ miles to Colley. Turn right onto Colley 1 mile to restaurant
on right after W 20th St.

Azar's Market & Cafe ⑪
2000 Colley Ave. © 757-664-7955 ⊙ M-Th 11-9, F-Sat 11-11, Sun 11-8
Middleastern with numerous vegetarian and vegan selections.
  • vegetarian friendly • alcohol • tables • wait staff • take-out

🚗 **From I-64E,** take exit 276 toward Naval Base onto Granby St/US 460W 4 miles
to E 21st St. Turn right onto E 21st about ¾ mile to Colley Ave. Turn left onto
Colley 1 block to restaurant on left. **From I-64W,** take exit 279A onto Norwood Ave
W ½ mile to Chesapeake Blvd. Veer left onto Chesapeake about 1⅓ miles to traffic
circle and take first exit onto Lafayette Blvd/US 247 about 2½ miles to Colley. Turn
left onto Colley about ⅓ mile to restaurant on left at W 20th St. **From I-264W,** take
exit 11B onto E Brambleton Ave 2¼ miles to Colley. Turn right onto Colley 1 mile
to restaurant on right.

Health Food Center ⑪   ♿
1701 Colley Ave. © 757-625-6656 ⊙ M-F 10-7, Sat 10-6
🚗 **From I-64E**, take exit 276 toward Naval Base onto Granby St/US 460W almost 3 miles
to W 38th St. Turn right onto W 38th about ¾ mile to Colley Ave. Turn left onto Colley
about ¾ mile to store on right. **From I-64W,** take exit 276C toward US 460W left onto Little
Creek Rd and right onto E Admiral Taussig Blvd about ¼ mile to Granby. Turn left onto
Granby and follow directions above. **From I-264W,** take exit 10 onto E City Hall Ave to St
Pauls Blvd. Turn right onto St Pauls ½ mile to Brambleton Ave. Turn left onto Brambleton
about 1 mile to Colley. Turn right onto Colley under 1 mile to store on left.

Health Food Center ⑪
7639 Granby St. © 757-489-4242 ⊙ M-Sat 10-6
🚗 **From I-64E,** take exit 276 toward Naval Base onto Granby St/US 460W about
½ mile to store at Wards Corner. **From I-64W,** take exit 276C toward US 460W
left onto Little Creek Rd and right onto E Admiral Taussig Blvd about ¼ mile to
Granby. Turn left onto Granby to store.

Machismo Burrito Bar ⑪
409 W. York St. © 757-624-2424 © Daily 11-9
Build-your-own burrito: vegetarian beans and "meat," vegan cheese and sour cream, brown rice.
  • vegetarian friendly • vegan friendly • tables • self-service • take-out

🚗 **From I-264W,** take exit 11B onto E Brambleton Ave 1¾ miles to Botetourt St.
Turn left onto Botetourt and right onto York St to restaurant on left. **From I-264E,**
take exit 10 and follow signs for St Pauls Blvd onto US 260 and right onto St Pauls
almost ½ mile to Brambleton Ave. Turn left onto Brambleton about ½ mile to
Botetourt. Turn left onto Botetourt and right onto York St to restaurant.

Organic Food Depot ⑪
1912 Granby St. © 757-623-8999 ⊙ M-Th 10-7, F 10-8, Sat-Sun 10-6
Homegrown produce from Pungo Farm in Virginia Beach.
  • organic produce

🍎 **From I-264W**, take exit 11B onto E Brambleton Ave about 1 mile to St Pauls Blvd. Turn right onto St Pauls about 1 mile (becomes Monticello Ave) to E 19th St. Turn left onto E 19th 1 block to Granby St. Turn right onto Granby to store on left. **From I-264E,** take exit 9 on left and follow signs for St Pauls onto US 260. Turn right onto St Pauls 1⅓ miles to E 19th and follow directions above.

Raput Indian Cuisine 🍴
742 W. 21st St. ✆ 757-625-4634 ⊙ M-Th 11:30-2:30, 5-10, F 11:30-2:30, 5-10:30, Sat 12-3, 5-10:30, Sun 12-3, 5-9
Traditional Indian fare with separate vegan menu. Lunch buffet.
   • vegetarian friendly • vegan friendly • alcohol • tables • self-service • wait staff

🍎 **From I-264W**, take exit 11B onto E Brambleton Ave about 1 mile to St Pauls Blvd. Turn right onto St Pauls 1 mile (becomes Monticello Ave) to E 21st. Turn left onto E 21st ¾ mile to restaurant. **From I-264E**, take exit 9 on left and follow signs for St Pauls onto US 260. Turn right onto St Pauls under 1½ miles to E 21st and follow directions above.

The Taphouse Grill 🍴
931 W. 21st St. ✆ 757-627-9172 ⊙ Daily 4pm-2am
   • vegetarian friendly • vegan friendly • alcohol • tables • wait staff

🍎 **From I-264W**, take exit 11B onto E Brambleton Ave about 1 mile to St Pauls Blvd. Turn right onto St Pauls 1 mile (becomes Monticello Ave) to E 21st. Turn left onto E 21st about 1 mile to restaurant. **From I-264E**, take exit 9 on left and follow signs for St Pauls onto US 260. Turn right onto St Pauls under 1½ miles to E 21st and follow directions above.

PORTSMOUTH

Organic Food Depot 🛍
341 High St. ✆ 757-673-2900 ⊙ Tues-Th 10-7, F 11-8, Sat 10-6
Homegrown produce from Pungo Farm in Virginia Beach.
   • organic produce

🍎 **From I-264E**, take exit 7B right at fork onto Effingham St ½ mile to High St. Turn right onto High 4½ blocks to store on right after Court St. **From I-264W**, take exit 7 toward Effingham right at fork toward Downtown Portsmouth. Veer left at Bart St, turn left onto Port Centre Pkwy and continue onto Court about 4 blocks to High. Turn right onto High to store.

PURCELLVILLE

Healthway Natural Foods 🛍   ♿
160 W. Main St. ✆ 540-338-2240 ⊙ M-Th 10-7, F 10-8, Sat 10-6, Sun 12-5
   • organic produce

🍎 **From VA 7W**, take exit for Hwy 7 left at fork toward Winchester/Purcellville and turn left onto Berlin Tpke/VA 287 about ¾ mile to E Main St. Turn right onto E Main (becomes W Main) about 1⅓ miles to store on left after N 21st St. **From VA 7E**, take exit toward Purcellville onto E Loudoun St about 2 miles to store on right after N 23rd St.

RADFORD

Annie Kay's Whole Foods 🛍
601 3rd St. ✆ 540-731-9498 ⊙ M-F 9-7, Sat 9-6, Sun 12-6
   • organic produce

🍎 **From I-81S,** take exit 109 onto Tyler Rd/VA 177N about 2⅓ miles to Rock Rd. Turn left onto Rock about 1¾ miles to Wadsworth St. Turn right onto Wadsworth 1¼ miles to store on left at 3rd St. **From I-81N**, take exit 105 onto VA 232N 4 miles to Wadsworth. Turn right onto Wadsworth to store on right at 3rd.

RESTON
Whole Foods Market 🛍 🍴 ♿
11660 Plaza America Drive ✆ 703-736-0600 ⏰ Daily 8-9
• organic produce • vegetarian friendly • salad bar • cafe • self-service • take-out

🚌 **From Toll Rd 267**, take exit 12 north onto Reston Pkwy/VA 602N (left from 267E, right from 267W) and make first right onto Sunset Hills Dr under ½ mile (past 2 lights) to store on right in Plaza America.

RICHMOND
Ellwood Thompson's 🛍 🍴
4 N. Thompson St. ✆ 804-359-7525 ⏰ Daily 7-10
• organic produce • vegetarian friendly • salad bar • cafe • deli • bakery • tables • self-service • take-out

🚌 **From I-95S**, take exit 76 onto I-195S toward Powhite Pkwy about 2⅓ miles to Cary St exit. Turn left onto Cary past hwy 1 bock to store at N Thompson St. **From I-95N**, take exit 74A onto I-195N (Downtown Expwy) about 3½ miles to Cary St. Turn right onto Cary 1 block to store at N Thompson.

Good Foods Grocery 🛍
1312 Gaskins Rd. ✆ 804-740-3518 ⏰ M-Sat 9-9
• organic produce • vegetarian friendly • deli • bakery • take-out

🚌 **From I-64**, take exit 180 (180A from I-64W) south on Gaskins Rd S about 2½ miles to store on right in Gayton Cross Shopping Ctr.

Good Foods Grocery 🛍
3062 Stony Point Rd. ✆ 804-320-6767 ⏰ M-Sat 9-9
Take-out items made at the Gaskins Rd store.
• organic produce

🚌 **From I-195**, take Powhite Pkwy to Forest Hill Ave exit. Turn west onto Forest Hill (right from I-195S, left from I-195N) about 3 miles to store past Huguenot Rd in Stony Point Shopping Ctr.

Harrison St. Coffee Shop 🍴
402 N. Harrison St. ✆ 804-359-8060 ⏰ M-F 8-8, Sat-Sun 11am-3pm
• vegetarian • vegan friendly • tables • self-service

🚌 **From I-95N**, take exit 74C onto E Broad St about 1½ miles to N Harrison St. Turn left onto N Harrison past first block to restaurant on right. **From I-95S**, take exit 76B toward US 1/Belvidere St right onto W Leigh St 3 blocks to N Harrison. Turn left onto N Harrison under ½ mile to restaurant.

Ipanema Cafe 🍴
917 W. Grace St. ✆ 804-213-0190 ⏰ M-F 11-11, Sat-Sun 5:30-11
Vegetarian, vegan and one fish choice.
• vegetarian friendly • vegan friendly • alcohol • counter • tables • wait staff

🚌 **From I-95N**, take exit 74C onto E Broad St about 1¼ miles to N Belvidere St. Turn left onto N Belvidere 1 block to W Grace St. Turn right onto W Grace 3½ blocks to restaurant on left. **From I-95S**, take exit 76B toward US 1/Belvidere left onto W Leigh St 1 block to Belvidere. Turn right onto Belvidere ⅓ mile to W Grace. Turn right onto W Grace 3½ blocks to restaurant.

Panda Vegetarian Restaurant 🍴
948 W. Grace St. ✆ 804-359-6688 ⏰ Daily 11-10
Vegetarian Chinese and veggie sushi. Buffet dinner option Friday to Sunday.
• vegetarian • vegan friendly • fresh juice • tables • self-service • wait staff • take-out

🚌 **From I-95N**, take exit 74C onto E Broad St about 1¼ miles to N Belvidere St. Turn left onto N Belvidere 1 block to W Grace St. Turn right onto W Grace 4 blocks to restaurant on right at N Harrison St. **From I-95S**, take exit 76B toward US 1/Belvidere St left onto W Leigh St 1 block to Belvidere. Turn right onto Belvidere ⅓ mile to W Grace. Turn right onto W Grace 4 blocks to restaurant.

ROANOKE

Roanoke Natural Foods 🛍 🍴 &

1319 Grandin Rd. ℂ 540-343-5652 ⊕ M-Sat 8-8, Sun 12-6 Deli M-Sat 10-4, Sun 12-4
• organic produce • vegetarian friendly • fresh juice • cafe • deli • bakery • counter •
tables • self-service • take-out • co-op

🛒 **From I-81**, take exit 143 onto I-581 about 5½ miles to exit 4W. Merge onto US
11AltW/460W about 1 mile to 10th St NW. Turn left onto 10th about 1 mile to US
11N/Campbell Ave. Turn right onto 11 (continues left onto 13th St and left onto
Grandin Rd) about 1 mile to store on right after Memorial Ave.

SPRINGFIELD

Healthway Natural Foods 🛍 &

6402-4 Springfield Plaza ℂ 703-569-3533 ⊕ M-W, F 10-7, Th 10-8, Sat 10-6, Sun 12-5
• organic produce

🛒 **From I-95N**, take exit 169A-B toward VA 644/Springfield. Follow ramp toward
Old Keene Mill Rd/Springfield and merge onto 644W under ½ mile to Bland
St. Turn right onto Bland and left onto Springfield Plaza to store. **From I-395S**,
continue onto I-95S about ¼ mile, merge onto Old Keene Mill Rd/644W and
follow directions above.

Whole Foods Market 🛍 🍴 &

8402 Old Keene Mill Rd. ℂ 703-644-2500 ⊕ Daily 8-9
• organic produce • vegetarian friendly • salad bar • cafe • self-service • take-out

🛒 **From I-95N**, take exit 169A-B toward VA 644/Springfield. Follow ramp toward
Old Keene Mill Rd/Springfield and merge onto 644W about 3 miles to store on
right after Rolling Rd. **From I-395S,** continue on I-95S about ¼ mile, merge onto
Old Keene Mill Rd/644W and follow directions above.

STAUNTON

Cranberry's Grocery & Eatery 🛍 🍴

7 S. New St. ℂ 540-885-4755 ⊕ M-Sat 9:30-4:40
• organic produce • vegetarian friendly • fresh juice • alcohol • cafe • tables • self-
service • take-out

🛒 **From I-81**, take exit 222 toward Staunton onto US 250W/Richmond Ave (right
from I-81S, loop around right from I-81N) about 2 miles to Greenville Ave. Turn
right onto Greenville across tracks, left onto Commerce Rd and first right onto S
New 1 block to store on right.

STERLING

Healthway Natural Foods 🛍 &

46900 Cedar Lakes Plaza ℂ 703-430-4430 ⊕ M-W, F 10-7, Th 10-8, Sat 10-6, Sun 12-5
• organic produce

🛒 **From VA 7W (Leesburg Pike)**, turn right onto Cedar Lakes Plaza to store in
Shops at Cedar Lakes. **From VA 7E,** turn left onto Cedar Lakes Plaza.

VIENNA

Amma Vegetarian Kitchen 🍴

344-A Maple Ave. E. ℂ 703-938-5328 ⊕ M-Th 11:30-2:30, 5:30-9:30, F-Sat 11:30-
10, Sun 11:30-9:30
No-frills South Indian vegetarian fare.
• vegetarian • vegan friendly • tables • self-service • take-out

🛒 **From I-495**, take exit 46A toward Tyson's Corner/Vienna onto Rt 123S (Chain
Bridge Rd, becomes Maple Ave E in town) under 3 miles to restaurant. **From I-66**,
take exit 62 toward Vienna north on Nutley St SW (loop around right from I-66E,
right from I-66W) about 2 miles to Maple Ave W. Turn right onto Maple 1 mile
to restaurant.

Sunflower Vegetarian Restaurant 🍴

2531 Chain Bridge Rd. ✆ 703-319-3888 ⏱ M-F 11:30-10, Sat-Sun 12-10
Mostly Asian with American overtones.
· vegetarian · vegan friendly · tables · wait staff · take-out
🚘 **From I-66**, take exit 62 toward Vienna north on Nutley St SW under 2 miles to Maple Ave. Turn left onto W Maple and U-turn at James Madison Dr and make sharp right onto Chain Bridge Rd to restaurant on left.

Whole Foods Market 🛍🍴   ♿

143 Maple Ave. E. ✆ 703-319-2000 ⏱ M-Sat 8-10, Sun 8-9
· organic produce · vegetarian friendly · salad bar · cafe · self-service · take-out
🚘 **From I-495**, take exit 46A toward Tyson's Corner/Vienna on Rt 123S (Chain Bridge Rd, becomes Maple Ave E) about 3 miles to store on left after Park St. **From I-66,** take exit 62 toward Vienna north on Nutley St SW under 2 miles to Maple Ave. Turn right onto Maple about ½ mile to store on right.

VIRGINIA BEACH

Azar's Market & Cafe 🍴   ♿

108 Prescott Ave. ✆ 757-486-7778 ⏱ M-Th 11:30-8:30, F-Sat 11:30-9:30
See Norfolk location for description.
· vegetarian friendly · alcohol · tables · wait staff · take-out
🚘 **From I-264E**, take exit 17B to first light at Independence Blvd. Turn right onto Bonney Rd 1½ miles to Prescott Ave. Turn left onto Prescott to restaurant on right. **From oceanfront**, take I-264W to Rosemont Rd exit. Stay in center lane at bottom of ramp. Continue straight onto Bonney about 1 mile to restaurant at Prescott.

Fresh Fair Cafe 🍴

700 19th St. ✆ 757-491-5383 ⏱ M-Th 7-7:30, F 7-6:30, Sat 8-4:30
· vegetarian friendly · fresh juice · tables · self-service · take-out
🚘 **From I-264E**, turn right onto Cypress St 3 blocks to restaurant at 19th St. **From oceanfront**, go inland on 19th ½ mile to restaurant at Cypress..

Health Food Center 🛍

5312 Kemps River Drive #105 ✆ 757-523-8961 ⏱ M-F 10-7, Sat 10-6
🚘 **From I-64**, take exit 286B onto Indian River Rd (VA 407S) about 1 mile to Kemps River Dr. Turn left onto Kemps River about ⅓ mile to store in Kemps River Shops.

Heritage Health Foods & Organic Cafe 🛍🍴   ♿

314 Laskin Rd. ✆ 757-428-0500 ⏱ M-F 10-6:40, Sat 9-7:40, Sun 11-6:40
A "holistic lifestyle department store."
· organic produce · vegetarian friendly · fresh juice · cafe · deli · tables · self-service
· take-out
🚘 Take I-264E to end. Turn left onto Pacific Ave about ½ mile to Laskin Rd. Turn left onto Laskin to store on right.

Machismo Burrito Bar 🍴

525 N. Birdneck Rd. ✆ 757-422-6010 ⏱ M-Sat 11-9, Sun 11-4
See Norfolk location for description.
· vegetarian friendly · vegan friendly · tables · self-service · take-out
🚘 **From I-264E**, take exit 22 left at fork and merge onto Pavilion Dr to N Birdneck Rd. Turn left onto N Birdneck about 2 blocks to restaurant on left. **From the beach**, go inland on 22nd St ½ mile to Cypress Ave. Turn right onto Cypress 4 blocks to end and turn left onto 24th St about ½ mile to N Birdneck. Turn left onto N Birdneck about ¼ mile to restaurant on right.

Organic Food Depot 🛍️

4301 Commuter Drive, #105 ✆ 757-467-8999 ⏱ M-Th 10-7, F 10-8, Sat-Sun 10-6
Homegrown produce from Pungo Farm in Virginia Beach.
  • organic produce

🍎 **From I-264**, take exit 19 toward Princess Anne onto VA 410/S Independence Blvd/S Holland Blvd under 1-1½ miles to Commuter Dr. Turn right onto Commuter to store on left.

Virginia Garden Organic Grocery 🛍️

3640 DamNeck Rd. ✆ 757-427-0378 ⏱ M-Sat 10-7
Produce from local farmers, grab-and-go foods.
  • organic produce

🍎 **From I-264E**, take exit 17A and veer right onto VA 410/Holland Rd about 4½ miles to Dam Neck Rd. Turn right onto Dam Neck about 1¼ miles (past Princess Anne Rd) to store on right in Virginia Beach farmers' market. **From I-264W**, take exit 19A onto Lynnhaven Pkwy 3¼ miles to Holland. Turn left onto Holland 2 mile to Dam Neck. Turn right onto Dam Neck and follow directions above.

WARRENTON

The Natural Marketplace 🛍️

5 Diagonal St. ✆ 540-349-4111 ⏱ M-F 9-6, Sat 9-5
  • organic produce • vegetarian friendly • fresh juice • deli • take-out

🍎 **From US 15N/17N (becomes Falmouth St)**, veer left onto Rt 211/Waterloo St and first right onto Diagonal St to store on left (2-story yellow house). **From US 15S**, turn left onto Blackwell Rd 1 mile and veer right onto Diagonal to store

WHITE MARSH

Healthy Solutions 🛍️

4858 White Marsh Shopping Center ✆ 804-693-2450 ⏱ M-F 9:30-6:30, Sat 10-4
  • organic produce • fresh juice • counter • take-out

🍎 On US 17 between Hickory Fork Rd & Feather Bed Ln on east side in White Marsh Shopping Ctr.

YORKTOWN

Food, Herbs & More 🛍️

2821 Denbigh Blvd. ✆ 757-898-0100 ⏱ Tues-Sat 10-6
Small selection of homemade foods and a picnic table outside.
  • organic produce • vegetarian friendly • deli • take-out

🍎 **From I-64E**, take exit 250B for VA 105E toward Yorktown onto Ft Eustis Blvd across hwy and right onto Jefferson Ave 3 miles to N Denbigh Blvd. Turn left onto N Denbigh almost 1½ miles to store on right. **From I-64W**, take exit 255B-A onto Jefferson almost 1½ miles to N Denbigh. Turn right onto N Denbigh almost 1½ miles to store.

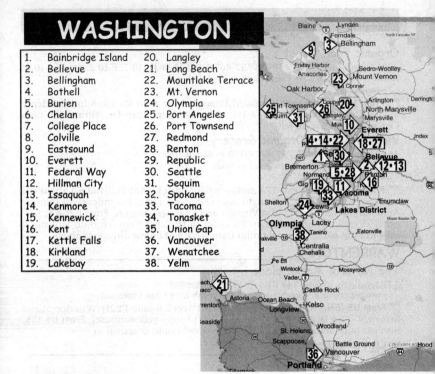

WASHINGTON

1.	Bainbridge Island	20.	Langley
2.	Bellevue	21.	Long Beach
3.	Bellingham	22.	Mountlake Terrace
4.	Bothell	23.	Mt. Vernon
5.	Burien	24.	Olympia
6.	Chelan	25.	Port Angeles
7.	College Place	26.	Port Townsend
8.	Colville	27.	Redmond
9.	Eastsound	28.	Renton
10.	Everett	29.	Republic
11.	Federal Way	30.	Seattle
12.	Hillman City	31.	Sequim
13.	Issaquah	32.	Spokane
14.	Kenmore	33.	Tacoma
15.	Kennewick	34.	Tonasket
16.	Kent	35.	Union Gap
17.	Kettle Falls	36.	Vancouver
18.	Kirkland	37.	Wenatchee
19.	Lakebay	38.	Yelm

BAINBRIDGE ISLAND

Emmy's Vegehouse 🍴
100 Winslow Way ✆ 206-855-2996 ⏱ M-Sat 11-7:30
Vegan Thai/Vietnamese to take out or eat at the outside tables.
• vegan • tables • self-service • take-out
🚗 **From WA 305**, go west on Winslow Way (right from WA 305S, left from WA 305N) about ⅓ mile to store on right at Madison Ave.

Real Foods 🛒 🍴
764 Winslow Way E. ✆ 206-842-3333 ⏱ M-Sat 7-8, Sun 9-8
"Breakfast bowls," soups, salads, paninis and pizzas.
• organic produce • vegetarian friendly • organic focus • fresh juice • cafe • deli • tables • self-service • take-out
🚗 Store is about 2 blocks east of WA 305 on Winslow Way E across from the ferry terminal.

BELLEVUE

Nature's Pantry 🛒 🍴
10201 N.E. 10th St. ✆ 425-454-0170 ⏱ M-F 9-7, Sat 10-6, Sun 11-5
Raw foods available on the daily menu.
• organic produce • vegetarian friendly • fresh juice • deli • tables • self-service • take-out
🚗 **From I-405**, take exit 13 (A from I-405S, B from I-405N) and follow ramp onto NE 8th St W about ¾ mile to 102nd Ave NE. Turn right onto 102nd to store at 10th St. **From I-5**, take exit 168B toward Bellevue onto WA 520E about 6 miles (across water) to Bellevue Way NE exit. Merge right onto Bellevue Way about 1½ miles to NE 10th St. Turn right onto 10th 2 blocks to store at 102nd.

Udupi Palace 🍴
15600 N.E. 18th St. ✆ 425-649-0355 ⏱ Daily 11:30-2:30, 5:30-9:45

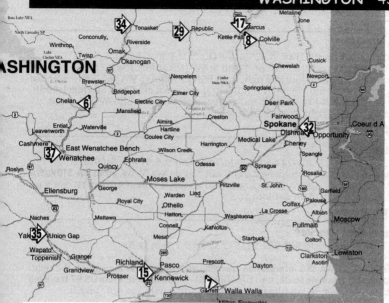

North and South Indian vegetarian with a lunch buffet.

• vegetarian • vegan friendly • tables • self-service • wait staff

📷 **From I-405**, take exit 14 toward Redmond onto Hwy 520E about 2 miles to 148th Ave NE. Turn right onto 148th ¾ mile to NE 20th St. Turn left onto NE 20th ½ mile to 156th Ave NE. Turn right onto 156th to restaurant on left.

Whole Foods Market 📷 🍽

888 116th Ave. N.E. ✆ 425-462-1400 ⏰ Daily 7-10

• organic produce • vegetarian friendly • salad bar • cafe • self-service • take-out

📷 **From I-405S**, take exit 13B right at fork (signs for NE 8th St W) to 112th Ave NE. Turn right onto 112th, make first right onto 12th St across hwy and first right onto 116th Ave NE to store on left (across from hospital). **From I-405N**, take exit 13AB right onto NE 4th St and right onto 116th under ½ mile to store on right.

BELLINGHAM

Community Food Co-op 📷 🍽

1220 N. Forest St. ✆ 360-734-8158 ⏰ Daily 7-9

• organic produce • vegetarian friendly • fresh juice • cafe • deli • bakery • tables • self-service • take-out • co-op

📷 **From I-5**, take exit 253 onto Lakeway Dr (right from I-5S, right onto King St and right from I-5N) almost ¾ mile (becomes E Holly St) to N State St. Turn left onto N State, left onto E Chestnut St and left onto N Forest St to store.

Terra Organica 📷 🍽   ♿

1530 Cornwall Ave. #101 ✆ 360-715-8020 ⏰ M-F 7-10, Sat 8-10, Sun 9-10

All food and beverages are organic or wild-crafted.

• organic produce • vegetarian friendly • fresh juice • organic focus • cafe • bakery • counter • tables • self-service • take-out

📷 **From I-5N**, take exit 253 right onto King St then right onto Lakeway Dr about 4 blocks to where Lakeway veers right onto E Holly St. Take E Holly ½ mile to Cornwall Ave. Turn right onto Cornwall to store on right. **From I-5S**, take exit 254 onto Ohio St toward State St 2 blocks and veer left onto State ½ mile to E Champion St. Turn right onto E Champion 2 blocks to Cornwall. Turn left onto Cornwall 1½ blocks to store on left.

BOTHELL

Tru Health

18001 Bothell-Everett Hwy. ✆ 425-415-8410 ✆ M-F 10-6, Sat 11-4

🍎 **From I-5,** take exit 183 east on 164th St SW (left at fork toward Mill Creek and left from I-5S, right at fork and right from I-5N) 2 miles to WA 567/Bothell Everett Hwy. Turn right onto WA 567 1¼ miles to store on left after Vine St. **From I-405N,** take exit 26 toward Mill Creek and merge onto 19th Ave SE/WA 567 about 2½ miles to store on right after 183rd St SE.

BURIEN

The Grainery 🛒

13629 1st Ave. S. ✆ 206-244-5015 ✆ M-Tues, Th-F 9-6, W 9-8, Sat 9:30-5

🛒 Burien is about 3½ miles west of I-5 exit 154 on WA 518W. **From WA 518W/WA 509 intersection,** store is 1 block west and about ¾ mile north on 1st Ave S on west side between 138th & 136th St.

CHELAN

Bear Foods Market 🛒

125 E. Woodin Ave. ✆ 509-682-5535 ✆ M-Sat 9-7, Sun 11-5
  • organic produce

🛒 **From US 97/WA 150 intersection traveling west,** store is at the end on the right. **From WA 150 traveling south,** turn right onto E Woodin to store. **From US 97 traveling east,** turn left onto W Woodin under ½ mile (across water) to store on left.

COLLEGE PLACE

Andy's Market 🛒

1117 S. College Ave. ✆ 509-529-1003 ✆ M-Th, Sun 7-9, F 7-1½ hours before sundown
Fresh carrot juice made daily.
  • organic produce

🛒 **From US 12,** turn south onto Gose St (right from 12E, left from 12W) 2¼ miles (becomes College Ave) to store on right (after tracks).

His Garden Bakery & Cafe 🛒 🍴

28 S.E. 12th St. ✆ 509-525-1040 ✆ M-Th 6:30-6, F 6:30-4, Sun 8-4
During the growing season food comes from their organic garden.
  • organic produce • vegan • organic focus • fresh juice • deli • bakery • tables • self-service • take-out

🛒 **From US 12,** turn south onto Gose St (right from 12E, left from 12W) 2 miles (becomes College Ave) to SE 12th St. Turn left onto SE 12th to store after corner.

COLVILLE

Mt. Sunflower Natural Market 🛒

358 N. Main St. ✆ 509-684-4211 ✆ M-F 9-6, Sat 10-5
Mainly supplements but some packaged foods.

🛒 Store is on US 395 (Main St) just north of WA 20 (3rd Ave) on west side.

EASTSOUND

Orcas Homegrown Gourmet Market & Deli 🛒

138 North Beach Rd. ✆ 360-376-2009 ✆ Daily 8-8
  • organic produce • vegetarian friendly • fresh juice • deli • take-out

🛒 **From the ferry landing in Orcas,** take Horseshoe Hwy north over 8 miles to Eastsound. Store is in town.

EVERETT

Sno-Isle Natural Foods Co-op 🛒

2804 Grand Ave. ✆ 425-259-3798 ✆ M-F 8-8, Sat 10-8, Sun 10-6

• organic produce • vegetarian friendly • fresh juice • deli • take-out • co-op

🍎 **From I-5N**, take exit 193 left onto Pacific Ave about 1 mile to Grand Ave. Turn right onto Grand 3 blocks to store on left in Everett Public Market Bldg. **From I-5S**, take exit 194 right onto Everett Ave about 1¼ miles to Grand. Turn left onto Grand 1 block to store on right.

FEDERAL WAY

Marlene's Market & Deli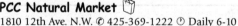

2565 S. Gateway Center Place © 253-839-0933 ⏰ M-F 8-9, Sat 9-8, Sun 10-6
  • organic produce • vegetarian friendly • fresh juice • deli • take-out

🍎 **From I-5**, take exit 143 toward Federal Way onto S 320th St (right from I-5S, left from 5N), right onto 319th Pl and straight onto Gateway Center Blvd to store in Gateway Ctr.

HILLMAN CITY

Lola's South City Bakery 🍴

5607 Rainier Ave. S. © 206-725-0443 ⏰ Tues, Th 10-6, W 10-5, F-Sat 10-7
Sandwiches, salads, pizza, house-baked breads and desserts.
  • vegetarian • organic focus • tables • self-service • take-out

🍎 **From I-90**, take exit 3 (3A from I-90W) south on Rainier Ave about 3 miles to restaurant on right at S Findlay St. **From I-5**, take exit 151 east on S Graham St (left onto S Albro Pl and right onto Swift St S 3 blocks from I-5S, left onto Swift and left onto S Graham from I-5N) 1½ miles to Rainier. Turn left onto Rainier under ½ mile to restaurant on left.

ISSAQUAH

Pabla Veggie Cuisine 🍴

1420 N.W. Gilman Blvd., N3 © 425-392-4725 ⏰ Daily 11-3, 5-10
Vegetarian Indian with buffet available at lunch.
  • vegetarian • vegan friendly • alcohol • tables • wait staff

🍎 **From I-90E**, take exit 15 toward Renton right at fork onto 17th Ave NW. Turn left onto 17th Ave NW to NW Gillman Blvd. Turn left onto NW Gillman to restaurant on left in Meadows Shopping Ctr. **From I-90W**, take exit 15 left onto 17th across hwy and left onto NW Gillman to restaurant on left.

ISSAQUAH

PCC Natural Market 🛍   ♿

1810 12th Ave. N.W. © 425-369-1222 ⏰ Daily 6-10
  • organic produce • vegetarian friendly • deli • take-out • co-op

🍎 **From I-90E**, take exit 15 and follow left exit lane (Lake Sammamish State Pk) to light at 17th Ave NW. Turn left onto 17th Ave NW 2 lights to store on right in Pickering Pl Shopping Ctr. **From I-90W**, take exit 15 (Hwy 900/W Renton) to the right. Turn right at light into Pickering Place to store.

KENMORE

Bastyr University Cafeteria 🍴

14500 Juanita Dr. N.E. © 425-823-1300 ⏰ M-F 8-6, Sat-Sun 8-2 Hours differ when school is not in session
Bastyr focuses on natural medicine. The cafeteria is open to the public.
  • vegetarian • tables • self-service

🍎 **From I-405S**, take exit 26 onto Hwy 527 and turn right onto 228th St SE under 1 mile to Meridian Ave S. Turn left onto Meridian continuing onto 80th Ave NE 2½ miles total to NE Bothwell Way. Turn right onto NE Bothwell under 1 mile to 68th Ave NE. Turn left onto 68th continuing onto Juanita Dr NE 2 miles total to restaurant in Bastyr U cafeteria. **From I-405N**, take exit 20A left onto NE 116th St 1½ miles continuing onto Juanita 4 miles to restaurant.

KENNEWICK

Chamomile Garden Cafe & Bakery 🍽

201 N. Edison St., Ste. 258-260 © 509-783-7464 ⊙ Tues-F 10-5, Sat 10-4
Tea shop and cafe serving vegetarian lunch from 11-2.
 • vegetarian • vegan friendly • tables • self-service

🚗 **From I-82/US 12E**, take exit 5A onto WA 240E toward Kennewick about 4⅓ miles to Edison St exit. Turn right onto Edison 1¼ miles to restaurant on right after W Clearwater Ave. **From I-82W**, take exit 113 onto US 395N about 1½ miles to W 27th Ave. Turn left onto W 27th about ¼ mile and at traffic circle take first exit onto S Union St 1 mile to W 10th Ave. Turn left onto W 10th over ½ mile to S Edison. Turn right onto S Edison about ¾ mile (becomes N Edison) to restaurant on left.

Highland Healthfood Superstore 🛍

101 Vista Way © 509-783-7147 ⊙ M-Th 9:30-8, F 9:30-5, Sun 12-5
🚗 **From I-82/US 12E**, take exit 5A onto WA 240E toward Kennewick about 7 miles to US 395S. Turn right onto 395S almost 1 mile to Visa Way. Turn left onto Vista to store on right. **From I-82W**, take exit 113 onto US 395N about 4¼ miles to Vista Way. Turn right onto Vista to store.

KENT

Nature's Market 🛍 🍽

26011 104th Ave. S.E. © 253-854-5395 ⊙ M-F 9-8, Sat 9-7, Sun 10-6
 • organic produce • vegetarian friendly • fresh juice • deli • tables • self-service • take-out
🚗 **From WA 167**, take N Central Ave exit and merge onto 84th St S. Continue to follow Central Ave then E Valley Rd almost 1 mile to E James St. Turn left onto E James continuing onto S 204th St 1⅓ miles total to 104th St SE. Turn left onto 104th 1 block to restaurant.

Punjab Sweet 🍽

23617 104th Ave. S.E. © 253-859-3236 ⊙ Daily 11-8:30
Indian vegetarian.
 • vegetarian • vegan friendly • tables • wait staff
🚗 **From WA 167**, take N Central Ave exit and merge onto 84th St S. Continue to follow Central Ave then E Valley Rd almost 1 mile to E James St. Turn left onto E James continuing onto S 204th St 1⅓ miles total to 104th St SE. Turn left onto 104th to restaurant on left after 236th Pl.

KETTLE FALLS

Meyers Falls Market 🛍 🍽

160 E. 3rd St. © 509-738-2727 ⊙ M-Sat 8-7, Sun 10-6
 • organic produce • vegetarian friendly • deli • bakery • tables • self-service • take-out
🚗 **From WA 25/WA 395/20 intersection**, store is 1 mile west on WA 295/20 (aka W 3rd Ave) on south side between Meyers & Narcissus St.

KIRKLAND

Cafe Happy 🍽

102 Kirkland Ave. © 425-822-9696 ⊙ M-Sat 11-8:30
Vegetarian Taiwanese. Mostly take out with a few tables.
 • vegetarian • vegan friendly • tables • self-service • take-out
🚗 **From I-405**, take exit 18 toward Kirkland west on NE 85th St about 1 mile (becomes Central Ave) to 3rd St. Turn left onto 3rd 2 blocks to Kirkland Ave. Turn right onto Kirkland 2 blocks to restaurant on right.

Lakeshore Veggie House 🍽

15 Lake St. #103 © 25-889-2850 ⊙ Daily 11-9
Asian vegan.
 • vegan • tables • wait staff

From I-405, take exit 18 toward Kirkland west on NE 85th St over 1 mile (becomes Central Ave) to Lake St. Turn left onto Lake to restaurant on right.

PCC Natural Market

10718 N.E. 68th St. © 425-828-4622 ⏲ Daily 7-11
  • organic produce • vegetarian friendly • deli • take-out • co-op

From I-405, take exit 17 left onto NE 70th Pl (2 lefts from I-405N). Follow NE 70th onto NE 72nd Pl, then NE 68th St about ¾ mile to store on right in Houghton Village Shopping Ctr.

LAKEBAY

JED's Good Stuff

9013 Key Peninsula Hwy. N © 253-884-1034 ⏲ M, F 10-3, Tues-Th 10-6

From WA 16, take WA 302W exit onto Purdy Ave and take WA 302W 5⅓ miles continuing onto Gig Harbor Longbranch Rd 3 miles to store after 92nd St KP N.

LANGLEY

Green Living Natural Foods and Apothecary

630A 2nd St. ⏲ 360-221-8242 ⏲ M-Sat 9-6
Wraps, rice bowls, soups, salads, raw foods. Vegan with one exception.
  • vegetarian • vegan friendly • fresh juice • tables • self-service • take-out

Langley is on Whidbey Island. From WA 525, go north on S Coles Rd (right from WA 525W, left from WA 525E) 2½ miles to 3rd St. Veer right onto 3rd to first left onto De Bruyan Ave. Go 1 block on De Bruyan and turn right onto 2nd St to store on left between De Bruyan & Park Ave.

LONG BEACH

THC Organic Market

811 Pacific Hwy. S. Ste. 20 ⏲ 360-642-3650 ⏲ M-Sat 9-6, Sun 12-4
  • organic produce • fresh juice

From Hwy 101S, turn right onto Pacific Ave about 1¾ miles to store after 8th St.

MOUNTLAKE TERRACE

Manna Mills

21705 66th Ave. W. © 425-775-3479 ⏲ M-Sat 9-8
  • organic produce

From I-5, take exit 179 west on 220th St SW (right from I-5S, left from I-5N) about ⅓ mile to 66th Ave W. Turn right 66th 1½ blocks to store on right between 218th & 216th St SW.

MT. VERNON

Skagit Valley Food Co-op

202 S. First St. © 360-336-9777 ⏲ M-Sat 8-9, Sun 9-8
  • organic produce • vegetarian friendly • vegan friendly • salad bar • cafe • deli • bakery • counter • tables • self-service • take-out • co-op

From I-5, take exit 226 west on Kincaid St/US 536 (right from I-5S, left from I-5N) to light at 3rd St. Turn right onto 3rd 5 blocks to store at S 2nd St (after underpass).

OLYMPIA

Olympia Food Co-op /Eastside

3111 Pacific Ave. © 360-956-3870 ⏲ Daily 9-9
  • organic produce • vegetarian friendly • salad bar • cafe • deli • tables • self-service • take-out • co-op

From I-5, take exit 107 west on Pacific Ave (right from I-5S, left from I-5N) under ¼ mile to Lansdale Rd. Turn left onto Lansdale to store on corner.

Olympia Food Co-op/Westside 🛍 ♿

921 N. Rogers St. ✆ 360-754-7666 ◷ Daily 9-8
• organic produce • co-op

🍴 **From I-5,** take exit 104 onto US 101N about 1¾ miles to Black Lake Blvd exit. Take ramp toward West Olympia right onto Black Lake (becomes Division St) about 1⅔ miles to Bowman Ave. Turn right onto Bowman about ⅓ mile to store at Rogers St.

The New Moon Cafe 🍴 ♿

113 4th Ave. W. ✆ 360-357-3452 ◷ M-F 7am-2:30pm, Sat-Sun 8-2
Breakfast options for vegans, vegetarians and the bacon-and-sausage crowd.
• vegetarian friendly • vegan friendly • tables • wait staff

🍴 **From I-5S,** take exit 105 toward State Capitol and follow 105B toward Port of Olympia onto Bay Dr ¼ mile to Plum St. Turn right onto Plum ½ mile to State St. Turn left onto State St ½ mile to Columbia St NW. Turn left onto Columbia 1 block to 4th Ave. Turn left onto 4th to restaurant. **From I-5N,** take exit 105 toward State Capitol/City Center and swing left via Henderson St onto 14th Ave SE ½ mile to Capitol Way S. Turn right onto Capitol ⅓ mile to Talcott Ave. Turn left onto Talcott 1 block to Columbia. Turn right onto Columbia 5 blocks (¼ mile) to 4th. Turn right onto 4th to restaurant.

Traditions Cafe & World Folk Art 🍴 ♿

300 5th Ave. S.W. ✆ 360-705-2819 ◷ M-F 9-6, Sat 10-6 (until 8 when there's live music)
Vegetarian quiche, lasagna, enchiladas, sandwiches and salads.
• vegetarian friendly • tables • self-service

🍴 **From I-5S**, take exit 105 toward State Capitol and follow 105B toward Port of Olympia onto Bay Dr ¼ mile to Plum St. Turn right onto Plum ⅓ mile to 5th Ave. Turn left onto 5th ½ mile to restaurant. **From I-5N**, take exit 105 toward State Capitol/City Center and swing left via Henderson St onto 14th Ave SE ½ mile to Capitol Way S. Turn right onto Capitol ⅓ mile to Talcott Ave. Turn left onto Talcott 1 block to Columbia. Turn right onto Columbia 4 blocks (about ¼ mile) to 5th. Turn left onto 5th to restaurant.

Urban Onion 🍴

116 Legion Way ✆ 360-943-9242 ◷ M-F 7-9, Sat 8-10, Sun 8-9
• vegetarian friendly • alcohol • tables • wait staff

🍴 **From I-5,** take exit 105 (105A from I-5S) toward State Capitol/City Center onto 14th Ave SE (straight from I-5S, swing left from I-5N) ⅓-½ mile to Capitol Way S. Turn right onto Capitol ½ mile to Legion. Turn right onto Legion 1 block to restaurant on left corner at Washington St in Hotel Olympian lobby.

Voyeur Cafe 🍴

404 E. 4th Ave. ✆ 360-943-5710 ◷ Daily 11:30am-2am
Everything on the menu can be made vegan—even the steak and chicken dishes.
• vegetarian friendly • vegan friendly • organic focus • alcohol • tables • wait staff • take-out

🍴 **From I-5S**, take exit 105 toward State Capitol and follow 105B toward Port of Olympia onto Bay Dr ¼ mile to Plum St. Turn right onto Plum ⅓ mile to 5th Ave. Turn left onto 5th ¼ mile to Adams St. Turn left onto Adams 1 block to 4th Ave. Turn left onto 4th to restaurant. **From I-5N**, take exit 105 toward State Capitol/City Center and swing left via Henderson St onto 14th Ave SE ½ mile to Capitol Way S. Turn right onto Capitol ⅔ mile to 4th. Turn right onto 4th to restaurant.

PORT ANGELES

Good to Go! Natural Grocery 🛍

1105 S. Eunice St. ✆ 360-457-1857 ◷ M-F 8-6
• organic produce • vegan • deli • take-out

🍴 **From Hwy 101 traveling east,** merge onto E Blvd/E Lauridsen Rd ½ mile to S Eunice St. Turn left onto S Eunice 1 block to store on left at E 11th St. **From Hwy 101/E 1st Ave travling west**, continue on Hwy 101/E Front St to N Race St. Turn left onto N Race over ½ mile to E 8th St. Turn right onto E 8th 2 blocks to S Eunice. Turn left onto S Eunice 6 blocks to store on right.

PORT TOWNSEND

The Food Co-op 🛍️ 🍴   ♿

414 Kearney St. ℭ 360-385-2883 ◷ M-Sat 8-9, Sun 9-8
* organic produce * vegetarian friendly * fresh juice * deli * tables * self-service *
  take-out * co-op

🏠 Take Hwy 20 to Port Townsend. Store is at the first light in town at corner Sims
Way (aka WA 20) & Kearney St.

REDMOND

Mysore Masala 🍴

16650 Redmond Way ℭ 425-558-7858 ◷ Daily 11:30-2:30, 5-9:30
Indian vegetarian with a lunch buffet.
* vegetarian * vegan friendly * alcohol * tables * self-service * wait staff

🏠 **From I-405**, take exit 18 for State Hwy 908 east on NE 85th St (left at fork
and loop around from I-405S, merge right from I-405N) about 3 miles (becomes
Redmond Way) to Cleveland St. Turn right onto Cleveland ½ mile to Avondale
Way. Turn left onto Avondale and left back onto NE Redmond heading west about
1 block to restaurant on right between 168th & 166th Ave NE.

PCC Natural Market 🛍️   ♿

11435 Avondale Road N.E. ℭ 425-285-1400 ◷ Daily 6-10
* organic produce * vegetarian friendly * deli * take-out * co-op

🏠 **From I-405**, take exit 20 east on NE 124th St (left from I-405S, right from
I-405N) about 3½ miles continuing onto NE 128th St about 1 mile to Avondale
Rd NE. Turn right onto Avondale 1 mile to store on left.

Preet's 🍴

8440 160th Ave. N.E. ℭ 425-867-9400 ◷ Daily 12-3, 5:30-9:30
Indian vegetarian.
* vegetarian * vegan friendly * tables * wait staff

🏠 **From I-405**, take exit 18 for State Hwy 908 east on NE 85th St (left at fork
and loop around from I-405S, merge right from I-405N) about 3 miles (becomes
Redmond Way) to Cleveland St. Turn left at Cleveland onto 160th St 2 blocks to
restaurant on right at NE 85th Way.

Teapot Vegetarian House 🍴

15230 24th St. N.E. ℭ 425-373-1888 ◷ Daily 11-9:45
Vegan Chinese.
* vegan * tables * wait staff

🏠 **From I-405**, take exit 14 onto WA 520E about 2 miles and exit onto 148th Ave
NE ½ mile to NE 24th St. Turn left onto NE 24th about ⅓ mile to restaurant on
left after 152nd Ave.

RENTON

Pabla Indian Cuisine 🍴

364 Renton Center Way S.W. ℭ 425-228-4625 ◷ Daily 11-3, 5-9:30
Vegetarian Indian with buffet available at lunch.
* vegetarian * vegan friendly * tables * self-service * wait staff

🏠 **From I-5S,** take exit 157 onto WA 900E (MLK Way, becomes SW Sunset) about
3⅓ miles to Hardie Ave SW. Turn right onto Hardie to restaurant in Fred Meyer
Shopping Plaza. **From I-5N**, merge onto I-405N via exit 154. **From I-405**, take exit
2 toward Renton/Rainier Ave onto WA 167N (Valley Fwy, becomes Rainier Ave) to
7th St (1 mile on I-405N, ¼ mile on I-405S). Make sharp left onto 7th and first
right onto Hardie about ¼ mile to restaurant.

REPUBLIC

Ferry County Co-op 🖐

34 N. Clark St. ✆ 509-775-3754 ⏰ M-F 7:30-6, Sat 10-4
• organic produce • vegetarian friendly • deli • take-out, co-op

🍎 Republic is at the crossroads of WA 20 & 21. **From WA 20,** take Clark St north 1 block to store on right.

SEATTLE

Arya's Vegetarian Place 🍴   ♿

1121 N.E. 45th St. ✆ 206-524-4332 ⏰ M-Sat 11:30-9
Thai vegetarian with a buffet option.
• vegan • tables • self-service • wait staff

🍎 **From I-5,** take exit 169 east on NE 45th St (merge onto 5th Ave NE and left from I-5S, veer left onto 7th Ave NE and right from I-5N) about 5 blocks to restaurant on right after 11th Ave NE.

Bamboo Garden Vegetarian Cuisine 🍴

364 Roy St. ✆ 206-282-6616 ⏰ Daily 11-10
Chinese vegetarian.
• vegetarian • vegan friendly • kosher • tables • wait staff • take-out

🍎 **From I-5,** take exit 167 and follow Fairview Ave N to Valley St. Turn left onto Valley (becomes Broad St) about ½ mile to Harrison St. Turn right onto Harrison to 5th Ave. Turn right onto 5th about ¼ mile to Roy St. Turn left onto Roy to restaurant between 4th & 3rd Ave.

Cafe Flora 🍴   ♿

2901 E. Madison St. ✆ 206-325-9100 ⏰ Tues-Th 11:30-9, F 11:30-10, Sat 9-2, 5-10, Sun 9-2, 5-9
Gourmet international menu emphasizing local foods.
• vegetarian • vegan friendly • organic focus • alcohol • tables • wait staff

🍎 **From I-5S,** take exit 168 onto Hwy 520 to first right (Montlake Blvd exit). Stay in right lane past Montlake intersection onto Lake Washington Blvd. Follow Lake Washington (winds through arboretum) about 1 mile to light at E Madison St. Turn right onto E Madison 1 long block to restaurant on left at 29th Ave E. **From I-5N,** take exit 164A (Madison St). Follow long ramp right onto Madison about 2 miles to restaurant at 29th.

Carmelita 🍴   ♿

7314 Greenwood Ave. N. ✆ 206-706-7703 ⏰ Tues-Th, Sun 5-9, F-Sat 5-10
Gourmet Mediterranean-influenced menu emphasizing local produce.
• vegetarian • vegan friendly • organic focus • alcohol • tables • wait staff

🍎 **From I-5,** take exit 172 west on 85th St (right from I-5S, left from I-5N) about 1⅓ miles to Greenwood Ave. Turn left onto Greenwood about 11 blocks to restaurant on left between N 74th & 73rd St.

Chaco Organic Canyon Cafe 🍴

4757 12th Ave. N.E. ✆ 206-522-6966 ⏰ M-F 7-8, Sat 9-8, Sun 10-5
Vegan with a daily raw foods menu.
• vegan • organic focus • fresh juice • counter • tables • self-service • take-out

🍎 **From I-5,** take exit 169 east on NE 50th St (left from I-5S, merge onto NE 7th Ave and right from I-5N) about 5 blocks to NE 12th St. Turn right onto NE 12th to restaurant on right.

Cyber-Dogs 🍴

909 Pike St. ✆ 206-405-3647 ⏰ Daily 10am-12am
Internet cafe, breakfast and vegetarian hot dogs. Near the Convention Center.
• vegetarian • vegan friendly • alcohol • tables • wait staff

🍎 **From I-5S,** take exit 165B for Union St right onto 7th Ave 1 block to Pike St. Turn right onto Pike 2 blocks to restaurant on right at 9th Ave (across from the express lanes on ramp). **From I-5N**, take exit 166 right onto Olive Way, right onto Melrose Ave 2 blocks and right onto Pike across hwy to restaurant on left.

Flowers Bar & Restaurant ⊤⊤

4247 University Way N.E. © 206-633-1903 ⏰ Daily 11-11
Vegan lunch buffet from 11-4 but no meatless entrees in the evening.
 • egetarian friendly • vegan friendly • alcohol • tables • self-service
🛏 **From I-5**, take exit 169 east on NE 45th St (merge onto 5th Ave NE and left from I-5S, veer left onto 7th Ave NE and right from I-5N) about 5 blocks to restaurant on right after 11th Ave NE.

Georgetown Liquor Company ⊤⊤

5501-B Airport Way S. © 206-763-6764 ⏰ M-F 11-11, Sat-Sun 2-11 (bar closes much later)
Video games, multiple TV screens and hearty vegetarian fare.
 • vegetarian • vegan friendly • alcohol • tables • wait staff • take-out
🛏 **From I-5S**, take exit 162 toward Michigan St onto Corson Ave S and turn left onto S Nebraska St and left onto Airport Way S about ⅓ mile to restaurant on left at Lucile St. **From I-5N**, take exit 161 left onto Swift Ave S continuing onto 15th Ave S about ½ mile to Lucile. Turn left onto Lucile about ¼ mile (across hwy) to Airport Way S. Turn right onto Airport Way 1 block to restaurant.

Hillside Quickie's Cafe ⊤⊤

324 15th Ave E. © 206-325-6429 ⏰ M-F 12-8, Sat 12-7, Sun 12-6
Small vegan deli-style restaurant.
 • vegan • alcohol • tables • self-service • take-out
🛏 **From I-5S**, take exit 166 toward Denny Way/Stewart St onto Eastlake Ave E. Turn right onto Stewart, left onto Denny, and left onto E Olive Way ⅓ mile. Continue onto E John St almost ½ mile to 15th Ave E. Turn left onto 15th to restaurant. **From I-5N**, take.exit 166/Olive Way. Veer right onto Olive Way and follow directions above. ♿

Hillside Quickie's Vegan Sandwich Shop ⊤⊤ ♿

4106 Brooklyn Ave. N.E. © 206-632-3037 ⏰ M-Sat 12-7
Vegan sandwiches, salads and accoutrements.
 • vegan • tables • self-service • take-out
🛏 **From I-5**, take exit 169 toward NE 45th St. Follow ramp for NE 45th/U of WA and go east on NE 45th (right from I-5N, left from I-5S) about ⅓ mile to Brooklyn Ave NE. Turn right onto Brooklyn about ⅓ mile to restaurant.

In the Bowl Vegetarian Noodle Bistro ⊤⊤

1554 E. Olive Way © 206-568-2343 ⏰ Daily 12-9:30
Tiny bustling eatery with big selection of Thai noodle dishes and curries.
 • vegetarian • vegan friendly • tables • wait staff • take-out
🛏 **From I-5S,** take exit 167 toward Denny Way/Stewart St. Merge onto Eastlake Ave, veer right onto Stewart and turn left onto Denny under ¼ mile to E Olive Way. Turn left onto E Olive to restaurant on left. **From I-5N**, take exit 166 right onto Olive Way under ¼ mile to restaurant on left after Denny.

Lucky Palate 🛍

307 McGraw St. © 206-352-2583 ⏰ M-Tues 8-6 and at various other times so call
Mainly home-delivery but store sells "Grab-and-Go Meals" and other homemade items.
 • vegetarian • vegan friendly • organic focus • deli • take-out
🛏 **From WA 99N (Aurora Ave),** turn right onto Queen Ann Dr, left onto 6th Ave N and continue on Morgan St/Queen Anne/Nob Hill Rd about ½ mile total to W McGraw St. Turn right onto W McGraw to store on left. **From WA 99S,** turn right onto Queen Anne and follow directions above.

Madison Market/Central Co-op 🛍️

1600 E. Madison St. © 206-329-1545 ⏱ Daily 7-11
• organic produce • vegetarian friendly • fresh juice • deli • tables • self-service • take-out • co-op

🍎 **From I-5S,** take exit 165B for Union St right onto 7th Ave 1 block to E Pike St. Turn right onto E Pike 1 mile to E Madison St. Veer left onto E Madison 2 blocks to store on left at 16th Ave. **From I-5N,** take exit 166 right onto Olive Way and right onto Melrose Ave 2 blocks to E Pike. Turn left onto E Pike ¾ mile and veer left onto E Madison 2 blocks to store on left.

Mother Nature's Natural Health Store 🛍️

516 1st Ave. N. © 206-284-4422 ⏱ M-F 9:30-7, Sat 9:30-6
One table inside and one out.
• vegetarian friendly • deli • tables • self-service • take-out

🍎 **From WA 99S (Aurora Ave),** turn right onto Roy St ½ mile to Warren Ave N. Turn left onto Warren 2 blocks to Republican St. Turn right onto Republican 1 block to 1st Ave N. Turn right onto 1st to store on right past Seattle Ctr. **From WA 99N,** exit onto Western Ave ⅓ mile to Battery St. Turn right onto Battery and left onto 1st ½ mile to Denny Way. At Denny turn right onto 1st Ave N about 4 blocks to store.

Patty Pan Grill 🍴

5402 20th Ave. N.W. © 206-782-1558 ⏱ M-F 11:30-6, Sat 12-5
Quesadillas, tamales, falafel, soba and more. Limited seating plus benches outside.
• vegetarian • vegan friendly • counter • self-service • take-out

🍎 **From I-5S,** take exit 172 onto N 85th St 1 mile to Aurora Ave N. Turn left onto Aurora 5 blocks to N 80th St. Turn right onto N 80th 1 mile to 8th Ave NW. Turn left onto 8th 1⅓ miles to NW Market St. Turn right onto Market ¾ mile to 20th Ave NW. Turn left onto 20th to restaurant on left. **From I-5N,** take exit 179 and veer left onto 7th Ave NE to NE 45th St. Turn left onto NE 45th 1 mile and veer right onto Midvale Pl continuing onto N 46th St then NW Market St 2 miles to 20th Ave. Turn left onto 20th to restaurant.

PCC Natural Market 🛍️   ♿

600 N. 34th St. © 206-632-6811 ⏱ Daily 6am-12am
• organic produce • vegetarian friendly • fresh juice • deli • bakery • take-out • co-op

🍎 **From I-5S,** take exit 169 and follow ramp to NE 45th/U of WA to NE 45th. Turn right onto 45th almost 1 mile to Stone Way. Turn left onto Stone Way almost 1 mile to N 34th St. Turn right onto 34th about ¼ mile to store on right at Evanston St. **From I-5N,** take exit 167 on left toward Seattle Ctr right onto Fairview Ave, left onto Valley St and right onto Westlake Ave N about 1⅔ miles to 4th Ave N. Veer right onto 4th across water (becomes Fremont) to N 34th St. Turn right onto 34th to store.

PCC Natural Market 🛍️   ♿

7504 Aurora Ave. N. © 206-525-3586 ⏱ Daily 7-11
• organic produce • vegetarian friendly • fresh juice • deli • bakery • take-out • co-op

🍎 **From I-5,** take exit 172 toward Aurora Ave N west on N 85th St (left from I-5N, right from I-5S) under 1 mile to Aurora. Turn left onto Aurora (Hwy 99) ½ mile to store on right before Winona Ave N (turn left onto Winona for parking).

PCC Natural Market 🛍️   ♿

5041 Wilson Ave. S. © 206-723-2720 ⏱ Daily 7-10
• organic produce • vegetarian friendly • fresh juice • deli • bakery • take-out • co-op

🍎 **From I-5,** take exit 163 (163A from I-5S) for W Seattle Bridge/Columbian Way. Take fork toward Columbian Way, then get into right lane. At third light ("Y" intersection) bear left onto S Columbian Way (becomes S Alaska St) over 1 mile to Rainier Ave S. Turn right onto Rainier to second left (S Edmunds St). Turn left onto Edmunds ¼ mile to 42nd St S. Turn right onto 42nd and left onto S Ferdinand St ½ mile to 50th Ave S. Turn right onto 50th (becomes Wilson Ave S) 1½ blocks to store on right.

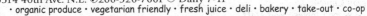

PCC Natural Market

6514 40th Ave. N.E. ©206-526-7661 ☉ Daily 7-11
• organic produce • vegetarian friendly • fresh juice • deli • bakery • take-out • co-op

From I-5S, take exit 171 (NE 71st St/NE 65th St) onto 6th Ave NE to stop sign at NE 70th St. Turn left onto 70th ¼ mile to Roosevelt Way NE. Turn right onto Roosevelt ¼ mile NE 65th St. Turn left onto NE 65th 1½ miles to 40th Ave NE. Turn left onto 40th to store on NE corner. **From on I-5N**, take exit 170 (NE 65th St/Ravenna) left onto 8th Ave NE to NE 65th St. Turn right onto NE 65th and follow directions above.

PCC Natural Market

2749 California Ave. S.W. © 206-937-8481 ☉ Daily 7-11
• organic produce • vegetarian friendly • fresh juice • deli • bakery • take-out • co-op

🚗 **From I-5**, take 163 (163A from I-5S) onto W Seattle Bridge 2 miles to Admiral Way ramp. Take Admiral Way 1 mile to California Ave SW. Turn right onto California to store on right.

Pizza Pi

5500 University Way N.E. © 206-343-1415 ☉ Tues-Th, Sun 12-10
Vegan pizza and calzone.
• vegan • tables • self-service • take-out

🚗 **From I-5S**, take exit 169 left onto NE 50th St ½ mile to University Way NE. Turn left onto University 2 blocks to restaurant on left at NE 55th St. **From I-5N,** take exit 170 right onto NE Ravenna Blvd under ½ mile to University. Turn right onto University 2 blocks to restaurant on right.

Silence-Heart-Nest

3508 Fremont Place N. © 206-633-5169 ☉ M, W-F 7:30-3, Sat-Sun 7:30-4
• vegetarian • vegan friendly • tables • wait staff • take-out

🚗 **From I-5**, take exit 169 onto NE 45th St (merge onto 5th Ave NE and turn right from I-5S, turn left onto 7th Ave NE and left from I-5N) 1 mile to Stone Way N. Turn left onto Stone Way about ¾ mile to N 35th St. Turn right onto 35th under ½ mile to Fremont Pl N. Veer right onto Fremont Pl to restaurant on right.

Squid & Ink

1128 S. Albro Place © 206-763-2696 ☉ Tues-Sun 9am-12am
• vegan • tables • wait staff

🚗 **From I-5**, take exit 161 right onto Albro Pl from I-5S, left onto Swift St and left onto Albro from I-5N about ⅓ mile to restaurant on right between 13th & Ellis Ave S.

Sunlight Cafe

6403 Roosevelt Way N.E. © 206-522-9060 ☉ Daily 8-9
• vegetarian • vegan friendly • alcohol • tables • wait staff

🚗 **From I-5S**, take exit 171 toward NE 71st St/NE 65th St onto 6th Ave and follow across hwy on NE 70th St about ¼ mile (2 blocks) to Roosevelt Way. Turn right onto Roosevelt about ⅓ mile to restaurant after 64th St. **From I-5N**, take exit 170 (Ravenna Blvd) toward NE 65th and follow ramp (becomes 8th Ave) to 65th. Turn right onto 65th 2 blocks to Roosevelt. Turn right onto Roosevelt past first block to restaurant.

Sutra Vegetarian Cuisine

1605 N. 45th St. © 206-547-1348 ☉ W-Th 6 & 8:30, F-Sat 6:30 & 9
Prix fixe 4-course menu with 2 nightly seatings. Reservations suggested.
• vegetarian • vegan friendly • organic focus • alcohol • tables • wait staff

🚗 **From I-5**, take exit 59 west on NE 45th St (right from I-5S, left from I-5N) about ¾ mile to restaurant on left at Woodlawn Ave.

Teapot Vegetarian House ⑪

345 15th Ave. E. ℭ 206-325-1010 ⏰ Daily 11:30-10
Vegan Chinese.
  • vegan • tables • wait staff
🚌 **From I-5S,** take exit 166 toward Denny Way right onto Stewart St and left onto Denny across hwy about ¼ mile to E Olive Way. Turn left onto Olive (becomes E John St) about ¾ mile to 15th Ave E. Turn left onto 15th 3 blocks to restaurant on left. **From I-5N,** take exit 166 right onto Olive (becomes E John) about 1 mile to 15th. Turn left onto 15th 3 blocks to restaurant.

The Flying Apron ⑪

3510 Fremont Ave. N. ℭ 206-442-1115 ⏰ M-Th 7-7, F-Sat 7-8, Sun 8-6
Vegan, wheat-free and mostly gluten-free baked goods and lunch.
  • vegan • bakery • tables • self-service • take-out
🚌 **From I-5,** take exit 169 west on NE 45th St (merge onto 5th Ave NE and right from I-5S, turn left onto 7th Ave NE and left from I-5N) 1 mile to Stone Way N. Turn left onto Stone Way about ¾ mile to N 36th St. Turn right onto N 36th ⅓ mile to Fremont Ave N. Turn left Fremont 1 block to restaurant on left.

Tilth ⑪

1411 N. 45th St. ℭ 206-633-0801 ⏰ Dinner M-Th, Sun 5-10, F-Sat 5-10:30 Brunch Sat-Sun 10-2
Featuring local and organic foods.
  • vegetarian friendly • organic focus • alcohol • tables • wait staff
🚌 **From I-5**, take exit 169 west on NE 45th St (merge onto 5th Ave NE and right from I-5S, turn left onto 7th Ave NE and left from I-5N) about ¾ miles to restaurant on left at Interlake Ave N.

Veggie Veggie ⑪

4537 University Way N.E. ℭ 206-547-6500 ⏰ M, W-F 10:30-9:30, Sat-Sun 11-9:30
Thai vegetarian in the university district.
  • vegetarian • vegan friendly • tables • wait staff
🚌 **From I-5**, take exit 169 east on NE 45th St (merge onto 5th Ave NE and left from I-5S, veer left onto 7th Ave NE and right from I-5N) under ½ mile to Brooklyn Ave NE. Turn right onto Brooklyn 1 block to NE 47th St. Turn right onto NE 47th and right onto University Way 1 block to restaurant on right.

Wayward Cafe ⑪

901 N.E. 55th St. ℭ 206-524-0204 ⏰ Tues-Sun 9-4
Vegan collective serving reasonably priced "home style" food.
  • vegan • tables • self-service
🚌 **From I- 5S,** take exit 169 left onto NE 50th St across hwy and 3 blocks to NE 9th Ave. Turn right onto 9th 2 blocks to restaurant on right at NE 55th St. **From I-5N,** take exit 169 onto 7th Ave about ⅓ mile to NE 55th. Turn right onto NE 55th 2 blocks to restaurant on right.

Whole Foods Market 🛍 ⑪   ♿

1026 N.E. 64th St. ℭ 206-985-1500 ⏰ Daily 7-10
  • organic produce • vegetarian friendly • salad bar • cafe • self-service • take-out
🚌 **From I-5S,** take exit 171 (NE 71st St/NE 65th St) onto 6th Ave NE to stop sign at NE 70th St. Turn left onto 70th about ¼ mile to Roosevelt Way NE. Turn right onto Roosevelt about ⅓ mile to NE 64th St. Turn left onto 64th to store in Roosevelt Square. **From I-5N,** take exit 170 (Ravenna Blvd) toward NE 65th St onto 8th Ave NE to NE 64th St. Turn right onto 64th 2 blocks to store at Roosevelt Way.

SEQUIM_____

Sunny Farms Country Store 🛍

261461 Hwy. 101 ℭ 360-683-8003 ⏰ Daily 8-8
  • organic produce • vegetarian friendly • deli • take-out

Store is on Hwy 101 about 1 mile west of town on north side between Carlsborg & Mill Rd..

SPOKANE

Huckleberry's Natural Market

926 S. Monroe St. © 509-624-1349 ① Daily Store 7-10 Cafe until 9
• organic produce • vegetarian friendly • organic focus • fresh juice • salad bar • cafe • tables • self-service • take-out

From I-90E, take exit 280 toward Lincoln St right onto S Maple Ave 5 blocks to W 10th Ave. Turn left onto W 10th 5½ blocks to store between S Madison & S Monroe St. **From I-90W**, take exit 280B right onto Lincoln, left onto W 2nd Ave and left onto S Monroe ½ mile to W 10th. Turn right onto W 10th to store.

Lorien Herbs & Natural Foods

1102 S. Perry St. © 509-456-0702 ① Tues-F 10-6, Sat 10-5
• organic produce

From I-90E, take exit 281 for Division St left onto E 4th Ave continuing onto E 5th Ave about 1 mile to S Denver St. Turn right onto S Denver 2 blocks and turn left onto E Newark Ave 5 blocks (becomes S Perry St) to store on right. **From I-90W**, take exit 282B onto E 2nd Ave and turn sharp left onto Liberty Park Pl across hwy and right onto S Hogan St through park to E 5th Ave. Turn right onto E 5th 1 block to S Denver. Turn left onto S Denver and follow directions above.

Mizuna

214 N. Howard St. © 509-747-2004 ① Lunch M-F 11:30-2:30 Dinner Daily 5-9
Gourmet vegetarian, vegan and seafood. Music on weekends.
• vegetarian friendly • vegan friendly • alcohol • tables • wait staff

From I-90W, take exit 280B right onto S Lincoln St about ⅓ mile to W Main Ave. Turn right onto Main 3 blocks to Howard St. Turn left onto Howard to restaurant on left. **From I-90E**, take exit 280 (Maple St) toward Lincoln. Turn left onto S Walnut St and right onto W 3rd Ave under ½ mile to S Lincoln. Turn left onto S Lincoln and follow directions above from Lincoln.

One World Community Kitchen

1804 E. Sprague © 509-270-1608 ① W-Th, Sun 11-3, F-Sat 11-8
Pay what you can afford, take what you can eat, get more if you like. Music on weekends.
• vegetarian friendly • vegan friendly • organic focus • tables • self-service

From I-90E, take exit 281 left onto S Division St ½ mile to E Sprague Ave. Turn right onto E Sprague 1⅓ miles to restaurant on right. **From I-90W**, take exit 282B onto E 2nd Ave and turn right onto S Helena St 3 blocks to E Sprague. Turn right onto E Sprague past second block to restaurant.

TACOMA

Antique Sandwich Company

5102 N. Pearl St. © 253-752-4069 ① Daily 7-7:30 (until 10 Tues if there's open mike)
Casual dining with sandwiches, salads, soup, quiche and such.
• vegetarian friendly • tables • self-service

From I-5, take exit 132 toward Bremerton/Gig Harbor onto WA 16W (38th St W exit on left from I-5N) about 3⅓ miles to 6th Ave exit toward WA 163. Turn left onto 6th 1 block to N Pearl St. Turn right onto Pearl 3 miles to restaurant.

Marlene's Market & Deli

2951 S. 38th St. © 253-472-4080 ① M-F 9-8, Sat 9-7, Sun 10-6
• organic produce • vegetarian friendly • fresh juice • deli • take-out

From I-5, take exit 132 toward Bremerton/Gig Harbor and take S 38th St W exit (toward Sprague Ave from I-5S, toward Tacoma Mall from I-5N). Veer right onto S 38th about ½ mile to store on right in Best Plaza.

Quickie Too 🍴

1324 S. Martin Luther King Way ✆ 253-572-4549 ⊙ M, W, F 11-8, Tues, Th, Sat 11-6, Sun 11-3
Vegan diner food based on tofu, tempeh, seitan and grains.
• vegan • tables • wait staff

🏠 **From I-5**, take exit 132 toward Gig Harbor/Bremerton onto WA16 W to S Sprague Ave (almost ¼ mile from I-5S, about 1 mile from I-5N). Take S Sprague 1¼ miles to S 12th St. Turn right onto 12th ½ mile to Martin Luther King Way. Turn right onto MLK to restaurant.

TONASKET

Okanogan River Natural Foods Co-op 🛍 🍴

21 W. 4th St. ✆ 509-486-4188 ⊙ M-F 9-6, Sat 9-5, Sun 12-4
• organic produce • vegetarian friendly • deli • tables • self-service • take-out

🏠 **From US Hwy 97**, go west on 4th St (left from 97N, right from 97S) 1 block to store.

UNION GAP

Mill Creek Natural Foods 🛍

4315 Main St. ✆ 509-452-5386 ⊙ M-Th 9-6, F 9-5, Sun 12-5
Half food, half supplements and body care.

🏠 **From I-82E**, take exit 36 right onto E Valley Mall Blvd ⅓ mile to Main St. Turn left onto Main about 1¼ miles (through town) to store on left after Washington St. **From I-82W**, take exit 38 toward Union Gap right at fork and onto Main to store on right.

VANCOUVER

Whole Foods Market 🛍 🍴

815 S.E. 160th Ave. ✆ 360-253-4082 ⊙ Daily 8-10
• organic produce • vegetarian friendly • salad bar • cafe • self-service • take-out

🏠 **From I-205**, take exit 28 east on SE Mill Plain Blvd (left from I-205S, right from I-205N) 2½-3 miles (becomes SE Mill Plain Rd) to SE 160th Ave. Turn right onto SE 160th to store on left.

WENATCHEE

Wenatchee Natural Foods 🛍

222 N. Wenatchee Ave. ✆ 509-665-9999 ⊙ M-F 9:30-6, Sat 10-4, Sun 11-3
• organic produce • fresh juice • counter • take-out

🏠 **From US 97 & US 2 intersection,** go south on US2/WA 285/N Wenatachee Ave about 3⅓ miles to store on west side north of 2nd St.

YELM

Yelm Food Co-op 🛍

404 1st St. ✆ 360-400-2210 ⊙ M-Sat 10-7
• organic produce • co-op

🏠 **From US 510 & US507 intersection (aka Yelm Ave)**, go south on 1st St S 2 blocks to store on left after Yelm Park. **Traveling northeast on US 507**, store is at the beginning of town on right at Morseman St.

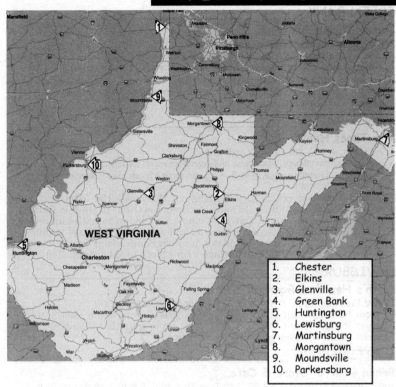

WEST VIRGINIA

1. Chester
2. Elkins
3. Glenville
4. Green Bank
5. Huntington
6. Lewisburg
7. Martinsburg
8. Morgantown
9. Moundsville
10. Parkersburg

CHESTER

Nila Jo's Natural Nutrition

637 Carolina Ave. © 304-387-3255 ⏰ Tues-F 10-6, Sat 10-3

🏠 **From WV on US 30 (Lincoln Hwy)**, take WV 2S exit towards Chester left onto Co Hwy 30/6 1 block to Carolina Ave. Turn left onto Carolina and cross back over hwy under ¼ mile to store on right at 6th St. **From OH,** after crossing the river take WV 2S exit towards Chester and veer left onto Carolina to store.

ELKINS

Good Energy Foods

214 Third St. © 304-636-5169 ⏰ M-Th, Sat 9-6, F 9-7, Sun 12-4

🏠 **From Rt 33E/Rt 219S intersection**, go south on Randolph Ave (right from Rt 33, left from Rt 219) 2 blocks Kearns St. Veer right onto Kearns 2 blocks to 3rd St. Turn left onto Kearns to store right. **From Rt 33W/Rt 219N intersection**, go north on Randolph about ½ mile to 3rd. Turn left onto third 2 blocks to store on left.

GLENVILLE

Country Life

211 N. Lewis St. © 304-462-8157 ⏰ M, W-Th 10-6, F 10-3

🏠 **From US 33/US 119**, store is at Church St 2 blocksNE of Main St.

GREEN BANK

Sweet Thyme Inn 🍴

Rte. 92/28 ✆ 304-456-5535 ⏰ Call ahead
A place to stay the night and dine. Non-guests call ahead.
· vegan · organic focus · tables · self-service · wait staff

🚗 **Traveling south on US 250**, merge onto SR 92/28 about 8 miles to Green Bank. Watch for Inn sign on right before BP station. **Traveling north on SR 92**, watch for Inn sign on left after BP station.

HUNTINGTON

Raw Times Health Bar 🍴

417 12th St. ✆ 304-781-0690 ⏰ M-F 10-3
Not all raw but everything is made fresh and vegetarian except for tuna.
· vegetarian friendly · vegan friendly · organic focus · fresh juice · counter · tables · wait staff · take-out

🚗 **From I-64W**, take exit 11 for WV 10 toward Downtown/Hal Greer Blvd and veer right onto WV 10/16th St 2½ miles (becomes Hal Greer) to 6th Ave. Turn left onto 6th 4 blocks to 12th St. Turn right onto 12th 2 blocks to restaurant on left at 4th Ave. **From I-64E**, take exit 6 toward Huntington onto WV 52W ½ mile to WV 60 exit toward W Huntington/Adams Ave. Merge onto Adams about 2½ miles (becomes 5th Ave) to 12th. Turn left onto 12th 1 block to restaurant on left.

LEWISBURG

Edith's Health & Gourmet Store 🛍

128 W. Washington St. ✆ 304-645-7998 ⏰ M-Sat 9:30-6, Sun 1-5
🚗 **From I-64**, take exit 169 toward Lewisburg/Ronceverte south on US 219/N Jefferson St (right from I-64E, left from I-64W) 1½ miles to US 60/Washington St. Turn right onto W Washington to store on right.

MARTINSBURG

Green General Store & Cafe 🛍 🍴

209 S. Raleigh St. ✆ 304-262-9978 ⏰ Tues-Th 8:30-7, F 8:30-8:30, Sat 10-8:30
· vegetarian · vegan friendly · organic focus · tables · self-service

🚗 **From I-81**, take exit 13 toward downtown Martinsburg east on King Street about 1 mile to Raleigh St (after tracks). Turn right onto Raleigh to store on right (blue house with front porch).

Healthway Natural Foods 🛍 ♿

740 Foxcroft Ave. ✆ 304-263-7728 ⏰ M-Th 10-7, F 10-8, Sat 10-6, Sun 12-5
· organic produce

🚗 **From I-81N**, take exit 12 toward Martinsburg right onto Winchester Ave/WV 45 and make first left onto Foxcroft Ave ½ mile to Martinsburg Cir. Turn left onto Martinsburg ¼ mile to store. **From I-81S**, take exit 13 toward Downtown left onto King St almost ⅓ mile to Foxcroft. Turn right onto Foxcroft almost ¾ mile to store.

MORGANTOWN

Maxwell's 🍴

1 Wall St. ✆ 304-292-0982 ⏰ M-Th 11-8:45, F-Sat 11-9:45, Sun 11-1:45
· vegetarian friendly · vegan friendly · alcohol · tables · wait staff

🚗 **From I-68W**, take exit 7 toward Pierpont Rd right onto Cheat Rd 1 mile to US 119. Turn left onto 119 continuing onto College Ave under 3 miles to University Ave. Turn left onto University ⅓ mile to Wall St. Turn right onto Wall to restaurant on right. **From I-68E**, take exit 1 toward Downtown/University Ave left onto US 119 (becomes US 19/University) about 4 miles to Wall. Turn left onto Wall to restaurant. **From I-79N**, take exit 148 onto I-68E and follow directions above. **From I-79S**, take exit 152 left onto US 19N 2¼ miles. After crossing river, turn left continuing on 19 3 blocks to Wall. Turn left onto Wall to restaurant.

Mountain People's Co-op 🛒 🍴

1400 University Ave. ✆ 304-291-6131 ⏱ M-Sat 9-8, Sun 10-6
 • organic produce • vegetarian • vegan friendly • deli • tables • self-service • take-out • co-op

🚘 **From I-68W,** take exit 7 toward Pierpont Rd right onto Cheat Rd 1 mile to US 119. Turn left onto 119 continuing onto College Ave under 3 miles to University Ave. Turn left onto University ⅓ mile to store on left after Water St. **From I-68E,** take exit 1 toward Downtown/University Ave left onto US 119 (becomes US 19/ University) about 4 miles to store on right after Wall St.. **From I-79N,** merge onto I-68E and follow directions above. **From I-79S,** take exit 152 left onto US 19N 2¼ miles. After crossing river, turn left continuing on 19 about 4 blocks to store.

MOUNDSVILLE

Yamuna's Natural Foods 🛒

RD 1 Box 319 ✆ 304-843-4811 ⏱ Tues-Sun 1:30-5:30

🚘 **From I-70W,** take exit 5A on left onto I-470W to exit 2 (Bethlehem). Turn left onto E Bethlehem Blvd about ¼ mile to WV 88. Turn right onto 88 about 8 miles to end at US 250. Turn left onto 250 1½ miles to Palace Rd (look for Palace of Gold sign, also called Limestone Rd). Turn left onto Palace 4½ miles (past Palace of Gold) to store in Palace Lodge. **From I-70E,** take exit 219 onto I-470E about 8⅔ miles (across river) to exit 2 toward Bethlehem and follow directions above.

PARKERSBURG

Mother Earth 🛒

1638 19th St. ✆ 304-428-1024 ⏱ M-Sat 9-7, Sun 12-5
 • organic produce

🚘 **From I-77,** take exit 176 toward 7th St/Downtown onto Rt 50W (right from I-77S, left from I-77N) about 2⅓ miles to Plum St. Turn right onto Plum about ½ mile to store at 19th St.

WISCONSIN

1. Amery	12. Hales Corners	23. Mt. Horeb	33. Steven's Point
2. Appleton	13. Hayward	24. Neenah	34. Sturgeon Bay
3. Ashland	14. Hudson	25. Oshkosh	35. Tomah
4. Baraboo	15. La Crosse	26. Pepin	36. Viola
5. Brookfield	16. Luck	27. Pewaukee	37. Viroqua
6. Cumberland	17. Madison	28. Rice Lake	38. W. Allis
7. Eagle River	18. Manitowoc	29. Richland	39. Wausau
8. Eau Claire	19. Marshfield	Center	40. Wauwatosa
9. Egg Harbor	20. Menomonie	30. River Falls	41. Wisconsin
10. Gays Mills	21. Merrill	31. Spencer	Dells
11. Green Bay	22. Milwaukee	32. Spring Green	

AMERY

Indigo Iris Natural Food Market & Exchange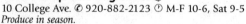
128 Keller Ave. ✆ 715-268-7052 ⏰ M-F 9-6, Sat 9-4
· organic produce

🛍 **From US 8,** go south on SR 46 6 miles to store in town (where SR 46 is Keller Rd) on east side at Center St in big blue bldg before tracks.

APPLETON

Kindred Spirits Organics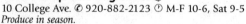
10 College Ave. ✆ 920-882-2123 ⏰ M-F 10-6, Sat 9-5
Produce in season.

🛍 **From I-41S,** take exit 145 onto Hwy 441S under 1 mile and exit onto College

Ave 2¾ miles to store on right in City Center Plaza. **From I-41N**, take exit 137 right at fork toward Appleton onto College 3 miles to store on left. **From I-10E**, exit toward S Oneida Rd and turn right onto Oneida and sharp left to stay on S Oneida 2 miles to College. Turn right onto College to store on left.

ASHLAND

Black Cat Coffee House 🍴   ♿

211 Chapple Ave. ✆ 715-682-3680 ⏰ M-F 7-7, Sat-Sun 8-5 (1 hour later in summer)
Sandwiches, salads, pizza, nachos and such. Outdoor seating in summer.
• vegetarian • organic focus • alcohol • tables • self-service

🍎 **From US Hwy 2**, go south (away from water) on Chapple Ave 1½ blocks to restaurant on left after Main St.

Chequamegon Food Co-op 🛍   ♿

215 Chapple Ave. ✆ 715-682-8251 ⏰ M-Sat 9-8, Sun 10-4
Fresh sandwiches in the cooler.
• organic produce • co-op

🍎 **From US Hwy 2**, go south (away from water) on Chapple Ave 1½ blocks to store on left after Main St.

BARABOO

The Grainery 🛍

127 3rd St. ✆ 608-356-9768 ⏰ M-Th 9-6, F-Sat 9-5
• organic produce

🍎 **From US 12, WI 136 & WI 33 intersection**, go east on WI 33 (aka 8th Ave) almost 1½ miles to Ash St. Turn right onto Ash 5 blocks to 3rd St. Turn right onto 3rd to store on left.

BROOKFIELD

Cafe Manna 🍴   ♿

3815 N. Brookfield Rd. ✆ 262-790-2340 ⏰ M-Sat 11-9
Raw food-friendly. Built and stocked using sustainable principles.
• vegetarian • vegan friendly • organic focus • alcohol • tables • wait staff • take-out

🍎 **From I-94W**, take exit 305B onto Hwy 45N about 4½ miles to exit 44 for Capitol Dr E. Keep left at first fork and right at second fork toward W Capitol and merge onto W Capitol about 4½ miles to N Brookfield Rd. Turn left onto N Brookfield to restaurant on right. **From I-94E**, take exit 295 toward Sussex left onto Hwy F about 2½ miles and take ramp onto Capitol Dr 3¼ miles to N Brookfield. Turn right onto N Brookfield to restaurant.

Health Hut 🛍

19035 W. Bluemound Rd. ✆ 262-821-2122 ⏰ M-F 10-8, Sat 10-6
• organic produce

🍎 **From I-94W**, take exit 297 and follow signs for Barker Rd N/Bluemound Rd. Veer left onto N Barker and right onto W Bluemound 1 mile to store on right (past the ice arena and before Brookfield Rd). **From I-94E**, take exit 297 toward US 18E and follow signs for Bluemound Rd E onto W Bluemound/Hwy JJ to E Moreland Blvd. Turn left at E Moreland and stay right on E Moreland/US 18E 1 mile to store.

CUMBERLAND

Island City Food Co-op & City Bakery 🛍🍴   ♿

1490 2nd Ave. ✆ 715-822-8233 ⏰ Store M-F 9-5:30, Sat 9-3 Bakery opens at 8
Fresh baked goods and organic coffee in the bakery.
• organic produce, bakery • tables • self-service • wait staff • take-out • co-op

🍎 **From junction US 63 & WI 48**, go north on Main St 4 blocks to store at Water St.

EAGLE RIVER

Grass Roots Health Foods 🛍️

3440 State Hwy. 70 E. ☎ 715-479-6299 ⏲ M-Sat 10-6, Sun May-Dec
• organic produce

🍎 **From US 45, WI 32/WI 70 intersection**, go east 1½ miles on WI 70 and make sharp right onto Old Hwy 70 to store on right.

EAU CLAIRE

Just Local Food Cooperative 🛍️

772 First Ave. ☎ 715-577-5564 ⏲ M-F 9-7, Sat-Sun 9-5
• organic produce • co-op

🚗 **From I-94**, take exit 65 and follow signs for Eau Claire north on SR 85 1¼-1½ miles to W Clairemont Ave. Turn right onto W Clairemont 1 mile to Menomonie St. Turn right onto Menomonie ½ mile continuing onto Water St 1 mile to 1st Ave. Turn left onto 1st ½ mile to store on left between Ann St & W Grand Ave.

EGG HARBOR

Greens & Grains 🛍️

7821 Hwy. 42 ☎ 920-868-9999 ⏲ Daily 10-5
• organic produce

🚗 Store is on Hwy 42 in town between Harbor School Rd & CR E in white bldg with purple trim.

GAYS MILLS

Kickapoo Exchange Food Co-op 🛍️

209 Main St. ☎ 608-735-4544 ⏲ M-F 11-6, Sat 9-6
• organic produce • co-op

🚗 Store is at intersection WI 131 & WI 171.

GREEN BAY

Kavarna 🍴

112 S. Broadway ☎ 920-430-3200 ⏲ M-Sat 9-10, Sun 11-6 Kitchen closes 1 hour earlier
Soups, sandwiches, wraps, pasta. Live music Friday nights.
• vegetarian • vegan friendly • alcohol • tables • self-service

🚗 **From I-43N**, take exit 180 onto WI 172W almost 4 miles to Webster Ave exit toward WI 57/Riverside Dr. Turn right onto 57N (Riverside, becomes Monroe Ave) 3 miles to E Walnut St. Turn left onto E Walnut almost ⅔ mile (across river) to Broadway St. Turn left onto Broadway to restaurant on right. **From I-43S**, take exit 189 right onto Atkinson Dr under ½ mile to US 141S. Turn left onto 141S 1⅓ miles to Broadway. Turn right onto Broadway ¼ mile to restaurant.

HALES CORNERS

Health Hut 🛍️

5610 S. 108th St. ☎ 414-529-2989 ⏲ M-F 9-8, Sat 9-6
• organic produce

🚗 **From I-43N,** take exit 59 on left for Layton Ave toward Hwy 100 right onto S 124th St 1 mile to W Grange Ave. Turn left onto W Grange over ¾ mile to S 113th St. Turn right onto S 113th ⅓ mile to first left onto W Parnell Ave ⅓ mile to S 108th St. Turn left onto S 108th to store in K-mart Plaza. **From I-43S**, take exit 5A onto W Forest Home and take WI 24W ramp on left onto W Forest Home 2 miles to W Scharles Ave. Turn right onto W Scharles and second right onto S 108th to store.

HAYWARD

Second Street Market

10583 Kansas Ave. ✆ 715-634-2944 ◷ M-W, F 8-7, Th, Sat 8-5, Sun 12-5
• organic produce • vegetarian friendly • deli • counter • self-service • take-out

☕ **From US 63 (W 1st St) & WI 27 (Main St) intersection**, go north on Main 2 blocks, turn right onto 3rd Ave and left onto Kansas Ave to store on left.

HUDSON

Fresh and Natural Natural Foods

1701 Ward Ave. ✆ 715-377-9913 ◷ M-Sat 9-9, Sun 9-7 Hot lunch bar M-F 11-2
• organic produce • vegetarian friendly • deli • tables • self-service • take-out

☕ **From I-94**, take exit 2 north on Carmichael Rd (left from I-94E, right from I-94W), turn left onto Frontage Rd and continue onto Coulee Rd about ¾ mile to 18th St. Turn right onto 18th 1 block to S Ward Ave. Turn left onto Ward to store in Plaza 94 Shopping Ctr.

LA CROSSE

Hackberry's

315 5th Ave. S. ✆ 608-784-5798 ◷ M-Th 11-9, F-Sat 9-10, Sun 9-9
• vegetarian friendly • alcohol • tables • wait staff

☕ **From I-90**, take exit 3 toward La Crosse (3A from I-90E) onto US 53S over 4 miles to Main St. Turn left onto Main 2 blocks to 5th Ave. Turn right onto 5th to restaurant on left.

People's Food Co-op

315 5th Ave. S. ✆ 608-784-5798 ◷ Daily 7-10
• organic produce • deli • bakery • tables • self-service • take-out • co-op

☕ **From I-90**, take exit 3 toward La Crosse (3A from I-90E) onto US 53S over 4 miles to Main St. Turn left onto Main 2 blocks to 5th Ave. Turn right onto 5th to store on left.

LUCK

Natural Alternatives Food Co-op

241 Main St. ✆ 715-472-8084 ◷ M-F 9-6, Sat 9-4
• organic produce • co-op

☕ **From Rt 48**, turn south onto Main St to store on right.

MADISON

Monty's Blue Plate Diner

2089 Atwood Ave. ✆ 608-244-8505 ◷ M-Th 7-9, F 7-10, Sat 7:30-10, Sun 7:30-9
Typical diner but many vegetarian options.
• vegetarian friendly • alcohol • counter • tables • wait staff

☕ **From I-39/I-90**, take exit 138B toward Madison onto Hwy 31W 2-2½ miles to E Washington Ave exit. Take E Washington toward Madison 1⅓ miles to S 4th St. Turn left onto S 4th across tracks and right onto Winnebago St under ¼ mile to Atwood Ave. Turn left onto Atwood about 2½ blocks to restaurant on right.

Mother Fool's Coffeehouse

1101 Williamson St. ✆ 608-259-1301 ◷ M-F 6:30am-11pm, Sat-Sun 8am-11pm
Vegan soups but mostly hot drinks and vegan dessert.
• vegetarian • vegan friendly • tables • self-service

☕ **From I-39/I-90**, take exit 138B toward Madison onto Hwy 31W 2-2½ miles to E Washington Ave exit. Take E Washington toward Madison about 2½ miles to S Ingersoll St. Turn left onto S Ingersoll 3 blocks to Williamson St. Turn right onto Williamson to restaurant on right.

Two Degrees Cafe ⑪
307 W. Johnson St. ✆ 608-257-7888 ⏰ M-F 9-8 Sat 9-6, Sun 11-5
In a LGBT-friendly, collectively owned bookstore.
 • vegetarian • vegan friendly • tables • self-service

🚗 **From I-39S/I-90E/I-94E**, take exit 135A-B toward Madison onto US 151W about 4¼ miles to N 1st St. Turn right onto N 1st and make first left onto E Johnson St ½ mile continuing onto E Gorham St 1¾ miles to N Bassett St. Turn left onto N Bassett and left onto W Johnson 2 blocks to restaurant. **From I-39N/I-90W**, take exit 142A on left and merge onto US 12W/US 18W toward Madison under 5 miles to exit 263 for John Nolan Dr. Merge onto John Nolen 2¼ miles to S Broom St. Turn left onto S Broom ½ mile to W Johnson. Turn right onto W Johnson to restaurant.

Whole Foods Market 🛒 ⑪   ♿
3313 University Ave. ✆ 608-233-9566 ⏰ Daily 8-10
 • organic produce • vegetarian friendly • salad bar • cafe • self-service • take-out

🚗 **From I-90/94**, take exit 142A toward Madison onto US 12/18W 9 miles to exit 258 (Midvale Blvd/Verona Rd). Turn right onto Midvale over 2½ miles to University Ave. Turn right onto University to store on right.

Willy Street Co-op 🛒 ⑪
1221 Williamson St. ✆ 608-251-6776 ⏰ Daily 7:30-9:30
 • organic produce • vegetarian friendly • fresh juice • deli • salad bar • tables • self-service • take-out • co-op

🚗 **From I-39/I-90**, take exit 138B toward Madison onto Hwy 31W 2-2½ miles to E Washington Ave exit. Take E Washington toward Madison about 2¼ miles to S Baldwin St. Turn left onto S Baldwin 2 blocks to Williamson St. Turn right onto Williamson to store on left.

MANITOWOC
Natural Market 🛒
302 N. 8th St. ✆ 920-682-1489 ⏰ M-F 8:30-5:30, Sat 8:30-3
🚗 **From I-43**, take exit 152 toward Manitowoc east on County Hwy J (left from I-43S, right from I-43N) about 3½ miles (becomes Waldo Blvd) to N 11th St. Turn right onto N 11th 1 mile to Buffalo St. Turn left onto Buffalo 2 blocks to N 8th St. Turn left onto N 8th to store on left.

MARSHFIELD
Plan-It-Earth Health Centers 🛒
148 N. Central Ave. ✆ 715-384-7100 ⏰ M-Th 9-6, F 9-7, Sat 9-5
 • organic produce
🚗 **From WI 97 & WI 13 intersection**, store is 2 blocks north of WI 13 (aka Veterans Pkwy) on 97 (aka Central Ave) on west side before Arnold Ave.

MENOMONIE
Golden Leaf Cafe ⑪
1706 Stout Rd. ✆ 715-231-5323 ⏰ Summer Daily 7-6:30, Winter Daily 6:30-8
Vegetarian soups, salads and vegetarian and organic meat paninis.
 • vegetarian friendly • organic focus • tables • self-service • take-out
🚗 **From I-94E**, take exit 41 south on WI 25 about 2 miles and veer left onto US 12/WI 29/Crescent St (on south side of Lake Menomonie) about 1 mile (becomes Stout Rd) to restaurant on left at 17th St. **From I-94W**, take exit 45 toward Menomonie left onto CR B 1½ miles to SR 12. Turn right onto SR 12 about 2¾ miles to restaurant on right at 17th St.

Menomonie Market Food Co-op 🛒
521 E. 2nd St. ✆ 715-235-6533 ⏰ M-F 7-8, Sat-Sun 8-7
 • organic produce • vegetarian friendly • deli • take-out • co-op

🍎 **From I-94**, take exit 41 south on WI 25 (right from I-94E, left from I-94W) about 2 miles to US 12/WI 29 (on south side of Lake Menomonie). Veer left 1 block and turn right onto 2nd St E to store on right.

MERRILL

Mustard Seed Natural Food 🛍️
801 E. 1st St. ℮ 715-536-7565 🕐 M-Th 8:30-5, F 8:30-6, Sat 9-4
🍎 **From US 51,** take exit 208 toward Merrill west on WI 17/WI 64 (right from US 51S, left from US 51N) about 1¾ miles to N Stuyvesant St. Turn right onto N Stuyvesant and left onto E 1st St under ½ mile to store on left at N Scott St.

MILWAUKEE

Beans & Barley 🛍️ 🍴   ♿
1901 E. North Ave. ℮ 414-278-0234 🕐 Daily 8-9
  • organic produce • vegetarian friendly • fresh juice • alcohol • cafe • deli • bakery • counter • tables • wait staff • take-out
🍎 **From I-43S**, take exit 73C onto N 8th St to North Ave. Turn left onto W North almost 2 miles to store on right after Oakland Ave. **From I-43N**, take exit 73C onto N 7th, turn right onto W North and follow directions above.

Bombay Sweets 🍴
3401 S. 13th St. ℮ 414-383-3553 🕐 Daily 10-10
A no-frills vegetarian Indian eatery.
  • vegetarian • vegan friendly • tables • self-service • take-out
🍎 **From I-43S**, take exit 314A right onto W Holt Ave (becomes Morgan Ave) ½ mile to S 13th St. Turn right onto 13th to restaurant on left. **From I-43N,** take exit 314A-B left onto Howard Ave ¾ mile to 13th. Turn right onto 13th almost ⅔ mile (past Holt) to restaurant.

Carini's La Conca D'Oro 🍴   ♿
3468 N. Oakland Ave. ℮ 414-963-9623 🕐 Vegetarian buffet Tues-F 11-2
This typical Italian restaurant is noteworthy for the weekday vegetarian lunch buffet.
  • vegetarian friendly • tables • self-service • wait staff
🍎 **From I-43S**, take exit 76A-B toward Capitol Dr onto Green Bay Ave to Capitol. Turn left onto Capitol (WI 190E) about 1¾ miles to Oakland Ave. Turn right onto Oakland about ½ mile to restaurant on left after Edgewood Ave. **From I-43N**, take exit 76A onto Capitol and follow directions above.

Casablanca 🍴
728 E. Brady St. ℮ 414-271-6000 🕐 M-W, Sun 11-10, Th-Sat 11-12
Middleastern with vegetarian lunch buffet. Friday music and belly dancing.
  • vegetarian friendly • alcohol • tables • self-service • wait staff
🍎 **From I-43S**, take exit 73C onto N 8th St to W North Ave. Turn left onto W North about ¾ mile to N Holton St. Turn right onto N Holton ½ mile to E Brady. Turn left onto E Brady 1 block to restaurant on left. **From I-43N**, take exit toward WI 145 right at fork (signs for Hwy 145S/McKinley Ave) onto WI 145 under ½ mile to N 6th St. Turn left onto N 6th under ½ mile to W Walnut St. Turn right onto W Walnut ¾ mile (across water) to N Water St. Turn left onto N Water 1 block continuing onto E Brady 2 blocks to restaurant.

Outpost Natural Foods 🛍️ 🍴   ♿
100 E. Capitol Drive ℮ 414-961-2597 🕐 Daily 7-8
  • organic produce • vegetarian friendly • fresh juice • salad bar • cafe • deli • bakery • counter • tables • self-service • take-out • co-op
🍎 **From I-43S**, take exit 76A-B toward Capitol Dr onto Green Bay Ave to Capitol. Turn left onto Capitol (WI 190E) about 3 blocks to store on left in River Glen Market Plaza. **From I-43N**, take exit 76A onto Capitol and follow directions above.

Outpost Natural Foods 🛍 🍴   ♿

2826 S. Kinnickinnic Ave. ℃ 414-755-3202 ⏱ Daily 7-9
 • organic produce • vegetarian friendly • fresh juice • salad bar • cafe • deli • bakery •
 counter • tables • self-service • take-out • co-op

🍎 **From I-794E,** take exit 3 left at fork and left onto S Carferry Dr ⅓ mile to S
Lincoln Memorial Dr. Turn right onto S Lincoln and second right onto E Russell Ave
½ mile to S Kinnickinnic Ave. Turn left onto Kinnickinnic under ½ mile to store on
left. **From I-794W,** take exit for E Oklahoma Ave right onto E Oklahoma under ¼
mile to S Kinnickinnic. Turn left onto Kinnickinnic ½ mile to store on right.

Palomino 🍴

2491 S. Superior St. ℃ 414-747-1007 ⏱ M-F 3-11, Sat-Sun 11-11
A tavern (with pool tables) offering vegan bar foods.
 • vegetarian friendly • vegan friendly • alcohol • counter • tables • wait staff

🍎 **From I-794E,** take exit 3 left at fork and left onto S Carferry ⅓ mile to S Lincoln
Memorial Dr. Turn right onto S Lincoln and second right onto E Russell 1 block to
S Superior Ave. Turn right onto S Superior to restaurant on left. **From I-794W,** take
exit for S Carferry left onto S Carferry and follow directions above.

Riverwest Co-op Grocery & Cafe 🛍 🍴

733 E. Clarke St. ℃ 414-264-7933 ⏱ M-F 7-9, Sat-Sun 8-9
 • organic produce • vegetarian • vegan friendly • organic focus • cafe • deli • tables •
 self-service • take-out • co-op

🍎 **From I-43S,** take exit 74 onto N 8th St and turn left onto W Locust St almost 1
mile to N Pierce St. Turn right onto N Pierce 3 blocks to E Clarke St. Turn left onto
E Clarke 1 block to store on right at Fratney St in Schlitz bldg. **From I-43N,** take exit
74 onto N 7th St, turn right onto W Locust and follow directions above.

Stonefly Brewing Company 🍴

735 E. Center St. ℃ 414-264-3630 ⏱ Daily 5-10
Bar with Tofu Wingers, edamame, Tofu Pot Pie, Tofu & Tater Tots and more.
 • vegetarian friendly • alcohol • counter • tables • wait staff

🍎 **From I-43,** take exit 74 east on N Locust St (merge onto N 8th St and left from
I-43S, merge onto N 7th St and right from I-43N) 1 mile to N Pierce St. Turn right onto
N Pierce 2 blocks to E Center St. Turn left onto E Center to restaurant on right.

MT. HOREB

Trillium Natural Foods Community Co-op 🛍

517 Springdale St. ℃ 608-437-5288 ⏱ M, F 8-6, Tues-W 10-6, Th 10-8, Sat 10-4,
Sun 10-2
 • organic produce • co-op

🍎 Take US 18/151 or WI 78 to Mt Horeb. Store is ½ block west of 78/92 roundabout.

NEENAH

The Red Radish 🛍

447 S. Commercial St. ℃ 920-720-3281 ⏱ M-F 8:30-7, Sat 9-4
 • organic produce • fresh juice

🍎 **From US 41,** take exit 131 east on WI 114/W Winneconne Ave (right from US
41N, left from US 41S) about 1½ miles to S Commercial St. Turn right onto S
Commercial 2 blocks to store on right.

OSHKOSH

Nutrition Discount Center 🛍

463 N. Main St. ℃ 920-426-1280 ⏱ M-Sat 9-6, Sun 11-3
 • organic produce

🍎 **From Hwy 41S,** take exit 124 south on US 45/Jackson St about 5¼ miles to
Church Ave. Turn left onto Church about ⅓ mile to N Main. Turn right onto Main
to store. **From Hwy 41N,** take exit 117 right onto 9th Ave about 2 miles to S Main.
Turn left onto Main about ½ mile to store.

PEPIN

Pepin Natural Foods 🛍 🍴

1015 3rd St. ☎ 715-442-3354 ⏰ M, W-F 6-5, Sat-Sun 8-5
Also home to Third St. Deli & Juice Bar and Seconds on Third consignment shop.
• vegetarian friendly • fresh juice • deli • counter • tables • wait staff • take-out
🛍 Store is on south (river) side of Hwy 35 at Locust St.

PEWAUKEE

Good Harvest Market 🛍 🍴

1850 Meadow Lane ☎ 262-544-9380 ⏰ M-Sat 8-8, Sun 10-6
• organic produce • vegetarian friendly • cafe • counter • tables • self-service • take-out
🛍 **From I-94W**, take exit 293 left onto Grandview Ave and make first right onto Silvernail Rd about ½ mile (back to hwy), U-turn onto Silvernail almost back to Grandview and turn right onto Meadow Ln to store on right. **From I-94E,** take exit 291 toward Waukesha onto Meadowbrook Rd and turn left onto Silvernail 1½ miles to Meadow. Turn right onto Meadow to store on right.

RICE LAKE

Main Street Market Whole Foods Cooperative 🛍 🍴

1 S. Main St. ☎ 715-234-7045 ⏰ M-Th 10-7, F-Sat 10-5:30
• organic produce • vegan • deli • table • self-service • take-out • co-op
🛍 **From Hwy 53**, take exit 143 toward Rice Lake onto Hwy 48E/W Knapp St (right from 53N, left from 53S) about 1⅓ miles to Main St. Turn right onto Main ½ mile (2 lights) to store at Messenger St.

RICHLAND CENTER

Pine River Food Co-op 🛍

196 W. Court St. ☎ 608-647-7299 ⏰ M-F 8-6, Sat 9-5
• co-op
🛍 **From US 14/6th St/WI 80 intersection,** go south on 80 (aka N Main St) 8 blocks to W Court St. Turn left onto Court to store on left. **From US 14/Orange St/WI 80 intersection,** go north on 80 (aka S Main) 7 blocks and turn right onto Court to store.

RIVER FALLS

Whole Earth Grocery 🛍

126 S. Main St. ☎ 715-425-7971 ⏰ Daily 9-7
• organic produce
🛍 **From I-94,** take exit 10 toward River Falls onto WI 65S (left from I-94W, right from I-94E) almost 8 miles to N Main St. Continue on N Main almost 1½ miles to store in town on right.

SPENCER

Plan-It-Earth Health Centers 🛍

101 W. Clark St. ☎ 715-659-5436 ⏰ M-F 9-5:30, Sat 9-12
🛍 Store is 2 blocks west of WI 13 on north side of Clark St (aka WI 98).

SPRING GREEN

Spring Green General Store 🛍 🍴   ♿

137 S. Albany St. ☎ 608-588-7070 ⏰ M-F 9-6, Sat 8-6, Sun 8-4
• vegetarian friendly • tables • self-service • take-out
🛍 **From US 14**, take WI 23S about ½ mile into Spring Green. Turn right onto Jefferson St 1 block to Albany St. Turn left onto Albany to store in blue bldg next to railroad.

STEVEN'S POINT

Steven's Point Area Food Co-op 🛍

633 2nd St. ✆ 715-341-1555 ⏰ M-F 9-8, Sat-Sun 10-5
• organic produce • vegetarian friendly • deli • bakery • take-out • co-op

🚗 **From I-39**, take exit 161 toward Stevens Point onto US 51 Bus about 1 mile (third light) to 4th Ave. Turn right onto 4th ½ mile to 2nd St. Turn right onto 2nd to store on right.

STURGEON BAY

The Healthy Way 🛍

218 S. Madison Ave. ✆ 920-746-4103 ⏰ M-F 9-6, Sat 9-3, Sun 11-3
• organic produce

🚗 **From WI 57 northbound**, turn left onto Green Bay Rd continuing onto S Madison Ave about 1 mile to store on right between Pine & Oak St. **From WI 57 southbound**, turn right onto S Neenah Ave ⅓ mile to E Redwood St. Turn left onto E Redwood 1 block and turn right onto S Madison 2 blocks to store.

TOMAH

Natural Connection 🛍

1012 Superior Ave. ✆ 608-372-3914 ⏰ M 10-4, Tues-F 10-5, Sat 10-3

🚗 **From I-90**, take exit 41 toward Tomah north on WI 131 (left from I-90E, right from I-90W) about 1½ miles (becomes Superior Ave) to store on right at Milwaukee St.

VIOLA

Viola Natural Foods Co-op 🛍

110 Commercial St. ✆ 608-627-1476 ⏰ M 2-4:30, 6:30-9, Tues-Wed 7:30pm-9:30pm, Th-F 2-6, Sat 12-4

🚗 Store is on WI 131 (aka Commercial Dr) at WI 56 (aka Main St).

VIROQUA

Viroqua Food Co-op 🛍

609 N. Main St. ✆ 608-637-7511 ⏰ Daily 7-8
• organic produce • vegetarian friendly • deli • take-out • co-op

🚗 Store is on US 14/US 61 (aka Main St) about 1 block north of WI 56/W Broadway St on east side.

W. ALLIS

Health Hut 🛍

2225 S. 108th St. ✆ 414-545-8844 ⏰ M-F 9-9, Sat 9-6
• organic produce

🚗 **From I-94**, take exit 305A or B and merge onto I-894E/45S. **From I-894**, take exit 1E west on W Lincoln Ave (right from I-894E, left from I-894W) ⅓ mile to S 107th St. Turn right onto S 107th 1 block to W Grant. Turn left onto W Grant 1 block to S 108th St. Turn right onto S 108th to store on right.

WAUSAU

Back to Eden Natural Health Store 🛍 🍴

2221 Grand Ave. ✆ 715-849-1299 ⏰ M-Th 9-7, F 9-6, Sun 10-5
• organic produce • salad bar • tables • self-service • take-out

🚗 **From I-39N**, take exit 187 onto WI 29E 1½ miles to exit 171 toward Schofield. Merge onto W Grand Ave/Bus 51 about 1 mile to Schofield Ave. Turn left onto Schofield ½ mile to E Grand Ave. Veer right onto E Grand 1⅓ miles to store on right after Eau Claire Blvd. **From US 51S**, take exit 192A left onto WI 51 2 miles to E Grand. Veer right onto E Grand about 1¾ miles to store on left after Kent St.

WAUWATOSA

Milk'n Honey 🖐
10948 W. Capitol Drive ✆ 414-535-0203 ⊕ M-F 10-7, Sat-Sun 10-5
   • organic produce • vegetarian friendly • deli • take-out

🚘 **From I-94**, merge onto US 45N (exit 305B from I-94E, 305A from I-94W) about 5 miles to exit 44 (WI 190E/Capitol Dr E). Turn right onto W Capitol 3 blocks to store on left at Mayfair Rd.

Outpost Natural Foods Co-op 🖐 🍴   ♿
7000 W. State St. ✆ 414-778-2012 ⊕ Daily 7-9
   • organic produce • vegetarian friendly • fresh juice • salad bar • cafe • deli • bakery • tables • self-service • take-out • co-op

🚘 **From I-94**, take exit 307A toward 68th St/70th St to 68th and go north (left from I-94E, right from I-94W) about 1 mile to W State St. Turn left onto W State 1 block to store at 70th St.

WISCONSIN DELLS

The Cheese Factory Restaurant 🍴   ♿
521 Wisconsin Dells Pkwy. ✆ 608-253-6065 ⊕ M, W-Sun 9-9 summer, off-season Th-Sat 11-9, Sun 9-7:30
Many vegetarian/vegan choices plus an old-fashioned soda fountain.
   • vegetarian • vegan friendly • tables • wait staff

🚘 **From I-90/94**, take exit 92 north on US 12 (left from I-90S/94E, right from I-90N/94W) about 1 mile to restaurant on right.

WYOMING

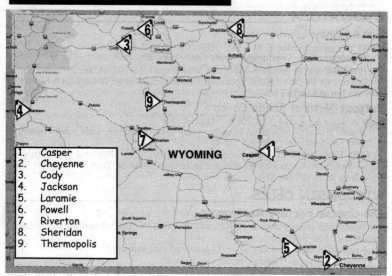

1. Casper
2. Cheyenne
3. Cody
4. Jackson
5. Laramie
6. Powell
7. Riverton
8. Sheridan
9. Thermopolis

CASPER

Alpenglow Natural Foods

109 E. 2nd St. ✆ 307-234-4196 🕐 M-F 9:30-6, Sat 9:30-5
  • organic produce

🍎 **From I-25**, take exit 188A south on N Center St (right from I-25S, left from I-25N) ½ mile to E 2nd St. Turn left onto E 2nd to store.

CHEYENNE

It's Only Natural

1802 Dell Range Blvd., Ste. 7 ✆ 307-635-0488 🕐 M-F 10-6, Sat 10-5
Heavy on supplements but some food.

🍎 **From I-25**, take exit 12 onto Central Ave (left from I-25S, right from I-25N) about ¾ mile to WY 219/Yellowstone Rd. Turn left onto Yellowstone and first right onto Dell Range Blvd about 1½ miles to store on right after Frontier Mall.

Noah's Ark Nutrition Center

1900 Thomes Ave. ✆ 307-778-2088 🕐M-F 9-6, Sat 9-5
🍎 **From I-25**, take exit 10D onto Missile Dr ¾-1 mile to W 19th St. Veer left onto W 19th over ½ mile to store on left at Thomes Ave (behind jail).

CODY

Mountain High Health Foods   ♿

1914 17th St. ✆ 307-587-1700 🕐 M-F 9:30-6, Sat 9:30-5
🍎 Take US 14/16/20 into Cody. Store is in shopping area at top of hill.

Whole Foods Trading Company

1239 Rumsey Ave. ✆ 307-587-3213 🕐 M-Sat 9:30-5:30
🍎 **From US 14 traveling east,** take Sheridan Ave (aka 14) to 12th St. Turn left onto 12th 1 block to Rumsey Ave. Turn right onto Rumsey to store. **From US 14 traveling north,** turn left onto Sheridan to 13th St. Turn right onto 13th 1 block to Rumsey Ave. Turn left onto Rumsey to store.

JACKSON

Jackson Whole Grocer 🛍️ 🍴
974 W. Broadway ✆ 307-733-0450 ⏰ Daily 7-11 Cafe/Deli 7-8
• organic produce • vegetarian friendly • organic focus • fresh juice • salad bar • cafe • deli • bakery • counter • self-service • take-out
🏪 Store is on W Broadway (US 89/26/191) about 1½ blocks past WY 22 intersection between Powderhorn & Scott Ln on south side.

LARAMIE

Big Hollow Food Co-op 🛍️
119 S. 1st St. ✆ 307-745-3586 ⏰ M-F 10-7, Sat-Sun 10-5
• organic produce • co-op
🚗 From I-80, take exit 313 north on US 287/S 3rd St (left from I-80E, right from I-80W) 1 mile to E University Ave. Turn left onto E University 2 blocks to store on right at end where it turns left onto S 1st St.

Jeffrey's Bistro 🍴
123 E. Ivinson Ave. ✆ 307-742-7046 ⏰ M-W 11-8, Th-Sat 11-9
Over half the entrees can be made vegetarian. Poultry and fish but no meat.
• vegetarian friendly • alcohol • tables • wait staff
🚗 From I-80, take exit 313 north on US 287/S 3rd St (left from I-80E, right from I-80W) almost 1 mile to E Ivinson Ave. Turn left onto E Ivinson 1 block to restaurant on right.

Sweet Melissa Vegetarian Cafe 🍴   ♿
213 S. 1st St. ✆ 307-742-9607 ⏰ M-Sat 11-9
Soups, sandwiches, salads, lentil loaf, lasagna, portabella fajitas.
• vegetarian • vegan friendly • tables • wait staff
🚗 From I-80, take exit 313 north on US 287/S 3rd St (left from I-80E, right from I-80W) 1 mile to E University Ave. Turn left onto E University 2 blocks and turn left at end where it turns left onto S 1st St to restaurant on right.

Whole Earth Grainery 🛍️
111 E. Ivinson Ave. ✆ 307-745-4268 ⏰ Tues-Sat 11-6
🚗 From I-80, take exit 313 north on US 287/S 3rd St (left from I-80E, right from I-80W) almost 1 mile to E Ivinson Ave. Turn left onto E Ivinson 2 blocks to store on right.

POWELL

Wyoming Natural Health Food & Supplements 🛍️
180 S. Bent St. ✆ 307-754-9266 ⏰ M-F 9:30-5:30, Sat 10-4
🏪 Store is just north of US 14/14A on east side of S Bent St.

RIVERTON

Graham's Gluten Free Market 🛍️ 🍴
414 E. Main St. ✆ 307-857-6155 ⏰ M, Sun 10-5:30, Tues-F 8:30-5:30
• organic produce • vegetarian friendly • salad bar • tables • self-service • take-out
🚗 From US 26/Rte 789 intersection, go west on E Main St almost 4 blocks to store on north side before Broadway St.

Wind River Mercantile 🛍️ 🍴
223 E. Main St. ✆ 307-856-0862 ⏰ M-Sat 10-5:30
• organic produce • vegetarian friendly • fresh juice • cafe • bakery • tables • self-service • take-out
🚗 From US 26/Rte 789 intersection, go west on E Main St 5½ blocks to store on south side between 3rd St E & Railroad Ave.

SHERIDAN

Good Health Emporium 🛍️

933 Werco Ave. © 307-674-5715 ⏰ M-F 10-6, Sat 10-4
• organic produce

🚗 **From I-90**, take exit 25 toward Sheridan/Bull Horn west on E Brundage Ln (left from I-90E, right from I-90W) ⅓ mile to S Coffen Ave. Turn right onto S Coffen 1 block to Werco Ave. Turn right onto Werco to store on right.

THERMOPOLIS

Nature's Corner 🛍️

530 Broadway © 307-864-3218 ⏰ M-Sat 8:30-5:30

🚗 **From US 20/WY 789 & WY 120 intersection**, store is 1½ blocks east on WY 120 (Broadway St) between N 4th & 5th St on north side.

EATING ON AND OFF THE HEALTHY HIGHWAY

As the *Healthy Highways* listings reveal, there are many food establishments that strive to serve healthy fare. However, no matter where you eat, it takes attention to maintain good eating habits when you aren't in charge. There is no question that is it much easier to have a better meal or snack when choosing *Healthy Highways* locations, since they provide greater choice and better and more varied ingredients. But even these establishments may serve some items you wish to forgo, such as processed grains, refined sugars, hydrogenated fats, animal products, and the like.

We want to emphasize the idea of *better and more varied ingredients*. Much is made of the benefits of avoiding "fast food," but little is said about the potential gains from eating in more health conscious places. A good diet is not about what you don't eat, but what you do. Great variety is always the key to healthful eating, as it increases your chances of obtaining a full range of nutrients.

Fast food restaurants are mostly based on just a small pool of ingredients—beef, chicken, cheese, eggs, potatoes, white bread, iceberg lettuce, tomatoes. Conversely, health-oriented eateries focus on a wide range of produce, grains of all kinds (usually in the whole form), and non-animal proteins like soy products and beans. Many also incorporate local and organic ingredients.

Nonetheless, in any eating place, there can be pitfalls. If you go for the bread and butter (or olive oil), eat rich sauces and fried food, drown your salad in dressing, drink excessively (whether it's real juice, soda or a sweetened hot beverage), or indulge in dessert (always a temptation), your diet may be higher in calories, fat, sugar, and salt than you realize.

To assist you, here are some ways you can continue to enjoy the fun of dining out, without being done-in by dinner.

Dining Out Tactics

When looking for a place to eat, there are often too few or too many options. Sometimes it's easier to rationalize that one meal can't really have a big impact on our overall diet, so why make the effort to choose well. Perhaps this reasoning held up 20 years ago, when eating out was less popular. But this attitude is obviously not sensible in a society that gets more than one-third of its calories away from home.

You Are Where You Eat

To a large part, *where* you eat dictates *what* you eat. This, of course, is why we assembled *Healthy Highways* in the first place.

If there is no suitable listing in *Healthy Highways*, consult the yellow pages under "health food stores," "vegetarian" or look through the various "restaurants." Start by eliminating places that are unsuitable. Then scout around to find eating establishments that are in tune with your objectives. Another tactic is to ask locally where you might find a place with vegetarian options or real "homemade" food.

Be adventurous about trying other cuisines. Many cultures feature more vegetables and diverse ingredients than conventional American eateries. Indian, Thai, Chinese, Japanese, Ethiopian, Mexican, and Middle-Eastern restaurants all present possibly healthful dining opportunities.

The Waiting Game

It's easy to consume a meal's worth of calories before your meal arrives. Do you order alcohol or a soft drink to tide you over while waiting in a restaurant, or use the bread and butter—or chips and salsa—to curb your hunger? Here are some ways you can cut down on "unintentional" eating.

- Eat a small healthy snack beforehand to keep you from becoming too hungry.
- Order sparkling water with a wedge of lemon to keep you occupied.
- Order salad right away.
- If no one at the table objects, ask to have the bread held until the food is served. Otherwise, place the breadbasket or chips out of your reach to avoid reflexive munching.

Mental Grazing

It's easy to be tempted by food you see being delivered to other tables or by the choices of your eating companions. Be confident in your decision.

Quit the "Clean-plate Club"

One of the biggest risks people who eat out face is enormous portion sizes. If you eat in places that serve large portions and lots of "free" extras, you may have to learn to hold back, share dishes with a companion or ask for a "doggie bag."

Consider wrapping up part before you dig in. If you are uncomfortable about asking for a take-home sack before the meal has even arrived, bring in your own container and set some food aside right away without drawing attention. If you are traveling with a cooler, it's easy to preserve leftovers for a second meal. Moreover, many motels and hotels have small refrigerators in the room, an option we always ask about on the road.

Sharing is Saving

It isn't unusual to order one dessert for the table. By extension, people are becoming increasingly comfortable sharing an entree and adding an extra salad or appetizer. Another way to cut down is to order an appetizer or soup plus salad, instead of a full dinner. The outcome of these strategies is both a healthier bank account and body.

Have It Your Way

How many times have you ordered a seemingly healthy dish, only to be surprised by what actually arrives at the table? If a menu item is unfamiliar, inquire about how it is prepared to make sure it suits your needs and taste. Ask about seasoning, sauces, if the soup is made with animal broth, and such. If anyone gives you a hard time or you feel embarrassed, just say you are on a "special diet." (You are!)

Insure your satisfaction by making reasonable requests beforehand. If they agree, you have the right to expect your request to be honored. If you are brought something other than what you ordered, be polite—but send it back.

Here are some ordering options:

- Order vegetables with care so they don't arrive swimming in a pool of butter or sauce. You can always season them with a splash of vinegar or lemon and pepper.
- Whenever appropriate, get the sauce or gravy on the side.
- When you order your salad ask for dressing on the side. Better still, request some oil and vinegar or a wedge of lemon in order to moderate the amount of fat and salt.
- Specify that your toast be brought dry. That way you can control the amount of butter that goes on it.
- Ask to substitute a baked potato, salad or other vegetable for chips, fries, white rice or pasta.
- Load up sandwiches with healthy extras like lettuce, tomato, cucumber slices, fresh pepper strips, mushrooms, and such. (And don't forget the vegetable toppings on pizza.)
- When ordering something broiled, specify no (or light on) added fat.
- If you like something on the menu that is fried, ask if it can be broiled instead.
- Always ask if there is whole wheat bread or brown rice.

The Portable Pantry

When embarking on a trip that allows for a little extra luggage (perhaps as little as a purse, briefcase or backpack), it's a good idea to pack a few staples that can greatly improve your away-from-home meals. By adding a cooler, you can extend the selection. And don't forget to include a few utensils—knife, spoon, fork—plus napkins or paper towels, plastic bags and twisters.

Here are some favorites:

- Bottled water
- Juice
- Cheese
- Cottage cheese
- Yogurt
- Nuts
- Nut butters
- Hummus
- Whole grain crackers
- Whole grain bread
- Cut-up vegetables
- Fruit
- Honey/maple syrup
- Mustard, hot sauce, soy sauce, and other favorite condiments

Savvy Snacks

There is nothing inherently wrong with snacking. As a matter of fact, eating small meals interspersed with snacks over the course of a day is an excellent way to keep your energy up and blood sugar levels more uniform.

If you think about typical snacks, you will probably conjure up foods high in sugar, fat and/or salt. This is hardly surprising since thirty percent of the money spent on food advertising each year in the U.S. is for candy, gum, mints, nuts, chips and other salty snacks, crackers, cookies, baked goods, and soft drinks. Not only do these snack choices provide calories without any real sustenance, for carbohydrate-sensitive individuals they can trigger overeating. By choosing smarter snacks with the right balance of nutrients you can satisfy hunger and even boost your nutritional status.

- Always carry something healthy to munch on. (A traveling sister-in-law keeps her energy up by carrying soy nuts to sprinkle on salad or yogurt.)
- Most commercial trail mixes are high caloric. You can adapt them by "diluting" with a ready-to-eat whole grain cereal or create your own mix with the cereal, favorite nuts, seeds, and dried fruit.
- Bean dips like hummus are readily available. Cottage cheese is another good protein-rich snack.
- Buy vegetables along the way to use with dips instead of chips.
- Pack a box of whole grain crackers for snacks (or when restaurants have no whole grain alternative).
- Pick up bags of plain popcorn at natural foods stores rather than the "natural" chips, which are still packed with fat and calories (even many of the "baked" versions).
- Spread slices of apples or pears with natural peanut butter or other nut butters. Although nut butters are best refrigerated, they can be safely kept at room temperature for a week or two while traveling.
- A container of yogurt is a better choice than a fast food snack.

Portion Distortion

If you've bought a muffin lately, you may have noticed how they seem to be expanding. Once a typical muffin weighed about 2 ounces; nowadays muffins are simply huge, often weighing five to six ounces. Bagels have undergone a similar expansion. Since the U.S. government standard for a serving of breadstuff is one ounce, just one of these items can be the equivalent of five to six servings.

These additional government-defined serving sizes illustrate the disconnect between health recommendations and reality: One serving = ½ cup cooked pasta (about 32 strands of spaghetti), 10 French fries, 15 grapes, ½ cup nuts (a small handful), four ounces wine (roughly half a teacup). Are they kidding!

The information below will help you to better assess what's on your plate. The number of servings listed next to each grouping is the recommended daily intake in the Dietary Guidelines for Americans. After the serving sizes are some visual aids (*in italics*).

STANDARD SERVING SIZES

BREADS/CEREALS/GRAINS
(6-11 servings daily)

1 serving =   1-ounce slice bread (*CD case*)
"   1 tortilla or 3-inch pancake (*compact disc*)
"   ½ small muffin, English muffin or bagel
"   ½ cup cooked cereal, rice, pasta (*cupcake liner*)
2 servings = 1 cup pasta (*half grapefruit*)

MEAT AND NONMEAT PROTEINS
(2-3 servings daily)

1 serving =   2 to 3 ounces meat, poultry (*cassette tape*)
"   2 to 3 ounces fish (*checkbook*)
"   1 cup cooked beans (*baseball*)
"   4 to 6 ounces tofu (*deck of cards*)
"   2 eggs
"   ¼ cup roasted soybeans/soynuts (*2 ping pong balls*)
"   ½ cup nuts or seeds (*modest handfull*)
"   4 tablespoons nut butter(*2 ice cubes*)

MILK AND DAIRY PRODUCTS
(2-3 servings daily; 4 servings ages 9-18 or over 51)

1 serving =   1 cup milk or yogurt
"   1½ ounces hard cheese, chunk (*3 dominoes*)
"   1½ ounces hard cheese, slice (*computer disc*)

VEGETABLES
(2-5 servings daily, but more vegetables is always better)

1 serving =   1 cup raw leafy greens (*man's fist*)
"   ½ cup vegetables, cooked or raw (*light bulb*)
"   1 medium potato (*computer mouse*)
"   ¾ cup vegetable juice

FRUIT
(2-4 servings daily)

1 serving =   1 medium fruit (*tennis ball*)
"   ½ cup cut-up fruit (*7 cotton balls*)
"   ¼ cup dried fruit (*small egg*)
"   ¾ cup fruit juice

SIX HEALTHY HIGHWAYS' "RULES FOR THE ROAD"

1. Choose different ethnic foods when possible. *Gained*: New foods, greater variety, new experiences.

2. Order vegetarian. Even if you aren't a vegetarian, seize every opportunity to eat like one. This will automatically improve your diet because meatless dining depends on beans, grains, vegetables, fruit, nuts, and seeds. *Gained*: More variety, more fiber, less saturated fat.

3. Go for salad and vegetables (but go light on dressing and sauce). There is no such thing as too many vegetables. *Gained*: Numerous vitamins, minerals, fiber, health-protecting phytochemicals.

4. Avoid unnecessary fats. Chefs are accustomed to using butter, oil and other fats when they cook, so don't add to this yourself. Be sparing with dressings, sauces, butter on bread (even the trendy olive oil.) Order foods poached or broiled instead of fried. *Gained*: Less fat, fewer calories.

5. Always ask if there is whole grain bread or brown rice. Even if there isn't, with enough requests they may start to stock it. *Gained*: More fiber, greater restaurant awareness.

6. Just desserts. Many of us find dessert hard to pass up. Even in health-oriented eateries, desserts are often calorie-laden. Look for lower fat options (sorbet, biscotti), something fruit-based (apple crisp, strawberry shortcake), or a treat with some nutritious ingredients (baked custard, rice pudding). If you can't resist something really indulgent, suggest sharing. *Lost*: Empty calories, fat and sugar.

Happy Trails,
Nikki & David

RESOURCES
(In no particular order.)

AAA: Emergency number in all fifty states. 1-800-AAA-HELP

Better World Club: Environment-oriented automobile association. www.betterworldclub.com 866-304-7540

Disability Travel and Recreation Resources: www.makoa.org/travel.htm

State and Local Governments On The Net: All state, county and local town websites. www.statelocalgov.net/index.cfm

Recreation.gov: Recreational activities to weather maps. www.recreation.gov

Road Closures: Construction, weather, road conditions, traffic, etc. www.fhwa.dot.gov/trafficinfo/

Rail Travel: www.traintraveling.com/usa/

Hostelling International-USA: Hostels, educational programs and travel advice. www.hiusa.org/index.shtml 301-495-1240

Green Hotels Association: Find hotels with an environmental viewpoint. www.greenhotels.com 713-789-8889

Reserve America: Online reservations for federal, state and private campgrounds. www.reserveamerica.com

RV Travel: RV campgrounds and more. www.allcampgrounds.com

The National Park Service: www.nps.gov/ Headquarters 202-208-6843

Traveling with Pets: Dog-friendly lodgings, restaurants, beaches, attractions, and more. www.dogfriendly.com 877-475-2275

National Public Radio: Find public radio stations for your trip. www.NPR.org

Farmers' Markets: Farm markets throughout the US. www.ams.usda.gov/farmersmarkets

Rails-to-Trails Conservancy: National network of public recreation trails from former rail lines. www.railtrails.org 202-331-9696

Entertain the family en route: old-fashioned traveling games. www.travelwithkids.about.com/cs/printgames/a/gamesprint.htm.

Festival Fun: Online information about festivals and events throughout the US. www.fulltiming-america.com/festivals/index.html

Quirky America: Museums, festivals and destinations on the fringes of mainstream tourism. www.eccentricamerica.com

Swimmer's Guide: An international directory of full-size, year-round swimming pools open to the public. www.swimmersguide.com

Yoga Finder: Find a yoga class, retreat center or event. www.yogafinder.com

Conversation cafes: Plug in to the local scene. www.conversationcafe.org

Weather: Current US weather or 5-day forecast. http://cirrus.sprl.umich.edu/wxnet

ORGANIZATIONS OF INTEREST TO RESTAURANTS

Greening Ethnic Restaurants: Helps ethnic restaurants adopt environmental principals. www.thimmakka.org 510-655-5566

Green Restaurant Association: Encourages ecologically sustainable restaurant industry and certifies restaurants that meet certain criteria. www.dinegreen.com 858-452-7378

For more travel resources visit us at HealthyHighways.com

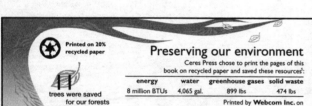

EAT WELL
The YoChee Way
GUIDE AND
275 RECIPES

Zero fat · calcium-rich · Low-calorie · High-protein

The Easy and Delicious
Way to Cut
Fat and Calories
with Natural
YoChee (Yogurt Cheese)

Nikki & David Goldbeck
Co-authors of American Wholefoods Cuisine

1-886101-09-4

CONTENTS:

- 275 recipes (with nutritional analysis) for every meal and in between
- Simple instructions for making YoChee
- Quick and easy recipes marked
- Creamy soups and sauces with little or NO fat
- OneLESS Egg recipes — YoChee is the natural egg extender
- Healthier (& tastier) versions of such favorites as pizza, quiche, wraps, lasagna, pesto, stuffed mushrooms, deviled eggs
- Appealing ideas for vegetables
- Rich desserts like brownies & cheese cake with less calories and fat
- Web community at www.YoChee.com

312 page illustrated paperback

HOW TO
Save Fat & Calories, Boost Calcium & Protein With Natural
YoChee® (Yogurt Cheese)

YoChee is the new name for the age-old food called yogurt cheese. YoChee can help you overcome today's most pressing dietary concerns — particularly those linked to calcium, fat and calories. Its rich taste makes it hard to believe that YoChee has zero fat and is low in calories. In fact, it has all the renowned health benefits of yogurt. But YoChee is even better than yogurt since it is spreadable, less tart and a more versatile cooking ingredient.

The Healthy Spread You Use Instead
You don't have to cook to get the benefits of YoChee. The smooth, creamy texture makes YoChee the perfect substitute for cream cheese, sour cream, mayonnaise, butter and margarine. With just 10 calories and no fat, you save 40-100 calories and 5-10 grams of fat per tablespoon by using YoChee instead.

If You Can Use a Spoon, You Can Make YoChee!
YoChee is made in minutes by spooning yogurt into a draining device.
Gravity does all the work. Fun for Kids too.

Deluxe YoChee Maker
This self-contained unit has a reservoir to hold the drained liquid and a lid to provide a clean, sealed environment. The durable stainless steel strainer is specially designed to promote quick and thorough draining. Holds about 1 quart yogurt to make 2 cups YoChee. Dishwasher safe.
Material: Plastic/Stainless steel
mesh size: 5x5x5"

THE HEALTHIEST BOOKS IN THE WORLD

AMERICAN WHOLEFOODS CUISINE: Over 1,300 Meatless, Wholesome Recipes from Short Order to Gourmet by Nikki & David Goldbeck. A classic of contemporary vegetarian cooking, plus 300 pages of valuable kitchen essentials. Considered "the vegetarian *Joy of Cooking*" by authorities from *Food & Wine* to *Vegetarian Times*. Over 250,000 in print. *(580 pages/Paper)*

THE ABC'S OF FRUITS & VEGETABLES AND BEYOND by Steve Charney and David Goldbeck. Introduce kids to the alphabet *and* good food. 26 clever poems plus recipes, activities, jokes, shopping tips, and more. Beautifully illustrated, fun for all ages. Used in educational programs. *(112 pages, Color illustrations/Paper)*

THE GOOD BREAKFAST BOOK by Nikki & David Goldbeck. 450 vegetarian recipes to jumpstart the day. Quick weekday getaways to elegant brunches. Great for families. Includes recipes suitable for vegans, as well as people with wheat, dairy and egg sensitivities. *(206 pages/Paper)*

EAT WELL THE YOCHEE WAY by Nikki & David Goldbeck. Enjoy rich creamy dishes without the fat and calories. High-protein, calcium-rich YoChee (yogurt cheese) is the ideal substitute for cream cheese, sour cream or mayonnaise. Improve your diet without forgoing your favorite dishes. Simple directions for YoChee and 275 recipes. *(310 pages/paper)* Also available, YoChee makers (descriptions online)

EARTHLY BODIES & HEAVENLY HAIR By Dina Falconi. The bible of herbal body care. 450 innovative formulas for women, men, teens, babies and elders. *(250 pages/Paper)*

CLEAN & GREEN by Annie Berthold-Bond. The complete guide to nontoxic and environmentally safe housekeeping. 485 recipes based on harmless, non-polluting ingredients.100,000 in print. *(160 pages/Paper)*

.... ORDER VIA THE WEB, MAIL, FAX OR PHONE ....

____**Healthy Highways** $19.95 ....$ _____
____**American Wholefoods Cuisine** $21.95 ....$ _____
____**The ABC's of Fruits & Vegetables and Beyond** $16.95 ....$ _____
____**The Good Breakfast Book** $9.95 ....$ _____
____**Eat Well the YoChee Way** $18.95 ....$ _____
____**Earthly Bodies & Heavenly Hair** $17.95 ....$ _____
____**Clean & Green** $9.95 ....$ _____
____**Deluxe YoChee (Yogurt Cheese) Maker** $18.95 ....$ _____
____**YoChee (Yogurt Cheese) Funnel** $10.00 ....$ _____
BOOK TOTAL ....$ _____
US SHIPPING: First item $4.95, additional items $2.25 each ......$ _____
TAX (NY residents add local sales tax to merchandise & shipping)..$ _____
TOTAL ENCLOSED ....$ _____

Name _____ Phone _____

Address _____ State _____ Zip _____

V/MC/AE/D Expires _____ / _____ Email _____

Card# _____ — _____ — _____ — _____

Signature _____

*Orders must be accompanied by payment in U.S. funds or charged to Visa, MC, American Express or Discover. Faxed credit card orders accepted. Checks payable to Ceres Press.

CERES PRESS • PO Box 87 • Dept HH2 • Woodstock, NY 12498
Phone/FAX 888-804-8848 • visit www.HealthyHighways.com for online specials